THE OUTLINE OF KNOWLEDGE

EDITED BY

JAMES A. RICHARDS

THE ROMANCE OF EVOLUTION

BY FREDERICK H. MARTENS

VOLUME I

J. A. RICHARDS, INC.
NEW YORK

Typesetting, Paper, Printing and Binding
By THE KINGSPORT PRESS
Kingsport, Tenn.

CONTENTS

BOOK ONE

THE ROMANCE OF EVOLUTION

PART ONE

FROM ATOM TO APE

PART TWO

APE AND MAN

CONTENTS

BOOK TWO

THE ROMANCE OF HUMAN LIFE THROUGH THE AGES

BOOK ONE

THE ROMANCE OF EVOLUTION

BY

FREDERICK H. MARTENS

THE
ROMANCE OF EVOLUTION

PART ONE

FROM ATOM TO APE

WHAT DOES EVOLUTION MEAN

EVOLUTION sums up in a single word the story of life. Because it comes from a Latin root the word "evolution" seems mysterious. In reality it is a simple, everyday word, with a plain meaning. The books of the ancient Romans were written on rolls of parchment and *rolled up* on rods of wood or ivory. In Latin the prefix *e* means "out," and *volvo* means "to roll." And there you are: Evolution merely means "unrolling or "rolling out" a book to read it. That is what it meant in ancient Rome and that is what it means in modern America. And though we now "open" our books instead of "unrolling" them, we cling to the idea the old word conveys. We "unroll the scroll of history," for example.

So Evolution to-day still means, as in ancient Rome, unrolling the scroll or book that tells the tale of life through the ages. Now this book is more interesting than any Greek or Roman author ever wrote. It is a more thrilling and wonderful *true* story any fiction by any author written in any time. It has been told, time and again —for the *scientist*—in highly technical language, and with a detail which confuses the intelligent lay mind. And that is not as it should be, for it is too great, too true, too fascinating a tale to be known only to the specialist. It is humanity's tale of itself. It is the tale of how all of us happen to be on earth to-day. Unless we know the story of Evolution, *we do not know ourselves!* But if Evolution's story is read as it really runs, cleared of the technical jargon and confusing detail which break the thread of the greatest narrative ever told by Nature, the master story teller of the all time, it will make clear to you a hundred and one facts about yourself you never have ispected. It will prove to you that nothing that lives and breathes earth, whether it walk, swim or fly, was born by chance. Not only is it the most romantic story ever told. It is the clearest and most logical as well.

Nature never needed a course in story-writing. She plucks a *molecule,* an atom—the very smallest particle of matter of which the mind can conceive—out of the Nowhere and begins her tale. Then she unfolds her romance. It is a series of thrilling chapters full of exciting adventures that would seem pure invention were they not based on solid scientific facts. Then she waves her magician's hand —and the molecule has changed into man, into ourselves!

The theory of Evolution—literally the story of how life developed out of nothing into man, the most perfected of all living creatures— is the master key to all the problems of nature. We call the story of man's development after the races grouped themselves in nations: History. We call the story of how he discovered beauty in its various forms and developed it: Art. We call the story of how his mind developed in different directions: Religion, Philosophy, Science. All these stories are sequels to the first great romance of Evolution that tells how we came to be. They are sequels as vivid and breathlessly interesting as the story they continue. Why? Because change and variety are the very soul of all evolution. And all these stories are told in "The Outline of Knowledge."

But if we are to understand Alexander Dumas's "Twenty Years After," we must first read his "Three Musketeers." And if we are to understand these stories—History, Art, Literature, Science, Religion and Philosophy—we must first read the romance of Nature's Evolution, which made possible all the others. It carries us from the darkness of measureless space to the rosy dawn of the first civilizations.

And—a final word before our tale begins. There is nothing in the story of Evolution which offends the vital moral truth of religion. There is nothing which contradicts the *real inner* truth of Christianity. For, as a great thinker and devout man once remarked: "It is a poor religion which fears the truth." The truth of God and the truth of Nature are embraced in the same broad law of harmony.

CHAPTER I

OUT OF THE NOWHERE

WE have just said that Evolution is a story: the greatest story ever told. But we can also look on it as a drama—the greatest "moving picture" ever screened. Produced and directed by Nature—only its captions supplied by man—reel follows reel as the drama develops from its first beginning to its logical climax. And we, the audience, settle down to enjoy a treat no other "moving picture" can give us—for we are going to see the scroll of the ages unrolled! We shall be able to trace back our own individual life stories to the source of all life. We have seen a thousand and one pictures, but this picture we have never seen. For it is too vast for any purely human stage. It begins in the womb of time and space, and every earlier reel is a record of millions of years. It is a drama each of whose billions of actors passes from the stage once his part is played. It is a drama in which every one in the audience takes a part—though we may not realize it—for while he is watching the reels made by "casts" that preceded him, he himself is carrying out the unchanging laws of change, continuing in himself the evolution whose progress he can follow. He is playing his part in Nature's "moving picture" which leads out of the Nowhere into the Here.

The curtain rises. At first we see nothing. The world stage is missing, for the world has not yet been born, and the curtain goes up on the vast immensity of time and space. Before us lies the Nowhere—emptiness, darkness, space! Space, emptiness and darkness—a Nowhere so vast that it has no end. If our thoughts could travel millions of years in one direction through this dark and empty sea of space, they might reach a point where the Nowhere touches the shores of Eternity. And who knows where Eternity ends?

And there is something in this Nowhere that we cannot take and hold in our hand and which in spite of this is the most real thing there is. It is movement. The baseball catcher feels it when he stops a swift ball: it is the force behind the ball, the motion of the ball that makes it sting his fingers through his heavy glove. In the Nowhere this force was constantly flowing in mysterious waves, and gradually in the Nowhere these waves of movement, as they flowed, began to take on the form of a number of rings, like the smoke-rings, sent up in the air from a cigar or cigarette. These rings as

3

they whirled were sucked in toward their center like a whirlpool or vortex and each whirling ring of movement in space, as it whirled, turned into an electron—a unit of electric force so small that it cannot be seen through the microscope.

But movement does not stop. That like draws like is Nature's fundamental law, which everything must obey.* The electrons are attracted to each other, they are drawn to each other, millions and millions of them, and each tiny spark of power spinning on itself, spins toward its nearest neighbor and, when millions and millions have drawn together, we have an atom, which is simply the very tiniest bit of anything in the way of matter we know. And the atoms, whirling and spinning, in turn combine to form a molecule.

The mysterious currents and waves of movement have thrown off their uncountable electrons, the electrons—though each one of them keeps whirling—combine to form the atom; the atoms combine to form the molecule. Think of the tiniest grain of granulated sugar; if broken and examined under the microscope, you will see that it breaks up into still tinier grains; and if these again are broken they still break true to form into grains. Something has at last come out of the Nowhere—matter; gaseous matter, liquid (the liquid atoms of water are not breakable because they are "continous") and, eventually solid.

Once the units of matter have shaped up out of the movement of the Nowhere Nature, the sculptor of the universe, is ready for work. But her clay has not the right "feel" and consistency as yet. Everything that she needs to make the ideal mixture of stuff with which to work, for that is all it is—though artists usually give it a high-toned name and call it their "medium of expression"—is so hot that all these atoms exist only as gases—yes, water, fire and earth are still a vapory gas! But Nature knows—what are the few billions of years needed to change an electron into a molecule or a gaseous into a liquid atom to her—that her creative material, the stuff she is going to use in her work, will now adjust itself naturally.

All these atoms of energy that movement has flung into space, have been whirling around themselves and around each other, pulling towards them other atoms that attract them. The energy of these atoms throwing out light and heat in space begins to take shape as they push and pull at each other, and forms a great patch of glowing mist. Against the black nothingness of the Nowhere it stands

---

*Nature makes everything obey this law by seeing to it that there are two kinds of electrons: those which pull others toward them and those which push them away. The pulling (positive) electrons are drawn to one another; the pushing (negative) electrons repel each other, and it is the *positive*—in electrons as in everything else in Nature—that holds the *negative* together.

out like an ocean of fiery clouds or one great cloud-field of furiously revolving fire.

But this sea of fire as it spins furiously around itself is going through a process of evolution. Some molecules are heavier, some molecules are lighter and—like to like!—in the particular fire-patch that makes up their own cloud (for the fire-sea is made up of thousands of separate fire-clouds) the heavier molecules draw together to form a kind of burning core for the others which revolve around it. About the core-atoms form the liquid atoms, outside, lightest of all, the gaseous atoms whirl with the rest.

Nature smiles. Her "medium of expression," her raw stuff to work with is shaping up nicely of itself. She will let it continue to do so; and it does.

Whirling, blazing, tugging at each other, elbowing each other out of the way in the infinite reaches of space (sometimes coming to a "head-on" collision with the road-hogs of a Nowhere whose "traffic laws" were to evolve of themselves) the fire-mists of the cloud sea began to break up into roundish fragments known as spheroids. No, not globes. For a globe is something that already is round, while a spheroid, in this case, is something *trying to become round*.

It seems a small point to dwell on—the difference between a spheroid and a globe, but the whole idea of evolution lies in that difference. For every thing that is, is constantly striving or being compelled to change. The law of change is the law of evolution. Take your own case! Look back ten years: are you the same now as then? Are you the same in body, in mind, in thought, in feeling? Can you not, looking back, remember vague likings or interests, that ten years ago were still in "spheroid" form within you, but which have "rounded out" and changed just as all is ever changing?

As each of these cloud-spheroids, we have mentioned, kept revolving the parts that made it up, naturally kept shrinking together. For the denser, heavier atoms that made up the core of every cloud kept contracting and pulling the outer layers—liquid and gaseous—toward them. And, as they did this even the never-ending movement of every cloud around its own core—its axis or axle, the two words mean the same thing—like a wheel revolving around its pin, spun them into the great flaming spheroids ever growing rounder and rounder.

But Nature saw that there must be "traffic laws" for the bit of Nowhere which she had picked out as the starting-point for her experiments when she began changing motion into matter. We do not know whether she was moved by that wonderful logic of order and harmony which rules the universe (and which the policemen who interpret our own "traffic laws" do not always seem to understand) or whether she already had "picked a favorite" among the blazing spheroids. She took the great law of "pull," which draws all things together, and the law of "push" which tries to scatter them, and struck a balance between the two.

The biggest, hottest, most powerful of all the roundish fire-clouds —it is still so hot to-day that it has not passed out of the gas state— as it whirled around in space was "pulling" the others toward it, because its pulling power was greater than that of any others. If there was not something to balance this pulling power, the other fire-balls would be drawn into their big brother—the sun—and lose themselves in him!

So Nature saw to it that each other great fire-cloud as it careened through space threw out enough of the "push" pressure to keep it from falling into the sun. And the spheroids, shrinking and getting more solid at the core, and growing rounder and rounder in the course of millions of years, these two forces of "push" and "pull," while they spin around themselves, keep spinning around the sun, and the sun, standing in the "middle of the road," saw to it that none of his time-worn brother planets strayed from the straight and narrow path assigned them to the "great White Way" of the further heavens, into the mysterious distances of the Nowhere. There may be other "precincts," where other stars patrol other beats, unthinkable trillions of miles of time and years of space away, around some other radiant captain-star. But the members of our own "solar system"—for that is what we call the sun and all the stars and planets revolving around him—adjusted themselves "of themselves." The sun's "pull"* was not strong enough to drag his brother planets into his fiery jaws. The pressing-away "push" of the planets (the word comes from an old Greek root, which means "a wanderer") was not strong enough to let them push themselves out of the control of the sun, to wander off into the infinite. So Nature in regulating the universe did something we never have been able to do in settling the affairs of one lone, little planet. She struck a true balance of power; she found the true "middle of the road" which the old song bids us stick to. And, aside from the "irresponsibles" of the skies—comets, meteors, shooting stars and the like, usually more youthful children of the fire-mist, which seem to feel their heavenly oats—the planets settled down in space. Each one patrols a regular "beat" assigned by the

*Gravitation is the name we give the force or influence which makes things draw together. Radiant heat pressure is the force that pushes things away and scatters them. In some cases gravitation is stronger; in others radiation pressure is stronger. If gravitation wins out in the long run, everything that is will at last be gathered into a solid mass. If radiation pressure finally get the upper hand, everything will be scattered through space in eternal movement. If we know which were going to be the victor, we could tell whether everything that begins must end.

action of Nature's laws. Each—though the beats of some (as is the case among policemen) are longer than others—steadily "pounds" the the star-dust pavements of the skies on its own beat, while the sun holds out to burn.

But—Nature by now has chosen one bright particular planet from among the rest, and said: "This star looks good to me. This is one I shall use to preach the gospel of Evolution in a thousand and one different ways!" It is the one we call "the Earth." Somehow, it seems natural that the word "Earth" itself should be traced back to an old, old root-word—ar—which means "to plough." For Nature ploughed and harrowed the earth with fire of every kind until it took the shape she wished. Like its brother fire balls, Earth had been growing rounder. At one stage in the game Earth was pear-shaped and her greatest step in turning into a globe was when she shook off the pear-end. It turned into the Moon, and in turn settled down upon a "beat" of its own, where we will leave it for the moment, while Earth—with its glowing outer skin of gaseous fire, its middle skin of liquid fire and its inner core of more solid white-hot fire—finally whirled and spun and blazed itself into something like an orange flattened at both ends. Nature had picked "the star" of the cast in her first great reel: "The Universe"—the "star" so far as we are concerned, with the definite purpose of turning it into a *stage* for another drama, one which was to be played *on* Earth itself!

But why was the Earth constantly blazing and burning as it travelled through space, we may ask? First because motion in itself is a form of heat. And aside from feeding on itself Earth was feeding on the millions of swarming unattached electrons and atoms it struck as it rushed through the skies. Whenever motion is halted by striking anything at all, it turns into heat. Strike a match, for instance! The matchhead is in movement against a rougher surface: the atoms of that surface try to stop the movement of the match— and the heat produced sets the match blazing. But the blazing Earth was throwing off heat and light faster than it fed its flaming *outer* skin of fire. Its tidal-waves of red-hot gas as they kept rolling around it began to cool—just as a red-hot nail cools as the heat and light it sends off for a while disappears. But—this did not mean what we mean when we say "cool." It turned just cool enough for part of the gaseous fire to change to liquid fire. The liquid fire, being heavier than the gaseous fire, would sink through it and begin to form a thicker liquid crust about the inner core of burning gases.

And as more and more fire in liquid form sank down through the gas-fires that made up the surface layer of the earth, it grew thicker and thicker. From a kind of thick oil it became as heavy as fluid asphalt and gradually, a very, very little at a time—we must re-

member that Nature took billions of years to stage every least movement in a show whose "first night" was a bit of eternity itself—this
crust grew more or less solid. Inside its fiery heart raced the pulsing
tides of shut-up gases. Around these rolled and flowed the great
semi-liquid tides of red-hot hardening crust. Outside this lava-like
crust, whirled and raced with a speed too great to measure, the
feathery, flaming, flashing tides of gas—the sun-tides of light and
heat—in a glory and wonder words cannot describe.

The great semi-tides of blazing gas fail. They are gradually drawn
into the red-hot thickening tides of liquid fire, and these as they
thicken grow more and more sluggish in turn. They are turning
into a thin, *real* crust of glowing matter that takes in all the thous-
and and one things of which the earth is formed.

The atoms of the two great gases, oxygen and hydrogen, two atoms
of hydrogen to one atom of oxygen, when the right moment is
reached in the cooling process—we must remember that this "cool-
ness" is cool only when we compare it with extremes of heat—come
together and form *water*. But when it was cool enough for the two
gases that made water to form a liquid, the heat of the earth's crust
was still so great that it sent the water hissing from its surface in
vast cloud-banks of mingled steam and air, that probably hung above
the earth in a dazzling rainbow glory of colorful mists. But the
cooling continued, water abandoned its vapor form and returned
to earth to flow over it—the tides of fire, which destroy, were succeeded by the tides of water, which were to create. At first, the
earth-crust bubbled wherever it was thin; and the heart of fire beating fiercely within it burst through. Then a hundred volcanos would
vomit forth fire and red-hot molten rock; a hundred earthquakes
would twist and turn and tear the Earth's surface into all sorts
of new, fantastic shapes.

The tremendous waters that had filled in the cracks and holes of
the Earth's crust, the ocean- and river-beds, would be disturbed,
As the case might be they would be flung about—whole oceans like
the Atlantic, if your imagination can picture it—to fill the new
hollows the earthquakes made. Or, if it grew "too hot" for them in
one or another spot, they would once more be driven hissing into the
atmosphere. There they would hang, to fall back to earth with the
falling of the temperature as the sky rained lakes and seas in
these mightiest of cloud bursts.

All these outbursts are natural enough and so are their causes.
Old Earth, at this period of its existence, was young and full of
what is best expressed by a common every day slang word "pep." Its
fiery heart beat swift and high, and it never seemed satisfied, from
one million-year long day to the next with its outward appearance.
There, too, it was in harmony with the spirit of evolution. For

Evolution is a moving on and up. It means more than change—it means a change for the better. Every time, Evolution is an improvement and the face of the Earth to-day is an improvement on the face the Earth first wore. And if Earth could look itself in the face now it probably would agree to this.

In a way, every woman who has her face "changed" by a skin specialist, and old Earth itself, have done so by a process of shrinking. Of course, Earth was not fussy: a few extra ridges of callous in the shape of mountain ranges; a few extra canyon-wrinkles or gorge-pits did not matter. But the highest mountain levels and the deepest depressions we can see on or in the Earth's surface to-day are as nothing compared to those formed when its "face" first was taking shape. Mount Everest and Popocatpetl piled on the Himalayas; the Colorado Canyon dug ten times deeper! One cannot blame Earth for breaking into volcanos and earthquakes trying to look like something created and not the result of an accident. Youthful Earth's attempts at self-improvement were almost continuous. The law of attraction, of gravitation kept drawing the atoms of its fiery heart closer and closer. It was shrinking all the time, contracting without a stop. Here and there, *under* the outside crust, the heart-foundation would shrink away. And where there was nothing to support the outside crust—the crust naturally fell in with a roar of earthquakes or a flooding of oceans to fill the huge new hollows! Again, Earth's *surface* was shrinking, too, and where it shrank faster than the fire-heat beneath it, it would fold up or shrivel together in the shape of long mountain ranges.

Had there been nations in existence at that time, it would have been hard to agree on what belonged to them. One day the Earth's outer skin might shrivel a bit—and up would come the bottom of the sea to shake off its water as it turned into mountain plateaus. The very rock-foundation on which the Waldorf-Astoria in New York now stands once was the bottom of the sea, fathoms deep. Broadway, its course not yet traced, ran along the ocean's floor for the fish to travel. In the Andes Mountains, "the avenue of volcanos," the top of Mount Aconcagua, towering 23,393 feet in the air, was once part of an ocean bed.

There was another process Earth used to change its face, besides the one of shrinkage, outside or inside. The Earth had its own "face wash"—still the cleanest, purest and best to be found—and used it in liberal quantities to "tone down" and generally improve its surfaces. Water was this natural "wash" which never stopped carrying rocks, dirt and other things from one place to another. Some it dissolved—it is these melted solids that the sea washed out of the rocks, in the sea-water, which makes it taste salty—and others it carried along undissolved. And it always, everywhere, was on the move. When the sun's "pull" draws up water from the ocean, turning it into fresh water by leaving the salt behind, it is carried along the skies in cloud form till it is so cool that it is heavier than the air. And then the Earth's "pull" at once drags it down from the clouds again. It may seem to us, especially those of us who may be farmers, that Earth is not as particular as it might be. In other words, it might rain more when rain is needed, if the Earth "washed its face" oftener. But this is something we cannot control. Yet water, which the Earth has used for washing its face year in year out, ever since it had a face to wash, does more to change that face than any other thing in Nature. The water which falls back on Earth in rain, fills the rivers that are gradually carrying the land into the sea, where gravel, sand and clay result when the sea and the tides put rocks and other earth-stuff through the mill of motion and grind them fine. In this way the sea and the rivers that run down to the sea (and for that matter every other body of water) keep going on without a break through the ages, and as they move and act, slowly but surely, they change the Earth's face, and so long as the sun—93,000,000 miles away—holds out to "pull," the seas and waters of Earth will go on moving. And so long as fuel burns, producing the two gases or elements that combine to make water (oxygen and hydrogen), so long will there be water for the Earth to wash its face.

Earth's "letting off steam" by blowing white-hot lava through leaks in its crust—the crust which is now from 50 to 75 miles thick, and has only a small number of volcanic holes, like Mount Pelee, Vesuvius, Chimborazo or Kilauea left, compared to the many hundreds constantly spouting in the early days—got less frequent as the crust thickened. Nor has the constant wear and tear of the waters "washed away" land in the sense of removing it. Where the oceans wash some of the Earth's face away at one point they are piling it up in another. The Earth, instead of being worn away in the course of centuries, managed after each great natural upheaval it brought about to turn a brighter face in the way of dry land to the rest of the universe. It was as though Earth had anticipated Dr. Coué, and roared in the thunders of earthquake and hissed in the lava flow of volcanos: "Day by day, in every way, I'm growing better and better!" And it was true. The greatest bodies of water were flung into deep ocean beds, and broad continents increased in size. Earth had taken on the shape that Nature desired. It was ready to serve as the stage on which the next reel in Evolution's great serial picture would be shown.

It has a good "beat" in the heavens to patrol. Captain Sun was far enough away so that his heat would be a kindly, favoring influence, and his angry rays would not destroy. The pear-shaped

Earth had flung off that which had become the Moon, which had burned and shrunk itself out quickly—in a few billion years—for small bodies cool off more quickly than big ones. The Moon, while Earth, so to speak, was still a mere planet-youth, already was a dead shell of a world. Without air there is no sound, and the still, cold Moon was soundless and scentless. The Moon has the most wonderful flower-gardens in the world. Its flowers can never decay, for there is no moisture on the Moon, and they already have been dead for ages. Poured over plains hundreds of miles long, these magic gardens of the Moon, unseen by any eye, sparkle in all the colors of the rainbow. But they are blossoms of crystal. They are dead.

Yet this dead world whose heart of fire may have stopped beating, which would travel unseen through space if its surface did not catch up and cast off the sun's light like a reflector, has a use. Nature decided it would serve as a *brake* to regulate the power that makes the earth spin upon itself. When Earth first flung off the Moon into space, the Moon's "pull" on the Earth was very strong, because it was so very near. Then the Earth span round so fast that the day was only four hours long, (at least, we think so, for if it had spun much faster it would have spun itself apart), but the Moon-brake, "dragging" against Earth's motive power for millions of years, has slowed it down to a twenty-four hour day. The actual "brake" the Moon uses, by exerting its "pull" is a *tidal brake*, a brake made of the tides.

When the Moon is full it is nearest the Earth, and its attraction or "pull" is at its strongest. So strong is this "pull," in fact, that as Earth goes spinning round, the water comes flowing in to pile up as the high tide. And because the "pull" of the Moon acts on the *near* side of Earth's liquid heart in the self-same way it does on its surface waters, Earth's *whole body* is drawn toward it. And the Moon's "pull" is so strong that the near side of the Earth's more solid body is drawn closer to it than any water on Earth's more distant side is drawn to Earth. And at one and the same time the "moon-pull" piles up a high tide on Earth's far side as well. Nothing can be both on one spot and another at the same time. The water that is left as the high tides pile up under the "moon-pull" at the near and far sides of Earth, makes the low tides that lie between. The Sun does a little "braking" or Earth as well as the Moon. But being so far away the "sun-pull," while it "backs-up" the strength of the "moon-pull" when the full moon shines, "bucks" it at other times and pulls against it. When Moon and Sun pull together high tides are highest; when they get to pulling against each other low tides are lowest.*

*There should come a time when Earth's original four-hour day, which has already turned into a day of 24 hours (perhaps if Nature had been

It is clear that Earth was now placed to the best advantage for any further experiments Nature had in view. She had a "fixed beat" in the Universe, she was adjusted so that the "pulls" of other planets would be helpful—a good "pull" is helpful in any world, many think—and she was provided with tidal brakes as well as extra sun *ones*.

Earth, conceived in the womb of the Nowhere, had safely been delivered into space. Its birthday occurred one fine day, about 1,600,-000,000 years ago, it is thought. It had been nursed through a most stormy babyhood by Mother Nature and—by a process of "roughing" rather than "gentling"—was about ready to supply a scene of action for the sequel of Nature's first great reel "The Universe."

There remained but one more thing to do. Nature's sequel film was to be one of great climaxes, following fast upon each other. But its first climax, probably the greatest of all, was so planned that nothing could be overlooked which might help make or spoil it. And this last detail was the right kind of "atmosphere," the right kind of air, to surround the Earth.

Now there is air and air. The tiny electric molecule* (electrons) we have mentioned as the stuff made up of two or more atoms, are supposed to draw themselves, etc., etc., together out of the "ether," the "air" of the Nowhere—and everywhere else as well—which is filled with all sorts of shapeless currents, waves, and knots of vague radio-energies and other kinds of power of which we know but little. But each planet, as it went whirling off into space, carried some of this "ether" along with it and changed it into its own air, and this air has been part of the Earth itself since Earth began. This air is just that part of Earth's original outside layer of gaseous fire, and is made up of the gases left when the others had burned themselves out. And, for what Nature had in view the Earth needed an atmosphere of a rather special kind, not like that certain other planets had thrown out around themselves. Once she had made sure that this atmosphere was made up of the *two right gases,* best suited to her purpose, oxygen and nitrogen in the right combination (1/5-4/5) Nature knew she could plan her serious experiments. She felt that she had done all there was to be done before beginning to use the Earth both as a "stage setting" and one of the "cast" in her next reel, introducing "The First Living Thing On Earth."

a good Union organizer she could have arranged her laws to make it stop at eight) will increase to forty-eight hours or more. For while she applies her tidal brakes, the Moon is taking longer and longer to move around the Earth, because she is moving away from it. But this will not happen in our day.

*Nature, long before the dentists, knew that one combination of oxygen and nitrogen produces "laughing gas".

CHAPTER II

(Intermission)

In explaining what "Evolution" is the writer said he had written only the captions for this story Nature is telling. She is the author of the scenario. Now, you cannot write captions for Nature without getting to know her, even if you meet her only as a voice, in a vision that takes you out somewhere into space. At least that is where it seemed to be that the caption-writer met Nature, author and producer in one.

It was somewhere in space. The lusty young Earth was swinging down its beaten track in heaven to circle around the sun. It did not seem to need an air-blanket of atmosphere, for it was still spluttering white-hot and red-hot lava. On its way, the heat from its heart afire burst its crust. But drowning out Earth's spluttering, the writer heard what seemed to be a great organ making solemn music, playing a noble march with a swelling glory of sound. And as this music rang out with a splendid, stately swing, it seemed as though all the stars and planets were keeping time to it as they moved. Some planets, as they marched, took one turn in space, others two, and still others four. But all were caught up in the wonderful rhythm of the march whose music seemed born of the mysterious currents of energy that sprang from the countless stars as they went their way through space. It was what poets called "the harmony of the spheres."

But Nature cracked a joke—you will see later that she was too wise a producer to forget her "comics."

"I know what's on your mind. Just a spectacular film, you think. Big effects but no story. All time for a background. A bunch of wild young planets out for a good time in unlimited space, with everything 'wide-open and handsome,' kicking over the traces in heaven instead of Hollywood. A crowd of little stars, meteors and comets as the 'extras' for the mob scenes. But where's the story? While the planets are being "pulled in" by the law (of gravitation) Dame Nature comes along to play fairy godmother to young Earth, one of the bunch, and—just when you think something is going to happen—it's all over!"

But I shook my head. "No," I answered, "it did not strike me that way. What I thought was: Nature surely lived up to that sub-head of hers, "Grandeur!"

"You have the idea," was Nature's reply. "Grandeur—great-ness, dignity, the harmony of vast natural forces working together is what my picture, 'The Universe' means. It is a great dance spectacle or ballet-performance, with the stars as the dancers."

"I stretch my fingers out into the Nowhere, and the waves of energy and movement that always are quivering and trembling and stirring in the abyss of time begin to move in circles of light that grow brighter as they spin. Electron joins hands with electron, molecule with molecule, atom with atom.

"Soon the little dancers of the skies seem one great chain of fire-mist, only to break from each other as clusters of atom dancers cling together to make a smaller group of whirling dervishes of flame. Planets, stars and meteors—they keep on with the dance—turning like giant torches among their little brothers, who dance like swarming fireflies. Swirling, spinning, flying across heaven's great ranges, criss-crossing, bursting, colliding with each other in a crash of worlds run amuck, one would think all the light and heat and energy of the Nowhere had gone mad! But no; gradually order develops out of chaos. The stars and planets take up the stately procession around the sun that will go on from everlasting to everlasting, in a glory of light, while the great organ of the spheres peals the tune for their march.

"A picture like that needs no plot. And yet there is one. 'The Universe' is only the beginning. Its sequels will show how Evolu-tion's great plot develops. This picture was a prologue, an intro-duction, to introduce young Earth. In 'The Universe' he is the hero. In my next reel he has—and is—the whole stage at the start, and then drops the lead and turns into a stage-setting—something no 'movie-star' of your day can do. But Earth is not just a stage-set-ting in the reels which are to follow. It has to change its face, its scenery, again and again. It supplies all sorts of 'properties' with-out which the other members of the cast could not act."

"Besides," Nature's voice sank to an impressive whisper: "My next picture is a miracle picture, a picture of the greatest miracle and mystery the world ever saw. 'The First Living Thing On Earth' was the greatest miracle of all time, and the greatest mystery is the mystery of the origin of life. And yet—even the mystery of the origin of life can be explained. It is not hard to understand, if we will allow for just *one* unknown thing, one unknown 'quantity.' After all, if that could be explained the mystery of how life came to be would be no mystery at all.

"Far, far out in the Nowhere, past where the winds begin, where new mysterious forces and powers are forever being shot off into space by the shock of the electron waves as they meet, lies the mystery of the origin of life. Let us say it was born of three substances, in the most terrific heat, a heat like that of the planets when they went flaming through space.* This stuff is the true *stuff of life!* And this stuff of life, including its unknown 'quantity,' already formed part of the Earth when I set all the worlds marching down the centuries to cool off. Do we really need to know the mystery of life? When the earth was cool enough, one fine day, I simply took the stuff of life, gave it the right conditions for growth, and let it develop. And all Earth's life to-day has sprung from the one bit of the stuff of life that contained the unknown quantity.

"Let the mystery of the origin of life remain a mystery. The things we do not know and not the things we know are always the most interesting. It took millions of years and a thousand workings-over in the womb of the Nowhere to produce the something in whose mixture the spark of life was contained. Nothing that has life ever came out of lifeless matter. The life-spark had to be there! And the secret of the life-spark is still unrevealed.

"Earth in its earlier days was not Earth as we know it now. When the stuff with the life-spark was evolved—for it, like everything else, also was produced by change, Evolution—oceans hung in the skies in the shape of gas, electron and other energy currents of which nothing is known were rushing through space. The radioactivity in the heavens would make the greatest of our present-day radio corporations turn green with envy. In that part of the Nowhere where a hundred unknown forces were clashing, the right combination of light, heat, energy and matter came about, and the first actual spark of life was struck off from the crashing tidal waves of the vast radio currents that washed the stars. And that spark, that glow, that glimmer of life came down to earth out of the skies, to lie dormant—the way a bear lies dormant in winter—until things would be right on Earth for it to awake to activity.

"First Earth had to "blow off" all its steam. Its seas and oceans had to settle in their beds, and no longer hang above ground in a vapory blanket of steam; and then these great waters had to cool off to a certain temperature before the awakening could come and the mystery turn into the miracle. Yet, all said and done, why call the birth of the life-spark a mystery?

"The origin of life is simple when we get down to the main

*Two of its substances are positively known: carbon and nitrogen in a special kind of combination, Ammonium of Cyanite. It is the third, unknown stuff or "quantity" that is the mystery.

facts. Here we have movement, energy and heat in the Nowhere. They change and clash and mix. And, one day, out of all these lifeless things, the spark of life is struck off, and we have what makes things live. What if the spark never is struck off again in all the billions of years of time to come! One spark was enough to wake the whole world to life! After that life began a career of its own. No more sparks were needed to keep it going out of itself. Think of the smallest of sparks you ever have seen struck from the steel by the blacksmith's hammer! Then think of the spark of *living* fire held in a womb of *lifeless* fire until—still living, and not dying when the lifeless fire around it died—drawing on its life-substance (the bits of stuff, oxygen and sulphur and what not, its own carbon and nitrogen, *plus* the 'unknown quantity') beginning to *live* as an actual living thing! And then remember that first, tiny, flickering spark of life was brought forth by Evolution! Everything; every single thing that lives and breathes on Earth to-day, every plant, every tree and flower, everything that swims in the sea, that creeps in the swamp, that flies in the air, that burrows in the ground, that walks the earth—Man himself, comes from that one spark! There is nothing on Earth—nothing at all, save the dead matter which grows from without—that has not come out of the one tiny spark of life that made all the difference between "the quick and the dead," as the Bible says, between living matter and dead matter!

"Not the mystery of the *origin* of life,* but the miracle of the

---

*The story of the origin of life as Nature tells it above seems the "straightest"; the most natural and plausible story. A good many of us, however, like to wonder "what would have happened *if* or how things would have been if . . ." It is for their benefit that this note is added, so that if they feel like wandering off into a summer day-dream when they have read as far as the place marked, or want to call up visions in the crackling glow of the fire in winter, they can have a starting point.

Some think that life began on older planets than ours, Mars, Saturn, Venus; and that on some (like Mars) it still continues. Our own little Sun and the solar system of the Earth are like just so many dots when compared to the other suns and systems which may stretch from the beginnings of the Nowhere out into the eternity of space. Other, bigger earths than ours have cooled off and died. The spark of life may have fallen on them long before it fell on earth. Life's story, in different ways and amid different surroundings, may have been told on worlds without number before the first life was born on earth. On other worlds life, *living* life may have developed in *mineral* form instead of *vegetable* form! And somewhat in line with this idea is the one from another planet. But the story we have told, the one most scientists regard as the true story of life's real birth in the shallow waters of early Earth, is in itself romantic enough for anyone.

development of fire is the great mystery. And that mystery, as you shall see, is one that life itself explains as it unfolds in every living thing. That development is the plot of the greatest story ever told and it begins with my next picture. . ." Nature's voice grew lower and lower, the stately music of the star-organ sank to a soft murmur. When I opened my eyes once more it was time to caption the sequel to "The Universe."

CHAPTER III

THE FIRST LIVING THING ON EARTH

It was the dawn of life's first day on Earth. Somewhere, some-how, in the hot waters of the earliest Earth-Sea, stirred the spark of what once had been liquid fire. For untold millions of years the waters, seething and boiling above it where it lay, had been too hot to allow it to unfold, to grow by drawing together every least little molecule of its being into a living whole. It was life, it was alive, but it was not as yet living. "The Spirit of God moved upon the face of the waters," as the Bible so wonderfully says, and it almost seems as though every atom in the universe must have stopped mov-ing for the twinkling of an eye as the great moment drew near when the first living thing on Earth was to be born!

And that miraclous birth must have taken place during the dawn. For the dawn is the birth of day. We cannot help but think that life on Earth came into being with the rising sun, the same sun once washed by the same electron-waves that struck off the spark of life now coming into its own.

It may have been a brief dawn, but dawn it must have been. Earth was still a place of storm and strife. The land was still struggling with the sea, which was trying to cover it. The sun dawned in a brief glory of fiery red, much closer to Earth than now. Then, in the thick air that blanketed the world of those days, the huge storm clouds gathered, and the heavens were swept with storms that would make our cyclones and tornadoes seem like a tempest in a tea-pot. Most of us know what a really great thunder-storm is like. To gain an idea of the storms of Earth's first day of life we would have to multiply the storm our eyes have seen a hundredfold. The artillery of the skies crashed with a thousand guns where now we hear a hundred. When the battling cloud-masses rammed each other they burst in sheets of lightning miles long, which tore deep into the earth and seemed trying to join their brother fires leaping to meet them beneath the upper crust. Whole rivers and lakes were flung down on earth as the cloud-continents opened their sides, and cubic feet of land equal to city sites and whole counties were swept down into the sea, and swallowed by its waters. There they might lie for untold years while the earth hardened into shale, and the stone was ground to sand in the ocean's current-mill.

But it was probably in the red glory of the dawn and not in the lightning-torn darkness of day that the first living thing on Earth was born. And after that, nothing mattered. The inheritance of life was secured to Earth!

What was that birth like? Like all great things it must have been simple. The hot tides were racing over the steaming mud-flats—tides the crests of whose billows towered much higher than the Woolworth Building—and, obedient to the moon-"pull" flinging themselves against the land with the crash of a hundred buildings falling in a city stricken by earthquake. The spark of life it was no longer an *actual fire-spark* of course, but just a "spark" in the sense of being a throbbing bit of life-electron, an electron which had managed to cross the bridge between near-life and real life—lay quivering in the slimy mud. Amid all the tremendous motion of sea and air and land going on about it, it waited for the one perfect moment, the moment when temperature, surroundings, motion, everything—had reached the birth-pitch. Perhaps, for many thousands and thousands, of years that little life-spark which stirred in the mud had been waiting, waiting—and the moment had not come! Now it had arrived.

The spark moved, it groped, stretched, drew all the tiny, tiny particles, the bits of matter invisible to the eye which lay about it and were part of it into a whole—and the first cell, the whole world in an atom, so to speak, came to life! It was the *Algae*, the first living thing, the lowliest and simplest form of plant life. And from the moment its call or body had formed, it began for the first time on Earth to do those things which make life live. Rising in the pool when the ebb-tide had left, the green, jelly-like *Algae*, a bit of *protoplasm* or life-stuff, living life-stuff, set about eating the first meal ever eaten on Earth. It must have been a cafeteria breakfast, for the *Algae* had to help itself.

At first it drew in the food it wanted—the air and the soft bits of matter in the water—through the skin of its cell: it was all "mouth." Later it put out little tubes to gather its food and draw it into itself, and it also built a "separator" in its cell, where it could prepare its food for digestion. Once this was done, the first living thing on earth, the father (and mother) of all sea-weed, started its career. And it seems reasonable to think that the warm sea in which just the right degree of temperature had developed that morning of the dawn of life, then flowed just about where the North Pole has been discovered (or it may be, the South Pole). At both those points of the Earth's surface the water of the sea got cool sooner than elsewhere, because the sun did not burn down as strongly upon it.

So we may almost take for granted that the *Algae* was born in the then torrid waters of what now is the North Pole. The jelly-celled *Algae* floating happily on the waters, grew and flourished. And as it went on swimming, it grew new cells. Some were for its private use as an individual, others for its most important business in life. Since it was the only life on Earth, it would have to reproduce other little *Algae* to keep life going. Not long after it had equipped itself and looked after its own private interests as "the oldest inhabitant," it turned to the duty it owed the world at large. It began to make other little green *Algae* by the simple process of growing young cells and letting them split off from itself. With each new *Algae* cell-baby which thus broke the connecting thread that bound it to its father and mother in one, another guarantee of life's continuation on Earth was secured. After it had passed on life to other *Algae* it could die—for with life death came into the world—but life itself would go on! It did well, all things considered. It grew new cells whenever it needed them and its descendants inherited the trick of doing so. It did what it could and the *Algae* which followed it for many thousands of years did what they could, to perfect their cells. To this day the cell remains the standard simplest living form. Of the cells, the children of Earth's first living inhabitant grew, some were air—, some were water—and some were food-cells, as well as tubes as already mentioned.

But—while every member of a family has certain "family traits" in common with other members of the same family—not one single member of any family is exactly like any other one. (If you do not believe this, think of your own home folks, and you will see that it is true). So while the *Algae* family was spreading through sea-waters and along the shallow pools, the individual members of the family, as it scattered, were all carrying out Evolution's great law of change.

Some members of the *Algae* were what we call "conservatives" to-day. Conservatives, whether jelly-fish or anything else, are against change. They want things to stay the way they are. The conservative *Algae,* when their brothers began branching out, shook their sea-weed heads: "We do very well as we are, so why should we change?" And because they were too conservative to move with the times, they were left behind. When we look at a giant California Redwood to-day we can see what progress, what Evolution really means. The *Algae,* starting with their one cell, that clung to the past are just as they were then. They live their brief day and die. Their brothers, who tried to get ahead succeeded: they live in a magnificent tree which endures for centuries, as one of the noblest and most perfect forms that plant-life has developed.

The first split probably came when some of the more enterprising

Algae, instead of budding little baby cells that were imitations of themselves, and playing father and mother at one and the same time, decided to select one sex like the electrons—a positive and masculine sex—or a feminine and negative one. This division of the business of creating new life, to pass on into the world was the first great step in advance in the vegetable kingdom. Here and there different *Algae* already had changed their family names. Gradually, according to the food they ate, the waters or lagoons they lived in, they chose other ways and means of calling forth the life it was their duty to pass on to their descendants, which turned into Fungus plants, Mosses, Lichens and various sea-weeds of different kinds and colors.

Let us look into what for the sake of convenience we may call the "married life" of the *Algae* and most of their descendants. The object of marriage in those days was to produce children. In the earliest time, when a plant was all parent and all cell it simply split apart—and where there was one there were two. Then some enterprising *Algae* tried a new way. It built up a whole crowd of babies in one special inside cell *on* the outside cell of its own cell-body, then let it burst, producing a big family all at once.

The next step was the first timid stirring of the separate mother-instinct in the compound parent (though "instinct" is, perhaps, too strong a word to use). Somewhere, among the *Algae,* was one which instead of just growing a cellful of young, made its mother-self shape up in a little thread of tiny cells and beside it grew another little thread of cells to represent its father-self. Then mother-cell and father-cell passed into each other to make the first known "egg" of any kind, and when the "egg" was ripe it budded out as a new plant.

This wanting to be either mother or father but not both at the same time grew stronger as the centuries passed in their hundreds. In the meantime some plants had discovered a simpler way of carrying on—when they grew old, they simply joined cells and the union of the two old cells produced a fresh, lively youngster of a plant, ready to start all over again. This easy way of "carrying on" did not lead to higher things. The plants which took this easy road to eternal youth are still where they started. But the mother-and-father-cells, each with a responsibility of its own, had moved on to sex. The father-cell became the "live wire," the pollen-cell, while the mother-cell, became the egg-cell. And the egg, the passive, waiting life-stuff, could not wake into life until the pollen, the active life-stuff had come in contact with it. In various special developments of sex-organs all the lower, seedless plants that descended from the *Algae,* gradually worked themselves up into the Fern forms and got in the habit of "changing" off in reproducing themselves.

There would be a plant generation born of fertilized eggs, and then this generation of plants instead of eggs simply produced "spores," a kind of cell all ready to begin life, and the first step toward a real seed. But these "spores" would go back to building male and female organs to produce a fresh batch of eggs. This see-saw method of carrying on life was the best the plants could do before the first real seed was formed.

So now when we look, we see the sandy or muddy stretches of the Earth's first sea-shore, its mud-banks and lagoons, crowded with all kinds of plant-life. Already—let us say tens of millions of years have passed since the first *Algae* stretched out into life—there are plants in hundreds and hundreds of varieties, and they have passed out of the sea-water, out of the slime and mud of the lagoons to take root on dry land. We must remember that during these tens of millions of years plant-life has been evoluting without a stop. The children of the *Algae* have spread and changed and changed, and shifted and shifted, again and again. And shifting and changing about in the world, they have met other plants which could trace back their origin to the dawn of the first day of life but—these seemed to be strangers. In the case of other plants each individual member had been so busy grafting its *own special individual traits* on the *hereditary form* it had inherited, and intermarrying with other plants that introduced *a new lot of hereditary traits,* that no one, to look at the two distant relatives, would have known they had a thing in common.

The land plants among the *Algae's* swarming descendants were the ones which had found out that a plant can adapt its organs to drink in the oxygen it needs from the air, and draw up the other nourishment it must have out of the ground instead of the water. This came in part because each family, and each branch and variety of each family, had spread out as fast and as far as it could. All were producing more little plants than earth or water could possibly take care of, and each plant wanted to give its own the best chance. Suppose you were a highly developed *Algae,* and the Greatest Common Divisor or whatever it was that took the place of the stork in the *Algae* family brought you anywhere from 1,000,000 to 5,000,000 little *Algae* a year! To make clear that the whole world would not have been big enough to hold the entire family, if every member lived up to the family record, we need only multiply by 5,000. And then do a little more multiplying to cover the rest of the plants on earth, for we have considered only a single one.

These large families were the origin of the well-known phrase, "the struggle for life." And do not imagine an *Algae* did not know as much about the "struggle for life" as a poor bricklayer with two or a rich farmer with ten—an Algae had 1,000,000 at least—children!

So throughout plant life began the cruel struggle to get ahead of the nearest other plant before it got ahead of you. Stupid plants that were unable to change their shape or that of their cells to get at the carbon gas in the air or the sunlight did not live long enough to have many offspring. Where two plants were growing side by side each was trying to overtop the other, to "suffocate" it by cutting off its sunshine. That is how *leaves* came to develop for leaves are the mouths of plants. And if you shut off their sunlight, the raw carbonic gas the upper leaf-cells have sucked in out of the air cannot be taken in and used by the lower green cells. All earth was turned into a sort of vegetable slaughter-house, where the plants tried to "do in" each other before they were "done in" themselves. This fight that goes on now as it did millions of years ago, is the well-known "struggle for existence."

Along the mud-banks and on the dry land a thousand silent, murderous struggles were going on all the time. Earth's first *parasites* —things that live on and at the expense of others—and the "black sheep" of the *Algae* family came to light. As might be expected the very lowest kind of Fungi—for there are degrees of lowness among them—are the tiny Fungi-things that enjoy life in putrid, stagnant liquids, and in the blood and bodies of diseased animals. The very tinest forms of life we know *live* and *thrive* on our typhus, consumption, cholera, small-pox, influenza and other blood diseases. Dividing to make big families, they increase with terrific rapidity, while watched under the microscope. Their right name is "Bacilli," but they are generally known as "microbes," *Bacteria,* or "germs." About the only Fungus worth its salt is the yeast Fungus, which gives its "rise" to yeast and makes alcohol ferment.

When Nature began to separate plants into father-plants and mother-plants, each doing its share in the work of carrying-on life, she tried all sorts of queer sex experiments. Some plants might carry out, by means of special separate organs in its own body the whole process of fertilizing and developing its "egg." Other plants provided the most elaborate means of making sure that the form of life they stood for would continue, and might even draw in the winds to help them distribute the dust of generation.

Crowding, pushing, shoving, the whole plant-life of earth was engaged in this great fight for existence. The stronger and healthier plant, the plant more clever in taking advantage of sun and ground, of building up its body to feed and spread, was the one that survived. It survived because it was better fitted to live on than its brothers. There was no mercy in the plant-world for the "underdog." If a neighbor plant weakened under attack, if a stronger growth next it could undermine its vitality by stealing the nourishment out of the ground beneath its very feet with sturdier and more "pushing" roots, it did not hesitate a minute to do so. And when its rival had been killed, the murderer's tap-roots were pushing and struggling through the earth intent on feeding on the dying rootlets of the slain. The law of "survival of the fittest," as it is called, seems a cruel one. But we must remember that in plant life as in every other form of life, *Nature's ideal is the best.* Nature wants perfection, and she so arranges things in her great kingdoms that those fit to live, live and "carry on," while those not so well fitted do not last. The road of time which leads from the beginning of life on Earth to the noblest development of the vegetable kingdom is strewn with the invisible corpses of thousands of plant-life forms slain by the wayside!

In the deserts of sand the track the caravans follow is marked by the bleaching skulls of man and beast, the bones of those who have perished of thirst. In the vegetable kingdom no trace remains, in most cases, of the hundreds of millions of plants which have fallen victims to the struggle for survival. Their case has truly been one of "dust to dust." Wherever they fell, whether in shore waters or on far inland meadows, their dead atoms quickly fell apart in the heats of tropic suns, and returned to earth or sea again to furnish food for crowding others of their kind. There is one great exception to this general rule of dead plants whose very "bones" have perished, on which we shall touch shortly.

Nowadays, when a man is growing plants of any kind, seedling plants, let us say, he will go over his seed-beds and pull up what he calls the "rogues." These "rogues" are the plants which are not up to the standard, and hence not fit to survive. In the early days, when plant life was developing, Nature left this business of weeding out the "rogues" to the plants themselves. In the process many interesting plant families were destroyed, because the stronger plants had but one stand—and that was to keep going at any cost. But these weaker plants which had to go were "rogues" too, in a way. The standard set was Nature's, and they did not come up to it!

An interesting detailed life-history of every plant that ever grew on Earth could be written. But we must remember two things. Nature is following up her great scene, "The First Living Thing on Earth" with a picture of progress in which it took thousands and sometimes hundreds of thousands of years to make each step in advance. And if we crowd this great picture with too many details the great outlines, the very story itself, will be killed! Besides, though the first living thing on Earth was a plant, all the plant-life on Earth only stands for *one development* of Evolution, *along one line.* So we shall try to make the great steps, the great moments of our picture stand out clearly. Then you will "get" it.

Nature, all along the road of Evolution up to the time she evolved the highest of all her forms, has set her creatures to work trying all sorts of experiments, different methods of carrying along the spark of life from generation to generation—plant-life and every other— and never really has improved on the idea that every living thing had best be born of *two* parents. Speaking in a broad way, the living things that have tried to be both father and mother to their offspring (beautiful as the thought may be in itself) have not made the success of it that the ones did who separated into individual parents for the purpose. The lower things that first began to swarm on Earth as the *Algae* and its relatives spread out, were inclined to stick to the easier way of carrying on life by shedding a new cell every once and so often.

But others were trying hard to find a better way to do their part in Evolution—hand on the family *type* with the best "modern" improvements each was able to make. It was a kind of "free for all" race, the handicap being that as soon as a plant got *too* conservative, and clung to old, out-of-date methods in suiting itself to its neighborhood, the food it grew, or the manner in which it increased and multiplied, it soon was out of the running. Perhaps it lingered on to come down through the millions of years as one of Nature's shocking examples of how a lack of progressive spirit leaves plants, like everything else, just about where they started. There are *Algae* today, and a little tiny plant called *Flagellata,* which have not progressed much beyond the dawn of Earth's first day of life. There are others which have gone as far as they can in one certain direction—like the *Algae* which, in the form of great tangled masses of seaweed, grows heaped-up in tremendous banks in the mid-Atlantic until in spots it is a menace to navigation! But all plant-life might be said to express Evolution in its striving for *Beauty* (just as the great procession of planets in the universe stands for Evolution's way of expressing *Grandeur* and the *Sublime*). While the Algae and most of the other water-plants which remained in the sea went as far as they could along their own "blind alley"—once they had reached its end they could go no further.

Most of the plants which clung to the habits of their common ancestor ran the idea of "heredity"—the handing on of the shape and nature of a parent to its children—into the ground. They kept on budding separate little cell-children ("spores," as they are called) and thus forever shut themselves out from the higher levels of Beauty. For the plant which reproduces by cell or spore does not flower. It remains a plant that belongs to the lower of the two great orders into which plant life is divided.

The great plant families which succeeded the *Algae* tribes and their descendants were the lower kinds of Mosses and Ferns. (We must remember that other millions of years will pass before they develop their most finished shapes). These were the plants which were struggling out of the steamy swamps—for all that their atmosphere was so rich in carbon, the food their kind of plant liked best—on to the warm, low-lying earth all over the world. All three were seedless plants; "spore" plants. With them were the Lichens.

The Lichens were a curious kind of plant, because they are the first instance of a life-partnership of two plants, based on *business* (in this case *food*) *interests both have in common*. If we look at a Lichen with the naked eye it looks like a mushroom or toadstool. But when examined under the microscope, we see that it is not alone. On it are a number of tiny *Algae*—*Algae* which could make a living for themselves were they forced to, for they are like any other *Algae* we know. Here we have two separate plants living together in an *honest* partnership. The *Algae*, by means of its cell-grains, manufactures the carbon food both of them need; while the Lichen's roots draw up enough mineral salts and nitrates from the soil to feed the company. There is no affection about it, of course: but both plants having found that they could do business "at the same stand," did not hesitate to do so. Yet it was a "small business" after all, for it may have caused them to neglect the more important business of life, that of trying to turn into something better even if not bigger.

Some of the Mosses had by this time managed to bud out the simplest leaves known. But they had no true roots, like the Lichens and Ferns, and had clung to their simple cell-structure. Yet the Ferns were a family destined to go far and grow high.

The best kinds of Ferns—and in these early days of Earth the Fern family was one of a thousand branches, and spread from one end of the world to the other—had already, by dint of pushing and struggling, clinging to the best of their hereditary traits, and adding new improvements to their bodies, made great advances. They had gone as far as *seedless* plants could go along the path of progress traced out for them, and roots, leaves and stems already showed a big advance on those of the Lichen's partner. Their internal organs were complex and highly developed, and they had "veins" instead of cells like their distant forbears.

For millions and millions of years the Ferns were to rule the Earth, producing the finest and most wonderful examples of the one great family which, above all others, was best fitted to live through those long, long stretches of time. In their prime they had practically crowded most other forms out of their ruthless way, and had covered the world with enormous "Fern forests."

If we shut our eyes for a moment we can see the picture! We are looking from the sea—the monstrous "Tethys Sea," as it is called, the old, old mother-sea of our Mediterranean which, very small in comparison, represents the survival of the fittest in a much diminished form. It is a broken shore, with hundreds of islands and island reefs smiling in the sunshine as in the South Seas, and beyond them all the world is one great mass of green, that stretches as far as the eye can reach. Above, the crowding Fern-forests which slope upward with the lay of the land, a bit of sky, and curling up into the sky, the lazy smoke-wreaths of a volcano, on its good behavior for the day.

There is a little water-fern called the "Mare's Tail" which any reader who lives in the country knows. It grows along the creeks and brooks. In the golden age of the Ferns, it grew to be a hundred feet high! Even our familiar "Club Moss," that now creeps along the ground as a trailer, would climb as high as a hundred and fifty feet, and great "Fern-trees" would send tall, straight woody stems up into the air hundreds of feet high before spreading out their great green canopies of *fronds* (the special name we give the fern-leaf) above the ground. That is what the great "Fern-forest" looked like, gazing shoreward from the Tethys Sea!

Entering the forest we feel as though we were in a hot-house. The climate of the time was the hot, humid climate of the moistest tropics. There was no "fall of the leaf" from the giant Ferns. Summer and Winter were the same the year round; or rather there was Summer everywhere, from the Poles to the Equator. So they grew and flourished and gradually drove out all other plants. There was no "self-determination"—the phrase we read so often in the daily papers—for small plants in those days. Not with the Ferns about!

The great stalks with their tremendous heads of dark, feathery green shot up into the air of their steaming natural hot-house as though they meant to play ball with the clouds. Later on, as we shall see, plants had to protect themselves against the change of seasons. But the giant Ferns of those days died *only of old age*. They knew nothing of changes of temperature because the temperature never changed. And, in the end, they represented—together with the mosses, and many reeds and rushes, some with leaves and some without, which rose in the swamps—the one great plant. The Fern forest we gazed on from the Tethys Sea was only one section of the forest-belt which covered the Earth, and gave the landscape the special kind of look any particular tree gives a countryside when it grows in large numbers, and other kinds of trees are missing. The Fern forests ranged to the Poles. Where now the explorer treads the measureless frozen plains of ice, the great "Fern forest" grew to the blue skies, while a sun of red gold beat down on its leafy tops!

But we would not have felt at home in the great silent "Fern forests," silent, for all their lusty vegetable life, as the soundless crystal gardens of the Moon. Each Fern-tree looked like every other Fern-tree. For each trunk, as it rose stiff and straight into the air, was

I

covered with a uniform armor of leaf-plates, like the scales of a snake. And through all those thousands of miles of forest the trunk-scales of each tree were like those of every other, till the eye would have tired of the sight.

And the silence! It hung like a pall over all those spreading Fern regiments in dark, mournful green, a green which seemed closer in color to the dark leaf-mold that speaks of death and decay, than the bright, happy green of our spring. And why were the Fern-forests silent? Why, as they stood in their gloomy green dress was there an absence of that cheerful hum of life we take as a matter of course when we stroll in the woods?

The reason is plain. There were no birds, no bees, no butterflies— there were no *flowers* in the great forests of Fern! Try to imagine what it must have been like! No fluttering rustle of wings in the underbrush, no sudden burst of wild, glad music from feathered throats! No brightly-colored butterflies dancing in the sunbeams of some forest glade! And not a single flower!

Yet what is this peculiar metallic rustling and "moving" in the clump of giant Rushes yonder? Yes, "moving!" Not the Rushes themselves, for it is millions of years since these giant *Algae* children, the Ferns and Rushes, came out of the water to dry land! They are rooted fast now ashore; on the spot they have grown they must stand till they die! But other members of the stock of the very first *Algae*—who knows—may have managed to combine movement with growth. And there *is* a stirring in the Rushes—the great sword-blades bend, they sway! For a moment we glimpse a shadow, huge and brown, and then a distaste for this dark, gloomy wood overcomes us. There is something unreal about it, with its heavy fern-smell, its hidden horrors, its absence of bird-song and all those shy wood-land flowers that make a forest *a forest* for us. And we notice another thing: huge stretches of forest are choking to death in their own growth. In the Fern forest, too, the fierce battle for survival goes on. Some of the Ferns, in their greed for the sunshine and the upper air, have managed to change into Fern-creepers and climbers. Like enormous green snakes they wind themselves around the straight growers. They seem to be stifling and strangling them in their writhing folds, as they fling themselves from one tree to another, but ever moving higher and higher, to throw out *their* great leaf-fronds *above* those of the true Ferns marked for the slaughter. We will leave the dark forests of the Fern: they make us homesick for our own!

Yet the most wonderful of all wonderful things about the great Fern forests of early Earth is not their strangeness, their silence, their mystery. It is the fact that they are Nature's greatest example of how she can work backward as well as forward. Evolution is change, change that makes for improvement. With the Fern forests Nature reversed her Evolution—for our benefit!

When the Fern forests had been growing in savage splendor for millions of years things changed on Earth. The land and the sea resumed their old struggle. Over vast stretches the sea would rush in and bury the tremendous swamp-forests under the waves. When the waters settled, far, far down in their glassy deeps, stood mile-long avenues of Fern trees vainly stretching up their green tops toward the sunshine from which they were cut off forever. But—they had been struck in the full vigor of life, and this vigor was sealed up in them under the sea. Again hundreds of thousands of years went by. Many times new forests grew, only to be swept into the sea again in turn. And through all the change and life and movement in the world above, the Fern forests slept at the bottom of the sea, slowly turning to stone like enchanted princes.

In some regions where they had not been so deeply buried, perhaps, instead of turning to stone, their great trunks changed into the kind of spongy dead wood we know as peat. While sea and land fought together we must remember that the volcanoes played and the melted rock and lava flowed from them. So, while some Fern forests were buried under the sea and—perhaps hundreds of thousands of years later reburied under rocks and earth when the sea was driven away from where they lay—others were buried beneath the stone and lava. It was in this way that Earth kept adding one layer after another to her crust. Not as many layers as an onion grows about its core—but enough to give it its present thickness of seventy-five miles —seventy-five miles of rock, sand and lava layers; with the top earth-layer above them to keep its glowing heart in bounds!

Nature buried the Fern forests and left them. In time a creature was evolved on Earth that needed fuel, the hottest and best, to work out its own Evolution. And then Nature uncovered her forests of stone—and *coal* came into the world—the hardest kind is still known as *"stone coal."*

It was as though Nature had said: "A spark of fire was born out of the electrons' clash before the world began. It came to Earth and changed its form through the years, until part of it had turned into great forests of Fern. And now I have changed it from a *backward* vegetable into a stone that will burn. And this stone holds all the sunshine and clear bright heat the Fern drank out of the tropical air sealed up in its stony cells. I have changed it so that it is fire, fire turned to stone, and only waiting for the kiss of the flame to leap into burning!" And Nature had told the truth. Backward along Evolution's long road she had led the giant Ferns until they were ready to turn once more into what they had been in the beginning of time—fire, light, heat!

And the creature whose Evolution was still working itself out used the stone Ferns that had gone as far as Ferns might go in their development millions and millions of years before—for fuel! Their heat turned the wheels of progress, and supplied the warmth and comfort that encourage life to live and advance!

CHAPTER IV

THE LEAF

WE have just seen a panorama: The first living thing on Earth is born. It increases, changing into a thousand new shapes as its descendants change in the struggle for the survival of the fittest. In the end we reach a time when the greatest and most powerful of all these strugglers, the Fern, almost rules the vegetable kingdom, only to be buried and laid away for untold ages.

It is time to consider *how* the plants lived. The tale of their *inner* life is the tale of their Evolution. Without it we do not understand how they came to express energy, beauty and usefulness in so many ways. The plants whose story we have thus far told were all seedless plants—*they could not flower!* The rungs of the ladder leading up move from the *Algae* (the *Fungi* who devour the green carbon-food of other plants like animals are not an *upward* rung) to Mosses. The Mosses have a rudimentary stem and rudimentary leaves. The Ferns have leaves, but are seedless and, though they grew to tree-size in the Fern forests (and some still grow to tree-size) they are not real trees.

The leaf, which gave the plant a mouth with which to eat while its roots were drinking, was the starting-point for all higher development in plant life. The lower plants, floating on the water, drew in nourishment with every part of their outside wall. Throwing out a special "mouth" for eating carried the plants that did so into a higher class. The *leaf* was the greatest discovery in plant life: the one great step forward in its Evolution! All life turns on something that seems the most common, ordinary and everyday thing in the world—food. People with high brows often speak of it with contempt, but if they did not eat, their tongues would soon refuse to utter the word of scorn. Strength, beauty, intelligence, progress— all turn on food! The life that *eats best* ("best" does not mean most richly, but in the best way to grow stronger, bigger and better) is the life that goes on. But we must not look on all Evolution as a million-year struggle among everything that lived to snatch the bite from its neighbor's mouth just for the sake of eating.

Life eats to live, it does not live to eat. With the means of "inhaling" food at hand, the continued life of the plant on Earth in all its higher forms was made sure. It could develop, change, take on a thousand different shapes and colors, for it had built itself a combined *mouth, lung and stomach in the leaf,* and could secure food and plenty of stuff to get *energy* for all the experiments it might want to try.

While the leaves eat: the roots drink. The plant's first object in life is—so far as movement is concerned—to "stay put." Not that plants cannot move (the *Algae,* as we know, started out as "floaters"), for when they want to get away from a spot seed-plants go so far as to provide their seeds with little feather-threads, so that passing winds are sure to carry them off to new places in the shape of their little ones. But, in general, the first of May (or any other day) is not moving-day for a plant. A plant anchors itself in the ground with its roots and settles down "to live and die"—whether it be in Dixieland or elsewhere. And these root-anchors they throw out are as sensitive as the nerves in animal bodies. The larger roots grow tiny fingers, and while we think of them as being stiffly stretched out in the soil, like water pipes, the real picture is altogether different.

There in the darkness these little fingers, ghostly-white because deprived of the sunshine, are groping, feeling, stretching out in every direction. The plant that stands as though turned to stone on a windless day may be moving, pushing, struggling underground in the fierce struggle for existence. Its ghostly root-fingers are clutched and twined in the root-fingers of other plants, and while in the sunshine above the proud stalk and leaves hang motionless, its root-fingers may have found that stranglehold which means death to a rival!

But while the root-fingers are weapons of offence, they also are the plant's drinking-mouth and throat. They drink water and the main food that builds up their eating-mouths and cells of living green—nitrogen, sulphur and phosphate. Out of what it takes up from below ground and draws down from above ground the plant makes its "body-builders," called *protoplasm*—the building material out of which every living body of any kind is made, vegetable or animal. And—what would we do without the plants?—the plants are the only things that *know how to make protoplasm.* All other things that live have to get their "body-building" substance from the plants some one way or another.

It is a wonderful example of Evolution's way of using one and the same thing for different purposes. It is an example of Nature's system of "cooperation"—for by cooperation, working together, advantages and benefits are doubled. Nature, as we shall see later, has other life-forms under way besides plants. And those life-forms will need *protoplasm,* "body-building" stuff, to build themselves up with and keep going after they are built. What does Nature do? She does not put it up to the animals to scurry about for the building material to put up their house of life.

Not a bit of it. Working at both ends, so to say, with root and leaf, the plants found their way to build little food-bricks of life energy. There was no need of having too many bricklayers (Labor unions are supposed to agree with Nature in this idea) for the plants could supply the food-bricks for the whole house of life—and the other living things could pay the plants for them.

Nature knew what she was about when she made the first living thing on Earth a plant. Without plants—the bricklayers—the rest of the house of life could not have been built! Until plants developed, nothing else could develop, for there was nothing for anything else to eat. For the plant "makes" or "provides" everything except water, on which the animal lives. The plant could live on the lifeless stuff of earth from the very beginning, and flourish on it—the gases in the air, the salts in the earth, and water. And while it fed itself it was making the only food on which all other life could live. Not only does the "breathing" of the plants keep the air pure—in the right balance of its two gases, but—it feeds the bull that makes the brains and brawn of the lord of life's house, at the top rung of Evolution's ladder! And it feeds everything else that is not a plant. If we look back far enough we will find that the savage flesh-eating tiger is really a vegetarian. The deer and lesser beasts it feeds on are grass and plant-eaters. They are vegetable food in another form.

The real development of the plant into the higher forms comes with the Leaf, as has been said, and the Leaf really begins with the Fern-leaf or frond. Plant-life proves what a deep connection there is between every separate *part* of Evolution as a whole. Not until the big Ferns and Fern-like plants spread their tremendous leaves to the sun could other forms of life get very far ahead. Not until Reeds and other water-plants towered into the air out of the marshes, could animal life really get started. Life for the animals was a question of food, too, and not until the plants began to turn themselves into green, living "food-stands" could the creatures who lived on this combination of vegetable "bricklayer and brick" hope to develop. Even with the Rushes, Mosses and Ferns to draw upon, the best food-plants were lacking, and though the first insects were able to draw rich food from their juices, only a few lower animal types found them a satisfactory diet. Fortunately plant-life was moving on ahead of animal life fast enough to let the latter move on and up without interruption.

With sensitive plant-mouths opened wide above and sensitive root-fingers groping for food below; with more food to encourage them to adopt new forms, and new forms to encourage them to find more food, new kinds of plants grow new special organs for special objects, and put out leaves until they grow the *kind* of leaf that is best for each of them. And though mother and father are still united in the same plant body, they have become distinct "persons," so to speak. One might call the stamen, the male sex organ of all higher kind of plants, the father of the seed; and the pistil, the higher development of the egg-cell, its mother.

The first extra cells of early plants produced for this, that or the other purpose, now have grown into a whole hive of cells. These cells are almost like bees without legs or wings. The leaves are neuters. They eat, produce and bud new leaves at the end of the branches, somewhat like the *Algae* increased by division. This leaf-parenthood—with no suggestion of father or mother, is known as sexless reproduction, because sex does not enter into it. And then, to make sure of real children, the same plant will use its stamen and pistils, the real reproducing organs of all the higher kinds of plants, which with their surrounding petals form the Flower, to make Seeds.

But before passing from leaf to flower, we should remember that all the splendor of the trees, all the real beauty of vegetation, came after the Ferns had yielded ground to the higher kinds of plants—*the seed-plants that flowered*. And the higher, flowering and seed-bearing plants are practically all *land* plants. For though the first living thing came out of the sea, the true highway of Evolution which leads furthest lies on the land and not in the water.

CHAPTER V

THE FLOWER

Toward the end of their reign, a few Ferns had put out a feeler toward a flower in the shape of a floweret, a near-flower. We mention it to show that even a plant which seemed to have reached its highest *special* development, wanted to go further. But the attempts at a real seed-organ which these flowerets stood for did not amount to anything. The land and sea struggle began again, and Earth's first million-year long summer ended in a winter night which in turn lasted for other ages. Earth's circle around the sun was not a true circle: it was an oval circle. And as it span the Earth tilted to one side or the other. The reason for these long changing summer ages and ice ages was the tilting of the Earth as it went wobbling around the sun like a top as it span. Its nearness to the sun had nothing to do with it, for the Earth is really nearer the sun in winter than in summer. But this tilting then made the many thousand years winter in its northern half, and covered it with ice. When it tilted back again there would be another summer of ages. So these warm "spells" and cold "spells" were summers and winters hundreds of thousands of years long.

The winter in which the first great Fern-forests had gone, was followed by a summer which called forth more evergreens, yew and fir trees—they had begun to appear timidly at the end of the Fern age—and with them great palms known as Cycads. These evergreens and cycads became the ruling families and the evergreens supplied a new link in Evolution's chain.

The pines, hemlocks and cedars bore the first flowers ever grown on Earth—the pine-cone *was* Earth's first real flower, just as the pine-tree was its first flowering tree.

But in the earlier days of plant evolution things did not move with a rush. Earth was not suddenly covered with lilies and roses, nor did every kind of tree develop out of the crossing of related kinds in wild profusion. But just as in the other life forms that were creeping and crawling and finally walking about the Earth, a "wave of life" did sweep over the vegetable kingdom some millions of years after, when the summer and winter had reigned in turn, each for ages.

This time when the world was flooded with a sudden "wave of life," that carried most of the first forms of plants we know on its top, other life-forms had reached higher levels of development.

For Evolution "works things up" by getting every kind of life to help every other kind of life to get along. The plants struggle for existence among themselves, and so do all other living things. But the separate plants need the help of insects and birds to spread their pollen, their sex seed. And the more insects the more pollen is scattered, the more plants are fertilized, the more "cross-breeding" takes place.

And as soon as we get plenty of "cross-breeding," we get plenty of new varieties. Any number of *new kinds* of lilies result from continuous "cross-breedings." Some make changes in the cup, some grow a new kind of leaf, some even change their odor. And this keeps on and on, plant families and single plants changing from generation to generation, until there are more different kinds than can be counted. And so with roses, with hyacinths, with all the flowers of the night and day in all their infinite variety.

But—nothing in Nature does anything for nothing. No insect will act as a messenger boy unless it is paid in some way. Hindoo poets like to speak of pearls as tears. Brahma wept—tears which fell into the sea and became jewels. And others have said that the scent of the flowers is a breath of the gardens of Paradise which they have brought down to earth. But poets are not expected to stick to facts. The pearl is just hardened matter the oyster has spread around a grain of sand that irritated its tender flesh. It might be applied to a tear, but only to the tear that comes when we accidentally stick our fingers in our eye. And the same thing applies to the fragrance of the flowers.

They used fragrance* and color—anything and everything to "ring up" their insect messenger boys. The insect, drawn by the color and scent settled, on the flower. He needed no help in finding the sweet juice—honey—which the flower spread out near stamen and pistils, and after eating the insect would hurry off to another flower and brush off the dust of life he had gathered on the stamen of the first one on the pistil of the second. Even birds, the humming birds for instance, are delivering these flower "messages" in return for a honey fee. And the flowers even produce the "fragrance" some particular insect they have in mind likes best. Certain South American plants coax carrion-flies to carry their pollen, by making their large blossoms look and *smell* like decaying meat! The figwort throws out the perfume of *rancid mutton* to call in the meat-eating wasp. More poetic reasons could be found why flowers

---

*What give the flowers their fragrance are certain volatile (evaporating) oils that they allow to escape into the air.

(most of them) smell so sweetly and bud out in such beautiful colors; but these reasons are the true ones.

In this way as other life was increasing all the time, the plant life of our own time, which stands for the survival of the fittest through all the preceding millions of years, is the final outcome of the great struggle.

On the way many, many plant *kinds* have died out. All were not crowded out by their fellows. There is many a missing plant-link between the *Algae* and the Redwood or the Tuliptree. Some must have been swept out of existence by great natural changes. But starting with the *Algae*—with close relations in the "line of direct descent" as well as relations so distant that one would hardly know they were related—there are enough links in the chain to show how true Evolution's story is. They make plain that every little difference in a leaf, a stem, a bud, a flower; in feeding or bringing forth spores or seeds, might be the beginning of a hundred new kinds and families.

The intelligence in making changes for the better shown by the plants is marvelous; the cooperation with all other life to gain their ends is astonishing. Certain grasses hide their seed so cunningly in the ground that it escapes the close-cropping sheep. Others, like the bamboo, grow into trees but keep other family traits. Some plants grow soft and some hard wood cells, according as they wish to "buck against" or bend to the winds. And the thousands of different kinds of leaf-mouths that are put out to draw in food cannot be numbered. Desert plants grow hardly any pores in their fleshy leaves to prevent the water they want to keep from evaporating. The annuals are satisfied to live a brief season. They spring up from a seed, grow stem, leaf and flower and wither and die. Their work is done: their seed is produced and their tribe will go on. What more can a plant ask for?

But the long-lived plants are not so devil-may-care. They grow a stem that lasts from year to year, and put out fresh leaves, flowers and seed as the seasons go by. Some plants that go on from year to year in this way, like shrubs and bushes, prefer to grow themselves woody stems. Others keep life going by going into the earth. Their stems and branches are all underground, in the shape of roots and stocks; like the potato, the iris, the tulip or the artichoke. The spend-thrift, come-day-go-day annuals—the one year plants—are less protected against dying out, in spite of their seeds, than the saving bulb or root plants. The swollen base, the *bulb,* at the end of a lily or onion, answers to the tree or shrub *bark,* in which the stem-growers put away their life stuff during the winter months. Both preserve energy. They are Nature's choice by "natural selection," and Nature takes care of them—because they take care of themselves, while the "free spenders" die.

And in Madagascar an orchid grows a petal-cup 18 inches deep for a moth with a tongue of even greater length to "dip up" the pollen. And the plant's pollen is spread as it should be. The cocoapalm, often as not, hangs over the water that flows around a South Sea island. So its nut is given a fibre coat and stored with food for the long ways a current may take it to other island sands. These are all proofs of how wonderful Evolution works to carry out its purposes in plant life.

The South American orchids are too careful to put their honey out where insects who would steal it, but would give no return, can get hold of it. They hold it at the bottom of a long, fleshy petal. While the long-billed humming-bird for which it is intended is picking up the tiny insects which have drowned in the honey— for the humming-bird eats insects and does not care for the juice— the pollen of the stamens is rubbed off on its head and it can fly off about the plant's business.

The flowers that use the wind to carry their pollen do not have to "dress up." They need not paint nor perfume their petals. As the Bible tells us, "the wind bloweth where it listeth," and so their stamens (long stemmed) quiver in the least breath of air. The pistils are also long and feathery, and hang far out to catch the least atom of pollen-dust. Mostly they are the flowers of high-growing forest trees which can thrust their pollen to the winds of heaven, and feel sure it will be carried to the right pistil. But little wayside weeds do the same thing. It is simply that the plant in question prefers the wind to the insects as a carrier, and shapes its organs to make it easy for the wind to work. All the great foodgrasses—rice, wheat, millet, barley, Indian corn—are wind fertilized. As a rule they grow in God's great open on great windswept plains and fields, and their tiny flowers fling out their pollen with every passing breeze.

Just how do the plants go about reproducing? It is this way. While simpler plants used earlier, simple ways of handing on life and existed, that is about all they did do. The winners in the race were the ones who unconsciously realized that to obtain the best results for themselves and for their children, "Mother" must have a distinct, separate body of her own, and that "Father" must be provided for in the same way. It points a moral for all of us who are too eager to do everything ourselves. Evolution shows us in the plants that the *positive* and the *negative* principles—or, if you like it better, that which *"does"* and that to which something is *"done"*—should first be separated before being brought together to get results. All the plants that amount to anything, all the plants which have made their way in the world, are plants that gave up the weakening and degenerating habit of "inbreeding," *of applying the communistic idea of owning everything in common to their sex processes.* The better babies of plant Evolution were those whose parents separated into their own individual selves, male and female, as the case might be. What makes the whole story of plant life so fascinating is that even the ways in which the vegetables developed through Evolution, supply lessons we can take to heart.

Of course, there are still many low kinds of flowers which still stick to the old easy way of fertilizing themselves with their own pollen. But this lazy and slovenly manner of "inbreeding" tends to keep them poor and weak. Brothers and sisters (stamens and pistils on the *same* flower) and first cousins (stamens and pistils of *another* flower on the *same* plant) should not intermarry—not on the same family "tree" or plant. Fresh blood—and a little pains taken to secure it—is what the plants which have risen to commanding positions in the vegetable kingdom have kept after and secured. They did so by cross-breeding—using the winds and insects as pollen-carriers—and went on up to places of honor and power. The others became the "poor whites," the "hooligans," the outcast and scum populations of the plant world. Poor, "mean," degenerate, unsuccessful, because they did not improve the chances Nature gave them, they linger along, dying out, or being choked to death with ease by sturdier, "cross-grown" plants born of the common-sense idea of having two "regular" parents, a *father* and a *mother,* not a double-sexed "corporation" parent, done up in the original package, which could answer to neither name.

Once in a great while, where plants grow wild, Nature, as though to show that there are exceptions even to the general law of sex production, will have a plant or tree produce a bud or flower like none of its fellow-buds. A peach-tree will throw out a nectarine bud, or a moss-rose bud, different from any other rose-bud on its bush, will be born by an ordinary rose-bush. These rare variations of the regular family faces show how strong heredity is. They prove that the look or nature of some ancestor, far, far back, may sleep in the life-blood of the plant for generations before actually taking shape in leaf or petal.

To return to the mother-pistil. Its eggs, or young seeds, already have been produced, and must now be touched by the pollen which is to start them into life. This pollen—unless the flower is one of the degenerates we have told about—must come from the father-stamen of *some other plant.* The father-stamen which sends out the pollen, in turn, does not fertilize his *own* pistils with it, but sends it adrift to fertilize the pistil of *some other plant.* When the pollen-strewn pistil has ripened its seeds, it is known as the "fruit." In most cases the "fruit" bursts when ripe, and flings out its seeds or drops them on the ground. Some seeds are soft seeds, some have a hard jacket; some are kernels, some are nuts. But once they have been matured and have dropped from their mother-pistil a new generation of plant-life has begun.

CHAPTER VI

TREES AND THE ROMANCE OF THE FLOWERING PLANTS

In telling the details of the bitter war that all plants carry on against each other, their own brothers as well as all others, we have dwelt on their weapons and their way of fighting. The network of broader leaves they weave shuts off the life-giving sunshine; the hangman's noose of the creeper tightens around a dying trunk; the vicious, tearing, wrestling root-claws, are offensive weapons. All are used in a fight that ranges from the subterranean tunnels underground to the tops of the forest trees. It is leaf against leaf, root against root!

The very plant, though, that is sapping its brother's life-blood under its feet, may be fighting some parasite that has settled on it, and is busy while it commits murder with its roots, in building up a tougher leaf-texture or mixing up a poison-juice within its veins to keep from being killed itself.

Their different kinds of enemies, their different ways of life, the different kinds of places they live in, and the different kinds of ways they are forced to go about getting the same food from the air above and in the ground beneath is at the bottom of what is called the *origin of species* the starting out of different *kinds* of plants.

The grand-children of the first *Algae* that kept right on living as grandfather had done, are *Algae* still to-day. But a lot of them *had* to change, little by little, as they found they must grow root-fingers and mouth-lungs instead of eating and drinking through the pores of a cell. We know that every other plant must have developed out of the *Algae,* but this is how it happened. Some *Algae* have worked and strained themselves into Mosses, and one of these Mosses has stretched itself out into a Fern. Do the rest of the mosses step into the fern class? Not a bit of it. The first fern came of moss parents, but the other mosses remain members of the moss family, and keep on in it, though they may divide into green mosses and grey mosses and land mosses and sea mosses, each different from the other. The Fern, however, has gone off and started a new species or kind. And so it goes: some Fern—through all sorts of middle forms—gets to be a Palm. Then the same thing happens again. The ferns keep on their way and the palms theirs until after a while we get all the different *kinds* or *species* of plants. The missing links—the plants that are in between, like the generations of more ferny and less mossy plants between moss and fern—are the ones that get "lived down" and disappear. And this is one of the most romantic things about the whole story of plant life. We have the great line of ascent from the *Algae* to the tree. But all along the way while going on up, we do not lose the many separate kinds. On the contrary they keep on branching out into different families of the *same kind*. And so in the end we have all the thousands of different groups and kinds of plants, each divided into all sorts of families of its own kind, while the great line going up from the first living thing is unbroken.

Let us take the flowers. Old sentimental songs, before jazz came into the world, show us the bee as a gay insect deceiver. He goes buzzing around from flower to flower, making love, "kissing," and breaking flower-hearts. Is not actual reality far more romantic? The flower making rich stains within its own self, out of the air and sunlight, to blossom out in the beauty of color—gold, crimson, lilac, blue—a thousand shades, for the sake of its seed-children! Or, drawing the stuff of fragrance out of the dark, moldy earth, it turns it into exquisite odors in its body-laboratory for the same reason. Only the plant, of all living things, has turned its organs of generation—its flowers—into such a marvel of color and fragrance, made its body into such a glowing, radiant altar for the god of life!

Is there anything more romantic than the *little grain of corn* found in the Egyptian pyramid, which has held its life for *thousands of years,* and which placed in the ground sends up its green sprouts as though nothing lay between the sweating slaves who were dragging the great stone blocks to *build* the pyramid and the sweating scientists who *radio* the news of their discovery across the world? Nothing can restore King Tutankamen, as carefully preserved as the grain of corn, to life. He is dead for all time. But the grain of corn *lives* and the green shoots it sends up span the bridge of six thousand years between its past and present. That is romance!

Our rose, queen of all the flowers, probably is older than the famous Hanging Gardens of Babylon, and most of our flowers were developed in the last great "wave of life" which swept over Earth before the dawn of civilization. But we know that long, long before that Nature could point to the highest and finest form of flowering plant, the flowering tree. Three tree kinds, especially—the Cycad palm, the Ghinko tree, and the Sequoia and Eucalyptus—connect us with that far past which continues back to the first day of life on earth.

The "flowers" are the loveliest and most beautiful, the trees are the noblest and most perfect expression of the Evolution of plant life. The first plant-cell that budded another smaller leaf-cell out of its middle began the stem that grew into the tree. For as this leaf grew more leaves—all goes back to the leaf again—each out of the other, to stretch upward, the *stem* stretched out of itself. And once it had become a separate part of the plant it gradually grew stronger and thicker, a real *trunk*, and in the course of Evolution developed its boughs and branches *off from the main stem*, until it became a bush.

Some trees, like the palms, do not branch; but rise straight into the air from inside, because on the road from bush to tree they kept on making the main trunk thicker, and not branching out until high above ground. The first life in the inner heart of trunk-cells moves with each year into a new ring of live cells it has built up around the old one. The old cells die and turn into wood. Thus the number of rings in a trunk give an idea of how old it is.

The tree is the last and greatest thing the Evolution of plant life produced. The tree first developed from herb to shrub—there is a plant, the Spirea, which sometimes takes one form and then the other, and shows how it is done—and as a shrub was forced higher into the air by the "struggle for existence" in the densely crowded tropical forests of other shrubs where it grew. Among all those shrubs struggling up, each trying to get to the upper light and sunshine, the ones that "got there first" and "downed" the others, were the ones that survived and are the ancestors of all others of their kind.

It seems right that some kind of *evergreen* tree, for the Sequoia belongs to the evergreens, should be the one to link us with the past. And it is a pleasant thought that its noblest specimens are found in the United States, in the Sierra Nevada Mountains. There it still towers as its ancestors did before civilization dawned, over 300 feet high and with a trunk 35 feet thick. As to romance, we need only recall the grove of mammoth Sequoias at Calaveras, California, growing 4,300 feet above the sea. We know they were growing there some 1400 years ago. The leaves of the *same trees* that still drink in the golden sunshine there rustled in the wind when Peter the Hermit preached the First Crusade to take away Christ's sepulchre from the Mohammedans! Think of a life that may continue, who knows, until a Mohammedan crusade floods Europe in the centuries to come!

If the rich, heartening, piny odor of the Sequoia's flowers, its cones, might almost be called the odor of eternity, the Eucalyptus, the greatest of "gum-trees," which traces its descent straight back to a leaf in the dim, dim ages past, throws off a fragrant oil *from its very leaf,* instead of from its clustered flowers. Like the Sequoia, it is one of Earth's giant trees, and the oil it gives off is one of

Nature's most wonderful antiseptics. When the Eucalyptus oil is exposed to air a little miracle that has something touching about it happens. Ozone—the ozone that fills the ocean air, develops on the surface of the leaf, as though the great plant were breathing out all its longing for those wondrous *seas of an early world*, seas in which all our oceans could be lost, and *from which its ancestors had drawn that life-giving ozone* with its leaf-lungs *hundreds of thousands of years before!*

The Cycads (palms), are the "princes of the vegetable kingdom," at least so they have been called. But they are not on a level with the Sequoia or the Eucalyptus. Their stems are the stem of a broom, their flowers as simple as those of a rush. Yet they are a very numerous plant kind, with over 1,100 variations of family type. Their romantic associations with the last great Fern forests is forgotten in the fact that Nature, in developing them, made them the most generally useful of trees. From *one kind* of tree, distributed among its separate family members, we get: food, shelter and clothes, timber, fuel, sticks, fibre and paper, starch, sugar, oil, wax, wine, tannin and dye-stuff, resin and more, stored in them to serve the purposes of other earth-life as well as their own! Nature, while developing the rich profusion of the palms, kept in mind the development of other Earth-life. Both the Ghinko-tree and the Cycad are Ferns that are no longer ferns, but have not yet become true palms, though on the way to do so. They have survived and still flourish in separate family groups, linking the giant Ferns of early Earth-life with the ferns we know to-day on one hand, and *all* ferns with *all* palms on the other. Thus they are one of the striking examples of the "moving over" from one kind of living thing to another which we already have explained. In the same way, the bushes and shrubs from which the Sequoia evergreens and our own fruit- and nut-trees originally started before they changed by means of leaf, stem and flower into all sorts of different family groups, were here on earth before the first actual Sequoia itself set up house as a distinct family group. They had to be. We may not be able to trace out of the thousands and thousands that may have vanished, the one particular bush or shrub whose leaf, bud or stem *started* the Sequoia kind. But we know it lies *somewhere* along the road Evolution has followed from the *Algae* on. And, as we have seen, there are so many examples of the direct upward Evolution of each plant out of some preceding plant-form, that it is impossible to doubt the truth of it all.

The first great road which Evolution takes ends in a paradise of bloom and beauty, of fragrance and stateliness, of "flowers" and trees. We have travelled the road from its start with the first living thing on earth, direct to the tree that marks its end. We have followed from the spark of life born on the first day of life's past to the shadow cast by the giant Sequoia on the mountain-top of the present. But this unfolding of the whole vegetable kingdom out of the first life-cell is only is only *one* part of Evolution's story. We must return to the "bend in the road" where the first living *creature* on earth branches off, to follow Evolution's great highway, the one that leads to her highest and most perfect development. It is the first scene of this greater picture of progress that of "The First Living Creature on Earth" which continues the story of what came out of the Nowhere.

CHAPTER VII

THE WIND IN THE REEDS

(Intermission)

THE sound of music woke the caption-writer. It was not the solemn harmony of the planets he had heard played on the organ of the Universe. It was a different music. Soft and low at first, it rose to great, gusty, hissing, blowing outbursts of sound, only to die away again into tender, long-drawn sighs and moans. Nature was there, was busy waving the actors in her last scene off the stage. Glorious gardens of lilies, roses and other flowers were fading into shadow; immense forests were disappearing in the mists of time. But the great reeds and rushes of an early Earth-day still clung to the fringe of the stage, and the winds of space playing through them made music.

Nature looked at the disappearing plants with affection.

"Of course, such a thing as a human being has a long, long wait before appearing in this serial," she said, "but when I think of my plants I cannot help noticing how like human beings they are. Evolution has taught them a lot of things which man—if he ever develops—will have to learn all over again." And she settled down to explain some things plants and human beings had in common.

"In the first place plants breathe, eat, drink and marry, like human beings do. And when it comes to the business of life, some plants are night-workers and sleep during the day, and others (like most human beings) work by day and sleep by night. But when your own particular kind of insect, the one you need in your life-business sleeps by day, then you have to be awake and ready for him during his night-time working hours. Most of the *night-workers among the flowers* do not go in for colors. They do not have to rouge to attract attention. At night 'all cats are grey' as the proverb says, and the insect would not see her brilliant dresses. So they go in plain white, and put all their energy into throwing off a strong, sweet perfume.

"It is not modesty which keeps the jasmine, the campion, the tuberrose, the stephanotis and other night-bloomers in the simple white muslins of plant-dress. It is plain common-sense.

"Human beings close their eyes; the flowers fold their petals. Some are early risers and go to bed by noon like the crocus. Some never think of opening their petal eyes until dusk. When sleeping most of them let their leaves hang limp, just as human beings relax. Only the deep breathers stand up straight, to take in their heavy draughts of oxygen. And they will wake up in the night if light shines in on them. Of course, it is pretty well established that all plants are deaf and dumb. The trombone that Darwin played to some plants to get them to take notice, was just so much music thrown away, as I could have told him. But—that was before jazz: a bit of jazz, now ? . . ." Nature reflected for a moment before going on.

"So far as touch goes, there are *sensitive* plants. They have delicate, quivering hairs on their leaves. Touch the leaf with your fingers and it curls up. If an insect touches the leaf it so tickles and excites the leaf that it folds right up on it. And wise insects do not "touch" these plants. For, strange to say, while the majority of plants are vegetarians, these touchy ones are meat-eaters. With human beings the exact opposite is the case.

"And though they do not 'see' in the same way a human being does they do 'see' for all that. Some have 'eye-pupils' in their leaves, a kind of lens which gives them an image of light and darkness. Any number of plants grow regular 'eye-dots' along their surface to 'see' the light with.

"One of the most human things about a plant is its mother-love. Yes, I know that sounds rather strong, but what else would you call it? The mother part of the plant has ripened its baby into a seed. And the plant-baby has a little root to dig with, and a little shoot to climb with, and a pair of fat little leaves tucked away inside to breathe with when it bursts its jacket. That jacket points the way to the plant's mother-love! Many plant-babies do not stay with their parent plant to be brought up. Everything the plant-mother wants to do for her youngster has to be done in advance. So the mother sacrifices herself. She literally "puts herself" into things which will help her child along. She grows hooks on the seed-baby's jacket, so that it will catch and cling to anything in the way of wool, fur or feathers that may pass, and be carried away and dropped at a good spot on which to begin life. Other plant-mothers (dandelions), weave feather-sails or one long feather (clematis) to carry the babe to some happy food-hunting ground. The fondest mothers, that stay longest with their children, are the ones which leave their home stalk or stem and travel off with them. But they give up their own mother-life to do so! In the shape of what is called the "fruit," they have turned themselves into fats, oils and sugars—into food-packages—so that their little one shall not start out hungry on life's road.

"Of course, when we have a mother-fruit so anxious to get children started in a brand-new spot where the soil is fresh, that like the sandbox-tree of the West Indian Islands, it bursts its seed-capsules and 'shoots' its little ones into the air with a noise like a rifle-shot, there is no human comparison. And these sandbox-seeds are so heavy, and go through the air with such force, that they can cause a serious wound!

"But when a peach turns a rosy, golden cheek or an apple shines invitingly red in human eyes, it is just a fruit-mother begging to be devoured. She has turned herself into a sweet, tender pulp to draw humans or birds. Her young, provided with hard or stony coats (to protect them against the digestive juices of animal stomachs) must be dropped in good places. And so the mother offers herself her own "flesh," so to speak, to anything that will eat her and, in return, drop her young where the ground will be well manured! But while fruit-mothers try to call attention to themselves, nut-mothers hide. They show a green coat on the tree and a brown one on the ground. And the sharper the teeth the squirrel grows, the harder grows the nut it must crack. In the case of nuts, hazels, cocoanuts, chestnuts, acorns, almonds and others, the nut-mothers lay themselves away in rich starches or oils around the actual seed-baby.

"And here we get in touch with the human again. Such a seed-baby is born with 'a golden spoon in his mouth,' for food is the only gold that is current in the vegetable kingdom. The simpler plants, too, are very human in the way they scatter around big seed-families to 'make their own way in the world,' without doing anything to help them along. It is in the plants high up in the social scale that you find the mother-love which turns its affection into food. In human beings this is altogether different. Riches and poverty have nothing to do with mother-love there. And often the mother who has the least of this world's goods cares the most for her little ones. The California poppy is one of the happy-go-lucky plant mothers. She had to start life with nothing and on nothing, and get busy at once combing the air for food as soon as she struck the ground. And every child in her immense family still has to do the same. The young cocoanut, however, is a rich plant's son. Its food-bank has such a big balance in it that the youngster can grow forty or fifty feet high on it without ever having to 'stir a stump' to hunt up a meal! The higher members of the grass family, a family which 'came in on the ground floor' so to speak—wheat, rice, Indian corn, barley etc.—all store up food for their young to start life with.

"But man makes no difference between the plant-mothers that want to be eaten like the apple, so that baby seeds can be spit out and start life right; and the plant mothers who have turned into food only for the sake of their offspring. When human beings are eating nuts and tubers—potatoes, yams, turnips, bee-roots, etc.—they are literally robbing the plant-children's savings-banks of the food-currency placed to their credit. But—as in all others cases—the fittest are the only ones to survive. Human beings have a higher purpose in life than plants, so the potato must suffer!

"Though plants are great 'stay at homes,' what we know as 'club life' was an old story to them long before the first athletic club was organized in ancient Greece. Club life among flowers started when a lot of small flowers found that they could attract insect 'visitors' better by 'clubbing together.' Look at a lilac or a fox-glove, and you will see what is meant! They are true examples of flower-clubs. The large-growing members of the lily tribe, families like the auratum, do not join clubs; but small-growing kinds, like the grape-hyacinth and the star-of-Bethlehem do. They are cluster-clubs, but you will find other sorts, like the individual daisy. For each daisy and dandelion is really made up of many tiny individual flowers, the better to draw insects!

There is a plant development of the club idea, the idea of an association for mutual benefit, which is almost human, so clever is it. In Guatemala there grows a twenty-foot Acacia-tree. Its trunk and branches are covered with hollow thorns. Little ants make holes in these thorns and settle down to housekeeping in them. And if any animal tries to eat the acacia leaves, out rush the ants and by stinging and biting, drive it away. These ants that live in the thorns also protect the tree from a more dangerous enemy, the "leaf-cutting ant." So the ants act as a *regular standing army* to protect the tree from its foes. But how does the tree pay its soldiers? By supplying food as well as lodgings. For drink each acacia-leaf secretes a honey-liquor in a gland at its base, and for solid food it grows a tiny golden pear, a little yellow fruit-point, at its leaf-base, attached to it by a thread. As soon as the food is ripe the ants cut the filament or thread and carry off the food. So here we have a plant, the acacia, which keeps and pays a standing army of ants to defend it against caterpillars, leaf-cutting ants and larger creatures! Such an alliance or association for mutual advantage goes far beyond any club life. Here it is a plant that seems to be the "thinking party" of the organization while the animal creature acts as a "hired man!"

When it comes to plant intelligence, there is one plant which, year in year out, stages a death-drama within its own flower, and causes the destruction of countless insects to make sure its pollen will get to the pistils of other plants of its kind. The fig is low in the scale of seed plants. Yet no scientist knows how it came to work out the system it uses, though it must have been a step by step process of Evolution. First the fig produces its flowers, some with stamens, others with pistils, in a tiny cave or chamber. Into a fig with stamens crawls a small wasp drawn by the scent. But so narrow is the entrance that its wings are stripped from its body, and it dies as soon as it has laid its eggs inside the egg-pods of the fig itself. Male and female wasps mature in the seedless galls (that is what a liquid from the wasp has turned the egg-pod into), and crawl out. They meet each other, copulate and the males die. But the females crawl out of the fig. On the way out they crawl over the flower-stamens, and become covered with the pollen dust. The wasps that then fly to figs with *pistils* and make them fertile with the pollen—become sterile: *they have no more young!* But these pistiled figs ripen and are eaten. The wasps that crawl into a stamen fig *do have young, but die as the first wasp did!*

And all this drama of life and death, of life at the cost of being barren, and fruitfulness at the price of death for the wasps, is arranged only so the pollen of the male fig flower can be carried to the pistils of the female one: There is nothing in human life to equal it!

"On the other hand we have some very interesting 'criminal classes' among the plants. Besides the low kinds of parasites, there are 'undesirables' and degenerates, including the beautiful orchids which squat in the crotches of other trees and the mistletoe, the "hanger-on" of the apple. As Evolution can on occasion work backward as well as forward (only then is it called *degeneracy*), it is not surprising that among the 'poor whites' of the plant world, we find some slipping further and further downhill, till they end up as parasites on some more vigorous plant.

"Practically all the 'crimes' committed in the vegetable kingdom are 'food crimes.' And, of course, in a stricter sense, one is not justified in speaking of them as 'crimes' at all. The South Carolina Venus's Fly-Trap, the California Pitcher-Plant, the Canadian Indian-Cup, and any number of South American jungle-growers that 'eat flesh' (for they catch small birds as well as insects at times), are only trying to get what would be a plant's idea of 'three squares' a day. They are the sensitives I have mentioned. Their sensitive bristles close on the insect that lights on their leaf, and prevent it from crawling out again, squirting plant-pepsin over it to dissolve it into a dinner. In the marshy soil where most of these plants grow there is but little nitrogen. So their surroundings drive them to eat the insects whose bodies contain a good deal. In some of the South American big-cupped varieties a five-inch layer of decomposing insects has been discovered as the bottom of the cup—the 'fruit' of their 'crimes'!

"An offender against *prohibition* is the Nicaraguan wine-palm. But it should be pointed out that *unless tempted by man it never distils any alcohol!* When chopped (this might be called its 'fall'), and an eight-inch hollow cut beneath its leafy crown, the palm sap will fill the hollow with a clear, yellowish wine, which the tree ferments in the sun. A wine-palm will 'make' as much as several gallons of its own brand in the course of twenty days! The *poisoners* of the plant world are also only poor, honest plants trying to protect themselves against animal foes. They bear poisoned leaves or berries or fruits only to protect themselves. Hops and hemp are both high-class plants. They have developed separate flowers for male stamens and for female pistils, to make sure of the best crossings and matings in breeding. Yet, though not criminal, hops are associated with *beer,* and hemp with *the hangman's rope!* And the famous Century Plant might be called a *suicide.* It is a lily flower, a member of the Agave family. In its native Central and South America it will grow for seven years or so, its tremendous big leaves, fifteen feet around at the base, doing nothing but eat and lay away food matter in their swollen leaf-bottom bases. And then, the Century Plant feels it must flower. It sends up a huge central stock twenty or thirty feet high and a foot thick at the bottom, with great quantities of beautiful yellow flowers. But as the big flowers unfold and their seed ripens, the Century Plant dies! It has emptied all of itself out into the flowers, and by the time the seeds are ripe the plant is done—it has committed a kind of *flower-suicide, bloomed itself to death!*

"And yet," Nature concluded, "some would say that plants are uninteresting! The great things to remember about plants, it seems to me, are these: They were the first things to live on Earth. If anything should happen to remove all plants from the earth at one and the same time, all other life would have to go, for no other living creatures could go on living without them. *When the plants die man will follow in a week's time!* And, last, they already point out most of the lessons of Evolution to the things which follow them. Their life, in spite of all its struggles, appears in a picture as a kind of "still life." But, if they do not show us much movement, they do give us two fine ideals to have and to hold: the ideal of Beauty, expressed by the flowers, and the ideal of Permanence. The greatest Sequoia that grows on the Coast and the very first *Algae* that opened its cell-mouth, breathe and have their being the same way, though millions and millions of years stretch between them! Beauty and Permanence are ideals Evolution has developed in a thousand different forms, but never more wonderfully than in the plants.

"And now to get back to my next reel, 'Earth's First Living Animals,'" Nature continued . . . and the music of the reeds carried me off on slumber's wings.

CHAPTER VIII

Have you ever played at putting "Pigs in Clover?" That is the whole secret of Evolution. It is putting all the animals (as they appear) in their right places. But in Evolution "the clover" is a long line that reaches from the lowest form on earth to the highest. And getting the line "straight" is the puzzle, the "pigs" are the counters in the game.

Our last picture showed, up to a certain point, how the descendants of the *Algae* had been turning into all sorts of different *kinds* of families of things, how they had been shifting themselves, their jelly-cells into new forms and shapes but—it was jelly, just the same, even if it may have grown a bit firmer or tougher. Their jelly cells, as the different creatures grew hard outside skins or sacks to protect them, or even put out claws, like the crab, might even change inside, but they were still *jelly cells*. *The fact is anything is a jelly-fish until it grows a backbone!* And that is the first big idea in all Evolution.

We have seen the *Algae*—certain families of them—moving up the line in one direction, the direction of plant life. There the *leaf* may be said to have first brought out a *backbone,* and the plants could progress right on up to the tree.

That is the object of Evolution—to move *up* the tree of life. Say you are climbing a tree. The first big boughs may be quite a way up the trunk. But you spy a small one that may give you a "step-up" to the first larger one. Then, as you climb, boughs spread out here and there in an irregular way. Sometimes there is a gap. You have to stretch and reach and catch hold of the next highest bough. But—*there always are boughs enough to make it clear that there is a top and that you are going to reach it!*

Evolution is something like that. Every new kind of an animal family is not as close to the next as one layer of skin is to the next in an onion. One family does not "dove-tail" right into the next. Evolution is like the tree we have just described. Boughs are missing here and there; sometimes there is hardly a foothold. And all the boughs that *branch off* go on to a separate end of their own. But it is the main stem we are climbing, and we know by the boughs that *are there,* that we can keep going up.

The *plant* bough of the great life-tree has been followed to its very end. Where did the *animal* bough begin? It began with the first little creature among the jelly-fish descendants that changed its diet.

It was written in the book of fate that only a creature that developed a *backbone* could climb the main stem of life's great tree. Up to a certain point the children of the *Algae* that did not keep on going in the plant direction, kept on developing in the water. They clung to the old ways—drawing in nourishment from lifeless matter in the water. But one day a little water-thing—it may have been an *Amoeba*—started to eat other *living* matter, and the first step in the *animal* direction had been taken.

After that, through hundreds of thousands of years, after eating other living creatures till they had become animal, by sticking to this diet and changing all the time, the descendants of the *Amoeba* "jelly-fish" had spread out into any number of families. But the *backbone* still was missing. They were still "jelly-fish"—all of them —in spite of shells and claws and spines and other things they had grown.

And now for a picture of all these creatures. For among them all is one which is going to take the *first step away* from the "jelly-fish," just as the *Amoeba* took the first step away from plant life. Remember all these sea creatures we are bringing together here already stand for an Evolution of millions of years! One form has been growing out of another and into still others. There has been cross-breeding between creatures akin, yet not of the same family, with brand new *kinds* of creatures being produced all the time. And each family, once it has begun, starts trying to get to the highest end of its *own little branch* of development—the sponge, the woodlouse the sea scorpion, the crab. But always there has to be some creature that makes a move up the *main stem.*

Out of the darkness of the past a picture of the shores and shallow waters of the early tropic sea flashes out. It is no "stern and rockbound coast." The things that went the plant way already fringe the lagoons as tall, thick clumps of reeds and rushes. The ferns spread and grow in the marshes filled with water, down to the shallow sea-pools and the great stretches of mud-flat along the shore. And here, in this swarming, struggling, fighting mass of early life, among the disgusting forms squirming and wriggling in the swamp-pools that are *life's cesspool cradle,* full of decaying vegetable matter, but alive with insect forms of horror, let us look for something resembling a *backbone*—for the backbone is the *only rung* of the ladder that will take life out of the jelly-fish class! Let us look into the water along the shallows, among all these creatures that have deveoped in the millions and millions of years since the first *Algae* split in two. Somewhere there *must* be the first faint shadow of a backbone among all these hundreds of families!

Here are sponges, some tiny, others monstrous in size, some spiral, some round in form. They furnish but little help on the upward road, for they have worked their way well *into their own one particular "blind alley" of progress.* They are sponges and will remain sponges. What entitles them to mention is the fact that they are animals; but they only are associated with progress in one way—in the shape of the bath sponge we use! Next come little *polyps,* jelly-fish that have grown tentacles, folk that never will settle on the land. But here is one polyp we ought to look at more closely. It is often called a "coral insect," but it is no insect. The right name is the "coral animal." The main point of interest about the tiny coral animal is that instead of trying to move upward *on land,* it has spent its life during all the countless generations that have passed, building *up land* for others—in the form of the lovely ringed *atolls* of the tropical Southern seas. A coral island is at the same time the home of all the rest of the particular coral family or nation that started building on that spot. For the living coral animal keeps right on living its little life out *on the bodies of its ancestors,* which turn to lime. When ages have gone by, one fine day the island rises smiling above the waters, flying birds drop seeds, and ocean currents wash cocoanuts ashore to sink into its top sands. Before long another green oasis of beauty has sprung up in the midst of the watery desert. But the coral polyps have but one "fixed" idea: that of building coral islands. They have no time for backbones, and so they are corals and water-animals to this day.

Here we can see mollusks and oysters and shell-fish of all sorts, lying lazily on the sand or moving clumsily about in search of food. One kind of these shell-fish show the start of a great family, and its decline, its going *back* to the start again. The first creature of the kind has a shell (all these shell-fish build their shells of lime) with a plain line of design. The next—a hundred thousand years have gone by—has added another line to the design. It is richer. A few more hundreds of thousands of years pass, and we have a whole group of lines, a rich and beautiful design on the shell of the mussel, a touching tribute to the great idea that beauty and progress are the same. And then—perhaps its special food grew scarce, perhaps there was some other reason—at any rate, the lines are fading from the shell! The mussel goes back to three, to two, to finally one line. And we know that to-day *not one of its kind* is left though a distant relative, the "pearly-chambered nautilus," a pretty colored shell-fish of tropic waters, still lives and "carries on."

We can almost see that all these spineless things, these things that drift and creep and crawl—mussels, sponges, and the rest of them—are only meant to go so far. There they must stop. It is the creatures with backbones that will rule, on sea and on land. To-day, even in the higher forms of animal life some of the stiffening of the backbone may be missing, here and there. And it is something to be guarded against, for without backbone everything tends to turn soft.

But what are these strange things? They are sea-urchins, round balls of living prickles. A sack of skin with *quills*. These sea-urchins, star-fish and stone-lilies are all a step above the coral animals! They have added a kind of stomach (a very primitive one it is true, and not the sort of stomach which will serve as a model for higher types, but still a stomach of sorts) to the gut, which is the nearest to a stomach the coral animals have. Most of them grow sharp prickles for defense, and *Algae* are their favorite food.

Then there are the woodlice. They seem to be something halfway between a land insect and a marine creature. We do not see them in the water, for they have turned some of their cells into air-tubes to breathe with on land, and live in damp places, under stones, just above high-water mark, though some have left the water for the woods. The mother carries her young in a pouch, like a kangaroo, and they have the crab habit of *shedding* their skins, sloughing off the old hard, cracked one, and coming out with a new soft skin. And here are all sorts and conditions of crabs. The simple sack of tougher "skin" that they used to share with the sea-urchins, they have, by adding lime, gradually turned first into a "soft" and then into a "hard" shell. Here is a little oyster-crab, who lives in and feeds on the oyster, and who is so tasty that we like to see him floating on top of an oyster stew! Here is the sponge-water-flea, only a tenth of an inch long and the giant-crab—ten feet around. We do not see the "gulf-weed" crab as yet. But he will turn up later, holding on to the back of some turtle, for that is the way he "beats his way" along the Gulf Stream.

What makes the crab an interesting figure is that, *for its own family*—and it is a large one—it has solved the secret *of leaving the water to live on the land!* Once there were only water-crabs, now there are land-crabs and they really—crabs, lobsters, water-fleas, water-centipedes, water-scorpions, and sea-lice—may be classed as *insects*.* What makes an insect and keeps it an insect is its queer system of *hinged joints*. Everything that grows its limbs on hinges, from the biggest crab to the tiniest ant, is an insect. Whatever the first water-thing was that threw out little pincers on the *hinged*

*This is not a strictly scientific classification, of course, but one which has a certain logic of convenience to recommend it.

plan, started the whole insect world! Its members were going to be useful to other higher forms of life in a hundred different ways, but in spite of all the tremendous number of different families on sea and shore—every insect in the world grew out of the first thing to grow *hinged limbs*—the insect tribe, like the mollusca tribe, ran itself into a "blind alley." It was evoluting, true, but only out along its own branches. No use to look for a *backbone* among the insects, they had gone in for *joints with hinges*.

So, though the robber-crab of the Indian Pacific islands climbs palm-trees in search of food, and there are many different kinds of land-crabs and water-crabs, they all belong to the insect family. And the insect family is an off-shoot from the main branch of the tree of Evolution that leads nowhere except—to other insects! *The main point about all these water-insects is that the land-insects developed out of them.* But in developing they clung to the same queer structures. They did not grow back-bones, but "jointed" legs and arms of all sorts and kinds, with sharp joints which always make them something uncanny, unnatural and unreal to us. They have hearts (except where food is concerned) of a kind, a hint at a brain, and their protective shell or crust (whence the name "Crustaceans"), but insects they are and insects they remain.

One special kind of very tiny crab, the *Copepoda,* is the most important of them all. It might be said to form the "plant-life" of the sea, to supply the vegetable food for all sea things, just as the plants on earth supply it to all land things. *Copepoda* lives on the tiniest bits of vegetable "microbes," which you could only recognize through a miscroscope, but it eats them by the trillions of trillions, and is eaten in turn by the larger forms of sea life *which depend on it as the land life depends on its plants.*

But stop—here are insects—long, soft, wriggly, that have not thrown out any weird limbs or joint yet. They almost seem in a class by themselves, to have stretched their jelly-cells out into a long, thick, flabby thread, instead of gathering it up into a flabby ball, like the sponge, or enclosing it in a hard shell of lime, like the mussels.

These worms, these long motionless water-worms, lying so sluggishly on a patch of *Algae,* are important. Some of these worms, later, are going to branch out into all sorts of families, and "inherit the earth" underground, for they are among the creatures that will move ashore, where they will do useful work under the ground in keeping it in shape for the plants to draw food from. Some will degenerate into disgusting parasites—we all know what a tapeworm is, by reputation only, it is to be hoped! But among all these sorts of different worms swarming here on the sea-bottoms and squirming along the cess-pool ponds, is one a little different from the others.

It has the first, soft, vague outline of a backbone! Less spineless than the rest of his tribe, this worm has gathered a thread of stiffening under its soft back. And among these creatures that seem so highly developed, each kind in its own way, it stands out. It means Evolution in the right direction! Yes, it has what we have looked for in vain among all the rest of this swarming life!

Another million or so of years will pass before this tiny thread of stiffening matter along the back of the lowly worm gets stronger and stiffer, gradually turns to a soft cartilage, soft yet firm compared to the rest of the body and, a *something around which the creature can keep on building*. No need to envy all these horrible *jointed* things so busy feeding on each other, budding new machine-like claws and wings and jaws and feelers. They are all *soft inside*. There never will be a great, strong, *central* thread on which their whole system of life can hang and grow, along whose stiffening will run a great central nerve whose crown is the brain, and from which all other bones will grow out. The things will not grow out on *hinges,* detachable, but will be *extensions* of the great thread of the body life, the *backbone!*

But it will take millions of years before this worm's great-great-great-grandchildren, after they have intermarried among themselves and among other like families, are going to work out their ancestor's vague suggestion of a backbone into something more definite.

When the next reel flashes out we see that the backbone has become a better one. It has been developing *in the sea!* While most of the horrid insect creatures with articulated joints have been swarming on to the land and have been increasing and multiplying into thousands of new species, what was begun in a *worm,* has developed in a *fish.* But it is not much of a fish, is this *lamprey.* It is one of the simplest and lowest of fishes, a parasite with only a fixed mouth, not even a jaw. Its backbone is soft, just cartilage. It is not the sort of a backbone to get very far. And here swims an eel. It has gone a step further than the lamprey and has evolved a real jaw out of the mere gaping mouth, but its backbone is still soft. And we find that though some of these creatures that clung to a soft backbone of cartilage grow to monstrous size, and fit themselves out with an armor of horny skin and terrible teeth, like the shark and ray, they have gone as far as a backbone without stiffening will take any creature. They still have no bones. They are lower forms, the higher forms are the ones with a backbone of *real bone, a vertebrae. The first creature with a real backbone was a fish, but a fish of a higher kind than lamprey or eel.*

It was a fish which did two things at one and the same time. We might call it by its family name, which was *Ganoid,* and say that while it was turning its soft cartilage spine into a hard bone one (by the mysterious action of its life-substances, which were building up within its body all the time) it also worked on an *air-bladder* (a floating gas-bag they used for swimming and to rise to different levels, letting out air) until its descendants, together with *the first real backbone,* had developed the lungs with which to "float" it out of water on to land. For it is clear that we will have to get our backbone back on land again if any higher forms are to develop there. Other Ganoids carried the hard, stiff backbone on into deeper and deeper water, and the many fish tribes they founded stuck to it. But that is another story, and the only branch of the family in which we are interested at present is the one working *up, out* of the waves. In the next chapter we will see how one particular *kind* of Ganoid brought its good, stiff backbone back to land, for future development ashore. And, underlying all other reasons, the main reason that brought this fish ashore was—food. The lagoons and seas were getting overcrowded and the fight for existence growing fiercer and fiercer. Food—the want and the need and the lack of food— are the driving power that brings about the greater changes in all early life.

CHAPTER IX

AND now, while animal life develops on Earth, we can see the creatures that are developing torn between the call of the sea and the call of the land. Some of them get used to the shore, then change their minds, and the call of the water takes them back into the sea again. There they throw off anything they may have developed for land use, and remain in the water. But in the long run, though it took millions of years, the call of the land proved the stronger. Yet through all these times we see creatures that cannot seem to give up the sea flopping or wallowing back to it. Sometimes as in the case of the whale and the seals they turn into a water animal with every land "improvement"; but marked off from the fish by the fact that they have warm blood while the blood of the fish is cold. To get their warm blood the whales had to go back to early land ancestors but in the end their longing for the water was too great. They returned to it, but returned to it as warm blooded animals and not fish. And to-day—so far as the big things that matter are concerned: skeleton, back bone, warm blood and manner of breeding and giving birth—we have a real "sea-cow" (as well as a land cow), that dates back to a land animal family. We mention this to show how all creatures were divided between this feeling for the sea, out of which they all came, and the land, where lay the greatest chances for "moving up."

The good Ganoids who brought the much-needed backbone ashore were Ganoids which were not satisfied with the breathing apparatus used by their kinsfolk. All fish, like all other things, had to breathe *air* to live. They breathed through gills, and thus drew in the air they needed out of the water. They had their backbone, and out of this backbone they had grown their fins*—the long side fins which later, changed in their shape and character, were to make two fore-feet or hands at the upper end, and two hind feet at the lower part and crawled. And these were not *hinged* joints in the insect sense of the body, or flappers for the things which did not swim but crept

---

*At first fins were just folds of skin, and were slowly "built up" and stiffened by gristle (cartilage) ribs in the course of time.

I

These fins were the forerunners of real limbs, developed out of a central bone, the backbone, that held together the whole body. The salamander of to-day shows the kind of fins that were to turn into feet.

The particular Ganoid family that "made" the land did so in the great hunt for food. Along and among the reeds and sedges on the shore were all sorts of insects, easily caught if one could only get at them. So—the thick, steaming atmosphere on land supplied all the "water" it really needed—it was just a question of being able to "breathe" while ashore. The gills would not do, for they were meant only for water-breathing, and the land air would not pass through their cell-meshes. So the Ganoid, without disturbing its gills (they were necessary while it was hunting food in the water) gradually managed to grow itself a sort of bag in its throat, *the first lung** swimming bladder. Now it could stay ashore for some time, and find the rich insect food it wanted.

The fish that were swimming about the ocean cared for none of these things. They were busy—once fins were the order of the day—in making bigger and better *fins*. But—the Ganoid which had turned "lung-fish" (as its descendants are still called) could not swim on land, up a mangrove trunk exposed by the tide. It had to crawl.

The chances are that if the Ganoids had never learned to *crawl*, Man would never have learned to *walk*. At any rate their fore-fins and hind-fins kept on taking more and more the shape of a thick, small limb ending in a fin-lap, something like the "flapper" the seal walks on to this day. Roughly speaking, it was something in the nature of an arm without a wrist-joint, ending in a flat palm, the palm being the fin-flap. Then, from the continual flexing, joints developed where the limb left the body and where it joined the fin. And the Ganoids that persevered through the thousands of years, finally, by continually pressing down their front fin-flaps on the mud and sand of the shore, had gotten them to turn into the *first* hands, while the hind fin-flaps turned into the *first feet*. With the continual spreading out of the fin-flap in one piece, the pressure gradually split it up into separate lengths. There were fin-bones in the fins, and it was a certain number of fin-bones joined together *under the skin* that made each of the fingers. Now the hands were really hands, for each had fingers, the *first fingers*. And—so does Nature cling to something which she has once decided upon—these

---

*Members of the Ganoid family that stayed in their "blind alley" of development exist to this day. One is the West African *bommi-fish*. It is a mud-fish of the Liberian coast, which uses its fins to follow its food over the mud, and along the mangrove-roots by the shore. Like the shark, it it a strange survival of a species which stopped at a certain stage of development, while other members of its same general family went on and up.

eighteen or nineteen Ganoid fin-bones never turned into more than exactly *five fingers* in each hand! From the fish's fin up to the most perfect kind of hand there is, there never have been (except by some accidental freak of deformation) more than five fingers on a hand! What caused these fingers to develop out of the fins, of course, was the need of clutching and holding.

In the meantime the Ganoid had been improving its lungs. And— a turning-point in the story of all life—there came a day when it decided to stay out of water for good and keep on living on land. Millions of years have passed—we must remember that the world may be 1,600,000,000 years old—and there was nothing left of the original Ganoid who had brought the things needed for animal Evolution ashore. Through continual breeding and changing while breeding new forms, it had turned into something which was not quite land animal and not quite fish, which could live on land and in the water.

Yet, for all that it was something betwixt and between, it was going up in the scale. Its backbone was all that could be desired for the moment; it had lungs; it had limbs, hands and fingers. And, together with a firmer skull it was improving its teeth. The teeth of the fish were originally all scales, every scale a tooth. Gradually this tooth-matter, which is called *dentine,* reached its best and strongest development in the jaws, though the unused scale-teeth were kept on as a covering by most of the things which swam about in the water. But the half-and-halves dropped their scales and snuggled their original tail-fins together to end in a regular tail.

The next step in advance made by the new families of things, half-land, half-water creatures, was taken by the Newt (which means "slow") or the Salamander. The Newt was so far removed from fins that it swam with its finless tail and snuggled its little hands close to its body. It lived in the water a good part of its time, feeding on shell-fish and insects of all kinds, and then returning to land to earthworms and slugs. In some of these betwixt and between forms *both gills and lungs* were in use, while others had taken to lungs altogether and dropped their gills. Again others, like the Frog, dropped their long tail. And all of them kept growing longer forearms.

But though these things all lived on land, *they had to be born in the water.* It was in the water that their eggs were laid and hatched out. And in the baby frog we find the strongest expression of that old, inherited feeling for the water. When it is hatched from its egg, it comes to life with a pair of gills, and does not use its lungs. But as it grows from a tad-pole with a fish-tail to a tailless frog, its gills die away, its tail is pulled in and vanishes, and its legs shoot

out. And once it has begun to use its lungs, it cannot stay under water for more than a certain length of time else it will drown!

The frog is a very important member of this constantly growing family of things that are at home in two elements, for the frog adds to what other low life forms have given us, *our hand as it is to-day!* Before the frog, hands were "all fingers," so to say. The frog worked out the first perfected hand—*a thumb and four fingers.* And this *thumb-print* the frog has left on Evolution's page ought to excuse it from all other uplift work, so important is it. Let it go on developing all sorts and classes of other frogs, of frog-like and toad forms. It has made another step toward the perfect body-structure which is Evolution's dream, and that is enough. But all these newt, frog and salamander things, though they have done their share in Evolution's work, cannot altogether get away from the water. In fact, so long as new life forms have to go through a complicated process of breathing *first* through gills before breathing through lungs, and having their eggs hatched out *only* in the water, we cannot get on.

Before we leave the early frog-creature it might be mentioned that somewhere between frog and crocodile life the *something* which developed in another family, has made the human *prima donna,* the greatest "singing actress" of modern opera. Some say that the Amphibian (half-land, half-water) frog was the first living creature whose throat had the necessary cords to allow it to utter the *first true vocal sound heard on earth,* distinct from insect chirp and reptile hiss! But other scientists lean toward the theory that Earth's first approach to a vocal sound was the curious piping noise made by the *unborn baby crocodile!* Buried deep in the glowing sands, it senses the moment when it should break its shell. And at that moment it utters the strange little vocal note which leads its mother to dig up the egg that holds it. This is one of the numberless questions in Evolution that have not as yet been definitely settled, for lack of evidence.

CHAPTER X

THE FIRST EGG WITH A SHELL

EVOLUTION, by letting one family of living creatures develop one thing, and another another, and then handing on new developments—a fin, a jaw or a tail—to still some other family, has already come a long, long ways. It is true that the jelly-bodied things, and the insect-things that grew out of them do not seem to have done much for us. But the jelly-bodied things produced the insects, and among the insects was the worm with the first spinal thread. And out of that thread came the *backbone,* the thing every real body must build up on. The head which was just an *end of body* in the worm, turned from a soft body-end to a *skull,* once it had a backbone to help stiffen it; the mouth-opening of the skull, a "one-piece" mouth, turned into hinged jaws that could open and shut; and the scales, the baby teeth that grew along the skin, were concentrated in the jaws. Meanwhile the backbone put out bones (ribs) for fins, and the fins, transferred to land, turned into little arms, all-finger hands, and, finally, true hands with thumbs. And in those pathetic first-draught skulls the very smallest, rudest and dimmest sort of near-brains were working in a sluggish way. Yet every once in a while an extra gleam of light would fall into some of those darkened skull cavities, those "thinking" organs which could not yet think, and were working only on the beginnings of instinct—and then there would be a slight upward move in some direction.

And, together with the creatures that really matter to us—the ones which grew or produced something or made a change in doing things which meant progress—all others were trying to get ahead in their own particular "blind alley" of development which, though it led them higher, led them higher only along their own particular family tree.

Here, too, we should mention that, as in the case of plant life, the animal creatures which did develop only represent *part* of all that swam and crept or crawled. The survival of the fittest played its part, and like the family of shell-fish we mentioned two chapters back, all sorts of crawly, wriggly, swimming or writhing things fell by life's wayside in the great rush for food. "Sink or swim, live or die, survive or perish"—it was all a question of food, not of liberty. And the creature that could not "rustle" its food, did not need to cry "Give me death!" Nature attended to that. Food was the one sole conscious object of existence in the early world. Hundreds of *kinds* of animal families have disappeared altogether. They passed out into nothingness—some more and some less advanced—and others took their places, and their kinds died out in turn. If we knew all the *kinds* of creatures that Nature has developed up to a certain point and then flung away, as the modeller does a bit of clay, no book would be able to describe them, so many are there.

Before going on with the creatures to which we owe our next upward step we might speak of the insects again. Their "blind-alley" had been getting more and more crowded. In their queer, many-jointed way—insects are neither flesh, fish, fowl nor good red herring—they had passed from water to land in enormous numbers. Let us take a look at them. The sea-scorpions have turned to land scorpions, and are as dry and scaly as once they were wet and scaly. The sea-lice have become wood-lice, and the crabs have branched out into all sorts of clans. The water-spiders now have land-spider brothers, but not one of them has yet learned to spin a web! The lord of the air, the tyrant of all other insects is the dragon-fly. Even the present-day "devil's darning-needle" is the last thing one would choose for a pet. And the dragon-flies of the early days were tremendous things, with wings that stretched as much as thirty inches or more, from tip to tip. We can imagine the air filled with the brilliant colored darting things, bronzy green, blue, black, with yellow bellies, with their repulsive, hairy heads, their shining metallic wings and their long, slender body, seemingly all sting. They fed on the eggs (larvae) of fishes floating on the water, the young of worms, and all sorts of water and land insects. They are interesting because they are a sort of insect double of the frog, in some ways.

They show the same longing for the old home-water. When they are young they have gills, and like the frogs' eggs, the dragon-fly's eggs are hatched out in the water, and the young dragon-flies all have gills through which to breathe. Watch one of these fierce insects devouring another one—probably a very distant relative. It would be bad enough if it pounced on its prey and got it over with. But no, it goes about the murderous business in so stealthy and treacherous a way that it makes one's blood curdle. Its large feelers support a kind of black face "mask," behind which it hides until the unwary water-spider draws near, when it suddenly throws itself upon it. Then the dragon-fly shows its true face. The mask drops, and the powerful "clutchers" hold its prey while the strong jaws take their time crunching it alive.

We must not take the dragon-fly's wings too seriously. Just as the tad-pole puts forth legs as it loses its gills, so the dragon-fly "moults" itself into wings. But they are *not true wings* in our sense. And they never helped the bird to develop. They are simply, as are all insect wings, hinged joints carrying a membrane, sail fashion. A true wing is a limb. But these wings are limbs only in the insect sense, like all those other hinged members the insects sprout. Like its distant relative the crab, the dragon-fly (and many another insect) sheds its horny coat or shell, from time to time, and comes out in a new suit.

But here is another and more repulsive looking insect flying about in the air. It is a lumbering thing, for all its big wings, and its body is awkward and does not seem built for flight, like the dragon-fly's. It is buzzing heavily about the great ferns—they have grown to giant size now like the reeds, sedges and mosses that all flourish beneath the hot burning sun and in the rich steamy air—but when it gets down to earth it can run fast enough. Yet what—what is it that makes it seem so strangely familiar?

And now it comes to us in a flash! It is its *manner* of running along the ground, swift yet furtive. It carries its gross, clumsy body along quickly on powerful legs. But there is something guilty and alarmed about its progress. It moves with a sort of stealthy rush. Why, it is nothing more nor less than a cockroach! A cockroach larger than the dragon-fly we have just watched devour its prey. A cockroach the size of a turkey-cock, that goes clattering and whirring through the air like a huge and horrible mechanical toy, though on the ground it runs softly and fleetly. And now we know what the brown shadow was we saw stirring long ago in the picture of the giant Fern forest that marked one of the great stages of advance in the vegetable kingdom! It was one of these brown monsters! The coackroach is just another "blind alley," this time leading the ugly children of these prehistoric winged giants, after a million year journey, to the kitchens of the twentieth-century apartment house. They have come down all the millennial years, losing their giant size by the way—Heaven be. praised—to send as harmless, yet filthy and disgusting parasites. In the kitchens of a race that sprang, indirectly, from a common ancestor—the worm—but has risen to the leadership of creation, they now scavenge as vermin!

While we watch these repulsive insects flying about in the prehistoric air, it might be said that the "selection" of Nature had a good deal to do with providing them with their many coats of horny armor, their shells and shields and tough outer coverings. They were all soft inside, they were all spineless. Without bones, they developed by drawing out their limbs into the joints or sections of which they are formed, and growing a tough coat for each new section. The insect with the best protective covering was the one Nature "selected" as standing the best chance of living* through the fierce struggle for existence with others. These shelled and armored insect families that have lived down to our day, stand for any number of others which have "gone by the board!"

But we must now pass from these forms who will do nothing— though there are so many different kinds of them—to build up the great stem of advancement, except by serving as food for other forms of life that are erecting it. Let us take up the next living rung in the ladder of progress. It belongs to a family which to this day is looked upon with scorn and loathing—the great family of the Reptiles.

Among all the "fish out of water," now grown into a huge swarm of lung-breathing half-fish and half-not-fish, some one member of one family first took a real step in advance. We already know that these Amphibians were the first *quadrupeds,* "things with four feet" (or hands) because these came as a natural result of a land life. But they still, like the frog, "kept one foot in the water." The amphibian which started the movement definitely away from the water was one of these lung-fish or salamander offspring. There was something the matter with its heart (which we will touch on later), but not with its intelligence. It was the first half-water, half-land thing to discover the way to lay an egg *with a shell!*

Eggs are eggs, we may think, and so long as they hatch out, what matter how they are laid. But we would be wrong, for the egg with a *shell* made all the difference between living on land and in the water.

Before we go further it may be well to mention that the reptiles, once that egg had been laid, started out in a bewildering number of families. From the frog and salamander tribes there developed all kinds of lizards (and their poor relations, the blind-worms) which did a good deal of work in developing all sorts of tongues, most of them too elaborate and special however, to pass beyond their own family. There were also snakes, crocodiles, land and sea turtles, and a number of horrible monsters which have completely vanished, though the others mentioned have come down to the present day. It may have been a salamander, it may have been a frog or a newt which laid *the first egg with a shell.* Let us say it was a salamander.

Let us say that the first egg with a shell was laid by a salamander of great intelligence, and with a liking for experiment. Dimly it may have felt that so long as eggs were laid in the water

*An exception is the family of "stick insects" and "leaf insects" which take on the look and color of the twig or leaf on which they rest and are the best example of "protective imitation"—The first real use of "camouflange"—by nature in the battle for survival.

with merely a soft outer skin, there would not be much chance for getting ahead. For it stood to reason that anything born *in the water* would have to have gills with which to breathe, even if later it did get back to land to use its lungs. Something must be tried. There is an old amphibia-reptile, called—do not laugh!—the *Palaeohatteria!* And since it is the oldest known reptile, it may have been the salamander that laid the first egg with a shell. The point about the first real egg-shell was that it could be hatched out on the dry, hot sand, and the little reptile which crept out did not have to bring a pair of gills along with it into the world to breathe. The reason the first egg-shell is important to us is that if the descendants of the original "fish out of water" were to get ahead on land, and become the ancestors of the things higher up, they would have to drop gills altogether.

Of course, this did not happen all at once. As we know, the frog and newt continued to hatch their eggs out in the water just as they did when the world was young. But even the sea-turtles, once they had formed it, clung to the habit of laying their eggs in the hot sand, and will still swim many weary miles of ocean to find a sandy beach.

And now we will see what the reptiles which hatched out of the first Salamander egg were like.

CHAPTER XI

WHAT CAME OF THE EGG WITH A SHELL

LET us watch a reptile-reel! Here, for instance, we can see just how some families of small lizards gradually drew their little feet more and more up into themselves until they disappeared, and stretched out their bodies till they grew as long and thin as a whip-lash and we have—a snake! A giant five-foot salamander comes lumbering along in search of food. He is one of the "big feeders" among the half-and-halves. And no sooner does he spy the small water-lizard than he scents a meal. The lizard gives itself up for lost—it sees a thicket of plant-roots, and just manages to dart in and get safely away as the salamander dashes up—too late! But the lizard owed its escape not so much to its tiny legs, but to its wriggling body. So the more wriggle (which means more body and less legs) the greater safety. To be able to wriggle out of sight fast was worth all the centipedes' feet to this kind of a lizard. And, sure enough, as he and his descendants scurry away to safety in clumps of water-reed or plant-root, they turn into wrigglers instead of runners. Their feet disappear (some snakes still have rudimentary signs of feet to prove where they went), and they keep on living this way in order to be able to "fight another day"—for all life was a fight then. The little fought to devour the less while the greater fought to devour them.

And so the snake, another example of Nature's "selection" of a race fit to survive (because it is a selection of Nature's choosing we call it "natural selection"), and all the other many families of snakes started with the *individual lizards* that were *the strongest and quickest wrigglers, the swiftest and most muscular ones.* For every water-lizard that tried to wriggle itself into a snake's skin did not escape. Only the best, the strongest, the quickest left descendants.

Out of all that wriggled, crawled and moved about the earth when the reptiles developed only certain "fittest survivors" live now, in the families of their descendants. We have snakes and serpents aplenty. We have lizards of every kind. We have crocodiles and alligators. But even the greatest of them are insects compared to

68

some of the early reptile families that "did not make the grade."
They were reptiles spelled with a capital R.

Let us take a look at some of the horrible and fantastic forms of
life which crept out of those first eggs with shells, to engage in
struggles which shook the earth, and lashed the waters of the ocean
into foam. A few moments ago we saw a water-lizard gradually
change into a land-snake to survive. One of the hugest and most
dreadful of all the reptiles which were *not* "fit" to survive was a
lizard, the great "fish-lizard" * of the early world oceans. After
it had worked its way to lungs, and even *brought forth its living
young* out in the waste of ocean waters without egg or shell, it spread
out its feet into flappers again (since it spent the greatest part of
its time in the waves), let its tail-end go back into a tail-fin, and
raised a huge upright fin in the middle of its back. The "fish-
lizard" was one of the most numerous of all the so-called "marine"
lizards of its day. Like others of the lizard tribe, it answered
"the call of the sea," the urge that impelled some of these things
which had become land creatures to return to the water from which
they sprang. There it was happy, its long, slender snout-jaws,
spiked with the sharpest of teeth, finding plenty of its favorite food,
the cuttle-fish or squid.

The life-story of the great "fish-lizards" is one of the strange
romances of that time when God's great open out in the sea knew
no law but the will of the reptile lizards, the giant sharks and the
monster "lizard water-snake." * We will draw back the veil of the
past and picture it as it probably was. In foaming billows the waves
are running along the reef-line of a coral island somewhere in Central Europe—for that is where the ocean is rolling then—a coral
island like those in the South Seas, where ferns and fern-palms rise
high and green, and the place of grass and flowers above the level
of the sands is taken by low-growing evergreen shrubs. But though
the flowers and grass are missing, the green fern-fronds bow in the
breeze, and a glorious, hot sun pours down its rays on an ocean as
blue as the blue skies above it. Suddenly the waters boil and bubble. A whole "school" of "fish-lizards" comes up from lower ocean
depths to the surface. There is nothing left in the waters of the
earth to-day that resembles them. Unlike the horrible "snake-
lizard," which is a lonely, blood-thirsty wanderer, they are friendly
fish among themselves, as a rule, swimming the sea-lanes together
in groups which may number anywhere from ninety to a hundred
lizards. As they swim they sport and roll about in the water like

* Ichthyosaurus is its scientific name.
* The Mososaurus, a "true" lizard which had taken to the water with
an enormous snake-body, with which it writhed through the waves, a
body covered with a scale-armor and with jaws armed with terrible teeth.

the porpoises most of us have seen, but there is nothing playful about the long, thin, sword-like jaws they thrust above the waves as they sport. Cuvier, France's greatest naturalist, gave the best description of the "fish-lizard" ever penned. "It is a creature with a dolphin's snout (only longer), a crocodile's teeth, the head and chest of a lizard, a whale's flukes and the *vertebrae* (bones) of a fish."

Here and there a group of the huge reptiles makes a sudden dive, down, down through the blue waters, fathoms deep, to chase the "hard-shelled" squids (all squids had hard shells in those days, like crabs and lobsters). The squid or cuttle-fish kept the lizards' sharp teeth in good condition, and they could digest them "hair and hide," with the exception of the horny tail end of the squids, which have been found by the dozen among the bones that had enclosed what was once the fish-lizard's stomach. These diving lizards are moving more quickly than the scurrying cuttle-fish, though the latter shoot themselves through the water at a great speed, blowing out the ink fluid from their ink-sacks to lead their pursuers astray. But all in vain. The oily patches of discolored water that spread on the surface here and there, and rise and fall lazily with the lazy swell of the great waves, are all that remain to show that a promising tribe of cuttle-fish has disappeared forever. More and more of the "fish-lizards" leave the school and die for squids.

The waters along the coral-reefs are a good hunting-ground, for the squids hide all around in the nooks and crannies of the coral-rocks. At last only three great "fish lizards" are left. One, somewhat apart, is floating idly along, but the other two seem to be watching each other. It is clear that there is some reason why they have not joined the rest of the divers, and, in another moment, we know what the reason is.

Have you ever watched two tiny American hedge-lizards in the spring of the year fight a regular duel? They fight to the bitter end, in their case the "bitten" end, till one of the young males struggling for the favors of some attractive "lizardess," has bitten its opponent's tail clean off. And what we have just described is taking place out in those vast waters, where the sparkling surf of a tropical sea—can we imagine anything more upside down in geography?—booms along coral reefs *in the middle of present-day Germany!* while the giant winged cockroach flutters among the fern-fronds that lean over the waves. The young male American lizard with its tail bitten off, may grow a new tail and survive—for lizards have the power—or it may creep off and die.

But the two colossal fish-beasts, each more than thirty feet in length, lash the waves into foam with their great tail-flukes and, as the whales do to-day, fling themselves up high out of the water and dart their long cruel "bills" at each other, trying to inflict a mortal wound. Sometimes a tremendous whirlpool develops in the water. It marks the spot where both have shot down in a deep sea dive, carrying their hatred into the black ocean depths the more easily to snap off fin or tail fluke of the enemy with their jaws, the more easily to rend and tear and slay. At length the battle draws to a close in the water whose color has been changed by blood and foam from its original peaceful blue till it looks as though a rain of red and white blossoms had fallen on the whole surface of the sea.

Out of the waves rises one of the two fighters which had disappeared. The other does not come up. Has it been killed, or is it only severely wounded? We cannot look below the waves. But woe to it if it has lost the use of its powerful tail, or if one of its jaws has been torn away. For the blood already has drawn the sharks, which have scented it from far, far away, to the scene. And the "fish lizard" who has lost love's battle will not last long after they appear. Wounded, its strength exhausted by its terrific struggle, the ravenous wolves of the sea will fling themselves upon it, and it will disappear in their gullets in the twinkling of an eye.

Nor does the victor and the mate it has won remain in the danger-spot. Already swimming swiftly, side by side, they have gained an opening in the coral reef, and followed by their squid-hunting comrades—which all made off when the sharks appeared—they crawl up the hot sands of the tropic beach on their finny flappers to rest in safety.

And now, another picture. A million of years have passed. The "fish-lizard" is dying out. Why? Because it has *deliberately made itself* "unfit to survive." Not with intention. It happened because a mollusc changed from a hard to a soft shell. It is one of the strangest tales in Nature's great book of a "Thousand and One Prehistoric Nights!" For hundreds of thousands of years the "fish-lizard" had been living on the fat of the sea. The squids never failed. When first it left the land to live almost altogether in the water, it shed the hard, armored shell that protected it. And now it was to perish, root and branch, to pass into the past, because a cuttle-fish did the same thing! The "fish-lizard" had gradually let its hard coat grow softer and softer, until it changed into a naked, blackish-green skin. This was so that it could shoot swiftly down through the waves after the squids it fed on. All that it kept—and it seemed enough—was its huge, long jawful of hard teeth. And then —*the squids started growing soft shells!* Instead of a coat like a hazelnut to protect their soft bodies they grew a thin, yielding membrane like a paper almond-shell. And that was the death of the "fish-lizards." After another hundred thousand years or so of "soup" diet, for this is what the squid now amounted to, the teeth they had kept strong and sharp crunching the tough shells of the old hard squids began to "go bad." The dentine, the tooth-stuff of their teeth, began to grow soft and flabby. Their teeth grew smaller, decayed and fell out. And toward the end of their time as a living family they had nothing left but the cartilage of their gums with which to "chew," we might say, seeing that the squid could be swallowed as we might swallow an oyster. But having lost their teeth they had no other weapon left to stand up against the terrible foes which surrounded them in the waters. In their younger days as a family they could, if need be, fight it out with a shark. But the sharks had grown to monstrous and horrible sizes, and they as well as the "snake-lizards" found the poor "fish-lizards" a tasty dish. It is easy to see how, exposed toothless and naked to the attacks of armor-plated creatures with as many as two- or three-hundred long, sharp cutting teeth in their terrible jaws, the "fish-lizards" which had lost their teeth disappeared completely. And all because the squid had changed its shell! The "fish-lizard" developed the egg in its own body and bore living young. And time, which destroys so many things, has passed down to us—it can actually be *handled* in the museum where it is kept—what was perhaps, the *last one* of the monster "fish-lizards" of the past.

All we need do is to look and see the wonderful picture it calls up. We see the lizard mother, the jaws of the monster whale-shark" * closing on her soft, defenseless body, pushing out the one last hope of the race in her dying agonies! For this little "fish-lizard" baby, which was born only to die in the slime where it fell and was found—millions of years later—lies rolled up, tail-fin meeting jaws, just as it must have been cast out, dropped, the last doomed life-spark of a race that passed as it was born!

Here we have a great reptile family removed; *because a squid shifted from a hard to a soft shell!* And yet, Nature, who swept away these great lizards, has preserved to this day on a few islands off the coast of Newfoundland, a small, simple, lizard-like creature, not nearly so highly developed as the great "fish-lizard," *one of the first of all reptiles,* which was crawling around a hundred thousand years before the first "fish-lizard" swam the seas! Come down in the egg from the "fish-lizard" days, it still lives its life unchanged from the times when half Europe was a tropical sea. It links the world of the first insect that flew with the age of radio transmission and the aeroplane!

Most of the other great prehistoric sea-reptiles have also gone the way of so much of Evolution's flesh. There were horrible near-turtles, like sea-dragons, whose small heads and fanged jaws rose

* Carcharadon.

at the end of long swan-like necks. There were other strange and weird marine things, but all that remain are the sea-turtles and water-snakes of the present day. The land reptiles—including the crocodile, which does not swim in the open seas—are so different in many ways, that we must give them a separate chapter.

CHAPTER XII

LIFE'S REPTILE NIGHTMARE ON LAND

HAVE you ever watched a group of lizards at play among the little ferns that grow in some forest clearing? How graceful they are, how pretty, *how harmless!* But look at them through a magnifying glass—the glass which man's ability has cut so as to make everything seen through it much larger. And now these pretty, harmless, inoffensive things take on a different look. There is something evil and sinister about them. There is something that makes us shudder—not deeply, for, after all, we know they are really tiny in size and not as large as they seem through the glass. But— it is the old, old *mammal* feeling stirring in us, though we do not know it. It is the old, old memory come down through the millions of years, that somehow—in spite of our knowledge that these tiny creatures can do us no harm—says they are evil and belong to an evil race.

The mammals—the animals which suckle their young at the breast (the Latin word *mammae* means "breasts," and so we get "mammals") which appear in the next chapter, grew out of the reptiles. The reptiles never got beyond laying their eggs, and leaving them to be hatched by the sun. Compared to a mammal the reptile is a kind of foster-mother, and not a true mother. That is the great dividing-line between reptiles and mammals, for the mammal is the first true mother among living things. And ever since certain reptile families took the first step—evolving a *real heart,* different from the reptile heart, a heart that separates the body's pure blood from its impure blood and became mammals—there has been war between mammal and reptile.

At first the new mammal things were mostly small creatures, hunted and devoured by the larger reptiles. Though fitter to survive than the reptiles, they often had a hard time surviving. When reptile meets mammal now, it may attack, like the crocodile or the snake, because it wants food, or because it has learned, out of its reptile life-experience that it is better to strike before being struck. But any creature born of an egg and mothered by the sun has only the bit of memory built up out of what happened to it in its own little life. It has only its own little *life-memory*. But the mammal, nursed at the breast, has a *race-memory*. It has a memory going back through the ages, to the time when it was a small hairy and furry creature, skipping about the trees and hiding in the brush, while the great reptiles tried to catch and eat it. And that is the reason why, as soon as we look at the harmless little lizard playing among the ferns, something as old as the first mammal rises in us, and tells us that it belongs to an evil tribe of fierce, deadly creatures, old, old enemies of *all* mammals.

Many of you have wondered why you have a sick feeling or a feeling of disgust when seeing a snake or a lizard. The reason lies in this old *race-memory*—a memory so old you do not know it is a memory—of the times when every kind of reptile was a mammal's born foe. The reptile has a *single creature memory*. When it dies that memory dies with it.

The lizards that grow more repulsive and dangerous looking seen through the magnifying glass are nothing compared to the lizard-reptiles of the golden reptile age. They lumbered about among the fern forests and crashed through the dripping rushes of the shallow pools in a nightmare of terrible shapes. Reptile life bred in the reeking swamps in shapes more horrid and awful than anything we can imagine. The truth of reptile creation is stranger than all the fiction of succeeding ages, its lizards more awful than all the dragons of human fancy. For things far more horrible than anything seen among the amphibians, the half-water, half-land creatures, were hatched out by the burning sun, creeping and wriggling from the eggs with shells that lay on the hot sands.

Most animals, except the very highest animal of all, have a way, sooner or later, of settling down to some special *kind* of food. We have already seen how the earliest things that ate *anything* and *everything* has a better chance to keep going than the ones that only ate *one kind* of food. One kind of food—whether insects, mollusc, flesh or plants, tied down the eaters to it. We have seen what happened to the great "fish-lizards" that ate only squid. No doubt many a race and family of animals was led by one kind of food into little "blind alley" of development, and had to starve there when some accident made its food disappear. It was not built to eat any other, and so had to perish.

In a general way great races of creatures settle down to one of two kinds of food—plant-food or animal food. They are vegetarians or meat-eaters. We often use the expression "a snake in the grass," but the opposite is never the case. The grass is never in the snake, for snakes eat insects and animals. Yet some of the hugest of the old reptiles never touched a living creature. They were innocent vegetarians, and browsed on the roots of water-plants or the leaves of trees.

There is a sloshing and stirring in the shallow pool whose sandy bottom rests on an underlayer of rock, and whose waters are covered with curious unflower-like looking, early water-lilies. A huge, smooth, naked black body, glistening with water, is pushing ahead through the pool. The body ends in front, in a neck that would make a very complete big snake if it were cut off, and in back in a monstrous tail, a tail thirty feet long! It is the "floating power" of the water that helps this great clumsy thing carry its huge belly, stuffed with lily-roots it has been gathering up from the bottom of the pool, and it would be sure to take Nature's prize as the greatest of waddlers. The tail of this "thunder-lizard"* is one of Nature's strangest and most curious freaks. Nature—as the reptiles, stimulated by the hot sun and plentiful food, were breeding and interbreeding among their horrible selves with a fertility passing belief—tried out all sorts of uncanny experiments. In the case of the "thunder-lizard," she made a start at developing a brain at the animal's *tail-end* instead of at its head-end! What brains the thunder-lizard" had in its head are not worth mentioning, for it holds the record of having the smallest brain-space—in spite of its eighty-four feet of length—of anything with a backbone that ever has lived on earth. But the nerves of its spinal cord, the brain-stuff, was piled up in an enormous mass in its monstrous tail, over the pelvis. Its cousin* also had the family tail, and this "tail-brain," piled up above the sex organs in these creatures, was three times the size of the "head-brain." The "thunder-lizards" have left no descendants to come down to us. Did their special food—the water-lily—die out where they browsed, and leave these huge tail-brained masses of reptile flesh to die of hunger? We do not know.

But the Iguanodon with a shorter neck, but a similar "tail-end" brain, has handed on its stupidity and its kind, not size of teeth to a harmless little South American lizard descendant, the Iguana. A famous naturalist has said: "The Iguana is the stupidist creature I ever met." It is evident that a tail is not the right place for a brain, and that Nature wisely decided it should survive in the *skull,* the "fittest" place for it, instead of in a *tail.*

The "rough-toothed lizard" **—you may see it as he stands "restored," in a museum—stood on its hind legs and stripped young trees of their leafy crowns. There were lizards which grew rows of fleshy spikes along their backs; there were lizards whose backs were blown out in a grisly fan with sharp points; there were lizards that

---

*Brontosaurus: the Greek word *bronto* means "thunder", and *saurus*—"lizard", and the earth must have thundered under the tread of this monster when it waddled along the swampy ground.

*The Atlantosaurus. Both reptiles are natives of Wyoming.

**Trachodon: from the Greek *trachys*—rough, and *odous*—toothed.

began to put forth horns on their upper jaws. It is surprising how like a three-horned rhinoceros the lizard looks which grew longer legs and put out two horns from the back of its head and one on the end of its snout. Some of these reptiles had smooth, slithering, naked skins. Some grew plates of tough hide to protect them. They had to. The flesh-eating kinds that tried to devour them had better teeth, so the vegetarians kept trying to grow a hide which would be tooth-proof, and protect them till they got their terrible tail-mauls working on the foe. But in spite of their huge bodies, these flesh-eaters were "soft." When winter came they were too clumsy to set out on the long hike by land or water to the promised lands of warmth, and most of them died of the cold. Besides, vegetarians—men or beasts—are at a disadvantage. The plant-eating lizards could turn the cells and tissues of their skins into hard, horny plates, shields to protect them from the quicker flesh-eating lizards. But they could not grow as good teeth. And the latter thought "thunder lizard"— or "rough-toothed lizard"—steak delicious eating. *Their* sharp teeth would crunch right through the hardest blanket of shell the vegetarian lizards could grow. If the great cold wave had not finished them off, the teeth of the fiercer meat-eating lizards probably would have done so. Some say that the plant-eaters would have died out anyway, because their *life-energy,* the life-stuff that should have gone into eggs to carry on the breed, was all being thrown into armor-plating their skins. So they were unfitted to survive, even in their own time, on two counts, and would have gone the way of the "unfit" had the cold not gotten them first.

The vegetarian lizards, the plant-eaters, all ran to solid, heavy bones. They needed them to support the weight of their huge bodies, which weighed tons. But the meat-eating reptiles, driven to do so, gradually bred lighter bones—more marrow and less bone matter. Why? Because they were hunters. They had to be more active than the reptiles they hunted. They had to be able to pounce quickly on them, and rip and tear before the clumsier lizards could use their tails. The plant-eaters grew great, solid hind-limbs to hold up their monster bodies when they rose up on them. They ran to clumsy "one-piece" legs. But the flesh-hunters developed longer and thinner legs, whose tremendous muscles answered quickly. Their bodies were big, too—the greatest of all these frightful beasts, with a heavy jawful of long, cruel teeth, measured forty feet from foot to tail! And it had a thick lizard tail almost as heavy as that of the Iguandon.

The "thunder-lizard" we saw emerge from the lily-pool has dragged its slow length up on the land, and stands for a moment on the pool's edge, as though resting. There is a rustling, a crashing in a clump of giant fern ten feet away. And suddenly, something like a monster kangaroo in shape—a great dark, smooth-skinned body, comes hurtling through the air! Forty feet of living flesh, tail and all, are shot off the ground by a contraction of all the muscles of the tremendous legs! The monster strikes the surprised "thunder lizard" almost before the latter knows it. For a short time the swamp heaves like a living thing as the enormous bodies thrash and roll about, crushing its lower fern-growth (a "lower" growth of "brush" more than eight feet high"!) But soon the "tyrant lizard's" * awful jaws have closed about the "thunder-lizard's" soft, long neck, near the head, almost cutting it in two. Its short forearms, with their long, sharp, tearing claws, are digging in the unfortunate vegetarian's back. As the "tyrant" lizard's" teeth meet in its neck, the poor plant-eater gives up the fight. It collapses, while the green jungle-ferns are drowned in red. And then and there the "tyrant-lizard" tears the dying "thunder lizard" limb from limb. A horde of waiting crabs, roaches and insects will soon strip every vestige of flesh from the huge bones. He is a typical example of his kind, is the "tyrant lizard!"

There are other reptiles that leap and jump on their prey, or rear on their hind legs to strike it. In fact, any number of different families have sprung from the crossings of the steamy marshes, with differences in shape and body and tail, in the size and arrangement of their teeth, feet and claws. Some, as they fight and breed, are beginning to develop something the great crocodile lizards have carried down to our day, the first *musk-glands,* the special glands which throw off a strong sweetly-sickish smell that betrays the reptile's presence hundreds of feet away. It is a little example of Evolution itself. Giving out a rank, heavy reptile odor on the living creature, to let other members of the family know it is around, it is now turned into a base for delicate perfumes. From the reptile the musk-glands, together with other things, later passed on to various mammals.

The crocodile-lizards are a reptile family which has come down with honor through the long long ages, like some of the turtle-lizards. Perhaps one reason was that the crocodile, which can run swiftly in spite of its short legs, and is even more at home afloat than ashore, could make its way to the promised land of hot sunshine without much trouble when winter came, instead of remaining to freeze to death. The great crocodile-lizards first stayed on the ground. They were satisfied to creep and run swiftly, to cling to their long lizard tail, to cover their bodies with a heavy armor of scales, and fill their jaws with long rows of cutting teeth. They seem to have been a more active kind of reptile, mentally, than

*The Tyrannosaurus

most of the others. One, as we already have seen, the "snake-lizard," deliberately left the land for the sea, and let its feet turn to fin-like paddles. Another, though, was even more ambitious, and founded a crocodile family which rose higher in the world than any reptile before or after!

Some low growth of reed-grass may have covered the vast North American prairies and plains, while the forest of Brazil stretched for thousands of dark green miles in South America when the "flying crocodile" first made the airs above them its range. The "flying crocodile," in which Nature went ahead and outdid the wildest dreams of poets to come, worked its way from the ground to the air for a reason. The poets say the lark flies up to greet the sun, but the "flying crocodile" only flew up to pounce down on its food. Whenever we see progress made by the inhabitants of the early world in some one direction or another, food is at the bottom of it, somehow or another.

In the plant world "great oaks from little acorns grew", and it is likely that the giant "flying crocodile" started life as smaller reptiles of the lizard tribe, which had taken to living in fern trees to be out of the way of larger lizard brothers ready to snap them up. Besides, insects with wings perched and fluttered around in those tree-tops, and made good food. But larger reptile lizards, let us say of the huge-growing turtle-kind, had a way of upending their clumsy, shell-covered bodies against a tree and "reaching up" for whatever flesh-fruit might be hanging in the top leaves. After centuries of jumping down and risking their tails, then scurrying away before the heavier enemy could turn and get back, the smaller lizards managed, by stretching and straining, to stretch a long sheet of gristle out from the end-finger of each fore-hand, each sheet of gristle connecting with one of their hind feet. This "wing-membrane" gave the tree-lizard a parachute or sail, by means of which it could "volplane"* down quickly, and escape its foe, without having to drop heavily on the ground. The lizards that "survived", the strongest in each generation of gristle-growers, grew wings that were larger and larger. They had to be, because now they had found a way to escape their worst enemies, these lizards, like all other reptiles in that glowing hot-house world, soon grew to giant crocodile size. They had to have bigger wings to carry their bigger bodies.

The "flying-crocodile", whose great triangular bat wings were all

*One of the strange examples of how Nature's creatures can move in any direction to develop, when there is a reason and if time be given them, are the *flying mammals*. These *flying mammals* are neither birds nor *flying reptiles!* They are full-fledged mammals, like the flying foxes and vampires, fruit and blood-sucking bats, the flying squirrels, etc., and have grown membrane parachutes or "volplanes" to help them sail from of twenty feet long, was an insect-eater, of the upper air. For it was toothless. The immense stretch of its wings could carry it up tremendous distances into the blue, and it could hang there for a longer time than a smaller flier. It may even have been able to balance itself there for hours. Probably it fed on fruits and insects, for which it needed no cutting and biting teeth. They could be "gummed down" by gums that were hard and bony.

There may have been some special insect, a high-flying insect, which formed its favorite food. We know the "fish-lizard" fed almost altogether on squid, and that the squid was the cause of its downfall. In its effort to reach and stay in the same air-levels that its special food-fly did, the early "flying crocodiles"* began to cast over ballast, just as balloonists do when they want their balloon to rise higher. These crocodiles are another wonderful example of Nature's way of letting the strongest individuals of a tribe or family, working in a certain direction for many generations, to get where they want to get. The "flying crocodile" first dropped all its crocodile teeth, big heavy things, and "went up one." Then its heavy lizard tail—the style of tail with which the "thunder lizard" could knock down a tall tree—went by the board. Then it pulled its hind legs up gradually into its body—who needs hind legs in the air?—to work their stuff into more wing-membrane. Next came the heaviest weight of all— it let all its bone-ballast go, and instead of solid reptile bones, its bones changed to bird-like bones, light and hallow. Instead of a heavy hide of horny armor, such as our crocodiles still wear, it grew a skin not much thicker than the silk of a balloon around these bones. The skull of this reptile "Wright brother" can be examined. It is as thin as parchment, while it would be hard for a strong man to lift the head of a large-sized crocodile of to-day.

We cannot help but admire this old reptile of the millions of years ago. Its race had put its mind to just one thing, and had stuck to it. And through Evolution, it produced the most perfect living flying-machine possible, working from the "volplane" angle, and not from the true wing angle. But, after all, it only had a reptile "thinking-cap" inside of its paperweight skull. It flew with its little finger and not with its brain!

Can you see the vast reaches of the Brazilian forest and, suddenly one tree to another, or rise in the air before darting at an insect or dropping into an orchard of fruit-trees. The huge earliest form of the vampire bat, a hideous blood-sucking South American creature, is supposed to have used its hideous "wings" to drop on the vast herds of native-born early horse-kinds that ranged the great South American pampas long before humanity was born. It is supposed *literally to have bled these horses to death,* so that when the Spaniards first landed there was not *one living native horse on American soil!*

*Its right name was Pterandon: which means "toothless flier".

shooting up, up, up out from that sea of green, this stuff twenty-foot
spread of kite-wing, up, up and still higher up, till it stands out against
the clear blue sky like a great brown shield flung to the clouds? It
hangs, trembling in the air, and comes volplaning down again with
dizzying swiftness only—as we think it is going to strike the green
tree-tops full tilt—to shoot up and away again at another angle. No
creature of the reptile kind ever went up so far and so high into
the blue as the "flying crocodile." It followed a "blue blind alley"
instead of a "green blind alley" and—very likely because its insect
food failed—disappeared absolutely from the face of the Earth.

But we like it best of all the great early lizards because, food or
no food, any striving up and on into the open blue of the sky seems
like a move toward freedom and light. The "flying crocodile" could
not stay there above a certain time, for all its "ballast-dropping" had
not led it to true wings. But one can't help but admire the one reptile that left the mud and slime of the swamp forever, that managed
to break off all connection with the land to live among the clouds, so
to speak. For even when the dusky tropic night ablaze with stars
sent it off to sleep, it shot high up into the twilight above the great
Atlantic, and zig-zagging softly down, came to rest on the breast of
an element as free and unconfined as the air itself.

But not all the lizards that grew "volplane wings" were like the
"flying crocodiles." Perhaps the most repulsive of the fluttering
things was the giant "bat-lizard."* Like its crocodile brother, its
lizard scales had changed their scale-stuff until they had turned
into a hideous, naked black skin. But it clung to its tail, which remained long, though thin. *And it threw away no teeth.* On the contrary, it grew a long bill filled with sharp teeth which it used to eat
up anything its own size or under that could be snapped up as it
zig-zagged in the air among the fern-palms. One of Sir Conan
Doyle's most exciting short stories is about an egg of one of these
huge "bat-lizards," discovered in the dense, streaming tropical
swamps of some Brazilian "jungle of doubt." The lizard-chick breaks
the shell laid untold millions of years ago, before an audience in a
twentieth-century London lecture hall. There it spreads its naked,
musky wings and terrifies a great crowd of people with its devilish
appearance and dangerous teeth. Who knows—in the hidden jungle-
lands of Africa and South America there may be reeking, fetid marshes
that have lain unchanged since Earth's early days. Perhaps, here
and there, there still linger some of the horrible forms of early
reptile life, waiting to be discovered. It would seem like a miracle,
but no miracle is beyond Nature, the greatest wonder-worker of all
time!

Perhaps the most curious of all the reptile "flyers," which were
neither true "birds" nor "bats," but just membrane-winged reptiles,

was a creature like an armless man,—and never a wing. It had a jawful of vicious-looking teeth, webbed feet—it was a water-thing, that lived on fish and had grown strong webbed membranes between its toes—and its lizard tail had shrunk away almost altogether. See it standing on a rock that juts out into a deep pool. As the "flying crocodile" gradually drew its hind feet up into its body, so this creature has drawn in its fore-arms. It runs down *almost just body*, from the long neck to the short hind legs that end in huge webbed feet. It dived for its food in the water, but then so did other lizards, and they turned their forefeet into fins or flappers to help them along. But—whether it was to dive more quickly or deeper we do not know—the "wingless bird" (the one word seems to contradict the other) lost its forefeet without growing anything in their place. It did not die out, it seems, like most of the other flying reptiles. This we know because in the bills of Arctic and Antarctic sea-diving birds —which later managed to "draw out" their ancestor's hidden legs and feet again in the shape of wings, we find traces of the teeth— imagine a bird with teeth!—the wingless reptile once had. But before many true snakes had developed out of the snake lizards came the blow that destroyed the reptile world. The snake form was not a very popular one for a lizard to change into in the golden reptile age, though there were land "snake lizards" as well as sea "snake lizards," and only a few small land—and water-snakes were to be seen. But the snakes came into their own later, as we shall see— after Earth's first winter.

CHAPTER XIII

THE SONG OF THE SURF

(Intermission)

THE steady beat of a pounding music rang in my ear. It rose in a long soft swell of sound that died in a murmur only to roll out again. It changed as it flowed, but with a more steady rhythm, and as my eyes opened on the long outer reefs of a coral-lagoon, where the great waves came curving in as clear as liquid blue glass, to foam across the coral and suck back again with a long-drawn sigh, I knew that the music I heard was the song of the surf. The white coral chimed like a bell under the stroke of the waves, and their solemn melody seemed one of sorrow.

"The voice of the great waters is always sad when the surf drives in to shore," said Nature, and waved her hand out in the direction of the open sea, beyond the pearly mist that hung above the rolling breakers. "Do the waves mourn the shrinking of the sea before its old enemy, the land? Do they sorrow for the great water-creatures of the past, whose like Earth will never see again? Or is the song of the surf just the lament of the waters for the passing of all things, even themselves, as they grow less and less with every thousand years of time? It is hard to say.

"The road of Evolution, now that the reptiles have come, is no longer a waterway: it is a land road. But let us see what the sea has brought forth since the first lung-fish with backbones crept ashore." Nature raised her hand. The coral reef and the mist-shrouded breakers disappeared. The song of the surf dropped to the softest of murmurs. I stood beside Nature on the silvery coral sand at the bottom of the lagoon, in a great basin of transparent water clear as glass, and light as day from the sunshine which filtered down from overhead. It was a strange world full of magic color, and bathed in a soft greenish light. Here and there long strings of pearly bubbles rose to the top, as eels and lampreys, moving sluggishly along the rocks, threw out the air from their gills. The surrounding coral-shelves were covered with the most wonderful sea-weed growths, green and scarlet, crimson and purple. Gardens of sea-anemones and sea-pinks flourished at the foot of rocks from which weird polyps,

83

half-plant, half-animal, looking like great snakes with a hundred heads, spread out long slimy arms, ending in fleshy pink fingers, writhing, stretching, hungry for any food, with a creepy motion that spread from the creature's root-ends to their uttermost tips. Curious sea-lilies grew in tangled clumps, with great twisted and woven masses of green stems, whose blossoms stirred as the sunlight kissed them below the water. And along the white sands and in dim, dark rock caverns there shuffled, and wriggled and squirmed all sorts of hideous small things. There were tiny squids, swimming backward as though shot from an arrow; there were big mussels with coiled shells, four or more feet around, lurking in dark corners with great, round eyes and gaping mouth, waiting for the golden-silver and rainbow colored fish which darted through the clear waters to come within reach. And here and there slim black water-snakes shot from one clump of sea-weed to another, some followed by the wriggling brood of young they bear alive, in the water, for the true water-snake lays no eggs in the sand.

And through all this life beneath the water Nature was leading me to a break in the coral wall that gave on the open sea beneath the reef. And now we stood at the top of a rise of sand which swept down in a long, steep incline to great abysses of darkness, where the very last soul of the sunlight has long since died away. Those are the deep caverns of utter cold and darkness. There, on the gray lime of Earth's earlier crust lie ghastly, swollen forms of life, white with the whiteness of all things that never see the light; blind with the blindness of all things that need no eyes; with a life-juice that runs a thousand times more cold and slow than that of the most sluggish reptile. There lie the horrors of a life that is life in death, a life so nearly slowed down that it touches on death, though it lives. There are the horrible things which still keep the secret of their hideous existence when the drag-net pulls them to the surface of the water. For even in their loathsome bed of frozen slime they obey the law of Nature. In a downward evolution they have sunk to the very bed-rock of existence. But they are the survival of the fittest to live in those horrid abysses. Their surroundings have changed their fate and made them what they are. The drag-net carries them higher and higher through the water which grows lighter and lighter. But tremendous pressure has made their strange, contorted bodies able to resist the pressure of the deeps. Once that pressure is removed, their cells fly violently apart. They explode in a shower of slime and mucous matter at the very moment when they are about to yield up their secret to science.

While my thoughts had strayed to this riddle of the fathomless deep, curious forms of finny life began to pass in the nearer waters, in a kind of review. Nature had called up the tribes of living things that had branched off from Evolution's great main road *after they had done their part*. They had left the main road to spread and develop in their own ways in the element out of which all life first came.

"Here are the 'fittest' of the countless army of living creatures that took the sea-road instead of the land-road, to go as far as water alone will carry them!" And as Nature spoke, the waters began to swarm with school after school of every kind of fish known. There— flashing by in a glory of color—were huge salmon, the family whose mothers dare death and wounds, leaping up the rocks to the clear fresh-water pools where their eggs are hatched out—a fish which lives in salt water, but whose mysterious law of life compels it to hatch out in fresh water. There were 'flying' fishes (true fish which have grown a kind of 'bat-wing' to take to the air when hungry jaws are after them) mackerels, sea-bass, tunny, and a thousand others, all the fishes that swim the salt seas. They were the true *backbone* fishes, the higher kind of fish that in build and shape went as far as fish may go. They flew past, their finned squadrons dashing by as though on parade, with a tremendous flutter of fin and tail, and a continuous sparkle as the underwater light shot a million jewelled drops of color from their glistening scales!

All these higher forms of fish had come down from the spawn of the strongest and sturdiest individuals of those which had survived the days of the first winter, for the cold thrust its icy fingers deep down into the surface waters of the sea, and slew life there as it did on land. The fish kinds, and the best fish of each kind, the ones that had the greatest vitality, that had the best "hold" on life, fled to warmer waters (like the land creatures) or got used to the colder ones. And the great, naked-bodied "snake-lizards" lay paralyzed in the grip of an icy current, gasping out their life as the cold found its way to their sluggish hearts and stopped the slow circulation of their chilly blood.

But many creatures used to lower deeps, where the temperatures were cold, keep on living and breeding without knowing that the world above the waters had changed. Nor did all the great families of fish and amphibians that vanished with Earth's first winter, its ice age, perish because of it. Sometimes, like the "fish-lizard," some little thing killed them. They would get used to one particular kind of food, and that food would die out. And, unable to get used to another kind of food, the fish in question would follow its food out into the great beyond.

"The great sea," said Nature, "is the most tremendous burial-ground, the most colossal cemetery in all the world. On earth all that dies does not remain in or on it. The dead *matter* of death in a thousand different ways, by the road of sun-ray, of plant-leaf and

plant-root, rises again into the air. There it is cleansed and puri-
fied, and comes back once more to make new life in a circle that
has no end. But while some of the matter of death in the sea rises
again into the air, far more remains, and the bottom of all Earth's
seas are carpeted by all the life that lived in it, powdered to dust
by the restless waves.

"Older than the other fish, going back to the worm-fish with their
stiffish backbone of cartilage, are the sharks and rays that are coming
now. They never found the *backbone* all the modern fishes own.
Restless wanderers of the seas, the curse of an endless hunger seems
to weigh on the sharks, and, savage slayers, they roam their special
"blind alley" of development as in the early days of time!"

They come shooting by in a darting whirl of speed, cruel, tooth-
rowed mouth agape, and now and again they fling themselves on
their backs and show their white bellies—for it is on upturned belly
that their hingeless jaw forces them to seize their prey! "None of
these sharks, terrible as they seem, can compare with the earliest of
their kind," said Nature. "There were giant sharks in those days.
The great 'whale-shark' grew to a length of more than forty-five
feet, with jaws and teeth to match, and it is easy to see how little
chance a poor, toothless 'fish-lizard' had which happened to meet it."

Now there darted by schools of the terrible sword-fish, or saw-
fish, a family of sharks which have worked their upper snout into one
long stabbing weapon. With this long, five-foot "saw," its teeth
standing out at each side, it strikes the other larger sea-creatures,
even the whale, and tears out their intestines, its favorite food.

The rays and skates swarm in larger schools. These huge flat
fishes, were first spawned in the Earth's early days. They had smooth,
flat, naked black bodies, their heads running back and seeming to
form part of the body, that looks as though it were made up of its
great flat fins. There are the electric rays or "torpedo fishes,"
which generate living storage-batteries of electricity in their nerves
powerful enough to kill lesser fishes.

The great "sting-rays" had a barbed spine at the end of their long
tails, a "sting" which they lash out to cut and maim. Most terrible
of all were the mysterious giant "devil-fish," the whip-rays which
grow twenty and more feet long and broad, and whose spined "sting-
ers" or tail-lashes cut even more deeply than those of their brothers.
The "devil-fish" gave a curious exhibition. First shooting down to
a tremendous depth, they would come speeding back with a force
that shot their 1500 or 2000 pounds of body a number of feet out of
water, to fall back with a thundering flap that sent huge "rollers" in
motion on every side! It is the way the rays "play" along the
Florida coasts and the shores of the Indian seas.

And now, in a writhing, weaving mass of hungry, twisting suckers, comes the whole horrible family of the cuttle-fishes or squids. First, the true cuttle-fishes, each with ten gliding suckers, feeling through the waters for something to seize and draw to the formless, gaping mouth-hole. Below them, as they swim above the sandy ground, crawl and sidle the smaller squids, the "hooked" cuttle-fishes, whose suckers end in a cruel curved hook or beak, and the flabby deep-sea squids, with suckers tipped with webbed cups for catching and closing on small fish. They are not a pleasant sight, but their hideous family has one beautiful member. School after school they come, the dainty chambered nautilus, with their rainbow colors, looking like beautiful fairy blossoms, among the slithering black shapes around them!

The long procession—forms of horror and forms of beauty, forms of brute strength and violence, like shark and ray, and others of gentle grace, like the fringed-finned gold—and silver-fishes—disappeared in the cloud of ink with which a rearguard regiment of passing squids scattered through the water. It was just as though a curtain were being dropped at the end of a play. I felt a drowsiness I could not control, and turned and looked back into the white basin of the lagoon. But as I did so all its light and beauty seemed to roll about me in a hazy cloud, and then the croon of the surf, humming softly and tenderly, above the reef, carried me off and I knew no more.

CHAPTER XIV

WHEN WINTER CAME

MILLIONS of years of summer—and then winter came! Everything living on earth to-day is a "winter child," so to speak. For every creature living on earth to-day has come down from the creatures that managed to get through Earth's first great winter,* its first Age of Ice, or get away to warmer lands while it lasted.

Beautiful are the great fern and fern-palm forests that cover marshy or mossy forest tracts that spread from the mudflats or Earth's spreading lowlands—for most of the land is flat—great sandy beaches, the dank, swarming ponds or blue lagoons, on and on and on, as far as eye can reach. A hot sun sends down its blazing rays, and under the blanket of steaming moisture it calls up from this lush, rich soil everything that has life, that swarms, breeds and feeds. It overbreeds and overfeeds, producing creatures even more strange in look and limb. For the heavy steam blanket is like the great glass pane over a hot-house that drives on life to bud and lay and bear, to grow to giant size, and pour out ever new forms of life in the great forcing-house.

Millions of years of summer! The torrid seas spawn forth marine monsters—sharks and rays that double and triple our whales in size, serpent-lizards huge and hideous, whose last fearsome children may still linger on in the hidden abysses of tropic waters**—life of a dead past—to alarm the sailor of our days.

The eggs that float on ocean currents or on the great green-scummed cesspools along the shores, that lie ready for the sun's hatching on the thousands of miles of sand-beach and mudflat would fill the earth three times over.

---

*There had been two winters of many millions of years, two great ice ages on earth before the first great winter came of which we write. But those winters came before the first *Algae* was born, so they did not affect any living thing.

**"Sea-serpent" stories are usually not believed. Yet there have been enough creditable eye-witnesses to show that *it is quite possible* that one or another of the gigantic "sea-lizards" or ancient days still roams the warmer oceans at the present day, cut off from its own past by millions of years.

But only a few out of their billions hatch out: the insects on land feed on the eggs of other smaller ones on land and on the water; and so on down. Insect eats insect, and reptile eats reptile and the great struggle never ends. The reeds and rushes, mosses and ferns slay each other in silence underground with murderous roots that twine, clutch and strangle. Winged insects pursue their prey in the air. The reptiles feed on each other or on reeds and plant-leaves. It is a ring of slaughter without beginning or end!

It is a circle of devouring teeth set in other flesh, while the plants link life with death and death with life, as they draw out of the ground the pith and marrow of the bones of the slain, only to be devoured in turn by the plant-eating reptiles, thus to continue the endless chain.

Millions of years of summer. There is rich food for all, for all *are* food. And life breeds faster than it can devour. Life grows denser and denser, richer in shapes of horror and wonder. Earth seems to have turned into one great slaughter-house, but though tooth and claw never stop tearing and rending, new creatures spring from the blood-soaked ground in ever greater numbers.

And then winter came! It came in cold waves of hundreds of thousands of years, each colder than the one before. For Earth had begun to cast up great mountain chains many thousands of feet high. Where they were flung up, the hot steam blanket that had mothered all the vast outpouring of life that bred beneath it disappeared. It was sucked up from the marshes, and the great fetid pools of stagnant water became dry. The moisture, sucked up the mountain side, fell again in tremendous rains. And the rains rushed down from the hills to make great rivers. Running water took the place of standing water.

The vast fern forests shivered, and on the breath of the cold wave countless numbers of creatures were swept away. They belonged to all families and all kinds, these first to fall. They were *the least fit to stand the cold.* There also were many insects, amphibians and reptiles unfit *among their own particular family* or tribe. They were the creatures with the least *vitality,* the least "hold on life." For everything that breathes has a *double* vitality. There is the vitality of its own *race,* the average time the life spark "carries on" in the creatures of its kind. And then each individual living thing has its *own individual vitality.* Some "let go" of life easily, and some cling to life when it seems they should be dead. Of all these creatures—insects, amphibians and reptiles—many were swept away on land and in the waters when the first chill wind of a thousand years blew over the Earth and struck them.

As one cold wave was followed by another colder one, food grew less, and when food died living was harder. But now, here and there, some tougher and stronger creatures of every kind were getting used to the cold, were beginning to take winter as a matter of course. But only here and there. Other creatures, led by that *sixth sense,* that strange instinct we cannot explain, which Nature gives her children who cannot think, started on a long, long journey for a promised land of eternal heat. They crawled over continents and swam the great Earth ocean, keeping on and on and on, with the one idea of finding their promised land, until they really did find it. There—for winter never covered *all* the Earth—they were safe!

Coming down the mountains, great rivers of ice slid slowly into the low-lying country till all Earth was ice, from India to Australia, and tropical Africa lay buried beneath great hills of frozen waters. It was the Angel of the Cold, with a freezing sword, who drove the reptiles out of their earthly paradise!

But there was summer beyond where the ice-rivers stopped. Even when millions of square miles of Earth were frozen stiff, and Earth's climate changed forever, so that the torrid golden summer of the reptiles never could return, descendants of the sixth sense fishes and mollusca, amphibians and reptiles which fled to the warmer parts kept on living, and have kept on living to this day. And that is why we still have certain kinds of great lizards, crocodiles and alligators and turtles (sea and land), and why a genuine old "first family" of the reptile age, the tortoise, is still laying its eggs to be hatched by the same sun that hatched those of its ancestors millions of years ago.

With animal, so it was with plant life. There is a strange continent where the plant and animal life of early Earth has "hung on" to our day—Australasia. There, in New Zealand, still stretch vast forest of ferns and mosses. Somehow, when the first winter of two hundred and fifty thousand years came, they "made the grade." When that first winter came the giant fern forests could not move. No sixth sense could help them: they were rooted to the ground. But as one wave of the cold followed another, they gained the toughness that carried them through, they grew hardened.

And—what a miracle of Nature!—not year after year, but millions of years after millions of years, from that *first fern forest of the golden reptile age* the shoots have been coming up, living and growing, continuing it down to our own day! We can still *touch* the ferns—in a way—that lived through Earth's first ice age, its first winter, after all these millions of years! Countless generations of fern-trees have grown and withered away in the same ground, and generation after generation, they have lived again after passing on their life to their descendants. And pith of their pith, stem of their stem, leaf of their leaf, they still look out over the seas—the same green trees that have continued the life of their race out of the dust and decay of past generations, bring it right down to the present day!

These trees which had not yet gotten far enough in the great evolution of plant life to produce *seed,* covered Earth before the first flower smiled! With them are mixed trees and flowers of the highest kinds of plant life. It is hard to find words to express the wonder of it. But you may get an idea of what a miracle it is, if you imagine Adam,* as the first of his kind, shaking hands with your own boy or girl!

These New Zealand ferns, and the reptiles and other creatures which have continued to exist down to our day represent the "survival of the fittest" through Earth's first winter of freezing ice. They stand for the "selection" which Nature made among existing families of living things; the *kinds* of life she meant to "keep going." All the rest she swept from life's checkerboard: the huge land and sea monsters whose bones still fill our museums; large and small, giant and dwarf, plant, insect, fish, amphibian and reptile!

She had decided to continue the Evolution of life with a "clean deck" of forms and life families. But she did not waste what had gone before, though out of every *hundred families* of living things only *one* was "selected" to keep its life going. Nature did not waste any of the great gains—*backbone, lungs* and *bone-structure, brains, jaws* and *mouths, skulls, feet* and *fingers, flesh* and *blood.*

And when winter came to Earth, Nature, as she swept so many of the living pawns, large and small, with which she was playing the great game of Evolution from her checkerboard, kept a pawn without which the game would have ended for *us!* It was the little reptile egg with a yellow-white shell, which hid the hope of progress for all higher forms of life—the reptile egg from which was to creep the first thing with a *true heart,* a *four-chambered heart,* the very first of all mammals!

---

*Evolution shows us that the story of Adam is a lovely, poetic way of accounting for a great truth, and one which must be regarded as what it is, *a beautiful story.* It has nothing to do with the facts *of Evolution,* which show us how everything has developed, step by step, out of something else that lived. No form of life woke up a finished product under a tree in Paradise, complete from head to foot. It had to make its way up *an inch at a time,* through a development lasting millions and millions of years.

I

CHAPTER XV

(The Birth of Motherlove)

IT was in the warm land of promise far beyond the great river of ice, in the dim ages of the first winter, that there crept from a reptile egg—a reptile egg like any other, so far as looks went—*the first reptile with a four-chambered heart!* It may have been a "freak," it may have been a "sport." No matter, it was a link in the great chain of Evolution which *had* to be, to move on and up—so Nature supplied it.

Once the first four-chambered heart beat on Earth, all the ages of progress which before this had been closed, were opened. For the mammal, the first warm-blooded creature had been born. Just as we must go back to the first real *backbone* for a real body, so we must go back to the first real *heart* for the beginning of *warm blood*.

Nature's great law of heredity (which already has been explained) "hands on" any new development of brain and body. She saw to it that the four-chambered heart, the heart which made *warm* instead of *cold* blood run through the veins of the body, came to stay. And there were other things (we will take them up in the next chapter) which helped to make warm blood the standard of advance, and perfect the new heart to make it work and beat in the best way.

Like so many other insect, fish and animal families, the other reptiles—those left after the first winter—kept on developing their own special branches. They kept on in the "blind alley" of cold blood and an imperfect circulation, and there they still have their being to-day. But the reptile that crept out of the "sport" egg, an egg hatched on dry land, was no longer a reptile—it was a *mammal!* From it sprang all the early mammal-reptile families.

This matter of a good heart and blood has a great deal to do with the fact that so much reptile life found its way to the scrap-heap when the first winter came. Some chapters ago we mentioned that the reptile heart had something the matter with it. The reptiles, to this day, have a heart with only three chambers, *three* big separating cavities: this means that they had a poor blood circulation, that the blood flowed sluggishly and unevenly through their veins. Why? Because only in a heart with *four* chambers is the blood that the lungs have cleaned from impurities *kept separate* from the blood which is still impure. A three-chambered heart is a make-shift bit of machinery, an imperfect, blood separator; a four-chambered heart is a perfect blood-separating machine. The three-chambered heart of the reptiles meant (and means to this day) *cold blood* and an imperfect circulation. When winter comes reptile blood does not grow warmer, it grows colder. The reptile must have the sun, must have *outside heat* if it is to live and thrive!*

The mystery of the first four-chambered heart is one that never has been fully solved. And yet—the brains which Evolution has slowly developed by means of that very same four-chambered heart has suggested the key to the mystery. One of Nature's ways of solving a puzzle which seems past solving is, every now and then, to have life bring forth a "freak" or "sport" form. Some creature will be born in a family of reptiles, for instance, which has inherited the traits and the shape of its reptile ancestors but—it has some absolutely *new addition* of some kind. Life has gone back through the ages to some tiny little spark of her own shaping matter she had overlooked, and suddenly—there it is: a "sport" or a "freak."

The long winter on earth had passed. Summer came again to the plains and shores, to the hills and valleys. All over the land the green life which had struggled through the winter years leaped into life. Selected ferns that had outlived the others once more rose in place of the forests sunk from sight beneath the soil which the sea had washed away, or which the ice had buried. And when those thousands of winter years were over, new plant kinds had grown up in the land to which all life had fled. Ferns already had been turning to fern-palms when the ice rivers began their slow move down the hills. Now the Earth sank back again, many of the great mountain ranges disappeared. And the tender fir and evergreens of various sorts, in their cones, their seedbearers, took the first step to the perfect flower, as the worm's soft cartilage led to the perfect backbone. And one fern, after many years of changing and producing has at last passed from cone to flower and—for the first time in all its history Earth smiled, where these big yellow flowers, coarse and clumsy, perhaps, compared to a golden yellow rose of to-day, but

---

*Bears, which are mammals and snakes, which are reptiles, "lay up" and sleep through the winter for absolutely different reasons: The snake burrows and hides because its blood temperature goes down with that of the air, and in its burrow it can just manage to live through in a torpid, half-frozen state till spring. The bear simply sleeps "on his fat."

real flowers for all that, spread over miles of plain on the dark-green ever-green shrub that bore them!

That first tremendous summer of steaming heat and moisture, with life spawning and breeding at tropical fever-heat, was never to return. The reptiles had been "fittest to survive" *during* that age. They were meant for it, and it for them. But when it changed they were unfit for the next and passed, leaving only the few "fit" ones which lived through to start things over again. Their monstrous size, their great plates of armored skin, their strength and ferocity could not save them. The sword of the ice angel passed over them and they were no more!

With a clearer, hot sun and less steamy swamp, with the ice rivers running down from the hills as the Earth sank in water, the reptiles spread out from their corner and once more covered the earth, where it was summer everywhere. But the early *"mammalreps"*—let us coin a word that shows these creatures came from reptile stock, but were more mammals than reptiles—had gone ahead of them.

During the age of ice Nature had been busy "selecting" her new kinds. In the overcrowded land of promise, where all life was huddled together during that long winter, only the strongest—the ones best fitted to fight and eat their way through at the expense of the rest—lasted over.

Now in those hot lands of promise there was a "cold fringe," where they touched the frozen parts of Earth. The ice covered Australia, South Africa, and India. North Africa and beyond was a land of promise. A "cold fringe" was the land nearest South Africa. Where now the Congo River flows through great steaming marshes and fetid swamps like those of the first Earth summer, it was bitter cold. The "mammalreps" that lived there were small active creatures, climbing trees or burrowing in the ground, and made hardy by the cold which their new hearts and warmer blood enabled them to stand, they developed in a way that left the reptiles and reptile peculiarities behind forever.*

It is fascinating to watch the new small fry of the mammal world sloughing reptile habits and coverings! Their hard reptile scales get softer and thicker, under the scales there grow hairs—wool out of horn—each scale giving way to a great number of separate hair threads—and *fur has come into the world!*

With this hair, fur or wool, which gave them a warm outside

---

*In some cases they took their time about it. Look at the present-day South American armadillo. Its gigantic ancestor, the armadillo of the early world, though a four-chambered heart pumped blood through its great body, still dragged along with huge turtle-shell that had come down in its family. And only changed in size, the armadillo of to-day has modified, but not yet cast it off.

covering and helped keep the warm blood moving in the coldest weather (the birds, which we will consider in our next chapter, *divided their* reptile-scales into tiny, downy feather-threads instead of growing hair and wool-threads around them also came skin-pores. And out of certain ones among these pores were develped the *breasts* of all warm-blooded mothers. It was these breasts which, while they nursed the little furry or hairy mammal babies that clung to them, brought true *motherhood* into a world which had not known it before. To this day the *living ghost* of that first coat of mammal hair appears *once on every human baby, three months before its birth,* though human beings have long since dropped the hairy coat which covered the bodies of the early mammals. This living ghost of the past is the thick, animal, "wool-hair pelt" (*lanugo*) which covers every child before it comes into the world!

But how did the skin-pores turn into a breast?

There are living on earth to-day animals which show us the successive steps of this wonderful evolution. The two animals at the very foot of the mammal ladder to-day are: a duckbilled water-mole and a porcupine ant-eater. Both are found only in Australasia. They have only one outlet for all the waste matter of their bodies, and though one has grown fur and the other bristles, *they still lay eggs,* which are hatched out, *like reptiles!* But after the eggs are hatched out, the little ones, while the mother lies on her back, draw fluid from certain *enlarged pores of the skin,* beneath which are glands filled with nourishing matter. These pores were the first move toward the mammal's nipple or teat.

Other creatures shows us the next step. These are the opossums, other ant-eaters—South American and Australian—and all sorts of small rat, rabbit and squirrel-things, the Tasmanian wolf (the thick pivot of whose tail still is fitted into its backbone just like a reptile's), and the kangaroos (which still sit and stand on their hind legs, resting on a tail like that of the old land-reptiles of the golden reptile age). These all—through crossings and intercrossings of thousands of years, and all the changes this would mean—are descendants of the first hardier mammals which flourished on the "cold fringe" of the warm world during the winter of ice. Some lived in trees, some burrowed underground, some dug on the surface of the earth, but all have one thing in common: the next step in the development of the breast: they no longer lay eggs, *but yet they do not bear their little ones outright,* ready to begin life!

It is a sort of compromise, a sort of "middle of the road" between hatching and birth. The children come from their mother in a very undeveloped state (embryos)—blind, helpless, "unfinished." Those of the great kangaroo, whose mother is larger than a sheep, are only *one inch long!* The babies by their mother are dropped into a pouch attached to her stomach, there to stay until they are full-fledged and able to hop out of it. These babies are born, one might say, before coming into the world. And now we can see what gradually happened to the enlarged pores of the water-mole mother. Gradually drawn out through the continuous suction of generations, they have become *nipples,* and to these nipples under the fur, the little inch-long, half-born kangaroo babies attach themselves, and draw out the fluid which is now a mother's milk, instead of the thicker nourishing moisture of the older gland-pores.

The nipples of these mammal-things were the beginnings of the *breasts* of all mammals, as the milk-glands grew larger, and the mammals moved upward. And these two stages of development are one of Nature's cleverest proofs of the harmony and beauty of her plan of Evolution, that makes everything grow, develop and improve in a natural way. The "blind alleys" into which the water-mole, the opossums and the kangaroos continued do not change the fact that these animals played their part in the new development, and that in turn other mammal races perfected what they had begun. And these mammals, growing a breast from a pore in their skins, go back clear to the amphibians—the frog and newt creatures which outlined the first real hand—for frogs and newts all have pores and glands in and beneath their skin, in which stuff gathers for various uses!

So pore and gland already were at hand. For ages and ages they had lain unused. The reptiles had no use for them. But they lay in their life-stuff, asleep until needed. And then, when the mammals came, and real hearts sent warm blood through their veins, Nature simply let them develop these pores and glands which had slept unused through millions of years of amphibian and reptile life, to let them bring up the living young they bore at the breast.

But the breast was more, much more than a mere organ for suckling the young of the mammal kind. It brought something into the world that the world had not yet known. It was in the breast that the feeling of repulsion of mammal for reptile, mentioned at the beginning of the chapter on "Life's Reptile Nightmare on Land," first sprang.

The reptile creeps out of its shell, and crawls and wriggles its way into the world without any *race-memories* to guide it. Its mother is soon through with it. It must sink or swim, survive or perish, altogether "on its own." If it survives it may build up a *life-memory* for itself: it may associate certain spots with good food or a narrow escape from death. And it will seek those spots out again or avoid them because of this experience that stays with it. But when that particular reptile dies, no matter how many eggs it may have laid, not one of its young begins life with any remembrance of what happened to its mother. It starts all over with a clean slate, so far as the feeling (*instinct*) which makes animals follow the *promptings* of these vague, dim memory pictures in their clouded brain goes. No creature *not* a mammal knows anything of a *race* past.

But with the mother's milk every mammal creature sucks in the memories, the instincts, the old, old things all the ancestors of its family and race have learned. The reptile does not continue in its brain anything known to other reptiles that went before it. The little mammal inherits the memory pictures, the *traditions,* as they are called, of its race. They are passed on to it with its mother's milk. And when these memory pictures stir in it, its *instinct*—which is the feeling that leads it to profit by what those memories teach— tells it what to do. So the reptile may be said to start its *race,* so far as tradition goes, all over again with each new member—in other words, *it has no traditions.* But each new little mammal born inherits and adds to the traditions, the memory-pictures, of all the other mammals of its race and family that went before it.

So old is this race memory, so far back does it go, that a child that never has seen a snake in its life will have the same creepy feeling of danger that sent a chill through its furry ancestors of millions of years, when they scrambled chattering up a tree as a great lizard ran to devour them. *With mothers' milk the first beginnings of feeling and tradition flowed out into the animal world!* The chorus of a foolish popular song begins: "Every little bit added to what you've got, makes just a little bit more." Foolish as words seem, the truth under the development of instinct never has been better expressed. The mammals which added a little bit to the sum total of the experience and memory of their race whenever a new brood of young were suckled at the breast, gave those young ones their "just a little bit more." And it was this added knowledge, the traditions, the memory-pictures of those gone before, added to those already there, that made *continuity, a something that keeps on going.* Each single reptile had to make and live in a memory-world of its own, and when it died, its world died with it. Each single mammal inherited the memory-world and traditions of all its ancestors, and when it died passed them on with new memory-pictures to its children. It is easy to see which race would be the one to advance!

But how did this advance take place? Through mother-love. Mother-love—was—as it still is—the strongest moving power and force in the world. Mother-love, which the reptile felt but dimly, was a close, tender bond of union between mother and child in the mammal world. It was mother-love which taught the mammals to develop brains; which first roused in them a vague affection for the other creatures *of their own kind and family!* It was the mother-love they drew in with their mother's milk that gradually taught them that while life still was a struggle for the "survival of the fittest," they could struggle to better advantage *together, as a family*—father, mother, brothers and sisters—than singly, each on its own hook. It was mother-love which led the way to the *grouping* of great mammal families in *herds* for mutual protection, where every single member of a race or tribe joined with every other one for defense against a common foe.

Later, some of the insects which in their "blind alleys" reached the highest point to which they could advance, the *ant* and the *bee* and others, also learned this lesson; and some of the more intelligent reptiles, too, though they never rose to the idea of *uniting in groups* to help each other, developed the affection of *mate for mate,* which leads them to join in attack or defense. But, generally speaking, *the real mother-love* which was to make these *inherited* instincts blossom out and bear their highest fruit, was confined to the mammals.

CHAPTER XVI

AT THE PARTING OF THE WAYS

THE series of thrilling pictures which thus far have shown Evolution steadily moving on and up, all make clear one great truth. In her work of building up and developing, bit by bit, out of cell and backbone, bones and skull, skin, muscles and nerves, hand, heart, breast and blood, a living creature was "growing, day by day, in every way, better and better." Nature had one clean-cut way of working. She took the backbone and lung from the fish that would bring it ashore—and let the fish that preferred the water seek their own "blind alley" of development. She let the amphibians develop hands, pores and a system of cold-blood circulation better than that of the fish. But she let the amphibians which clung to a half-water, half-land life go along as they were, and passed all their "new stuff" on to the enterprising sister who laid the first egg on dry land, and thus did away with gills. This was the reptile and—when the reptiles had been evoluting and "growing better" in this, that and the other way, and the time was ripe, the "sport" or "freak" egg with the four-chambered heart was hatched. The reptiles that clung to the old, imperfect three-chambered heart kept on in their "blind alley" of cold blood and sluggish circulation, and the mammals left them to move up higher.

In each case Nature had chosen some *race*—the poet would say to be the "torch-bearer," but we will say the "egg-bearer"—of Evolution, of progress. When she had evolved the mammal, she once more had to make a choice, to "select"—this time among the mammal races and families—one which would take the great main road leading *up*. For it stood to reason that, as before, the majority of families, after they had contributed to the general advance, would follow out their own "blind alleys" of development. Their evolution, though it might take them quite a ways, would be *away from* the main highway of progress.

But not until the numerous races of mammals, developing in all sorts of different directions, have split up into certain large *groups* or families more or less related to each other, does Nature make a final choice of the particular *mammal kind* she will select to carry on life, through hundreds and hundreds of succeeding improvements, to a climax where the mammal *stands on the threshold of the highest development of all!*

When that point is reached we have a vision of a dim, hairy creature, a creature repulsively animal in shape and appearance, yet with something of the divinity of humankind about it. We seem to catch a glimpse of it, half-shown, half-hidden in the gloomy, green shadows of a tropical jungle, looking out at us with eyes in which, *for the first time,* there gleams a spark of *more* than animal intelligence.

We are dining out. While the orchestra has been playing, our thoughts may have wandered far, far from the brilliantly lighted room, far from the beautiful women in evening gowns and the men in evening dress. Suddenly the music stops. We turn to the girl by our side and there—glowering down at us both above the long-stemmed table-glass with its fragrant bouquet of sweet peas—leans a shaggy, hideous form. It is bestial, with its great fang teeth, its hairy body, its huge outthrust, chinless jaw, the claw-fingers with nails broken by digging in the soil and stained by the juices of fruits which hang on high boughs. Yet *bestial* as it looks, we still can sense the *human* hidden behind the hairy mask. It speaks in the eye, which is not the eye of an animal, it trembles in the curious moaning and jibbering sounds which break from its hair-grown throat. The creature is trying, trying in an agony of effort, trying in vain, to tell us something!.... and then, as the brief hairy vision of a second, sprung from our wandering thoughts, is gone, we suddenly know what it was trying to tell: *the first story ever told*—the story of our race, *our own story!*

That is the story of the mammal which stands on the threshold of the highest development of life on earth—human life! But it is not yet time for that creature of the past to tell its tale, for Evoluion has not yet caught it up in the thread of its development. First its family kind must be separated from the vast throng of mammal races that crowd the Earth as the years roll by in their thousands.

While the ancestors of this mammal were developing unnoticed among hundreds of other small mammals, one in a crowd, so to say, the whole mammal family had come to a parting of the ways, and before we take up the tale of the mammals selected to follow the one road which was to lead them from the bestial to the human, we must throw on the screen of progress the splendid pictures of the great mammal development, and the great parting of the ways which occurred in the mammal world.

OUR KINSFOLK OF THE SEA

The mammals that first parted company from the early mammal tribes which—in spite of reptile habits and "looks"—were passing on the four-chambered heart with its double blood circulation from generation to generation, were the ones which could not resist the call of the sea.

They longed for the vast, blue deeps, and "a back to the water" movement already had been started for them by great lizards such as the "fish-lizard" and the "snake-lizard," which had left the land and taken to the water before mammals were thought of. The great "fish-lizard" died out; so did the "snake-lizard," but reptile lizard families into which the four-chambered heart had come by way of inheritance, survived the first ice age. They were great flesh-eating reptiles, lived through Earth's first winter and became *mammals* instead of *reptiles* of the sea. There is a legend an old story which declares that the mermaids live a life of joy and happiness for hundreds of years in beautiful palaces of coral and pearls in the ocean deeps. At last however they dissolve in white foam on the surface of the waves—for they are water creatures and have no souls! Something of the same kind happened to the mammals which at the parting of the ways took to the great sea-lanes. They are mammals, they bear their living young and suckle them at the breast, they are far, far more intelligent than the fish among which they live, but—they can never, rise to a "soul," the road of higher progress does not run into the water! So they were shut out of the glorious inheritance of the land animals, and have continued in their billowing "blind alley" ever since.

There are not so many great *races* of sea mammals, but each race has split up into many families. There are the *Seals*, for instance, which in the water have developed a fur more soft and beautiful than any save a few rare land mammals like the black fox of the Arctic. They have kept their far removed reptile ancestor's flappers or fore-feet, and the original lizard hind feet have turned into a kind of fin-flap, and they do not use them to move on land. But these flappers are thought to have been real animal fore feet in the dim ages when they went into the sea. For their *nearer ancestors* are supposed to have belonged to the first beasts of the bear tribe that developed. And they have also held to the old "meat-eating" lizard's liking for flesh food; though their bear-ancestors may have been flesh-eaters too. They eat fish and shell-fish, and even birds they may catch swimming or resting on the water. But they have the mammal instinct to *herd,* and go ashore to bear and suckle their young. The one baby of the gray seal, born in a cavern-end above tide-range is the aristocrat of the seal family. It is born with a beautiful long, soft white coat of fur that the "common seal" cannot show. For six weeks this baby is a real land animal, for it does not take to the water before the end of that time.

The *Walrus* ("whale-horse") a cousin of the seal, which has developed to a larger size, has sprouted the big teeth of some old reptilian forefather in the great pair of tusks which it uses to scrape and dig up the crabs and mollusc it eats, to climb the ice-foes, and to fight others of its own kind. The *Sea-Cows* live in the shallow lagoons, bays and rivers of warm countries. When the oldest sailors who ever sailed the Indian ocen saw a *dugong* (as the sea-cow which lives there is called) raise its head for the first time out of the water, *with its baby under one flapper,* they started all the mermaid stories which have been told ever since. Man, the distant relative who has gone so far ahead of the poor, stupid, lazy sea-cows—just as our land cows browse on Earth's grassy meadows and plains, so the sea-cows browse on the great undersea pastures of grasses and sea-weed—has already slaughtered off a whole family of these poor things, which lived in the North Pacific ocean, for the sake of their oil. But the *manatees* of tropic American, African and Australian coasts still live, and one can trace back their evolution from the first good-natured, sea-weed eating land mammal which carried a warm mammal heart into the cold water. Some of the sea-cow ancestors first clung to a couple of reptile tusks, but gradually they ran to hard gum—all they needed to chew their plant-food. There seems reason to believe that the sea-cow's ancestors took to the water much later than those of the seals. It is thought that longing did not strike them with full force until they were a well established land beast, a relative of the very first elephant-kinds. But once they gave in to the water-craving, their feet went back into flappers again, and they became water-mammals for good and all.

Oldest of all the water-mammals, probably, is the largest of the tribe, the whale. Some still think and speak of the whale as a "fish," but *the whale is no more a fish than is the cow or horse!* Its fish-like form is only the development of the old, old lizard body for the greatest ease and quickness in swimming. It is almost certain that all the whales that live go back to an old, old, ancestral whale of the golden reptile days named *Zugleudon.* By hook or crook the four-chambered mammal heart got into the whale race in the crossings and breedings which spread it in reptile circles, and from a three-chambered, cold-blooded, flesh-eating, old "water-reptile" family, there sprang a new mammal branch. The huge whales and whale-sharks (another curious cross-breed) which swam the early seas have died out; but in a much changed form their great-great-grandchildren still roam the waters. It is interesting to see how Evolution has changed the whale. The first mammals grew fur for warmth, and the protection of their skin. Perhaps, long, long ago, the whales wore fur coats, but finding the hair slowed up their speed in the water, they dropped all but the few bristles which still grow around their lips and in their nostrils. Deciding on another "chest protector," they gradually shed their hair, and grew instead a thick layer of fat "blubber" beneath their skins, which kept them warm, while letting them swim fast. But the remaining bristles show that they once were altogether covered with hair.

In the same way the whale changed its teeth to suit its food. It "dropped out" its old reptile teeth, and instead grew "whalebone" from the horny ridges of its upper mouth. To eat, it takes a great mouthful of water into its enormous jaws. The water is alive with tiny shell—and other fish. The long, slender, elastic whalebone blades fold back when the whale closes its mouth; the front row passing behind the back row in a groove between the tongue and lower jaw. Then, when the whale opens its mouth again, their elasticity straightens them out, and they act as a perfect strainer, the water running out between them, while all the little fish and shell-creatures are left behind to be swallowed. The big lower lip prevents the whalebone from being carried along with the rush of the water on its way out. And the whale's tail is in a *horizontal* position, so that it can rise easily for air, while a fish's tail always is in a *vertical* position.

If those who think of the whale as a "fish" could examine one they would see Evolution's proof to the contrary. Under the smooth, fish-like skin of their fore-paddles *are the bones, joints, muscles and even fingers of the old lizard fore-feet!* And, stranger and still, more convincing, buried deep in the interior of the huge breast, are the *rudiments of the hind legs* its reptile ancestors used! They are of no use to the whale to-day, but it seems as though Nature had said "Evolution can begin at any time, can begin anywhere, for race or individual! Here is the material of Evolution. In the shape you have taken and now you do not need it. But, if ever you wish to leave the sea, and take the road back to land once more, the count-less generations to come can start growing out their hind legs again!"

Black whales and ice whales, hump backed whales and sperm whales, the Biscay right whale of the North Atlantic, and the Japan-ese whale of the North Pacific—there are no very great differences among them. They still remain the hugest of all forms of mammal life descended from the early days of Earth, and the greatest among the mammal kinsfolk which took to the sea at the parting of the ways.

The *Dolphin* ("porpoise" or "bottle-nose") is another creature often mistaken for a "fish." In fact, before the world knew it was a mammal, it was eaten by pious Roman Catholics on "fish" days. But that happy time passed when it was discovered that the dolphin mother nursed her single young one, carefully floating sideways in the water to expose her breast to make nursing easy for her babe. In spite of its tenderness for its young, its real mammal instinct for *herd* life, and a seeming liking for human society, it has inherited the appetite of its old land-mammal ancestors, and is a greedy feeder on fish, crabs and molluscs.

One branch of the race got used to fresh water, and a number of dolphin families have forsaken the salt ocean and live in fresh water. One of these families is a poor, blind degenerate which has given up the clear surface waters, where most dolphins love to "play" about, and leap high out of the waves when they are "feeling good." Instead, this eight-foot dolphin which has "gone native" in Indian rivers like the Ganges and Indus, gropes its way along the muddy bottom waters, grubbing with its long snout for the small shell-fish that live there.

And these are the chief races—divided into many families—of the mammal kinsfolk who took to the sea-lanes at the parting of the ways.

OUR COUSINS OF THE AIR

Before ever the first mammal crept out of a reptile egg, the reptiles had been busy trying to reach the upper air and (after a fashion), they managed to do so. But the different "flying lizards" and even the great "flying crocodile" which literally almost *turned itself into* its huge membrane wings, were all working on the wrong idea. Their zig-zag spiral flights and flutterings through the air were really not flying.

But now, while most of the small "mammalreps" were still laying their reptile eggs, and were slowly working their way up to the skin-pore that was to develop into a real mammal breast—obscure creatures* of the opossum, rat, mole and rabbit kind, fighting the fight of life somewhere along the "cold fringe" of the warm land of promise—the real lizards were very busy.

Some of these reptiles probably were driven up into the air by the same reasons which took the older "flying lizards" there. Either they wanted to get up to catch insect food or (like the "flying fish" which leaps out of the water) they wanted to get out of the way of an enemy. But we must never think for a moment that they borrowed the ideas of flying from the old families of "flying lizards" which came before them. Not a bit of it. They made a fresh start and—hitting on the right idea—they made a success of it. They actually *flew*. Out of some one family, after attempts and trials without number, generations and generations of lizards that

---

*They have a scientific name: *Theriomorphs,* which means *"beast-like"*, to show that they were no longer reptiles. Some think that had it not been for the hair and fur they managed to grow their kind would not have lasted on into the summer after the first great ice winter. In other words, if they had not lived through, Evolution might not have gone on at all, or else have been put off for other thousands and thousands of years.

tried to get up into the air, there was born at last *the first true bird!* And, the first true bird was *neither reptile nor mammal.*

Where the "flying lizards" had been satisfied to grow a sheet of membrane out from a little finger that supported it, these early birds turned their reptile fore-arms into wing-arms. Their wings were limbs, real flesh and blood limbs, just as much limbs as the fore-feet out of which they had evolved. The wings of the "flying lizards" were not limbs at all. They were just sheets of membrane. But the *true wing* spread out from the body of the arm-joints on the plan of an arm with feathers on its rear edge.

Feathers were grown by these true birds just as mammals grew their fur and hair. The reptile scales that covered the reptile creatures on their way to become birds split and softened; but instead of giving way to fur, each scale split up into a different kind of lighter, fluffier thread, better for flying and these clung together thickly as feathers. The "Ancient Bird,"* as the first true bird on earth is called, held on to the sharp reptile teeth in its upper and lower jaws. Lizard-fingers peeped out from its wings, and it shook a lizard tail. For a bird it looked a good deal like a reptile. It was no longer than a crow, but—the wings it had were *real bird-wings,* and the feathers that stick out from its long, bony tail were *real feathers!* There is no stronger proof of the truth of Evolution than this skeleton ghost of the skies, that is gone. The "Ancient Bird" shows plainly that it had just crossed the boundary-line which divides a bird from a reptile. It shows it was evolved out of a reptile family and form. We have mentioned among the reptile-birds the strange wingless fish-eating divers which looked like an armless man. There is a wide gulf between the "Ancient Bird" and these water-fowls, but the reptile ancestry is still clearly shown in their teeth. Was the "Ancient Bird" one of this sort which had grown wings once it had found a mammal heart? Or was it a land bird? It is hard to tell—the main thing was that the bird, like the mammal, had developed out of the reptile, and that from now on there would be bird-life, and birds would fly about the Earth.

As a courtesy title, we might call the birds our *cousins.* We are related to them through our common reptile ancestors but—while the mammals, so to speak, are our *brothers* by right of heart and blood, the birds are a different species. The heart of the bird is a better heart than that of the reptile, for the reptile three-chambered heart makes a poor blood circulation. And while the birds' heart has only *two chambers,* the birds have secured a good blood circulation, even with a two-chambered heart. The two halves are entirely separate, and the blood of the veins and the arteries cannot mix. But the

* Archeopterix.

bird never could develop to the rank of the mammal in intelligence, for it does not bear living young, but still lays eggs like the reptiles from which it sprang. On the other hand, though it has no breast, it has developed much more mother-love than the reptile—for good blood will tell!—and gives touching examples of its love for its chicks by the way it feeds and fights for them, daring every enemy in defense of its nestlings. It has an eye like a reptile's but is so far removed from its ancestor, that it has lost the *evil hypnotic something* which the reptile eye still holds. The snake—though both came from a common stock—can hypnotize the bird with its glaring, sinister stare. On the other hand the bird's eye is much sharper, keener and quicker than the eye of a mammal.

The nearest approach to "suckling" its young of which birds are capable is probably offered by the pigeon. Both parent-birds, when their pigeon-chicks have crept from the egg, feed them with a milk-like fluid stuff, given out by certain cells in their crops which produce it. And if the young pigeon-chicks die during the period of this feeding, the parent birds are apt to follow them because of the swelling and bloating of these "milk-cells," from which they suffer just as a cow does whose udder is swollen with milk. It is clear from what has been said *why* birds are neither reptiles nor mammals, but a new living *kind* of their own.

The Evolution of the birds is one different from that of other living kinds of creature. Like Evolution in plant-life it is a thing separate and apart, but in another way. Plant life developed in "still life." The seed of the plant may travel from place to place, borne on the winds, or carried in the stomachs of birds and mammals. This seed may cross mountains and oceans in a sea-bird's gut before it is dropped on a distant island or shore to spring up hundreds of miles from the flower which bore it. But the plant *itself* does not move. The Evolution of the plant is an evolution rooted in one spot. It is the *Evolution of not moving*.

The Evolution of the bird is quite as special as that of the plant. It might be called the *Evolution of movement* in an element, the air, which is meant for the swiftest and freest movement; and element it shares only with the winged insects. But, like plant-evolution, it has moved *away from the mammal!* Plant-Evolution lost touch with mammal evolution (and that means, broadly speaking, human evolution) when the first *Algae* turned half-animal, and then the whole animal, and began to live on other *living things*. The plant continued on its way as a plant, while the plant-animal climbed the animal ladder. The Bird Evolution loses touch with mammal evolution when the first "Ancient Bird" spreads its heavy, scraggly wings, and opening its fanged beak, sails up with its feathered lizard-tail into the blue. For though it comes from the common reptile stock of mammal and bird, it has not become a mammal by flying out of the reptile class.

The early wingless birds* which seem to have followed the "Ancient Bird" and which later, after a great gap of years, may have grown out again the lizard fore-feet they had tucked into their body (as the whale did its hind ones) were followed by great early bird-creatures like an ostrich, which had short wings and tails and ran more than they flew. Some of these reptile birds with wings had regular tortoise teeth, and after them and before the coming of a crowd of early cranes, storks, comorants, gulls, penguins, flamingos, puffins, and others, millions of years go by. Details of gradual improvement in wing and the splitting up into such numerous families are lacking. Just as in the case of the reptiles from which they came, a good many of these early birds only grew little wings, but ran to a size of body which would have made an ostrich look like a bantam chick beside them. All their development seemed to go into enormous *hind legs*. Gradually more and more bird kinds we know to-day were evolved out of breedings and crossings of strains. We see the very earliest vultures, ostriches and albatrosses develop. But, in most cases, they were just rough "first attempts," clumsy "working models." Nature turns them out, and then leaves them to work themselves up (by means of the strangest and fittest to survive) into the best and most finished kind of thing their particular family can produce.

Coming down to a few hundred thousand years ago, the bones of a giant swan prove that our swans of to-day belong to a very old family. And the nearer we get to the time when mammal life has developed into the greatest number of different forms, the time when *the something which was to rise higher than all birds and mammals was stirring in the jungle shades,* the airs of the dead and gone past were filled with the flutter of wings. Parrots, ducks, pigeons, geese, herons and darters, (the first goose was one of the birds which "also ran" but did not fly) owls, railbirds and starlings, and hundreds of other families took possession of the air ther descendants now share with the aviator, the man-bird.

Curious links with the past are the bird families which have utterly died out since man first appeared on Earth. There is the sad tale of the *Dronte*. Let the curtain of time roll back to the year 1593, and rise on the beautiful island paradises of Mauritius and the Isle Bourbon, set like green jewels in the golden-sunned sea east of Madagascar. There, having lived ever since their ancestors had flown over from the Madagascan coast, we see a tribe on monster pigeons.

*The *Ichthyornis* ("fish-bird") and the *Hesperornis* ("Western bird") were early natives of Kansas.

When they first flew across the water their wings were large and powerful. But centuries of "soft" living have made them big and fat. You can see that though they are pigeons, they are as large as turkeys. And they have had such an easy life of it on the islands, that they never have used their wings. So their wings have grown less and less, until now they can no more be used for real flying than the poor, shrivelled little rear feet the "flying crocodile" let hang down behind when it had put all its strength into membrane, would do for walking.

And now we see an old-fashioned three-masted vessel anchor in the island bay. A crowd of thick-set, heavy-looking sailors, with odd-shaped hats, wearing queer clothes and carrying weapons which would make us laugh to-day, row ashore in boats. They have been eating mildewed salt pork and weevilly biscuit for six months—and then they spy the *Dronte!* It is the first fresh meat they have caught sight of in six months Naturally, the *Dronte* wants to survive, but then, so do the sailors. The result of the struggle for the "survival of the fittest"—hear the fat, clumsy birds squawk sadly as the sailors knock them over the head with sticks and stones !—was that when another boatload of Dutch sailors put in at Mauritius exactly one hundred years later (1693), there was *not one Dronte left to eat*! For the two seperate *Dronte* families which occupied the islands had been systematically "cleaned up" by the crews of the vessels which went out of their way to stop and take on "fresh meat." A whole bird species or family had gone out of existence.

Let the curtain stay up on this same isluand of Mauritius while we look at the *Dodo,* which lived there when the *Dronte* did. It is another overgrown pigeon-bird. See the giant reptile-head, without teeth, but still lizard-like, with a clumsy, but horny hooked beak larger than a large swan. Dark ash-colored, with a yellowish-white breast, it has wings which have degenerated from want of use, like the *Dronte's,* and a little short curly tail, which, together with its solemn head, makes it look as though it belonged in a "funny sheet." We see one of the Dutch sailors knock over a *Dodo* which comes his way—but if we could see his face when he tastes the first bit of Dodo meat that comes from the pot we would know that the *Dodo* is safe from further attack. Its flesh is nauseous and for that reason the *Dodo* lasted a little longer than the *Dronte.* Before the last *Dodo* lays the last single white dodo-egg on its little mound of grass, we might take a peep into a London street-showman's booth, in the year 1638. There a poor *Dodo,* brought to foggy London from its far island paradise, swallows "pebble stones as bigge as nutmegs" for the amusement of a London crowd. By the beginning of the eighteenth century the hogs which the Europeans had brought to the island of Mauritius, and which were not so particular about the taste of what they ate as the sailors, had completely put the *Dodo* out of existence. It is another variation of the "survival of the fittest." But even though the hogs may not have been the "fittest" to survive in one sense; they were useful to man, while the *Dodo* whose flesh and eggs could not be eaten, was not. It is easy enough to say, in the words of an old song: "The Dodo once lives, but it doesn't live now, Yet why should a cloud overshadow our brow?" The fact remains that a few living specimens of this interesting bird would be very helpful to the scientist who is always adding new details to the great story of Evolution.

And now for a look at the most curious of all these extinct Mauritian birds. See the *Solitaire!* A joker would say the name was appropriate, for the bird is a "card." Nearly three feet high, brownish gray with a white breast, it looks something like an overgrown hen with a heavy beak. It has hardly any tail or wings. It is another pigeon "gone wrong," a pigeon unable to fly. But what are these two Soltaires doing now? They rise on their three-toed feet, and begin to whirl around and around again, drawing nearer each other with every whirl. They take twenty or thirty of these "whirls" in five minutes and while they whirl they "rattle." And their rattles? They are the big "fighting knobs," round clumps of bone which grow on the wings of the male birds, and which rattle about in the thick callous skin which covers them. It is with these round masses of bone that the *Soltaires* are fighting out the same battle we have seen the great "fish-lizards" fight out in the tropic seas, and the tiny green lizards among the forest ferns. The last *Soltaire* is thought to have laid down on its nest of palm leaves to die, in 1761. The bird's flesh could not have been tasty or it would not have lingered so long.

The Garefowl of Great Auk was another almost wingless bird of the Hebrides Islands, the size of the goose. It looked like its relation the razor-bill. It passed out of life on this world in 1844. First it was killed by fisherman for its fat, then, strange to say, the remaining auks were hunted down for the sake of providing *natural history museums—the very institutions which should have tried to keep them alive in the interests of science*—with stuffed specimens!

The giant Groushe, or Capercally, whose bones have been found in the garbage-heaps of earliest man, in Iceland and Denmark, was such good eating through the ages that it became extinct in Scotland and Ireland, but has since been "resurrected" in those countries by the introduction of some *old stock* from Sweden. The New Zealand Moa, and another, a huge emu or ostrich-like bird that once lived in Madagascar, have disappeared. The latter not only laid an egg of tremendous size, but also laid the foundation for the Arabian Nights' tale of a gigantic bird called the "roc." Both have gone the road taken by most of the birds which did not develop their wings. After all, in spite of bird-shot and rifle, a bird on the wing has a better chance than two birds in the bush. And Nature has plainly pointed out that "the way of a bird in the air" is the way of the survival of the fittest for its race.

OUR BROTHERS OF HOOF AND CLAW

We have already raised the curtain for a moment on the thousands of years of summer* which came after the Angel of Ice, with his freezing sword, had driven the creatures of earth from their home-swamps to a distant land of promise. Let us look at this new world more closely. It is a bigger world, because Earth has taken back more land from the sea. It is a better world, because a higher *kind* of creature—the mammal instead of the reptile—is the ruling form of life. It is a world more beautiful, because the silent plants continuing on *their* way up and on, have produced new forms of strength and beauty, new flowers and trees. With those flowers and trees bees and butterflies have come into the world, to make us forget the horrible dragon-flies and winged roaches of the dark, steaming fern-forests.

This new world might be divided into four summer "months" with about a hundred thousand years to each "month." The first two months were hot, almost as hot as the golden summer of the reptiles, but with a cleaner, brighter heat and a purer air, less filled with moisture. Then came what might be called a glorious "Indian summer," and then a final summer month, at the end of which the Angel of the Cold once more stretched out *his* freezing sword of ice and called down Earth's second great winter, the second *Ice Age*.

And during each of these four "months" which make up the second great summer on Earth, Nature *leaves* a sign to make clear that she already has selected the *one* family of mammal kind which will be fitted by Evolution—by heredity, survival among all others of its race, and intelligence—to bring the *animal* to the threshold of a new life, a threshold which no other foot but that of an offshoot of this *one family* ever will cross—the threshold which divides *beast* from *man!*

But this "reel" of Evolution's great serial must also show our "Brothers of Hoof and Claw." Like plant, fish, reptile and bird, they develop, each after their own kind. One of these "brother" races is to father a new race of *animals* that yet are not *beasts*—and besides them the story of our *other* "Brothers of Hoof and Claw," as they move on into their "blind alleys" of development, rounds out the great story of Evolution as a whole.

First let us see the world as it may have looked in the early sun-

*Chapter XV.

gilded "months" of this summer which carries *Evolution's supreme mystery* hidden in its jungles' breast! See the little "mammalreps" eat and grow fat in this new summer of life! See them grow, increase and change—in skin, in shape, in color, in size, in fur and hair, in a thousand and one different ways—under the hot sun. The very lowest kinds have spread out in Australia—and there they stop. Africa and Australia had been one undivided continent. But suddenly the volcanoes roared, the ground trembled. And when the white-hot heart inside of the globe we live on beat quietly once more Africa and Australia had parted company! The Earth had sunk and a great "lost continent" lay beneath the waters of the ocean, fathoms deep.

The curious Australian "mammalreps" which still laid eggs or produced their young half-born, were cut off from the rest of the world. They lived and followed their "blind alley" in an island world of their own. And the other great families of other mammals shut off from them in Africa and Asia, never reached this island for that reason. These strange Australian beasts exist unchanged to-day, as living witnesses of *how a reptile gradually changes to a mammal!* But somewhere in Africa, favored by the golden sun and plenty of insect food, a creature of the *same general kind* as the Australian duck-billed watermole worked up to the next step in mammal life. It formed its young in its *womb,* and after that eggs and hatching and other makeshifts were over with for the mammal world!

Once the young mammal kinds were born alive *in perfected form,* they were ready to drink in all that their mother's milk could give them (as has been told in Chapter 15). We all know that the reptiles formed their eggs in *ovaries* in egg-chambers and then laid them: the mammal egg is formed in a womb and—unlike the reptile egg—is built up *of the mother's own blood!* Small blood-vessels connect the little body which is forming in the womb with the blood-vessels of its mother, and so the child becomes its mother's *very own* in a way much more intimate than in the connection between a reptile mother and her *egg.* The mammal, child of its mother's womb, is truly the "blood of her blood." The first African mammal mother that "went the kangaroo one better" took the big step ahead. Instead of *hatching her young inside herself in her ovaries,* to bring them out *half-born* after all nourishment inside the egg-shell was gone, grew connection blood-vessels between herself and her child. Thus she changed ovaries to womb, and crossed the great gulf which separates mammal from reptile and bird. Behind her the bridge of broken egg-shells on which she had crossed dropped into the gulf for all time!

So while the Australian links in the chain were left alone on their Australian island, the mammal families in Africa and Asia began to develop in a hundred and one directions, and to split up into a number of different races. At first, very likely, they were small. This was while they were changing themselves from reptiles to creatures that grew hair and fur to warm them, and bore their young and suckled them, and most of them lived in trees. The insect food on their trees, and in the ground increased with a sudden "wave of life" when a hot sun once more poured down on Earth. There was a great increase of all sorts of spiders, some of monstrous size. There were crawling bugs of every sort, and besides the centipedes, there were ants and caterpillars and worms without number.* The insect "wave of life" carried on to the insect-eating mammals. They, too, commenced to grow larger. And soon, as they grew, some of the larger mammals began to climb down from their trees to live on the ground. Some mammals, like the old plant-eating reptiles, had been vegetarians from the start. They now had more to feed on, for the seed- (grain) bearing grasses (as well as the grasshoppers) were spreading their carpets of green over the naked surface of the Earth. Still others fed on fruits or nuts, which with the coming of the earliest kind of bread-fruit trees, cocoanut-palms, and soft-pulped tropical fruits, supplied a good choice of their favorite food during those first hot "months" of the new Earth summer. Our brothers—for all mammals may be called "brothers" in a sense, since they all date back to the first mammal *womb* and the first mother's *breast*—fed, bred, flourished, and multiplied.

Then, one day, a good-sized mammal saw what looked like a large, fat insect and pounced upon it. But it was not an insect. It was one of its own small blood-brothers—a tiny mole or shrew. Without thinking, it had already gone into its big brother's mouth and—it tasted good! and with that one little act a whole great move away from insect food started. Certain mammal families began to prefer fresh meat to fresh insect. The old, old split of the rock into flesh-eaters and plant-eaters took place, and the mammals gradually divided into families that lived on meat, and families that lived on vegetables. It was the old, old story of the reptile age all over again.

The eaters of flesh, naturally, spent their time tracking and hunting down the eaters of plants. But the living, breathing "dinners" they hunted, had better kinds of brains than the poor, stupid, heavy-witted old reptile plant-eaters, which carried their brains in their tails. Some grew heavy body armor around their great frames and terible horns, like the rhinoceros; or great tusks like the early elephant. But most of the plant—and grass-eaters saw a great light.

---

*The increase in insect life with the development of mammals and birds was enormous—the species, the *kinds* of insects in existence to-day is put by Science at 10,000,000. With the mammals enormous numbers of parasite insects, such as various special kinds of lice and flies developed.

They realized that feet could be used for *running* as well as for walking or standing on. And so in their Evolution it was their *feet* which kept growing better and better adapted *for running at great speed*. While the brothers of claw and fang were growing bigger and better teeth, and stronger and heavier "action" muscles, in their great fore and hind leg-joints, the brothers of the hoof were overhauling their "running gear," and adding the latest improvements which Evolution could suggest. By throwing their weight on the middle front part of the foot, the needless toes gradually "dropped away." The meat-eaters soon found that they would have to "work for their meals," because their "dinners" in the raw had formed a habit of running away from them.

In these days our good old Earth is a fairly reliable place in which to live. It does not change so much. Once in a while some inner blood pressure sets Earth's white-hot, liquid heart a boiling under its seventy-five miles of "crust." Then Mount Vesuvius spouts fire and flame, or Tokio is shaken to pieces by an earthquake, or Mount Pelee turns a lovely tropical island like Martinique into a desert of gray lava. But all in all we do not do so badly.

It was different in the early summer days after Earth's first winter. We have seen how Australia was suddenly "shunted off" from the rest of the world, and how the waters of the sea made a "lost continent" of the land which connected it with Africa. And this sort of thing was going on all the time. Every now and then would come some great upheaval. Earth would throw up great ranges of mountains, raising the level of the land for millions of miles around. Or whole parts of the Earth's surface crust would "fall in" (for reasons already explained in Chapter 1) and deep seas would roll over the great forests buried beneath their waters. It seems certain that during those first summer "months" of a hundred thousand years apiece, South America and Africa were unbroken land until an "upset" flung the sea between them, and made another "lost continent."* And once, where the waters of Behring Strait now flow, one could step across from North America into Asia and never wet a foot.

The greatest and most romantic story of the land Earth lost to the sea is that of the "lost continent"* of Atlantis, which once lay between Europe and America, and over whose sunken glories the waters of the Atlantic now roll. (It is a story that will be told later.)

The main point about all these changes of the Earth's surface was that while the changes were taking place—changes that would make the maps in any school geography look as though the map-makers had gone crazy—the animals were "citizens of the world." They wandered from continent to continent, and spread here, there and every-

*This "lost continent" is known as Hellenis.

where. Though the waters might shut off one race from another in course of time, all races would keep on "shaping up" along the old family lines wherever it was. They would keep on in hoof, claw, hide or skin, as the climate, food, cross breeding and the survival of the fittest acted on them.

And all this time, while the mammal races were hunting or running away, the two clans of claw and hoof were busy dividing into new families, and through the selection of the strongest and best members of each family, they were building up "heredity"—family traits to be handed down from one generation to another.

The reptiles had had their golden age. Besides new crocodile kinds, the new summer brought forth big boa-constrictors and pythons, and the blind "burrowing snake," the only ones which still shows traces of their old lizard legs. But this was the animal's "big time" on Earth. And sometimes Nature seemed to joke. Have you ever examined a tiny model an inventor has made to show the *idea* of a thing? That seems to have been something Nature was fond of doing during the first summer "months" with a number of plant-eating families.

We have seen how, right from the beginning almost, the fish, reptiles and birds changed their "limbs" so as to make them fit the needs of *their special kind of life*. The "fish out of water" gradually worked their fins into flappers, then into fore-arms and feet with "fingers." And the plant-eaters that want to escape their brothers with sharp teeth and tearing claws will have to change their five-fingered feet into something easier to run with. And they do—though like all of Nature's changing this takes a long time. The planteaters are creatures that walk on all fours. So when it gets necessary for them to *run* on all fours, they begin to "pull in" their toes, so to say.

All the early kinds of vegetarian animals that do not grow much in the way of a horn or hide to defend themselves, improve their keeness of scent (it warns them when a tooth and claw brother is coming their way) and grow the kind of feet that will let them run away. And so the queer-looking first drafts of deer, antelope, camels, wild horses, cattle-kinds and pig-kinds—looking like the real thing seen through a blurred glass—began dropping their toes, one by one. First there were five-toed and four-toed grass-eaters, then three-toed ones, and finally, they had formed the rounded, horny hood which was the ideal foot for carrying them over the ground at high speed. And now for Nature's joke. It was her first "models" of these five-toed and four-toed grass-eating animals, as small as any inventor's model. They were tiny camels, tapirs, horses and deer—and must have looked something like the wooden animals that come out of a toy Noah's Ark!

Then, as those centuried seasons went by, these "runt" sizes grew larger and larger, dropping their toes as they grew, until some of them got to be enormous in size. One early pig-animal, the elephant —when it started out in life as a race, the elephant had no trunk, only a snout—grew so fast and so big, and put on such a dangerous set of tusks, that it did not have to run away from other beasts. The elephants kept all of their five toes, and they have come down in the family to this day. Others, like the rhinoceros, grew themselves plates of armor-hide and—to be sure they had enough—pushed out no less than *three* big sharp horns from their great skulls, while at the same time they changed their toes into a hoof. The result is that the descendants of the early rhinoceros use their hooves for running. Bu instead of running *away* from their enemies, they charge right down *on* them with their horns. Still other creatures, like the early seals and dolphins, far back at the beginning of Earth's second summer, perhaps, were related to the earliest bear-mammals. Maybe some of the other flesh-eating brothers of claw or tooth were too much for them, and gradually drove them into shallow waters, where through ages and ages of evolution they managed to turn back their fore-feet into flappers again. Perhaps, living along the sea-shore, they began to like a fish diet so well that they made the change from feet to flappers in the course of hunting their favorite food further and further into the water. We do not know exactly. But we *do* know that they were originally land mammals, and that for one reason or another, they "took to the water" and have stayed there ever since.

The pig-race which produced the hippopotamus, tapir and other pig families, was content with a tough hide. It grew hoofs, it is true, but built up such a tremendous body that instead of using them for running away with, it took to the great rivers and found safety from the flesh-eaters there. That is the way one great branch of the very earliest mammals split up into races and families, and after it had come down from the trees and taken to the great grassy plains, the forests, the rivers and the sea.

But what were the brothers of claw and tooth doing in the meantime? They had been just as busy, and some of the flesh-eating families, when they started out, were almost as hideous and terrible as any of the horrible lizards of the great reptile age. First of all, they grew improved editions of the great reptile teeth of their distant ancestors. And they developed, sharpened and improved the old reptile claws. Then they built out muscle and lightened their bones, to be able to leap and pounce on their prey with ease.

In those early summer "months," while trunkless elephant kinds rooted in the rich *tropical jungles* that ran along the shores of the *North Sea,* and three-horned rhinoceros beasts lumbered about the African forests, the flesh-eating mammals had already developed some horrible examples of what an early mammal could be like. Among the "first sketches" of familiar domestic forms that made life a burden for the camel-, horse- and pig-creatures which were trying to "speed up" to get away from them, were the very earliest "cat" and "dog" kinds. There was one huge monster, a sort of half-dog, half-hyena, but still so reptilian in appearance that we can only just glimpse the coming *real* dog in it, still thousands of years of Evolution away. And there were other beast-forms which were the most remote ancestors of the cat animals of to-day, things that produced the most terrible outbranchings of cruel claws and great tearing and cutting teeth. They kept on hunting and eating the plant-feeders, but were unable to stop the tremendous increase in their kind and number. Many other kinds of mammal creatures had given up trusting to their ability as "runners" to escape these devouring jaws. Moles, rabbits, hares, hedgehogs and a number of rat-creatures disappeared underground. There they were safe unless dug out. Opossums, sloths, squirrels and other tribes fled to the trees, where they had a chance for life. The bats even turned "night into day" and led a "night life" for safety's sake. The ancestors of the seals and porpoises took to the sea, and beaver-kinds and hippos to the rivers.

In fact, everything that was not strong enough to "stand up and fight" the brothers of fang and claw, "got from under" in one way or another or grew hoofs and ran away. Life was the same old struggle for existence over again. But now, all these mammals being more intelligent than the reptiles that went before them, thought out a hundred and one different ways of hunting and of escaping from the hunter. One might call mammal life one great, bloody game of "prisoner's base," except that no "prisoners" were made. It was of no use for a small beast to cry "Camarade!" and try to make out that it was some sort of thirty-second cousin of the big beast which had caught it. As soon as any meat done up in the "original package" was caught by a meat-eater, it was torn apart and went down its captor's throat. As soon as a relative was food, relationship did not count in the mammal world!

In this never-ending struggle—for the meat-eaters had to have meat to "survive," and the creatures they ate had to be able to dodge them if *they* were to "survive"—though many of the grass-eaters were "eaten up" and their families disappeared, others kept on going and other new families sprang up. Besides, we always find, in the great struggle for existence, now in one race, a flesh-eating one, now in another, a grass-eating one, or in the reptile or insect world, those sudden great "waves of life" (already mentioned) which make a family breed out tremendously, all at once. And we also find other great "waves of death," which strike them and wipe them out, sometimes for no apparent reason.

According to the kind of live meat they hunted and their surroundings, the big "dog" and "cat" families finally split up into any number of separate families. Among the "dog" families, coming down from the first of their general race, were the bears and wolves, big bears and little ones, gray wolf and timber wolf, the foxes, red, brown, black and white, the dingos or wild dogs, the hyenas and jackals, the badgers, otters, wolverines and many more. And— through a succession of perfectly monstrous forms—we get our lions and tigers, pumas, leopards, jaguars, cheetahs, the lynx, mongoose and other cats of to-day.

And as they hunted and killed and ranged the earth, the land was changing its appearance more and more. While every creature was developing keenness of scent (and many were budding the musk glands whose peculiar odor, a *family smell,* made it possible for them to recognize others of their own kind a long distance away), the world around them was growing more colorful and richer in plant life. Where once the forests grew but a few kinds of tree, there now spread vast stretches of gum, fig, ginkho and laurel. The willow hangs over the river-banks, and giant cactus-"trees" and cinnamon-trees bloom and blossom everywhere (among other places, where "Greenland's icy mountains" now stand). And in the hottest lands great jungles and swampy water and river-sides still make it possible for the grand-children of the reptiles who escape the first winter to "carry on"; for the elephants and hippos to feed, and for the *first, faint shadow of a coming new kind of animal* to be thrown on the screen of time.

While Nature, during the first two "months" of Creation's new summer, amused herself making "small-scale model" horses and camels on the plains, she was busy—deep in African and Asian jungles—with a more serious experiment. There she was producing *through Evolution* a number of small "trial" families of *monkeys,* five-fingered, long-tailed chatterers, which swung from the trees and lived on fruit and insect fare. She did this with a higher object in view. The *Adapis,* a queer cross between pig and monkey, she finally rejected, and it has disappeared. The *Lemur*—the word means "ghost," and it *is* a ghost, a spectral figure of "might have been"—the next step to an Ape— was chosen to carry on her experiment!

Meanwhile, during the third (Indian summer) month of this great summer of hundreds of thousands of years, the many mammal tribes, cat and dog, hoof and hide, reptile and insect, had been increasing and multiplying. The most hideous of all the great cats, the "lion-tiger," which killed a hippo with ease, a huge beast covered with reddish hair with the lion's great tufted tail, ravaged like a destroying angel for a time among the plant-eaters. But in the end all the creatures had "toed in" and grown good hooves. They now could run so quickly that the "lion-tiger" family *died out for want of food!* For the sickening, musky carrion reek the beast threw out was carried by the winds for hundreds of yards in advance of the beast itself, and the keen-scented grazing animals would "beat it" from wherever they were cropping the grasses, and disappear as soon as it tainted the air. It was another case of the "survival of the fittest." And, while all these beasts wandered and strayed across four great continents, the early elephant found its trunk! Before this it had been trunkless. It had only a snout like any other pig—for the elephant belongs to one of Earth's oldest mammal families, the pig or hog* family. But gradually, by stretching and straining their snouts—and by handing on each extension to some strong and hardy descendant to stretch a little further—some of the elephant kinds grew long, full-fledged *trunks*. Food, as in nearly all other cases, was the cause of this evolution. The early elephants, like any other pioneers found their food in the forest. And like any other pioneers, they had to "dig themselves in," to be able to feed. But the jungles and forests of those days were so thick-grown and hard to work into, that the most tangled jungles and forests of to-day are nothing compared to them.

The elephants, who were among the "brainiest" of all the mammals, had developed the *herd* instinct, the feeling for "society," at an early stage of their existence. When they found they must break a way through the tangled forests—without the axe, hatchet or matchete of the human pioneer—they built them an instrument out of their own bodies to do the work. They did not find it hard to get their enormous trunks to turn *up* instead of *down,* the way they grew at first, so that with them they could break heavy branches and lift great tree-trunks. But they needed something else. So they began to *draw* in their lower lip, and between the tusks they let upper lip and snout grow *out,* further and further—very gradually—until at last they had a trunk they could raise high in the air or pass along the ground, without moving their heads. It is a wonderful example of animal Evolution, and the true explanation of how the elephant came to have a trunk!

But during this time what was happening in Nature's jungle-laboratory? While the other mammals in their evolution are growing further and further into the "blind alleys" of their races and tribes, how is the *one* mammal race that is to have a "gangway" to reach a *more than animal* development, advancing?

Nature's jungle laboratory "comes alive" before our eyes. As

* Perhaps *heredity* explains why there are still human "pigs" and "hogs" in the world.

before, the screen shows us a heavy network of tropical vegetation. Ropelike twiners gorgeous with red blossoms twist about huge trunks, whose outlines are hidden by the spreading green leaves of other trees. It is a place of shadows, yet quivering with life. And now, something stirs in the dark, luxuriant foliage! The broad leaves are parting. For a half a second we seem to catch sight of a tall, hairy something and then—a blinding glare and blank whiteness! The film has burned! The pictures is destroyed at the very moment which would have revealed the mystery! But in the light of what comes after we have discovered the key.

.   .   .   .

We cannot restore the picture whose secret Nature still refuses to disclose. We cannot build up in flesh and bone the shadowy, hairy form that once lurked in that dark jungle cavern of tangled leaves. But we know (as the next section of Evolution's romantic story will show) that it was the primal *Common Ancestor*, the creature *more than ape but not yet man*, the man-beast which was the father of the two races: *apelike men* and *manlike apes!* This creature, the ancestor of both, was the first living creature to cross *the threshold which divides man from beast*. And as a proof that it *was* the Common Ancestor of the lowest form of man and the highest type of ape, it gave both man and ape *an inheritance they share to* this day: It gave them the animal *tail,* which to this day every human being has in fully developed form, *and longer than its legs, when seven weeks old in the womb* (often children are *born* with a short ape-tail, which has to be amputated). It gave them the beast-fur (*lanugo*) which covers every *human child* up to three months before it comes into the world. And it gave them the small animal intestinal gland known as the *appendix!*

Both tail and appendix are now only a source of trouble to their human possessors. Tail and hair usually disappear before birth, but the appendix remains as a source of trouble to its human owners. Yet, handed down from the first mysterious animal ancestor who crossed the threshold from the *bestial* to the *human,* both to man and to ape tail, hair and appendix are *actual outward signs of a great truth!* The Divinity that "shaped our ends" seems to have given them to man to remind him that in spite of his wonderful physical and mental development, in spite of a God-like intellect, he is still linked with *brute* Creation. If we go back far enough into the past, if we follow the tree of Evolution to the *Common Ancestor* of *both man and ape,* we are "flesh of his flesh and bone of his bone." More than ape, though not yet man, he links the cultured university professor with the hairy gorilla, the beautiful actress with the hideous chimpanzee. If we go back far enough, the ancestors of both these men and women and these apes we have mentioned *sprang from the same lions!*

The Evolution of all other forms of life now takes second place in Nature's great scheme of things. Step by step, from atom to *algae,* from fish to amphibian, from amphibian to reptile, Evolution, as we have seen, brings them to the highest point of development of brute creation: the *mammal.* There, out of a tremendous number of races, Nature's selection narrows down to *one*—and the threshold is crossed which divides *beast* from *man.* The story of "Ape and Man," the second section of Evolution's great serial, continues from this point.

PART TWO

APE AND MAN

APE AND MAN

CHAPTER XVII

THE FOOTPRINT IN THE SANDS

(Before the Rise of the Curtain)

SOMETIMES, when the last note of the music has died away at the "movies," there is a pause. The music has stopped, but the curtain before the screen has not yet gone up. We are keyed up, eager to see what is to come, and in another moment the picture will flash out, and its actors will live and move before us. But there is time, during those few moments of waiting, for our thoughts to travel far away. There is an Arabian Nights' tale in which a sultan dips his head for a *single moment only* in a basin of water! And during that fleeting moment of time, while his head is under water, he goes through years of adventure and excitement. He lives a whole lifetime in that second his thoughts were elsewhere. And it was thus, waiting for the curtain to rise, that the caption writer suddenly found himself behind the scenes with Nature, carried out of the present on the wings of fancy, during the second between the stopping of the music and the curtain's rise.

What he saw was one of the vast plains of that third "month" of a hundred thousand years after winter had gone from Earth, the "Indian Summer" month we already have mentioned. By that time, among all the mammals, one race had grown so in size and intelligence, in the strength of its own vast body and the combined strength of the *herd,* that it was the lord and master of the Earth. This was the *mammoth,* the gigantic early elephant, which feared no other living thing.

A tremendous herd of these huge beasts was grazing on the immense prairie which stretched before my eyes, while far, far in the distance gleamed the waters of a great river, a flash of silver where it was not hidden by forests of sycamore-trees. I could see why the mammoth's size made the lion-tiger and the cave-bear fear to attack it; though the stupid rhinoceros might charge it, only to lose the battle. This herd of mammoths grazing so peacefully on the tall prairie grasses, was led by five huge males, one of which seemed the chief of all. They were gray in color, and moved along like great towers, with feet like tree-trunks. Their immense tusks, ten feet long, were strong enough to pierce an oak, their trunks looked like long, black python-snakes, and their heads like huge rocks. They creaked along in a skin so thick and tough that it was like bark of an old elm-tree.

"To this day the elephant, the descendant of the mammoth, is the most intelligent of all mammals, man excepted," said Nature, pointing to the huge moving beasts. "I show you these creatures to prove that in developing them Evolution had gone as far as Evolution can go in any side-track that leads *away* from the main road.

"For these mammoths, like the elephant has to-day, had a *memory:* an *individual memory* and a *race memory.* They had brought *instinct* and *tradition* to the highest pitch to which any animal can bring them. They had made the *herd* a strong united body. The oldest and strongest beasts were the leaders—their memory went back the furthest. They regulated the movements of the herd, their social habits, their way of fighting. No other beast gave them trouble. They had a keen sense of smell, a clear, piercing eye. Look at their eyes—they do not have the vague look that those of the wild horses and wild cattle have!

"These enormous skulls you see held all sorts of *definite knowledge, actual ideas,* regarding the waters of the Earth, its plants, its other beasts. They knew that the barren and the fertile seasons of the year succeeded each other. They even could tell the sun from the moon, and knew that each took a different way through the skies. And these mammoths, by means of their wonderful trunks, whose ends were as sensitive and delicate as fingers, had stored up in their massive brain-cells all sorts of information unknown to us. It was passed from generation to generation. But—they had no *speech,* nothing except a few signs and trumpetings to express what went on in their massive brains. And that is the reason why these enormous mammals, larger, stronger, more intelligent than all the apes, never came into the inheritance of the smaller, weaker mammal, Man!

They could not tell what they knew! The brains of the cleverest and brightest of them were *shut up, jailed,* in a kind of solitary confinement. So they could not combine or compare a thought or memory with one another. That is what *speech* made it possible for *another race* of mammals to do. The mammoths were shut off *forever* from the flood of *spoken tradition* out of which grow new thoughts! And so their descendants, in course of time, had to give way to another race. Why? Because this other race *could pass on, by means of speech, all its experiences, its memories, its ideas,* and *combine them with other new ones!* The mammoths could hand down the simple gestures and signals every member of the herd understood. They could hand on the simple laws which ruled the social life of the herd. But in spite of all their advantages of good memory, keen sight and scent, and long, long life, their great-great-great-grand children now serve the other victorious mammal race, and obey its members. They carry these creatures, so much smaller and weaker than they are, on their backs. They move as the iron goad the elephant-driver digs in behind their big, flapping ear tells them to. They spend their lives dragging huge logs of teak in Indian or Burman forests, in "making a show of themselves" in circuses for the amusement of the children of a mammal folk they could crush like a fly beneath their huge forefeet. They fetch and carry, lift and even dance as those other mammals tell them. Look at them once more, for they are very, very near the dividing-line which separates *beast* from *man!* They came as near as any beast save the ape could come without crossing.

"And now," Nature went on, "let us see *not* the *handwriting on the wall, but the footprint in the sand* which told the mammoths: 'Thus far shalt thou go and no further!'"

The vast plain and its herd of towering grayish-black mammoths, grazing peacefully as they drifted across the prairie amid great companies of wild horses, gazelles and other grass-eating beasts faded away. Instead of the prairie I saw a forest clearing, through which a merry brook leaped between sandy reed-grown banks. "Bend over, and tell me what you see by yonder pussy-willows!" Nature commanded. I leaned over and there, firmly pressed in the moist sand, was the print of a *foot!*

It was not the foot of an ape, *for I knew that the toes of the manlike apes, except those of the gorilla, are all of the same length.* They have no thumb-toe, only five finger-toes! But here was the outline of the foot with *a big toe and a little left toe, a human footprint!**

"That footprint," said Nature, "was a sign that the mammoth race would never rule the Earth. And now—your second is over!" Without knowing how it had happened, the caption-writer once more found himself with his eyes fixed on the curtain, which at that very moment began to rise on a curious scene.

*This footprint—*the first human footprint known on Earth,* was probably made 40,000,000 years ago, and *still exists,* caught for all eternity in the sand that vanished foot once trod—sand now turned to *sandstone* by the passing of the ages. It was discovered by a Robinson Crusoe of Geology (the science of the Earth's crust), named Freudenberg, in 1918, *the first human footprint in the sands of time!*

CHAPTER XVIII

A TALE OF FOUR SKULLS

A GREAT background of dark green jungle, much like the one of which we caught a glimpse in the last picture of Part One of our serial, filled the eye. In the foreground of the picture was a little clearing of bare, dry ground slightly raised above the level of the surrounding swamp. And in the middle of this clearing—the jungle trees grew so tall on all sides that their tops were lost in the skies and must have grown together to form a roof, for not a gleam of sunlight pierced the shadows—burned a small brush fire. By its light, as the sparks flew when now and then a dry branch caught, a grisly sight was disclosed. Four skulls were ranged in a half-circle around the fire, four skulls bleached by the ages of time, yellowed and mildewed with the earth-stains of millions of years! And yet, there was a kind of ghastly intimacy in the way their sightless eye-sockets peered at each other across the fire, and their massive under-jaws stuck out, as though to challenge their nearest neighbor.

And now, by some miracle of Nature's stagecraft, a change comes over these dead bones! Around the fire the shadows thicken and darken. The fire itself is veiled for a moment and the gleam of the white skulls disappears. Then, as the shadows clear away again, where the four skulls had lain, stand four grotesque, repulsive, hair-covered figures. All have a strange family likeness, yet each differs in some one way from the other. And, though they *look* like the great apes which are known as "man-like" apes—the gorilla, the chimpanzee, the orang-outang and the gibbon—*they are not apes!* At least they are not apes as we know them, for the ape runs about on all fours and only stands by chance. But these hairy, apish things stand erect.

The creatures Nature's magic had called from the beyond—as the witch of Endor called up the shade of Samuel the prophet for King Saul—stood where the four white skulls had lain: two on one side, two on the other side of the fire which once more was burning brightly. In the middle was a space. And towards this vacant place in their midst all turned their shaggy heads and looked, until the first of the four, waving a hairy paw in its direction, croaked:

"Nature has used her magic, and made us rise from the dust of

death in the shapes we once wore to tell our tale! And since we must
obey the power which created us, we stand here, our dead bones
hidden by th flesh and hair of our living selves, and ready to do
Nature's will. We can tell our tales, stranger were never told! But
Nature has to supply the words we use, *for we lived before human
speech came into the world!* And one among us, our Common Ancestor, *more than ape though not yet man,* the father both of men and
apes, has not appeared.

"Only when the children of men have found something for Nature
to conjure and make magic with, a skull, a thigh-bone, a jaw, does
the creature that once owned it have to obey her summons! *And
not a bone of the great Common Ancestor ever has been found!* His
mystery is still hidden in the deeps of the African jungles, and Nature herself has no power to call him up from the dead." Motion-
ing his companions to squat, upon which they all dropped on their
haunches, the speaker, who looked to be the oldest as well as the
largest and hairiest among them all said:

THE APE-MAN OF JAVA'S STORY

"I know that in this world of to-day they call me the 'Ape-man of
Java.' But that is because men know no better. At first glance,
covered as I am with black, shaggy hair, with my slouching shoulders, my huge limbs, my heavy, shot-out jaw, I may seem to be an
ape. Yet with my mother's milk I drank in the knowledge that those
of my kind who had gone before me *had been more than apes!* We
had inherited the one gift Nature cannot give—for it is not in her
power to give it. We had *human souls!*

"The soul of every creature that lives, fish, reptile, beast or bird,
is *born at the moment the egg that holds it is formed!* That soul is
made up of tiny atoms of a distant past, the past of all life that has
gone before. Everything that lived before us has added some of
these *invisible atoms of soul* that are born with each new egg when
the egg is born, in ovary or womb. But all the many millions of
living things, until the Common Ancestor came, had *animal souls.*

For *what makes a soul human is a spark of the Divine,* and that
spark had been missing. Nature, great as she is, cannot supply it.
Only God Himself can do so. And God—who has created Nature,
performed the miracle Nature could not perform. *He gave the
Common Ancestor of us all, his human soul!*

"Yet not at the moment of his birth. He was born of his mother's
womb a beast. He grew up as a beast, and ranged the forests on
all fours. He lived and loved as a beast, and of the seed of his
bestial days were born the great apes which are our brothers in
blood, but not in soul. And then the spirit of God must have
breathed upon him! One day, in the glorious "Indian summer" of the

world, he rose and stood on his hind legs—and never again did he walk on all fours! His eyes changed: there was something in them that made them different from the eyes of every other beast, even the lordly mammoth. *The soul the beast had gained shone out from them!*

"Yet this soul, too, had to grow and change and develop through Evolution; through piling centuries of struggle and effort. For God had given our Common Ancestor only a soul-spark, only the least little ember-glow of the Divine fire! He must tend and feed it. He must nurse it until by its means he could master himself and all the world. But the soul-spark was there, and all of us who were born of his loins *after* its coming were born on the *human side* of the dividing line which separates man from beast; just as all those who sprang from his seed *before* God breathed upon him, had to follow the way of the beast for the generations to come.

"Yet God did not wish Man to grow vain in his own conceit, to glory in the fact that every living creature on Earth had to obey him. So Nature, together with the soul God gave him, has seen to it that he has carried over the threshold from his former beast-life *the three beast-marks of which we know*—hair, tail and appendix! And now to my own story.

"I was born into a far more beautiful world than this of to-day. It was in the last month of Earth's second great summer and—though I did not know it—the angel of the cold was drawing forth his sword of ice to strike the world again! In the island of Java, where I lived with my parents in a great tree-nest such as our cousins the chimpanzees build to this day among the boughs, I spent a care-free, happy boyhood after I had been weaned from my mother's breast. I would roll about and wrestle on the leaf-covered floor jungle with my little cousins the orang-outang cubs but always, *always I knew that I was different!* They were one thing and I was another, for all I could understand their grunts, and used the same grunts and signs they did to make my meanings clear. A little later, after my father had cuffed me a few times, and had gotten it through my thick skull that I would have to do my share toward providing the family meals, I was too busy hunting anything that could be eaten: fruits, snails, insects, even birds—though they were hard to catch—to have much time to play. And we already had a human habit that the friendly apes which were our neighbors did not observe. All the food we three caught was brought back to our tree and fairly divided by my father. The apes hunted food each for himself, except when there were baby apes in the nest; then the father brought the mother enough for herself and her young.

"And, in due time, in one of the ten or twelve scattered families of our own kind—for we no longer intermarried with our ape cousins, and the young male of our race would travel hundreds of miles to find a female with whom he could mate—I found a young creature as hairy and hideous as myself, and with grunts and rubbings of one hairy cheek against the other, we soon decided to build a tree nest of our own. And there we were happy. We had chosen a huge tulip-tree which overhung the banks of a stream, not far from where the great volcano of Lawu sent up lazy smoke-wreaths to the bright skies. But we were used to the volcano, which had been sending up the same kind of smoke-wreaths ever since we could remember.

"Now I know—for many are the things we come to know once we are dead!—that our island of Java was one of Earth's paradises. It was an isle of spices, where a magic palm-tree was supposed to grow deep, deep down in an abyss of whirling sea-waters, and let its big, swimming nuts be carried up to the surface of the waves. Above the Sunda forests which were our home floated the 'birds of paradise' the many-colored glory of whose feathers was to make the kings of later years pay golden rewards for their skins. I must smile at the pretty story told of them: that the male and female birds had no feet, and lived always on the wing in the blue sky, where their young were hatched out in a cradle twisted together on the long tail-feathers of both birds.

"The birds of paradise I knew all had feet and used them, and they laid their eggs in a nest like any other bird. But when, thousands and thousands of years later, they were hunted for their glorious feathers, their ugly feet, that only took up room, were cut off; and that was the way the story started. High up in the tree nest I had built with my mate, I sat one day working with a sharp stone on a bit of wood that had a heavy knob-end. I meant to make a throwing-stick with which I could strike a bird at a distance, and my heart was beating high at the idea of this new thing I was about to give the world, when—the Earth suddenly seemed to split in two! A tremendous shock flung my mate from the nest into the foaming crest of a fifty-foot tidal wave that swept along the stream, and so swiftly did it rush past, carrying along the entire river with it, that when I was hurled through the air a moment later, I fell in the dry river bed. And there, before I could pick myself up—even while Lawu spat fire and flame, and the Earth shook and rumbled—I was buried beneath the huge lava-wave which raced down from the volcano, and knew no more."

Solemnly the hairy figure of the "Ape-man of Java"* squatted down, and his nearest neighbor rose in his place:

*The skull and thighbone of the *Pithecantrapus erectus*, "the ape-man who walks", found in 1890, near Trimal, in Java, is regarded by scientists as making this creature the *middle link* between the Common Ancestor and man. His brain "capacity" was greater than that of the

THE DAWN-MAN'S STORY

"Of course, we other men-beasts with human souls already had begun to spread here, there and everywhere over the earth when you were building a tree-nest in your spice-island," said the second speaker to the first. "I too, lived on an island, and though there were no birds of paradise in my forests, it was a pleasant place— all flowering cinnamon trees, almonds and figs, and there were miles and miles of giant cactus in the sandy tracts. And when *they* were in bloom the *human* in me would stir, and I would squat on my haunches while the tears ran down my cheeks! It was what they now call the "beauty" of it that made me weep, but I did not know what it was: only that a feeling of softness and sadness would creep over me, so great that the tears came. And the chimpanzees would all skin down from their trees, and sit around me in a solemn circle, with sad faces—imitating my sad face—and filled with curiosity. But though we talked the same language of signs and grunts I could not tell them *why* I was sad yet hapyy, for they could not understand.

"But how my forest of pink-flowering cinnamon and blossoming almonds has changed! A pleasant river of clear, crystal water flowed through it and ran down to the sea, but now all that green and flowering wood is gone. The ground for miles around is all one great city,* and the clear waters of the river are soiled and stained.

"Perhaps you had no beast enemies in your spice-island, O my Javan brother, or the great black python, the snake of the rocks, lived far from where your tree-nest swung in the winds! But we—there were four of us, two brothers and two sisters—lived in fear of the great saber-toothed tigers that prowled and crept about at night, and would clutch a tree in their great paws and shake the chimpanzees out like so many plums. For a time, by nesting in the very highest branches of certain trees of great size we escaped and then, one dawn, when thinking all was safe we dropped to the ground, a great tan-colored body shot from the undergrowth and I saw my brother torn to pieces before my eyes.

"I once had seen a chimpanzee fling itself on a tiger when its mate had been seized, and in a madness of rage beat against its huge skull

largest orang-outang—and the orang-outang is nearer man than any of our other ape cousins. Its thigh-bone *proved* that it walked and stood erect. Its teeth were human, not ape-like. Strange to say the most beautiful statue of ancient Greece, the Venus of Milo, *still considered a standard of feminine beauty,* and this hideous "sample" of hairiest, early ape-like man had one thing in common—the arms of both were missing when they were dug up out of the earth!

*London rears its sea of houses where the Dawn Man's flowering cinnamon forest once spread on either bank of the Thames down to the salt sea waves.

with a heavy stone, only to be disembowelled with a sweep of the great beast's paw. Yet ten minutes later the chimpanzee's brothers and sisters had forgotten all about it. But again, when I saw my brother torn limb from limb something moved in me—even as I scurried away with my sisters—something that the 'oak-men' could not feel. It might take long and I might lose my life but—the cave-tiger must be killed! And it was then, O brother, that I found in my human brain the something with which I could slay the cruel beast at a distance!

"Long since my father had made himself a flinging club such as you were making when you were swept away. And thanks to that our folks had long since given up flinging stones at birds. They were uncertain and it was hard to get near enough to fling them. The flinging maul was good. But it was not good enough for a tiger. For days I sat by myself and hunted a dim thought: the thought of something with which I could make my kill—for the tiger must go. My sisters went off day by day and brought back food—wild fruits and cresses, birds' eggs, newts and frogs, and when the older one was lucky with the "flinging stick," a young stoat or rabbit. I never moved a finger. And at last, in a flash, it came to me, and I cried out with joy and danced until the chimpanzees came running up on all fours and, as is their way, imitated me, hopping and jumping about me in a ring.

Brother, I made me a sling.* Its cup was the skin of a mole, and its thongs were made of the guts of a sea-otter cast up on the beach. And I practised with my sling, whirling it around my head before I made my cast, and using the smooth round pebbles of the riverbed for stones till I could strike the head, the wing or the tail of a bird as it flew. And then—it was at noon when the sun is brightest—I, though my heart shook, sent one pebble after another crashing into the brush where the tiger hid until suddenly the bushes parted and it leaped out, its tail beating the ground. And while it stood there, its eyes blinking in the sun, I sent two pebbles speeding from my sling and put out the light of those eyes forever. And one pebble must have gone deeper and struck its brain, for with a great, strangled roar, the tiger suddenly dropped, twitched and was dead!

*The "throwing-stick", the sling, the "throwing spear" and bow and arrow all were invented by the human beasts to that they could hunt. At first the other animals were so tame that they could be "grabbed" and hit over the head with a stone. But *instinct* soon taught them to run from man: then he had to chase them. Killed with a "throwing-stick", the hunter would drink the fresh blood and suck the brain of his "kill" from the hashed skull, cutting it up with a sharp bit of flint. To this day the Australian "blackfellow" flings the kangaroos he has caught, into a fire until it is swollen by gases and the heat. Then he slits open the belly and devours the intestines as a Neapolitan does maccaroni.

"And after that the use of the sling spread to all human beasts of the island forests, and from far away they would come to me with gifts of mussels or rabbits to be shown how to make and use the sling. For the sling meant good hunting and plenty of flesh food. But the chimpanzees who had seen me kill the tiger drew away from me after that. Something of the fear they had felt for it they now felt for me. . . ."*

He broke off suddenly and squatted down in his place, while a silence rested on the strange group for a moment. Then the third ape-like man rose:

THE HEIDELBERG MAN'S STORY

"Brothers," said he, "you did well by our race! For *to nourish the human* in us we must eat *all* foods and not one or two foods only, like our beast brothers. And you who brought "throwing stick" and "sling" into the world started the things that came after and made flesh food sure for us for all time. Each of us is separated from the other by a hundred thousand years or more—for I lived in the middle European plains and forests and the ice-angel was drawing his freezing sword to prove that Earth's second summer was ending. "But had we not known how to eat and live on every kind of food, we would have gone the way of the beasts. Some of you who listen to my tale will smile and say: 'Heidelberg Man?* He must be the earliest ancestor of the Prince of Pilsen and the inventor of the first "stein!" Where does he "get off" tlaking about food, unless it is "liquid food," as the ads. call it?' But the fact that I was called from life at Heidelberg means nothing. There was no Heidelberg when I laid down my bones there. There was no 'liquid food'—and I'm not sure the world has been improved by finding the secret of sending the spirit that lives in hops and malt and grain up into our skulls to do a devil-dance there.

"Not that I would not have tried it," added the Heidelberg Man,

---

*Revenge is the reason here given for the invention of the sling. It has been done purposely, to stress the difference between the *human* and the *beast* soul. Only once in a while do animals remember injuries and seek revenge; for they live only in the moment, while man remembers and nurses the wrongs done him. The elephant, the descendant of the early mammoths and mastadons, is an exception, and will nurse a grievance for years, until it gets a chance to "even up". This speaker is *Eoanthropus* (Dawn Man), a skull plus jaw-bone found in England, with human teeth and a brain capacity bigger than that of the Ape-man of Java.

*Out of a single jaw-bone found in a Heidelberg sandpit Science has built up the huge, hairy-armed, apish *Homo Heidelbergensis,* "The Heidelberg Man". And with him were found some of the sharp flint-stone instruments he used to carve and scrape his "throwing sticks" with, to cut up animals he had killed and to do anything else wih. These flins are called *eolihs,* and were the very first human *tools.*

with a hairy grin, "because *early man had to try every new thing once* in order to rise above his fellow beasts. But to get back to the solid food. Often, wandering through the woods with my 'throwing stick' in hand (where I lived we had forests of oaks and larches, evergreens and beeches, instead of cinnamon-trees and figs) I would meet a poor blood brother who was going down while I was going up, face to face.

"I am no beauty," said the Heidelberg Man, shaking a mane that would have made any twentieth century girl shudder, "but I could not help but feel sorry for the 'tree-man.' Every instinct the poor, hairy wretch had, every vague hope and aim in its life was finding the trees on whose fruit it lived. It could eat nothing else, could not even *think* of eating anything else. It only had the tradition of its fathers and that tradition said: 'Fruit must ye eat!' I could not help the creature, but there was the blood-tie between us, so I would give it a friendly wave and grunt, and its dull eyes would light a little and grow *almost human, yet not quite!*

"Or, sometimes, I would run across a small family of the 'Blue-skinned Folk.' They, too, were eaters of one food: tubers and roots that grew in the ground. Poor pig-apes, with their huge, hyena-like heads and jaws, their heavy bodies covered with bluish hair, and using all four clawed hands to dig up the roots and tubers they had to have or die. Tremendous though their strength was they were doomed—no Evolution for them!—and if their tubers failed when some 'wave of death' struck the planet-world they died as well, for there was nothing else they could eat. No, brother," and the Heidelberg Man shook his heavy head, "our soul-spark never would have grown if we had not been able to feed it, feed it on *every* kind of food, vegetable and animal!

"But you spoke of the vast city of houses that has 'wiped out' your fragrant forests of cinnamon," he said, turning to the Dawn Man. "Do you know," he continued, "that I, I brought the *house* into the world!" And in his pride he beat his hairy breast with his great paw till the jungle boomed.

"Till I came, my folk had lived in tree-nests, like the rest of you. But I saw how snugly the beasts were housed in their caves and how they were sheltered from the storms and rains. And I said to myself: 'Shall the beasts live at ease in their dry caves while I, who am so far above them, shiver in the tree-tops?' And I found a splendid cave: high, dry and roomy, but—a hyena family lived there. The hyena was no blood-brother of mine. I drove out father, mother and cubs—in spite of all their snarling and showing of great, white fangs, for they are a cowardly folk—and moved in with my own mate and young. And everything you made later in the way of a house," he added, turning to the human ape who had not yet spoken, "is an Evolution of what my brain thought of: the first *shelter,* the first house. After me the human beast-folk never went back to their tree-nests. Caves and the hollow trunks of great trees were their homes, their houses. That is what I gave the world!" And again the jungle boomed as the huge human beast proudly beat its hairy chest. And then, while the boom of the Heidelberg Man's chest-blows still echoed through the jungle, the Neanderthal Man leaped up from his haunches:

THE NEANDERTHAL MAN'S STORY

"Brothers all!" he cried, "none will deny that you did well by the race! You tended and nursed the soul-spark, the God-given human something in our beast-bodies, until it bore new thoughts, until it found new ways of moving upward from bestiality! But I and those who lived between the time of the Heidelberg Man and myself— we went further than you ever dreamed of going. Over two hundred thousand years of time separate me from my Heidelberg brother, and in that time the angel of the ice swept across the world three times, driving human and other beasts before him, as he did when winter came for the first time. I lived in that fourth great winter age half a million years" (he turned to the Ape-Man of Java) "after you were buried beneath the lava of Mount Lawu!

"Even before me those of our race had taken great steps in advance. The human beast-folk, the many brothers who had sprung from the loins of our Common Ancestor *after* God had planted the divine spark of human understanding in him, thousands of years before the Ape-Man built his nest, had split up into many, many tribes, and had scattered all over the Earth. Some of us, for human creatures can 'go to the dogs' or 'the dingos' as we said in our day, *did not nurse our soul spark!* We let our soul-lights grow dimmer and dimmer until they flickered out and we perished with them. Some, mingling again with the beasts, were lost in the stream of *their* generations. Others, our first 'poor whites,' declined and decayed and died out!

"There were the 'Shoulderless Men,' of whom my great-great-grand-father used to tell my grandfather when he was a hairy little human cave-cub. For thousands of years they had lived in the forests and hunted with weapons, and grown strong in numbers. And then a blight seemed to fall on them. My grandsire said it was because they interbred too closely, for they dwindled and their young grew less and less in number every year. As they grew weaker, the great beasts grew stronger and more numerous, and after a time the great cats and cave-bears, and the fierce bands of wild dogs drove them to a land of half-flooded caverns and marshes.

"There a diet of fish and molluscs in the course of a few hundred years gave them long, narrow, chinless skulls, bodies like tubes, *almost without shoulders, with arms shooting out like a crocodile's fore-legs,* and a skin which was turning scaly like that of our old reptile ancestors. Even in my great-great-grandfather's time they had nearly vanished from the Earth!

"There were cannibals,* the 'Eaters of Human Flesh.' They lived in a middle-European land of rocky woods and caverns, and their huge, chinless lower jaws had not even as much 'speech' as we other Neanderthal Men had found—some twenty 'grunt-words' to help out our hand signs! And yet, their nauseating habit of eating the flesh of their own kind did not spring from a diseased craving of the stomach—it was not a beast trait! The marrow of split cave-bear bones tasted better. But what led them to eat 'their own,' was the same instinct, the human instinct, the religious instinct 'gone wrong,' which makes some South Sea island tribes of this day prefer 'long pig' (the pretty name they give the human beings they eat) to the ordinary 'short pig' of their islands. It was a dim feeling that when brave enemies of another tribe were devoured their bravery would enter into the body of those who ate them, and make him brave as well. And—do not laugh!—a deformed or sickly child after being fattened might be eaten by its family and tribe, in the moon of its birth *in a tender spirit of religious affection, as a sacrifice,* to the moon-goddess or the sun-goddess, to send it back to its ancestor and bring the eaters good luck!

"Then, too, there were the 'Eeaters of Worms.' They were a forest people who had 'gone soft' in the woods. They took to feeding only on snails, toads and roots, and abandoned all other foods. And as they grew smaller and weaker they gave up, one by one, their human habits. They travelled in separate *hordes.* In the spring the males and females would come together and mate like beasts, and then they would break up into separate bands which roamed the forests. And in the end the human spark flickered out and those who did not join some family of the 'Blue-skinned' apes and breed themselves back into animals again, died out and were forgotten.

"But we who kept the human spark in our natures alive, and fed the light of intelligence in our brains, we went up and on!"

For a moment the bestially human face with its great, sad eyes peering forth from its hairy mask, turned from its jungle brothers and swept the crowded house with a glance. And the audience watching felt a queer thrill, half-kindly, half-repulsive, as the old ancestral "call of the wild" swept over it in a tingling wave.

*With Neanderthal skeletons found in the cave of Krapina in Croatia, near the southern boundary of Hungary (1899-1905) were *human bones roasted and cracked for their marrow-fat,* showing that cannibal orgies had been held there by its cave-dwellers.

"Yet could *you* have seen us—seen me and the mothers and young of my own family squatting down for a meal, you would not have thought we had gotten very far. But, no matter, I must get on with my story.

"My real story—is the story of how I brought fire into the world. *Before me human beasts knew no fire!* We shivered in our caves and hollow trees, and ate our food raw. We had no real protection except our poor weapons against the huge cat animals and the great packs of wild dogs which downed us by sheer weight of numbers.

"Time did not exist for early beast-humans like ourselves. The hours, the days, the years went by, and we only gave a dim thought to their passing when our limbs stiffened, when our arms no longer could whirl the maul or fling the throwing spear, when we found it hard to keep up with the 'pace' set by the stronger and younger males of the tribe, as we wandered along in little *herd* groups of thirty, fifty or a hundred 'humans.' And when, male and female, we grew so helpless that we could no longer 'keep up with the rest,' some of the young and strong would dash out our brains with a maul! *But the bringing of fire into the world made the hands of the world-clock leap forward,* for all we knew nothing of time.

"This was the way of the finding of the fire! Once, all night long, a terrible storm had raged outside my cave. The lightning darted tremendous bolts of blue flame with never a stop, and many a giant forest tree lay smoking and smoldering when the storm passed with the dawn. I strayed out to see what could be found and there, amid the hot ashes of whole sections of forest which the lightning had set blazing, I saw the blackened bodies of all sorts of small birds and animals caught by the flames.

"Now the wise human creatures that live on Earth know all things, but to this day as in my time, the way to test food, to tell whether it were good or bad, is to *taste it*. I picked up a burned and blackened bird, rubbed off its crust of soot and smut, and set my teeth in it. Never, never had I taken anything so delicious into my mouth! It was humankind's first taste of juicy, roasted meat! And never again, thought I, would the raw flesh on which I had fed until then enter my mouth again. This was living! This was a new thing that was better than good! I danced about, eagerly tearing off more hunks of the delicious roasted meat, flinging the first bird away to pick up a burned rabbit, and then another bird. And when I had gorged myself so that I could hardly walk, I roared for my folk to come and share the great discovery I had made. But while they fed and grinned, mowing and licking their greasy and bloodied lips with joy, I was hunting eagerly among the ashes until I found what I wanted.

"It was a little pile of glowing embers. Quickly I built a small 'cage' of stones, tying it together with ends of gut, and scraping up the living embers, dumped them into it. Then I hurried to my cave with the cage, bidding one of my mates fetch dry twigs and grasses, and to be quick about it. As soon as she brought them, I sent her off for more, and then carefully began to feed the red embers, until a merry little flame leaped up and sang a happy, crackling little song: 'Roast meat! Roast meat!'

"And before long fire from my fire-cage found its way to all human forest-folk. All had fires that were fed night and day, and never allowed to go out. For if they did, we would have to wait the chances of another lightning storm and meanwhile go without the good warmth, the roast meat and the protection the flames gave us. And the women mates and the half-grown young ones in all the caves had a new duty—to gather the brush-wood to feed the fires.

"But always our hearts were in our mouths lest the precious fire go out. And once, when my tribe had been fighting with another about the right to hunt in a certain forest tract, we were driven back in such haste—for there were more of them than us—that our fire-cages were captured. For weeks we huddled shivering in the new caves where we had fled, mourning the loss of all that the fire had meant to us, and then . . . the weakest, laziest of all my sons found the way of calling up the fire-spark whenever it was wanted, and our future was once more made secure!

"He was a clever worker with his rude, flint tools (*eoliths*), the sharp, clumsy stones which fitted into the fist, and which we used to make other things, was my whelp. We had found out that by rubbing a flint-stone against wood that the wood crumbling off into a kind of warm meal which was the very best thing to feed to the red embers in the fire-cages when they began to grow dark and die. And one day this whelp of mine, his head filled with some dim idea about the wood-meal or dust being warm, *took up two bits of wood,* and began rubbing one against the other and . . . after he had rubbed for a long, long time, suddenly the meal began to smoke of its own self, and a red ember glow showed in the hollow of the bit of wood.

"His wild shout brought me running to him, and I saw what had happened. Never would we have to watch and tend and carry our fire cages again! Now we could have fire whenever we wanted it —and we did.*

"And with the fire all else came to our folk. I myself lived to see

*Either in this way or by the striking of sparks from the flint-stones was fire found and bound to man's service. And all the different kinds of "fire-sticks", the "fire-borer" of the Eskimo and the "boring-sticks" of Central Africa, the "fire-whirler" of the Hindoo and the Malay's wooden "fire-saw", in which a piece of wood is drawn sidewise through a cleft in another piece, are variations of this old idea.

the cave—the first cave, which my Heidelberg brother called the first house—turn into a first *real* house, for the first *real* house, *the hut,* grew up around the first fire!

"We might still use good caves and the hollow trunks of trees, but bit by bit, and branch by branch, the walls and ceilings of the first real homes grew up around the family hearth-fire. We could harden better weapons and tools in the fire; we could roast and cook our food, and no longer had to eat it raw. Warmth and shelter and protection all came with the fire. And the family, too, grew closer together *and something like a family feeling grew up with the glow of the flames!*

"But most of all, O brothers of mine," cried the Neanderthal Man, "the fire set us apart forever from our blood-brothers the beasts! In the cold damp darkness of the forest night, the chimpanzee or gorilla would creep shivering up to the outskirts of the great fire which blazed before our cave (before the huts grew about it), and warm its frozen hands, uttering little moans of pleasure! *But no ape ever learned to feed the flames!* It feared it, and much as it liked its warmth, had to freeze once the fire went out. And, low as we. stood in the human scale, brothers of mine, in those bestial days, we knew that we must lay fresh wood on the dying embers if we would not freeze, and that knowledge once and for all drew a new line between the beasts and ourselves, a line that never has been crossed!"

As the hairy figure resumed its squatting position in the silence which followed its last words, there was a stir and movement in the dark background of the jungle, and a group of other forms, some less, others more bestial looking than the four which had spoken, broke out through the shadowy wall of leaves. One, a stunted, wrinkled creature, seemed to be the spokesman: "We are your blood and soul brothers whose bones had not yet been found when Nature called you here with her magic spell! But now we have come! While the Ape-Man of Java was building his tree-nest in the island of spices, I was building mine in the Australian gumtrees.

"And there," he ended sadly, "we now are dying out.* For we who have gone but a little ways up the ladder of progress die when we meet the wise children of other human blood-brothers who sprang from the Common Ancestor's loins. Their soul-spark is so strong and radiant that we perish in the fierce light of its knowledge and power!"

The Neanderthal Man rose and answered with a sadness even greater than the others: "In a way, our fate has been the same.

---

*A skull of earliest man found in Australia is supposed to be *not* a Neanderthal skull, but to belong to a very primitive kind of man who lived before the True Men who followed the Neanderthal people.

Your race is fading from the face of the Earth. Mine has died out in Europe, and for the same reason, in the days after the last winter that Earth knew.

"We are the Abel-races of human-beasts. Where we do not perish, we linger as slaves. We strove and tried, we found us weapons and houses and fire, and a dim hope rose in our breasts that Evolution might carry us further and further upward. *But only the fittest survive among beasts or men, for that is the ancient law of life on earth, the law that has come down from the first day.* We were hunted down, killed, and destroyed by a stronger, taller, handsomer and less hairy race, which swept down on us out of the vast Asian lands where it had developed. In the Africa from which we Neanderthal men first came still live those of our kind. But they are subjects and slaves of the very race that swept the Neanderthal Men from Europe. The Neanderthal Man was Earth's first 'human under-dog.' We are even denied our human soul-spark, the soul-spark we had nursed and tended, and hoped to blow into a great flame of life and knowledge!"

The Neanderthal Man clasped and wrung his great hairy hands, tears filled his gloomy eyes.

After a moment he resumed: "A beast race swept off the checker-board of races dies without suffering. It hardly knows that it dies. But a man-race suffers, for black and hairy though it be, it thinks. Through hundreds of thousands of years of toil and struggle, we moved up, but so little at a time that we seemed to stand still. And then, at the moment when our chance seemed to have come—we were swept away as carelessly as a family of reptiles with their brains in their tails. Yet the great law of survival is the same for beast and man. The stern law of Evolution bids us give way to the fitter and stronger race than our own. And we cannot struggle against it!"

Here there was a sudden interruption. A large, hairy form pushed its way forward and cried excitedly: "I have just been discovered near Los Angeles,* and all the scientists say that I am older by tens of thousands of years than you are, Ape-Man of Java, and that my brain-development is something phenomenal, really phenomenal!" And to the Neanderthal Man the new-comer said patronizingly: "It's our California climate! Why, if you had only known enough to leave your barren European plains and emigrate to *my* country, you might be alive to-day! Hardly anything or anyone ever dies there. The California climate! . . ."

And now it was clear that all these fantastic, hairy shapes were

* Not until detailed study and investigation have made clear the type of the prehistoric men whose bones and skulls were discovered near Los Angeles (Mesa Pet) during March 1924, will it be possible to "place" them.

human in spite of *their appearance*. A loud burst of laughter, the slapping of hairy paws on hairy knees, and the great roar of merriment showed that they had a sense of humor, and *a sense of humor is one of the things that belongs to man alone and is not known to beast*. How the Californian would have taken it is hard to say had it not been for the fact that now, while the Neanderthal Man turned away his head and clenched his great gorilla fists, and the others all fell back, a tall figure came directly up to the fire and raised a commanding hand. A whisper rose on the air: "The True Man," and as it died the picture of the jungle and the ape-men gathered around the fire, vanished from sight.

CHAPTER XIX

A SEMI-SIMIAN CHEWING-CIRCLE

(For Ladies Only?)

ONE glance from Nature's piercing eye, as she peeped around the corner of the curtain at the caption-writer, where he sat in the audience—and he found himself behind the scenes. "Here is a little picture meant for you and the ladies, only! I doubt if the men would be interested," she said. "I want you *to see what the women of those human-beast days were like.* Man was the only 'big noise' in the forests of those days. The apish man whom you just have seen, would never have 'stood' for my showing any of their womankind in the same picture with themselves. *For woman was very, very unimportant then in the eyes of men.* Of course, it was long ago," she added hastily, "but they were just slaves,* a necessary evil in connection with the sex instinct, and useful for adding more food-hunting small fry to the family circle. It is sad to have to admit it, but all the finer and nobler feelings which humanity developed with regard to woman, and which has given her her true place in the world, as the better, purer and more ideal sex, the kinder, sweeter and more humane half of the human race, had not yet been born!

"We must remember that man was then still half-beast. Though he was tending his soul-spark, all the 'spark-plugs' were not working, and it is to be feared that so far as respect, reverence and tenderness *for the female of the species* was concerned, he was only 'hitting on one cylinder' of his better and less bestial nature."

Nature waved her hand. There, against the same jungle background which had framed the hideous, hairy figures of our forbears and so far as their appearance goes, for*bears* is the word that best expresses them) was squatted another and altogether different group

---

*The "giving away" of a prehistoric bride by her father may be pictured as follows: the father, clutching her by the back of the neck, flung her down before the man who was to be her mate, and in the simple grunt and guttural language of the primitives said: " . . . She is your woman. I will protect her no more. She shall bow before you, her master. She shall seek out the game you have killed and carry it over her shoulder. If she disobeys you put her to death." This is no exaggeration.

of figures. They seemed to be quite as hairy, but their faces were less hard; the outlines of their jaws seemed a little less heavy; there was a softer look about their outlines. There they squatted, a "chewing-circle." Though some were scraping away with eoliths, cleaning roots or cracking nuts between two stones, most of them were *chewing* the skins of deer and other beasts to make them soft and pliable for man's uses. A few, together with their own babies, *were nursing wild dog pups and little suckling pigs.**

It was a kind of "Semi-Simian Chewing Circle." You well-bred and sheltered women of this twentieth century (who, though you may sometimes speak of your men-folks as "brutes" and "beasts") will find it hard to realize the primitive depths from which you have risen, and *from which you have lifted male man!* Not until Christianity gave woman a place *beside* and not *beneath* man, and *romantic love* was born of *the ideals of Chivalry,* was womankind to take her place as the true beaconlight of civilization, the finest influence in man's dark upward road! And *now*—is it a step in advance or a step backward?—woman gives up her right to be man's romantic ideal, and puts herself *on an exact level* with him in the "business" of life! In all fields except those of heavy manual labor she works and "draws pay" as he does. She "looks out for herself." She makes herself independent of him. Are "womans' rights" and "suffrage" *the beginning of a better, bigger, higher life for all womankind?* Or, in another way, *are they a return to the horde life of the females among the "Eaters of Men, independent of the males, and "earning their* own keep," *once the mating season is over?* Does the *hearth fire* around which the family first gathered on Earth or the *electric light* on the desk of the independent woman office worker shine with a brighter flame? These are questions every woman *can only answer for herself!*

But with regard to our "jungle-girls," these brutish "soul-mates" of their bestial human men-folk, even in that far time and day, we can get an idea of what their family and tribal life was like by listening to their gossip. You delicate women of to-day, as you gather once a week in some friend's hospitable home—whether you call it a "social" club, or a "Thursday" meeting, or a "Sewing Circle" or what-not—are probably going back to an old tradition of the race. Around the jungle-fire, while the men were off on the hunt, many and many a time, no doubt, the women of the tribe or horde "got together," and "talked over" everything and everyone (who

* To this day the women of living, primitive races *show the feeling of kinship with the lower animals, the feeling that man and beast sprang from the same stock.* The Tierra del Fuego women suckle their young dogs; Samoans, young pigs; the "hairy" Ainu of Japan, baby bear-cubs; Australians, little dingos; some lower tribes in Siam, young monkeys; and some South American savages *even young muskrats!*

did *not* happen to be there). The only difference might be that where you delicate and well-bred women use the conversational "hammer," your "all-wool" jungle sisters used a "maul" or "throwing stick," and called a spade a spade when they did their "knocking."

"My son Nam came home yesterday. He had been gone for many moons, wife-hunting on the other side of the big forest," says one fond mother, scratching her hair cheek for—we blush to give romance *its wriggling foundation of truth!*—none of us, men, women or children, ever washed in those days. We were filthy beyond describing, and infested with vermin.

"And did he catch him a woman?" asks a friend. "If you want to call what he dragged home *that,* he did," replies the disgusted mother: (In those days a mother-in-law was very, very frank about a girl with whom her boy had taken up.) "A great, broad-faced thing, with a foolish grin that won't come off. Her silly people worship the Moon-goddess—as though any one with a brain above a chimpanzee's did not know that the Sun-god is the only one! But I'll train her. She need not think that because my son was kind enough to knock her over the head and drag her off with him she won't have to work!"

And Nam's mother gave the bit of mole-skin crammed in her mouth an extra vicious chew.

"Did you hear about her daughter Gomma?" one of the Chewing-girls whispers in an aside to the squatter next her, with a glance at Nam's parent. "No, what was it?" is the eager answer. "Our cave is so far at the end of the line that I never know what happens. And as for that great, chuckle-headed man of mine ever knowing anything about what's going on! . . . Please tell me!"

"Well, her 'Old Man' has a way of letting the rest of the family feel his fist,* and poor Gomma has turned up many a time with a face as black and blue as her flintstone necklace! At any rate, Gnug, my man, told me last week that some of the young males of the Gnaw-Gnaw tribe have been hanging around the upper spring, probably looking for girls to steal. Now, between you and me, I *see* any young Gnaw-Gnaw stealing Gomma—*if she does not want to*

---

*The chief of a group of families, the father, the "Old Man" of a family had the strongest fist's right of life and death over the others. Women existed to work and bear children. Morals, in our sense, had not been born. The "Old Man" of a family group including several women and girls paired with one or the other as he felt inclined. Growing boys were driven off as soon as they were old enough to rouse jealousy. If a daughter found her life at home too hard, and wanted to escape being "knocked down" to the highest bidder, she ran away with some man she preferred. Or—she took care *not* to "watch out", so that the wife stealers could get her.

be stolen! She is as strong as a cave-bear, and would think nothing of bashing in a Gnaw-Gnaw skull with the owners' own club—*unless* she thought she might be more comfortable sitting over a Gnaw-Gnaw camp-fire instead of her own. Anyhow—she's gone! And her 'Old Man' was so angry that he broke his finest flint eolith against the rock the other day. Now he is talking about getting all the men together to go on the war-path against the Gnaw-Gnaw, but I guess we women will have a word or so to say about that! Any cave-man has a right to knock his daughter about a bit. But he ought to be satisfied with pulling her hair, and not beat her up with the maul till she's black and blue. I think Gomma did just right!"

Meanwhile Nam's mother was confiding to one of her friends the details of the feast which was to celebrate her son's successful return from his wife-hunt. "Yes, baked fish, roasted aurochs and wild pig hams and oysters and mussels! And my daughter Snok has been grinding a delicious marrow-bone paste all morning!"

Alas, Nam's good mother does not tell us that the fish and the aurochs (a kind of early wild bull) are *very, very gamey indeed!* They have been kept *not* "on ice," *but just kept, if you know what that is, for five days,* in honor of the great event, so that they would have a flavor. We would not call that dinner a "feast," with these filthy, hairy creatures squatted around the fire, the Old Man and Gnaw twitching the skin under their shoulders, brows or muzzles as some of the larger carrion-flies buzzing about the meat settle on them. And we turn away in disgust as their large nostrils eagerly draw in the rank smell of the foul meat waiting to be devoured. Yet such was the case. All our brothers and sisters "under their skins" cared for in the way of an odor, was an odor with a "kick" in it. And that the house-keeping of early man always could supply. We think the garbage-pile a modern invention. Long before Nam's mother and the other older girls of the tribe gathered in their Chewing-Circle, the great garbage-piles (kitchen middens) made up of heaps of mussel-shells, bones and other garbage, rose higher wherever human squatted. You may have noticed the smell which rises when the hot sun beats down on the garbage-pile on the outskirts of town. Multiply it by a thousand and you have the odor of the "kitchen middens," as these early garbage piles are called by scientists.

Yet these were trifles in those days. But now we hear something which shows that, after all *these were true women,* that they had deep within them, *something of the beauty of faith, the trust in a higher power,* the soul's aspiration which all true women have to this day. It is a haggard, pathetic little creature speaking, while she nervously cracks marrow-bones.

"I can remember when my Gnaw came, a handsome, sturdy boy.

And an hour later I was up and about.* He was our only one, and my man and I did everything to make him grow up strong and brave. No one could handle a bow and arrow as he did. And then, only last week, when the others ran up the trees, he stood his ground as the great tiger leaped out among the young men in the forest. And he would have sent his axe crashing into his brain but—his foot slipped on a pile of leaves, and before he could scramble up the tiger had jumped—and all was over!

"But his father and I dug him a grave,* and lined it with smooth stones. There we laid him. And he seemed to be lying there asleep, with his head toward the East, where the Sun-god rises, to whom his life-spark had returned. His head rests on a flint-stone pillow his father smoothed with loving care. And in his hand we laid the axe he loved so well, the axe which would have saved him had he a chance to fling it. I know that my son, my strong son, my brave son, who never spoke harshly to the mother who loved him, is happy! He is a light-spirit in the golden fire-glow around the Sun-god, though his cheek is pressed against the pillow of death which not even a mother's cheek can warm!"

Nature laid a hand on my arm. "Let us leave them! Forget the dirt, the coarseness and the squalor of their life, and remember this mother's words. For in them lives *the beauty of mother-love,* strong and fine and noble. Just as the mother love of the first mammal-creatures for the 'blood of their blood' came into the world with their young, and set them apart from the reptiles; so this finer, purer mother-love *which lives on for its child beyond the grave* sets these mothers apart from the ape-mothers in the tree-nests, who wail when their young are stricken, and ten minutes later have forgotten the little corpse lying stiffly on a pile of leaves at the foot of a forest tree!"

---

*Child-birth, even among primitives to-day, seems one of the slightest of tasks. The early mother was about her household duties an hour or so after she had laid her tribute on the altar of tribal increase.

*The skeleton of a young Neanderthal boy, found in the Le Moustier cavern, Vézère, France, *proves clearly,* by the way the body was arranged, that these poor primitives loved their own and *believed in a life after death.*

CHAPTER XX

APES AND MEN

THE human apes have vanished from the scene, though the scene remains the same. And now, shuffling through the jungle brush, come the new figures. They do not stand erect, as did those human brutes who preceded them. No, they come running on all fours, or waddling along on their huge bow-legs in a way that shows this is not the way they usually move. They are the beast-brothers of the men-beasts we have just seen—the great *Anthropoid* ("Man-like") Apes!

They are tailless, but their arms are too long, and their bowed legs too short. The Neanderthal Men had already begun to shed his hair—for hair began to go when fire came into the world—but these creatures are hairy beyond description. None of them, in spite of the resemblance of their skulls to those of the human beasts, has a brain capacity anywhere near that of man. And though the ape-brain and the human brain *have the same fold, known as the "Ape-fold,"* the difference *in soul, in intelligence,* that has no "outward and visible sign" is there! The stomach of the apes is human in shape; so is the liver, gall-bladder and lungs. All share with man the *vermiform appendix.* But the regular arch formed by his teeth distinguished man from ape!

Let us take first look at the hideous *Gorilla,* largest of the man-like apes, over six feet in height, with powerful *tusks,* and a sullen, untameably ferocious disposition, shown in the black scowl on his hairy face. He is nearest the first ape-children of the Common Ancestor. The *Chimpanzee* is simply an offshoot of the gorilla stock, with a better brain, perhaps, but smaller and not so well developed a brute.

The shaggy, bestial gorilla, strange to say, seems to be the nearest blood-relative among the apes to the extinct (Negroid?) Neanderthal Man! Is it fanciful to take for granted that *the mother of the first gorilla-beasts,* littered *before* the human soul-spark entered into the Common Ancestor of men and apes, *was the same mother who, later, bore the first human ape-beasts?* From these later offspring, sired by the same father, we might trace the European Neanderthal

146

Man, and *the black tribes and races which have swarmed and bred in the vast dark reaches of Africa to the present day.*

In the same way, there seems to be a distinct family connection *between the chimpanzee and the black dwarf peoples* (Dwarves, Science teaches us, are the product of millenial years of hard living conditions, and not enough to eat). Perhaps the first chimpanzee creature was merely a stunted and undersized gorilla-cub of the days before the soul-spark. And, perhaps, the first dwarf human black race sprang from a similar "second-rate" *human cub* of the days after the *soul-spark!* Of course this is to some extent guess work. But it seems as though the blood of the same mother must originally have been handed down to the two races—of gorilla-beasts and gorilla-like men—*with only the saving grace of the human soul-spark* to light the deep gulf dividing them!

The Orang-Outang—the Malay word means "man of the woods"— a prouder, more human beast than the gorilla, is a member of the ape-race which has split up into various families. It builds its nests in the trees, and lives on fruit, *but its brain is more like the brain of man than that of any other ape!* The Ape-Man of Java might be called a *link in the line of human descent,* running parallel with the orang-outang. Here again, it seems quite possible to think that the second ape-mother* of the Common Ancestor's more bestial days was an ape-female of the orang-outang type. She went through the same process the earliest gorilla-mother had gone through—first she lit-tered *orang-outang beast-cubs.* Then came the *human* children she nursed at her breast after their father "had seen the light," the children born who had the human something their orang-outang half-brother lacked. There was the look of the orang-outang about them in body, but they had the *soul-spark!* Some scientists claim that from the man-orang-outangs, the half-brothers of the animal orang-outangs (through Evolution, the cross-breedings and mixtures of millennial years) have come the great dominant white races.*

Remains the *Gibbon!* There is something comical about the beast, smaller than its companions, when it turns its back on us for a moment. For the small, naked callous spots on its buttocks are plainly to be seen. *Yet we should not laugh at it!* For not only is the gibbon so swift and quick in its movements that it can catch a bird on the wing, but it often walks erect, like its distant cousin.

*We must remember that in that dim past all sorts of different early ape races and families, rough drafts of others to come, were being bred in Nature's laboratory, some to survive, others to disappear.

*These include the early Cro-Magnard people, the present European races which sprang from them, and the Asiatic family of Indo-Aryan races —like the orang-outangs, and Asiatic, not an African race. They may even include such low race-types as the Australian, the South Sea Island-ers (Samoans, Papuans, etc.) and the "hairy" Ainu of Japan.

Here again, might not we suppose a mother of the general gibbon type finding favor in his sight, in those dim, far days when the Common Ancestor had his being. Cannot we suppose her presenting him with simon-pure little gibbon-babies while both parents were no more than apes? And then, once the human soul-spark glowed in the beast-brain, might not her human ape-babies take after their gibbon-mother in looks, *yet carry in their tiny, hairy selves humanity's glorious inheritance?*

Nor need we turn up our noses at our Common Ancestor's "plural wives." *Morality, like everything else, is a product of Evolution!* There was no such thing as "morality" when the Common Ancestor lived and loved among the jungle thickets. There was no such thing as "morality" for millions of years afterward.* Only gradually, through a long, long process of Evolution, was "morality" developed among men. In the beginning all sex relations must have been on a purely animal basis: a basis of "catch-as-catch-can," and "anything goes." Gradually as the *family ideal* took a more definite shape, some kind of order came out of the mixup of sex relationships. And since our Common Ancestor did not even know what "morality" was, we must not judge him too severely for not having it, and "marrying"— if one may use the word—his wives when, where and as he found them!

To return to our gibbon. His range, at the present day, is from the Malay peninsula to Southern China and—a scientific theory connects this man-like ape with the Mongolian races of the world of to-day!

But glancing at these four apes, it almost seems as though the orang-outang holds himself more proudly erect than the others. The gorilla and the chimpanzee hang back somewhat in the rear; the gibbon looks as though it were not quite sure of its human blood-ties. But the orang-outang stands forward boldly. And in a way, it has a right to do so. *For the orang-outang is the ape whose special, distant human brother*—descended, perhaps, from the same earliest mother—*has gone higher and further than the rest of the descendants of the human children born by the Common Ancestor's mates!*

Some people like to "kid themselves along" that all the races of man have sprung from one common stock, are alike gifted, and equal in mind and brain, if not in body and statue. They like to think—for religious, sentimental or *humanitarian* reasons—*that there are no inferior races of mankind!* But every picture Evolution has thus far flashed on her screen, *proves the direct contrary!* There were inferior races among the *Algae,* the plants, the molluscs, the worms, the

*When we read the newspapers it sometimes seems as though the Evolution of morality has "dropped a stitch" recently, or that it has not evoluted as far and as high as it should have done.

fishes, the amphibians, the reptiles, the birds and beasts. And—either the inferior races do not "survive," as we have seen, or if they "survive" they sink lower, or remain on the inferior level of their own special "blind alley." It is Evolution's law. *The fittest always survive, and the fittest are the superior, not the inferior race, whether the race be a beast-race or a human one.*

Nature narrowed down her choice to the mammals in developing the great upward movement which was to end in man. Then she chose among the mammals *the one particular race, the Ancestor of the man-ape-family,* out of which to develop man himself. How this probably was done we already know. And then, *among the races of men,* Nature chose the *race of races* (or the family of races) which was to be the one superior race!

There were the early Neanderthal Men, probably Negroid races. There are the black tribes* of Africa to-day, the probable blood-brothers of gorilla and chimpanzee. *No amount of sentiment can make them the equals of the white races!* They are and remain inferior. Their brain capacity is less than that of the white race, just as the gorilla's brain-pan holds less than that of the orang-outang.

Nor do the yellow races, the Mongolian races, stand on a level with the white race, for they compare to it as the gibbon does to the orang-outang—and the gibbon falls short in the comparison! The so-called "brown races," in most cases, are branches of the great white stock, and Science has not yet decided whether the American Indian races ("the red race") is an offshoot of very, very distant Mongol ancestors, or whether it represents some one of the earliest human races of Europe. Perhaps such a race, in the years which separate the Ape-Man of Java from the Heidelberg Man, crossed from Europe to America over the land bridge which then connected the continents. If so, *they may be one of the very first shoots of what might be called "white stock."* This would explain why *normal white human beings do not shrink from mating with the North American Indian,* the "red man," *as they do from mating with members of the black and yellow races!*

That the Neanderthal Men had to go with the coming of the first "true men," members of the white race destined to rule the world,

---

*Why is the negro—in all his thirty-one or two shadings—black? It is a question we often find hard to answer. The foundation theory is a double one: 1. Nature makes the skin of dark races develop an excess of dark coloring matter as a protection against the *ultra-violet rays* of the tropical sun. 2. In the blood of the race (the gorilla-mother) was a *bias, a leaning* towards this black skin. This bias lies so far in the animal past that its origin is lost. But the *leaning* is carried on through the generations *in accordance with Evoluton's law of heredity.* Outward conditions: climate, soil and atmosphere, and food with an excess of carbon also help develop the tendency toward "color".

was one of Nature's tragedies. That the black races of Africa still are known as "the white man's burden," is its sequel. But—even Nature cannot make an evolutionary omelette without breaking eggs —if these *inferior races* had been the "fittest to survive," to rule and lead, *they would have survived!* For Nature plays no favorites, either with beast or man. They may not know it, but their fate is in their own hands. If, through hereditary and natural selection, they improve their breed and the brains of their breed, they rise and rule. If they cannot do so, they decline and serve.

And so the orang-outang knows what it is about, when it stands proudly forward among its fellow-apes. After all, it is the most intelligent member of *its family,* and the *nearest,* in blood and body, to the most intelligent member of the human family!

We must not think, because the Neanderthal Man probably belonged to a Negroid race, that the stages of his Evolution upward were not exactly the same as those of the white races growing up elsewhere—in warm, fostering Asian lands, where they had better opportunities, perhaps, than this black European. *The white races went through the self-same stages of Evolution.* They had to "think out" with which weapons to hunt. They had to move from treenest to hollow tree-trunk, to cave and hut of branches. They had to discover fire and learn the secret of calling it forth at will. They had to form their first families around their first hearth-flames.

But—when we heard the Neanderthal Man tell his pitiful tale we most likely thought: Poor devil! He did not get a square deal. He was handicapped from the start, and did not have a ghost of a chance! But it is likely that Nature knew (no matter what he thought) *that the Neanderthal Man had reached his limit of development!* Have his blood-brothers, the African black races really progressed during the same long ages of time while their white brothers reached the high places?

Nature knew that the Neanderthal race had reached its limit—its Evolution had stopped. Nature's motto is "Progress!" The "True Men"—the men of the "Aurignacian Age," the Cro-Magnard races, possibly the oldest white stock, capable of a development which knew no limits, must take the Neanderthaler's place. And they did, as the next picture will show us.

The shade of the first gorilla-mother of the ages may have wrung her hands in Evolution's dark limbo of the past, at seeing the children of her blood set back and those of the orang-outang advanced! *But the law of Evolution, the law of Nature knows no sentiment, is moved by no tears!*

CHAPTER XXI

THE COMING OF THE "REINDEER MEN"

Look well on the picture the screen unfolds before your eyes! It is a picture modern man has never seen, the picture of a great migration! Whole races, millions of men, women and children, with all they have and all they own, are moving across the surfaces of the Earth. Behind their hurrying feet the miles of green meadow-grasses and red and yellow meadow-flowers lie a brown, trampled dust! The rivers shrink to tricklets, for the vast hordes drink them dry! The land behind them is stripped of forest, for the trees have disappeared to feed their camp-fires! Only the patient rocks remain unmoved by the passing of the nations!

In the dim, golden lands of southern Asia and northern Africa, in the tropical river-countries that now lie buried beneath the waters of the Mediterranean Sea, the "True Men," the "Reindeer Men," white, which were to inherit the Neanderthalers' Earth "and the fulness thereof," had been working out their Evolution. And, century by century, driving the Neanderthal Men before them, their hordes swept on into Europe, as the Angel of the Ice put by the sword he has not since bared.

They had better brains and better bodies than the Neanderthal Men, did these tall Cro-Magnard races. They had far more of man and less of beast about them, and the "Reindeer Men" are so near ourselves that scientists call them "True Men," to mark the difference between them and the more gorilla-like Neanderthal peoples. They were a race of hunters, with better weapons and greater skill in using them than the poor gorilla-like men, and—they gave the latter no quarter! In the Cro-Magnards the soul-spark which glowed so dimly in the Neanderthal skull shone bright and clear. They de-

*Tell me where you were found and I'll give you a name, is what Science says to the early skeleton it digs up. The first "Reindeer Men", were found in a French grotto called Cro-Magnard. The Grimaldi race (found in a Mentone cavern, were honored with the family name of the Prince of Monaco, the gentleman who owns the "bank" at Monte Carlo. The so-called "Grimaldis" seem to have been a Negroid race. Of the two, the Cro-Magnard, "Reindeer" race appears to be the most important: the one which "lasted longest".

spised their distant, unknown brothers of the gorilla-blood, for their race ran back to the brainier orang-outang mother.* They were the "Reindeer Men" of the world's first great steppes or prairies. They stand for the silver age of the *human hunting-pack*. It came before the gold age of "husbandry" that saw the *first seed* sown in the earth, and the *first farms*** laid out to tie man down to *a home-soil,* and begin everything the words "homeland" and "native land" and "our own country" mean to us!

What brought these great hordes of men, women and children flooding out from their Asian cradle-lands into Europe? It was not ambition. It was not love for adventure. It may not even have been the desire for new hunting-grounds. To us who—unless the "Great War to end war" has changed things—fight for patriotic and commercial reasons, *climate* seems the last thing in the world to cause a war. Yet *climate* set these huge masses of men in movement and —so strangely does Evolution work—*Climate, change of climate,* caused the inferior Neanderthal people to be cut off root and branch.

Climate seems the most logical reason for this great swarming of the "True Men" out over Europe. For in the early days climate was not fixed and "did not stay put" as it does to-day. A great Ice Age would sweep down out of the north and—just as it forced the reptiles of millions of years before to find summer lands of refuge— would make the races of men move. We cannot begin to count up the bloody struggles between early races of men, the conquests, and massacres due *simply to a change of climate!* Races whom a cold wave had "dispossessed," would come flooding down into another continent, and there would find other humans already "sitting pretty," and quite ready to stand up and fight for their own hunting-grounds. They had to fight for them, in fact, unless they wanted to starve, or move on. No doubt the gorilla-like Neanderthal Men had much of the sullen, savage ferocity of their apish half-brothers. But the Cro-Magnards, the "Reindeer Men," were their superiors. The Neanderthal folk were hunted down without pity, and the victors scorned them so much that contrary to the usual custom they did not save the women to mate with, but killed them and their young as well as the men.

In every way there are signs of advance on the part of this new race. As we see them pass before our eyes on their tremendous "hike"

*An examination of their skulls shows that the "brain capacity" of the Cro-Magnard women was *greater* than that of the men of to-day!

**The first farmers did not come till Neolithic Man (The Late Stone Age Man) brought the first grain-seed, *purposely put in the ground to grow for man* from his Eastern home. The "Reindeer Man" knew nothing of tilling the soil, and must have had only the straight flesh or fish diet their hunting gave them.

from fast Asian homelands to the new European wildernesses they mean to take and hold, they do not seem so very different from the Neanderthalers they have come to destroy. They are taller and, perhaps, less hairy. But it is still a bestial, only half-human horde in appearance, a dragging, a jostling and pushing mass of hundreds and thousands of hairy bodies in a slow churning advance, which sends up the indescribable reek of the savage—one that is his very own and that he alone casts out—to taint the pure airs of heaven!

Yet, though they take over the caves of the race they trample into the ground, they also (toward the end of their time) build them huts, huts of branches. And these huts are already beginning to group themselves around a center hut. Among the Neanderthal folk the tribe is a hazy idea. They had not gone further than the *family*. These Cro-Magnards are beginning *the Evolution of Society!*

These great hordes, on their long trail, have the germ of what makes the nation of to-day. The family grows up around the family hearth-fire. But—if every family lived for itself alone, had gone on living *for* itself and *to* itself alone, where would we be now? Take the case of those in your own village, town or city who live a solitary life, a life apart from the rest of humankind. Is their life usually a normal or a happy one? The law of Evolution shows that the family is only the *start* of society. The lives of its members must be broadened out to take in other lives and their interests. And it is only by association with other minds that our own minds develop. It is by doing *our own share* in the bigger circle of life—the community, the nation—that we ourselves advance.

And this step these remaining hundreds of thousands are beginning to take. But they do so little by little. They have reached their European land of promise and a new scene greets our eyes. Once there they split up into a great number of separate tribes, *but all these tribes are loosely united in a race* which feels that all these "bunches" of folks are related in a general way.

When we say tribes, that does not mean that one "crowd" of these hunters lived in one "town" and another in another. There were no such things as "towns." There were no such things as "villages," at first. The "tribes," men, women and children, usually were "on the move." Unless we happen to be serving a "hitch" in the Navy or an army enlistment (or, perhaps were a Red Cross Nurse in France during the War) we cannot even imagine what the "moving" in this life was like.

"The "Reindeer Men" were hunters. They formed human hunting-packs instead of wolf or wild-dog hunting-packs. They had to "live with their game." Where their game went, they went, for they had no choice. So life must have been a kind of a savage "picnic" (with few of the pleasures taken for granted with that word), spent largely around the camp-fires which were shifted, and rebuilt again as the herds of reindeer, wild horses, antelopes, deer, musk oxen, bisons and other flesh-grazing beasts shifted their grazing quarters.

Let us take another look at the screen! It shows a vast, prehistoric middle European steppe, knee-high in waving grasses. Far to windward of the immense herds of reindeer and wild horses which lift their heads from time to time as they graze to sniff the air, is a "tribe" of hunters. The men of the pack are in advance, creeping up on the beasts to get within bow and arrow distance. Far back, on the edge of the forest, are the women. Suddenly the arrows hiss. Three reindeer and a bearded stallion leap into the air—the remainder of both herds set off in a thundering gallop across the steppe until the sound of their hooves die in the distance. Then the women come to carry off the kill over their shoulders and cut it up to roast. Nothing ever was *cooked, baked or boiled,* for there was not a Reindeer woman with a *pot, pan or kettle* to her name! Pottery had not been invented by some clever girl(?) or man. And along this steppe the hunters may linger for a week or so, while great new herds of beasts come drifting past over the prairie, as the days go by. Perhaps one of the young men returns in the evening with news that a herd of mammoths is on the way, and then all hands fall to work digging a great pit to trap one of the huge beasts. For man still fears the mammoth in open battle. He fights it with his wits. If the great lead beasts do not happen to come too close to the trap, and overlook it, the chances are that some member of the herd (grazing in a broad front hundreds of feet in length) may break through the layer of boughs and grass which hides the pit-mouth. And then, when its companions hurry up at its shrill squeals and trumpetings of distress, they find they can give it no help. When at last they leave it to its fate, the hunters are happy. They dance around the helpless beast, and bury their spears and arrows in it until it is dead—and then, "Oh, you mammoth-steak!"—is what the lips that nervously lick their chops say, without a word. But if the wise old mammoth chief ever scents the man-smell, then "it is all off." A trumpet-signal warns the herd, and each beast makes a circle to avoid the danger spot.

Man lives in the open with his game. Yet, little by little, there are certain groups of caves and more solid huts, perhaps, to which the hunters return in the seasons when game is scarce. And, perhaps once or twice a year, there are great "gatherings of the clans," big, open-air camp-meetings (not necessarily religious ones) where the folks "who all belong" get together to celebrate the fact. It seems going back pretty far—40,000 years ago—but the custom has lasted to our own day. We still like to "get together" for great family "meetings" and when all the Smiths in the states of the Union come together for a great open-air reunion, few of them think that the nameless "Smiths" of 40,000 years ago were doing the same sort of thing in *their* way.

That they had big "eats" is beyond a doubt, for scattered around the great open-air camping-places where the Reindeer Men used to foregather for centuries, are bones by the hundreds of thousands— reindeer, wild horse, wild oxen, bison and antelope. And all the marrow-bones had been sucked dry!

The Reindeer Men had something the Neanderthal Men did not have—a weapon which made it possible for them to stand up against the cave-bear and sabre-toothed tiger, and fight it on more equal terms. They had bows and arrows. And the Cro-Magnard fisher- men "flung a wicked" harpoon. The harpoon we are reasonably certain of, but fishing lines—well, one can hardly expect a fishing- line to last 40,000 years in good condition so that one can tell it *was* a fishing-line. Fishing-hooks "come in" a little later.

The truth of the matter is that the "Smiths" and other Cro-Mag- nard families, in the course of time, ate their way through the im- mense herds of reindeer, wild horses, antelopes, bisons and *aurochs* which at first covered the whole face of Europe in herds too large to count. The "Reindeer Men" ate up their game faster than it could breed, and it is easy to figure out what happened. Besides, early man—like the pioneer buffalo hunters on our American prairies in the West—was a wasteful hunter. When he made a good kill and shot down plenty of beasts, he cut off the very choicest portions only. He took the porter-house and left the rump-steak. In the same way the American buffalo-hunter, after shooting many more of a buffalo herd than he could possibly eat, would merely cut out the delicious tongues, and leave the rest of the body to be picked clean by eagles and hawks. And, just as the buffalo melted away, so must the reindeer herds of the "Reindeer Men"—for the herds that were not eaten "moved on." That was when fishing was taken up very seriously, but it was not enough. Some scientists believe, in a half- hearted way, that just before they disappeared a few of the "Rein- deer Men," with the true cow-boy spirit had managed to "wrangle" some of the bearded ponies. And others say that the glass of Kuy- miss you sip (if you do) in the drug store goes back to the first "Reindeer Man" who milked a mare. But like the vocal cry of the baby crocodile, scientific proof is lacking in these cases.

For something like 20,000 years the "Reindeer Men" hunted and ate their reindeer and bearded ponies (for that is about what the wild "horse" of those days amounted to) and "made out" until the herds thinned and began to move away. They "went in" to quite some extent for "dress" in the sense that the American Indians

I

used to, and painted their bodies red and white, black, crimson, brown and yellow—for though none of their "rouge-sticks" have come down to us, traces of the "rouge" they used have.* And— they lived as happy a life on God's great open spaces of steppe and prairie as circumstances allowed them to. But at the end of that time "something happened." What it was we do not know exactly. But they "faded out." We rub our eyes and—they are gone!

* *They wore not a stitch of clothing* of any kind, any of them, except the bit of skin they flung across their shoulders, which was a mere ornament, like the furs lady readers wear in summer.

CHAPTER XXII

OVER THE EDGE OF THE WORLD

(Intermission)

NATURE beckoned to the caption-writer and he followed her beck. "There is an honest-to-goodness break—a break of about 5,000 years—between the age of the *Reindeer Men* (the men of the "Old Stone Age") and the *Neolithic Men* (the men of the "New Stone Age") so an intermission surely seems in order. Besides, there are a few things about the 'Reindeer Men' and their disappearance that are easier told than screened.

"In the old, old days when *everyone thought the world was flat* and the Church threatened to put the great astronomer Galileo *to the torture* for saying *it was round,* the general idea was that when you came to 'the edge of the world,' you just walked off into space—that is, unless you watched out where you were going!

"And, in a way, the 'Reindeer Men' we have just seen seem to have come pretty close, as close as any one ever has, to walking 'over the edge of the world.' We find their eoliths and their weapons, the bone-piles that show what good feasts they had at the 'annual tribal dinners.' We find their drawings, and even the bone needles the Reindeer ladies used, and the skin flaps, mantlets and tippets they wore as they went about in 'native worth and honor clad.' But we do not know what became of them.

"No one 'shot them up' as they did the Neanderthal Men. They simply seem to have disappeared. We must remember one great fact about the primal dusk: that *it was a very twilight time indeed.* Many scientists have devoted their lives to this shadowy age of the past, and yet it is not possible to speak with absolute certainty (as is explained in the next 'Tangled Trails' picture) about the movements of the tribes and races which have wandered since 50,000 years ago, toward history's dawn over the wildernesses of Asia, Europe and Africa.

"And this very fact is what makes a 'Romance' of Evolution possible. The great main lines of Evolution's story stand out clear and strong, for every one to read. But we are continually running across the most interesting little mysteries. The scientific 'lights go out,' and when they are turned on again the world has changed, and we find we have to shake hands with a brand new race of early brothers.

"There is one theory which I rather like myself," Nature went on with a wink, "because it is *romantic!* I see in my mind's eye the horde of 'Reindeer Men' drawn further and further across the mid-European plains. The old 'annual camp-ground' gradually gets too far away to travel back to, and is abandoned. Why? Because the Reindeer Men must follow their food. And the herds, the great herds they have been slaughtering for so many thousands of years have at last 'taken the hint.' They have given up their old grazing grounds. Before the arrows of the 'Reindeer Men' they are drifting, drifting, on and on and on, west and north, ever west and north! The 'Reindeer Men'—who cannot live by fish alone—follow after them. And the great herds of reindeer and wild horse, of bison and wild ox, keep drifting across a sunny Siberia, on and on and on, to where the great land bridge connects Asia and North America, unbroken by Behring Strait. A slowly moving panorama of vast shaggy beast bodies and wild, hairy red- and yellow-painted huntsmen, they move on into the continents of mystery, and are lost to sight as the centuries close in behind them. They pass 'over the edge of the world,' and I like the picture, for it leaves the imagination leeway to think of what they may have done in their new home. They were 'True Men,' they were the dominant race, a white race . . . I see the ruined glories of Maya temples, the silvery towers of Mexico, the golden pavilions of Peru . . . the future stretches wide before them!

"Nobody knows, for instance, exactly *who* or *what* the savage islanders of Terra del Fuego, down at the end of South America, near the Antarctic pole, are? No one can tell from what race they sprang. Did the 'Reindeer Men,' tracking their vanishing herds down to the very edge of the Antarctic waters in the course of the centuries, follow them till they could go no further?

"Or again, perhaps, they balked at the land bridge, and managed to stay in the Asian plains and 'carry on' there. It seems as though some of the Reindeer folk stayed on in Europe—and that some of their blood still runs in European veins. The early Mongolian races are blood-brothers to the gibbon, but they also have a strain of this Reindeer blood, here and there. From them may have sprung the Aztecs. But I think that this first race of 'True Men' did cross 'over the edge of the world,' and that their blood has been handed down to the native Indian races of the North American continent.

"But in that 'Intermission' five thousand years long which came after the 'Reindeer Men's' time, when because of the great lakes the melting ice left in the lower lands the forests spread out and covered most of the great plains again, the shadowy 'People of the Painted Pebbles,' the *Azilians*,* drift into earth-life. Reindeer and mammoth had turned away to the Siberian plains, the first beast-race to live, the second to die out utterly. But in a great 'wave of life' the red deer came down into Europe to take the place of the reindeer and pony herds that had gone. And the deer grew and increased in the forests and it was in the forests that the 'People of the Painted Pebbles' lived.

"Truly has King Solomon said: 'There is nothing new under the sun.' Even in the serious business of developing the human race," continued Nature, "I could stop for a moment, to establish a 'new first time' record. Scientists are a serious race. Many of them hold that the pretty 'painted pebbles' of the 'Stag-Folk'—as the 'People of the Painted Pebbles' are also called, because they hunted and ate the red forest deer—was to 'make magic.' But this is not proven. The 'painted pebbles' of the Azilian folk seem like *Nature's earliest Mah-jong set!* They are small, rounded pebbles painted with bands and stripes, but with a greater variety of little 'letter-like' designs than the Mah-jong counters show. And with them are the flat bits of bone, painted in the same way.

"One great scientist has a rather grisly explanation for them. He says that the extinct Tasmanians used little stone plates, like them, marked with red and black lines—*and each little stone, thus marked, stood for a dead friend.* But we do not need to believe this, nor the other theory that the 'Stag-Folk' used their pebbles as the Australians do their *churingas,* or 'bull-roarers.' These are small bits of wood, attached to long strings. When the Australians whirl their 'bull-roarers' around their heads, strange, weird, moaning sounds are produced, and these sounds, so the savages say, *are the voices of their dead!*

"No, I like to think," said Nature, "that the 'People of the Painted Pebbles' were a gentle, happy race of forest dwellers. They had harpoons, which show that they fished in the forest streams and lakes. They had stag-horn lance-heads, which showed they hunted. They had awls and needles, which showed that their women, too, wore clothes for decoration if not for covering. But—to me they are *the very first people to bring the idea of pastime, of play, of a human game into the world!* Once early man had caught enough for the morrow's meals, he had all time on his hands. And I see the happy 'People of the Painted Pebbles,' gathered in little groups, in the long, lazy summer after noons, stretched out or squatting down in the forest clearings over the checkerboard of hard, smooth earth

*Named after the Mas d'Azyl, in France, where their painted pebbles were found.

which they may have used for their game, *in the first real development of the spirit of the play known to man.* What if they, too, were not fitted to survive in the contest with stronger races—the fact that they had turned from the flint spear-head to the bone one shows a 'going-back'—after all, they brought the spirit of play, of innocent amusement into the world, with their painted pebbles, a spirit which other human race-strains which probably absorbed the *Azilians,* persisted through all the ages of blood and horror to come."

CHAPTER XXIII

THE TORCH BEARERS OF THE DAWN

AGAIN, as the screen flashes from darkness into light, the great European plains stretch out before us. And again, as before, vast hordes of a new race, fresh human spawn of Nature's Asian nursery moves across them. But we see a difference between these folk and the "Reindeer Men." They are less shaggy—less hairy, and the fact makes them look more human. A few drops, here and there, of the blood of the first "True Men," the "Reindeer Men," probably flows in our veins, but most of it comes from this newfolk—the "Neolithic Men," the "Men of the Later Stone Age." They are probably, before all others, "our own kind" of people so far as blood goes.

These "Neolithic Men" who cross the threshold of the Primal Dusk, are moving out of the night of lowest barbarism and savagery into the faint, grey pallor of the civilization which precedes the Dawn of History. What they manage to "put over" in the five thousand years of time which, roughly speaking, still precedes the Dawn of History—for the Dawn of History does not really begin before the invention of the alphabet and writing makes a fascinating tale. But certain of the things the Neolithic Men "put over" are things which "do not screen," so to speak.

So, while the operator stops grinding out his film, allow the caption-writer to introduce to you an old friend: "Ladies and gentlemen, Dame Nature! Dame Nature would like to give an idea of the Evolution of certain things that were born and developed *out of the original soul-spark,* and to which practically all Man's advancement has been due ever since he *shook off the beast to become a human being!*

SOME REMARKS BY DAME NATURE TO THE AUDIENCE

"Kind audience, there are some things which simply won't screen! Of course, I can (and will) throw on an 'educational,' a chart of the way the human race 'spread itself out' all over the world. But an 'educational' film sounds so *unromantic,* and my great serial is entitled 'The Romance of Evolution!' Besides we know that an 'educational' picture is *not always* 'the spice of the program' for all those words are always flashed when an 'educational' is screened.

"But you must have the 'inside' of these three little stories—about how we came to spread all over the Earth, about how we came to talk, and about how we started to find a god or gods—because you cannot afford not to know! And since they will not screen, I will try to "put over" the three stories as *lectures*. No, not dry ones— but live and 'peppsy' and to the point. So here goes!'"

THE TANGLED RACE-TRAILS OF EARLY MAN

The tangled race-trails of early man are many and dim. We have seen the "Neanderthal Men" driven to take the long trail of the valley of the shadow as the human floods of the first "True Men" came rolling down out of the East. And we have seen the "True Men," the "Reindeer Men," drifting along after the great herds of bison and wild horse "over the edge of the world." And after them the feet of other hordes from Asian and African lands of mystery, the Neolithic peoples, make new rutted trails in the same patient earth.

They are the advance-guards of all the races of mankind which are moving and shifting in great streams over the world. They fight and destroy, or fight and "breed in" with the race they have whipped. But always they are drifting, for their moving trails and hunting trails tell us this. With Neolithic Man the things that hold men down to a certain place come into the world.

In the beginning early man was just early man. But there were "early men"—though we have given our main attention to Europe— wearing the trails of restless feet all over the earth, in the different continents. Yet the men who had come down in the three great early races of blood-brotherhood were meeting and mixing and "blending." This "blending" as we have seen in the case of birds, reptiles and mammals, makes "new breeds," new races. And instead of three or four "kinds" of men, we begin to divide up into many "races."

All "early men" are "early men" to begin with, just as a box of "assorted chocolates and bonbons" is all candy. But, say we have three or four straight or main "kinds" of candy: pure sugar, "black" chocolates, nut and fruit candies, this does not mean that we are tied down to them. No, by "mixing" and "blending" we get *all sorts of new varieties, made up out of the others*. It is as easy to "mix" thirty-one *varieties* of chocolate candies, as it is to "mix" negro (or other) races, for instance, until the same number of kinds results.

With all this mixing came increase in numbers and as climate, need of food or other reasons "set them going," the great waves of human life would rise in the Asian and African breeding-pools, to wear new trails in some one or another direction, to meet and "mix" with other families of men. And through the thousands of years of the world's dusk this shifting and interbreeding of races and tribes went on until all man-kind has become more or less related.

The details of "Who's Who" in this relationship—though scientists have written many books about them—make up the world greatest puzzle. We believe this, and we believe that, but we really do not *know*. Our great picture of these early trailings and interbreedings of the races of men is "blurred," a thing of shadowy shapes, moving in a dim and twilight world.

Naturally we are most interested in our "own kind of peoples," and they are the peoples of the "Caucasian" branch, which we have reason to think has come down through the "Orang-Outang" strain, and gradually has spread over Europe and America from its Asian homelands, where many distant "kin" to us may still live. There are—as a result of the "mixing" process—any number of different kinds of Caucasians: very, very blond and very, very dark; very white-skinned and very brown-skinned, with every kind of difference in nose, feature, build and level of intelligence. But they all are descendants of the Common Ancestor in the one line of descent we already have mentioned. To go into the different classifications of these Caucasian blondes and brunets, to try and explain why each one of their far, far more than "fifty-seven varieties" is thus and so, will lead us nowhere. It is enough to know that of the Neolithic races—we must always remember that they were not *one* race or tribe, but *many,* and that they followed and blazed their tangled-trails in hordes, one horde after another, like wave after wave of the same tide—the true blond, very white-skinned kinds settled, generally speaking, in a more northern belt of lands. The darker and brown-skinned ones, most of them, generally speaking, clung to the more southern European belt of countries; while still other branches spread out into Egypt and India and even may have carried their traits to the shores of the distant Pacific ocean. During five thousand long years of cross-fertilization and cross-breeding of race with race, producing *new races* out of a hundred and one different combinations, Evolution finally "simmered down" to the existing white races of to-day. Climate, food, tribal custom, habits of religious thought, all had their effect on length of leg, and height of cheek-bones, tallness and shortness, shape of skull and size of feet. And always the old ape-strain claimed its rights as well.

In the earlier days we had not drifted so far away from the "brotherhood of man" idea with respect to color. Early man (and sometimes present-day man seems to take the same stand) did not draw a "color line" where sex was concerned. There his trails were very, very tangled. "A woman is only a woman," as Kipling says, would appear to have been his motto, and to borrow another quote, from Emerson, "he hewed to the line and let the chips fly." Some of these human "chips" still show the hereditary ear-marks of those liberal-minded days. There is a touch of the "tar-brush" in various partly Caucasian Asiatic peoples, for instance. But in general the Caucasian races, though they have intermingled thoroughly with each other in all *their own* varieties, have held themselves aloof from the other blood-strains with which the Common Ancestor blessed the earth.

The folk of the Gibbon strain, the Mongol races, the people with yellow skins and straight black hair, after the first great "milling" of the human herds, for the most part settled down in Asia, and perhaps some found their way to the American continents. For it seems that we never really started things "off our own bat" in America, so far as being able to "point with pride," to *a real born-of-the-soil early race of man of our own!* America was settled by emigrants from the very beginning, long before the Irish, the Norsemen, or Columbus discovered our land, and Ellis Island was established. One favorite theory is that the dead and gone peoples who raised the wonderful temples that lie buried under tropical jungles in Yucatan, were descendants of a branch of the great Asian Mongol family of races, the folk of the gibbon strain. Another is that they were Atlantides, an early white race from the buried continent of Atlantis. There are things which seem to prove it, just as they lead us to believe that the Inca people of Peru, who also raised their golden house to the sun-god beneath the snowy mountains around Cuzco may have descended from the same Atlantides and not the early Reindeer Men who drifted "over the edge of the world" on their long trail after the vanishing bison-herds. Perhaps, after an Evolution of centuries, they blossomed out into the golden glory of a civilization so rich and colorful that it is a shame it had to be destroyed through Spanish bigotry and greed, like that of Mexico!

The Neanderthal Men—supposed to be of a European negroid (negro-like) race—disappeared early in the game of "kill or be killed." And though many hold that the primitive and degraded Australian is an early "white brother" gone to seed, the gorilla strain has held its own in darkest Africa and has left traces in various parts of Asia. Owing, perhaps, to some dim blood instinct handed down from the days of the first gorilla and gibbon mothers of the black and yellow races, there seldom seems less "race repulsion" between them than between the white and black races.

Later, the spreading of the gorilla strain even into white veins was made easy by a *thought habit,* a *religious point of view.* This was the doctrine of *Islam,* of the *Koran, which makes all men equals on the basis of its faith!* Among Mohammedan peoples *there is no color line, only a religious line of difference.* It is strong enough to overcome any other feeling or prejudice, and in the East, especially, accounts for *the little bluish circle under the fingernails of Caucasians who have a drop of negro blood in their veins—the one unmistakeable mark of the old gorilla strain,* carried down from the jungle mother of the past. Hands and face, body and hair may be Caucasian; everything may be white about a person. But the *one drop of the black strain* will persist, *for heredity claims its own!* In the same way the so-called *"Mongolian eye-fold"* goes with the *drop of Mongol blood* in Caucasian veins.

There are many mysteries in connection with these tangled early race-trails which never have been solved. There are traces which rose to a high level in the arts and pleasures of life, and built great cities and monuments of stone, with temples and palaces, toward the end of the Neolithic times, and which have vanished so completely that we can only guess what they were or from whence they came. Cities of stone lie covered with the rank growth of African jungle associated with dim legends of a vanished "white race." Gigantic ruins and monumental pillars erected to gods whose memory has perished with the race which worshipped them, rise on lonely South Sea islands, and Science is at a loss to explain them. The lifeless stones which have outlasted the many, many generations of living creatures still hold their secret, which only the lazy blue swells which have been rippling along the same silent white sands for thousands of years could disclose!

All these tangled "race-trails" which once crossed and crisscrossed in the great dim open of the early past breathe the romance, the sadness of all things which have passed forever. In our own land and time, almost within the memory of living generations, we have seen the rutted "race-trails" of our own "Forest Indians," worn deep by the tread of thousands of mocassined feet covered by farms and cities, buried under hay-fields, orchards and pastures, or seas of brick and stone. They lie deep down, beneath steel rails and trolley tracks, dispersed by the sewer- and gas-pipes, and the hundred and one underground appliances of modern man. Now and then one survives, like the famous "Mohawk Trail," coated with macadam, as part of a "state road," to serve the autoist. And the wheels of progress skid along at the rate of thirty miles an hour where painted "braves" held to the steady jog-trot of their war or hunting "hikes." Our ancient Indian trails ran from the Canadas to the Mississippi and on down to the sea, linking the life of the tribes from the Seminole swamps to the Athabascan lakes. Yet if it is hard, even with written records to help us, to trace the ancient trails of this great family of tribes, the "forest Indians," the difficulty of tracing the tangled trails of the early folk in the thousand of years which preceded History's Dawn, is a thousand times harder.

The tangled trails of the early races are like the beast-trails of the ages before man. Many trails were worn in the patient earth by the races and tribes of beasts, by reptiles and mammals. The fittest to survive still follow the new trails which have branched out of the old ones, and have led them to their highest point of separate race development. Other trails by the thousands have been "washed out" in the sands of time by the waves of race-death: their makers were unfit, in some way or another, unable to compete with other life, or they were swept off by disease.* Again, other forms of early life walk the trail of their own "blind alley," through some freak of Evolution, as they did millions of years ago. Among them is the Newfoundland newt or salamander which is as old as the first Amphibian, and the Australian duck-billed mole, which goes back to the day of the first mammal.

And so it is with the races of men. Out of the crossings of the tangled trails of all the continents the civilized peoples of to-day represent the survival of the fittest feet. All along the line tribes and races have been dying out, from the Neanderthal Man to the Tasmanians; or have been "taken up" in the "race body" of other conquering nations, as the Assyrians were absorbed by the Persians in the early days of History. And still others, like the primitive savage peoples of to-day, keep on in their own treadmill, living the life of fifteen or twenty thousand years ago, *bits of a dead past, still "carrying on" in the midst of a living, twentieth century world!* We will return to these early peoples of the Stone and Neolithic Ages, who still linger among us—though they are dying out like the duck-billed mole and kangaroo—in the "Romance of Life Through the Ages"—people like the Eskimo, the Terra del Fuegians, the Weddah of Ceylon and others. The thing to remember is that *their continued* existence *does not disprove the law of the survival of the fittest.* They simply take a longer time dying, owing to the fact that they live in the waste places of the earth where civilized man, because of climate and other reasons, does not bother them. Yet they are passing, and the day will come when their trails are

---

*Most of us may not know that disease has not been on earth a long time, *relatively* speaking—only about 25,000,000 out of a possible 100,000,000 years. Scientific investigation has reached this conclusion. It is pleasant to think that some 25,000,000 years ago *there was no disease in the world.*

dead trails like all others made by naked feet in the age of the auto and the railroad.

For the great law of Evolution always works out in the same way. When an inferior race, man or beast—no matter what its particular degree of advancement may be—is brought into the presence of a superior one, and has to compete with it—it dies out. The civilization of the ancient Aztecs was romantic and colorful. Its great shrines gleamed with jewelled, barbaric idols. A people in love with love, laughter and war, with the musical chiming of silver bells, blossoming flowers and glorious feather-dresses of humming-birds' wings. The Aztecs yet waded ankle-deep in the horrid blood-stream of human sacrifice. But color and romance fell before the Spanish sword, as did the gentler culture of the Incas, with its golden temples and its fountained palaces of white-robed sun-virgins. Our own North American Indians practically have died out where they have not been absorbed by the stronger Caucasian blood. Everywhere the weaker race dies out, and fades away before the stronger, the one *fitter to survive*.

Beast has changed to man, man has split up into thousands of families and clans of human beings. But they are still subject to the one great *law of survival,* modified by the *law of natural selection* which "breeds in" their own special race "points," and the *law of heredity* which hands them on to the coming generations. And that is the main thing to remember about the tangled early "race-trails"—that they lead to the same goal, to which all Evolution has led and still leads!

When the Dawn of History begins to brighten, "dark" or "brunet" *white races* are to be found in Northern Africa (the early Egyptians), along the Mediterranean coasts—Italy and Spain—as far as India (Dravidians). Mongol races swarm in the interior of Asia and are established in the river-valleys of Asia Minor (Summerians). In inland Europe, ranging from the inland lakes (Switzerland, etc.) where the "Lake Dwellers" built their houses in the waters, the "blond" or "Nordic" white races stretched up and on into the frozen Scandinavian north. In their African "back country" lurked great, swarming black tribes. This is where the great "world hike" of the tangled trails of early man seems to have brought the main groups of races.

CHAPTER XXIV

"OUT OF THE FULNESS OF THE HEART. . ."

THERE is no truer word in the Bible than the saying: "Out of the fulness of the heart the mouth speaketh!" For out of early man's need, his urge, his necessity, to make his own meanings clear to others—in other words, "out of the fulness of his heart"—his tongue learned to talk. But not all at once. Spoken language, like everything else, went through its many centuries of Evolution before it really could be called "speech."

The beasts talked long before man. *All beasts have a "language" of their own!* We already have seen how the mammoths had developed their language of trumpet-signals and trunk-gestures. And if we care to watch the animals about us to-day we actually can "see" them talk. Take a dog's tail. It can express all sorts and shades of meaning, from deep affection to rage. He has friendly "play" growls, and "the real thing" at his throat's end, and he can express our phrase, "angry beyond words," in the silent but understandable language of biting jaws. Ants and other insects talk to each other by means of their "feelers." Birds have a variety of notes: chatter and gossip-notes, plaint-notes, mourning-notes, joy-notes, signal cries to set the flock in movement, and the "song without words" of their mating-time. Horses and cattle "converse"* by rubbing nostrils, lowing and neighing.

The apes go a step further. Our own American ape-professor, Mr. Garner, has proved that the gorilla and chimpanzee each has about 20 actual word-sounds at its disposal and uses them daily, though it helps itself along with all sorts of signs and gestures. Interesting in connection with the birth of "speech" is the fact that the *gibbon is the only one among the apes which can "sing!"* Of course, it takes a great professional naturalist to say, as one of them has done, that the song of the gibbon *"charmed him."* If they sang as well as that, we would long since have had "gibbon choruses" singing "be-

---

*The most "tongue-tied" man has reason to pride himself on his advance if he compares himself with the lower forms of life. It is estimated that hens and pigeons each have a "language" of about 12 sounds; dogs (aside from their "tail-words") have 15 different sounds to express meanings; cattle and horses run to 22—*but even the most word-poor man has 300 words at his disposal.*

168

hind the scenes" in musical comedies while the chorus-girls without voices let the silent language of their limbs speak "the fulness of their hearts." But it is a scientific fact that a gibbon in the London Zoological Gardens has been heard to sing *a regular chromatic scale,* beginning with the fundamental E, and going up a full octave. The idea has been expressed that the love-songs the gibbon sings to its mate in its leafy bower *prove the existence of vocal chords inherited from the Common Ancestor of both gibbon and man, and that man, at last, developed this "singing voice" into a "speaking, voice."*

This theory, that speech was developed out of song, is not unreasonable. The first rude attempts at speech on man's part may very likely have been "sing-song" cries, running up and down the scale of vocal sounds, and gradually being chopped off into special "root-word sounds." But earlier than any speech save grunts and cries, must have been the mute language of signs or gestures. *A few signs would explain of the very earliest man's dim mind-pictures;* a pointed finger, a clenched fist, even a shrugged shoulder—we use them to-day, just as we did, perhaps, when we bade our mate good-bye with a wave of the hand, as we swung over the edge of our tree-nest and shinned easily down some fifty feet of trunk.

But "spoken" language itself was "long a-coming." It grew very, very slowly out of the life of family and clan. All first words were *fact words*—and had to do with facts. The theory advanced by some scientists, (we cannot believe they are serious) that woman's desire to "have the last word" had much to do with bringing about the development of human speech, has not been proved. Spoken language grew slowly because early man expressed himself *in motion rather than in words.* The dramatic moments of his life were "acted out," in big tribal dances: there were hunting dances, in which he pantomimed his triumphs as a killer of big game in "motion," better than he could have "told" them in speech. There were mating-dances and sex-dances, in which action and gesture expressed the inexpressible so clearly and artlessly that with all the words at our disposal, modesty (as we understand it) forbids our even attempting to describe what these dances "said." There were religious dances and funeral dances and pantomimes, which with cries and drum-beat made words unnecessary to express their meaning.

Yet, little by little, more and more words, in every tribe and race of men, were added to the existing stock. Perhaps the *Neanderthal Man* went the gorilla ten or fifteen words better, and gradually progressed to fifty or seventy-five of the simplest sound-words, each standing for some idea having to do with the practical things of life: food, beasts hunted, etc. And this word-stock *Neolithic Man* may have increased until he was the pround possessor of something like eight-hundred or a thousand words—"down on the farm" in Europe, Poland, Russia, Hungary and other lands, the simple peasant has not many more this very day!

And, in somewhat the same way that Evolution works in other fields, it seems to have worked with regard to language. In a broad general way, "speech" has developed in four big "groups" with all sorts of "original" or "primal" tongues that do not fit into any of the "big" four. Race development is a matter of blood, of how the race-blood expresses itself in body and appearance. Language is a matter of brain, of how the brain thinks. Because, if you get right down to it, *the sound part of language, speech, is just a "medium" to put across the idea behind it,* and so, in a way, the matter of language gets back to race and blood again, for *the races which have a common blood-stock have the same general way of thinking and expressing their thoughts. They think along the same lines.*

Down in the bed-rock of their grammar, their sounds, and "the way they put ideas," the way the words that stand for the thoughts are "hitched" together in sentences, the way the different "parts of speech" are fitted to each other, *the way the people that use them think*—certain big groups of languages are alike. The most important is the *Aryan* (Indo-European) "bunch of languages." Probably, when spoken language really began to "shape-up," it went hand in hand with "sign language."* And how important sign language was, is proved by the elaborate systems earlier man must have thought out in the course of time, and which primitive peoples still use.

Sign-language came before speech-language. It means expressing ideas by a crude outline gesture. Before they could "talk," the North American Indians, from Baffins' Bay to the Gulf of Mexico, had a

---

*A "language-map" would show it covering most of Europe, and reaching out to India. No matter how different English, German, Dutch, the three Scandinavian tongues, French, Spanish and Italian, Greek, Russian, Bulgarian, Armenian, Persian and the Indian languages derived from the Sanskrit *sound, look, speak or read,* they belong, in a very broad way, *to races whose minds when they think work the same way.* They are all sound-variations and word-variations of *a same, identical habit of using the brain in thinking.*

In the later days of the Neolithic peoples, the far-away ancestors of a Frenchman and a Bulgarian might have had a pleasant chat about an ivory carving or a "trade deal," and each have understood every single word the other said, *because the old, original Aryan root-language* had not yet "split up" into branches. But—that was a long time ago—five or six thousand years at least. The fact remains that most of these languages of the Ayran bunch are Caucasian root-languages, and are used by the blond white (Nordic) races.

"standardized" sign language which all the tribes understood. Our Boy Scout "smoke signals" are a survival of the "smoke language," which came with the invention of fire. *Smoke columns* and the way the smoke was made to move and rise sent "wordless messages" over great distances in early days. *Bone whistles* and *"whistle-talk"* came in with later Neolithic Man. To this day the islanders of Gomera and the negro tribes on the Atlas-rim of the Sahara Desert use their hunting-pipes or whistles to have a "chat," miles away, and exchange *whole sentences,* using a separate note for each syllable, across long distances. The happy Neanderthaler or other primitive who first knew the delight of drawing a booming sound from a hollow tree-trunk was the "man behind" the drum. *Drum-langauge* is still an important one among the Stone Age people living at the present day. It has been worked out into an elaborate system of *"drum telegrahy"* by some African tribes. In Kamerun, for instance, the drum sends tribal calls, war-signals, important news and ordinary "gosip" over long distances. *Science blushed* when she made her pains-taking records of what the "drum language" of the simple African had developed by way of *"swear"* and *"cuss"* words! The *Finger-talk* of the Australian anticipates the elaborate systems of finger-language used by our deaf mutes of to-day.

But sign-language is limited: word language can express anything. So it forged ahead. The trails of early languages are as tangled as those of race. Besides the Aryan languages mentioned there is a "bunch" of languages of the Keltic peoples, usually "hung on to" the Aryan group like an appendix. And, like an appendix, they seem to have out-lived their practical usefulness. At a Welsh Eistedfodder, in the Scotch highlands, or in remote Irish of Breton (France) rural districts, there may linger a few old men or women who speak some Keltic tongue. But even in Ireland, where independence has given "the good auld tongue" a new lease of life, the rich Keltic brogue will probably keep on lending flavor and strength to the spoken English word. *The Irish always will be able to use English without giving any one the idea that they think from the same angle an Englishman does!*

The language groups known as the *Semitic* and the *Hamitic* are also mainly "white folks talk" languages. Some of the Semitic languages have faded out with the tongues that spoke them: the languages of the Babylonians, the Assyrians, the Phoenicians and other peoples of history who have "gone West." The chief ones that have lived through to to-day are: Arabic, Syrian, Abysinian and Hebrew (with its large family of "Yiddish" dialects). Speaking broadly the Semitic languages are the languages of the early "water-front" peoples of the Mediterranean. *But the way the brain works behind their words, seems to prove that they go back to other non-Aryan races of the early Neolithic* world, which developed their own ways of thought and speech *away from the bigger bunch of the Aryan white peoples!*

Languages are like races of beasts and of men. They seem to have shaped up, at times, out of race-combinations. That is why, in every big language-group, we have all sorts of special "thought-kinks," due to crossing of thought-strains. In a broad, underlying way for instance, an Englishman and a Russian may get a certain idea by the same process of reasoning. But each one has so many race-angles—added one by one, the way a diamond cutter puts a new "facet" on a diamond—that *when they get the thought into language,* it will "come out" altogether different in each case. The *Hamitic* languages have their *quick* (Modern Coptic, Berber, Galla and Somali) and their *dead* (ancient Egyptian, ancient Coptic, Lydian) the tongue of the people of King Croesus, (one of history's earliest multimillionaires). Etruscan (the language of the race which lived in Italy before the Romans came), and the vanished Ethiopian tongues. In the main, the races which speak Hamitic languages are Caucasians, and the Hamitic group probably developed off by itself at the same time as the Semitic group did, or even earlier.

The great group of *Turanian or Mongol Languages* is a very tangled one. There are *dead tongues* of the early Turanian (Mongol) days: Sumerian and Accadian, the languages of the older people who lived in Mesopotamia before the Semitic races got the better of them and "took them in." And there are a multitude of *living Mongol tongues,* of which Chinese,* and its branches are probably the most important. A "bunch" of these Mongol languages (which have been called Uralian or Altaic) include the Manchu dialect (the language of the Tartar conquerers of China), Turkish, Kurdish, the Kalmuck and Tartar dialects, Magyar, (Hungarian, for the Mongol strain in the modern Hungarian race shows in language

---

*Chinese, Burmese, Thibetan, Siamese, Annamite, Cambogdian, Korean and perhaps Japanese, are "one-syllable" languages. They vary a single syllable to express many ideas; we find new syllables for new ideas. *They show the deep gulf which yawns between the way in which the Caucasian and the Mongolian races think!* And this *difference* between the kinds of languages is very interesting because it gets at the *rock-bottom difference* between the white and the yellow race. The white race is ever developing, ever improving, ever going on. It stands for continual movement and progress in every field of human activity. The yellow race, generally speaking, develops and improves—*up to a certain point.* Then it stops. When a certain point of development is reached the Mongol goes no further. He represents *a clinging to the past.* The white races represent a *moving toward* the future. The Mongol races have originated many things—gunpowder, for instance—they never have developed them to their limit of development. That has been the work of the white races.

as well as in other things), the tongues of the Samoyeds, the Finns and the Lapps.

The tongues of gorilla-land are tangled to an extent which is only to be compared with the race-varieties of its inhabitants. What adds to the confusion is the fact that there is hardly any written language in darkest Africa, language exists only in the spoken form, though some dialects have been reduced to a system by missionaries. The *Bantu* languages form the biggest group. As might be expected they betray how the negro brain (its development is stopped when the child passes into the adult stage by the pressing down of the *frontal skull bone*) works out its limited range of thought. Of course, the "African" dialects of the American negro, the Negroid French of Haïti and Creole Louisiana, and the Negroid Spanish of certain other islands, are not original Negro tongues. They simply give the negro an opportunity to use a tongue which is understood. *He thinks in the same way in other words.*

And now come the languages with question-marks. Everything in the world comes from somewhere, and it stands to reason that these languages must have had a root, a race-root or a tribe-root language, out of which they grew. But it seems to be a question of "Where, oh where, is my little dog gone?" No one can tell how certain "little dogs" of human speech strayed away from their original masters, who have passed out of life and history. They have left them behind, with their "tail" (where it was separated at the root-end) "cut short," begging to be told "how come" they are left stranded without any respectable big group language to tie up with.

The mysterious *Basque** race (which has supplied excellent thrifty and industrious sheep-herders to the American West) lives on amid surrounding Spanish peoples in a province of Spain. It has been supposed, vaguely, once upon a time, to have been perched up in the Caucauses Mountains. The Basques *may*, in language and blood, be distant relatives of the earliest races of India. They *may* come from an early Neolithic race which worked out a "language" before the ancient Egyptians and other Hamitic races set up their own kind of speech. Their language *may* be connected with our American Indian tongues, another "question-mark" group of languages. It merely shows that language-trails are as tangled as race one.

Beautiful and highly developed languages like that of the ancient Mexicans, and the poetic Quichua tongue of Peru, hang suspended

---

* Our own preference is that the Basque language like that of the earliest Egyptians, the Etruscans, the Berbers, and, perhaps, the Maya and Quichua (Peruvian Inca) tongues are off-shoots like those who spoke or speak than of the Neolithic Caucasian inhabitants of Atlantis, the Lost Continent.

in the scientific twilight of doubt, together with the Hottentot's simple speech, and such primitive things as the Papuan dialects of the New Guinea savage. Australian, Terra del Fuegian and Eskimo —tongues without a future—are still as baffling as the beautiful and expressive Iroquois languages of the "Six Nations," of our forest Indians. We may think this or the other, but we cannot take away the question-mark from the language, until we take it away from the origin of the first men who spoke it.

As in the case of the tangled trails of the human races, we can fix on an outstanding fact amid the tangled trails of the world's languages. Out of the fullness of man's heart he found speech. Little by little, by the law of Evolution, speech improved and developed. Like the mammals developed out of the reptiles, a "body" of simple speech grew out of the simplest sound-words. Then, as the many different races of early man came into being four or five great "group languages" were developed. And then, as the races kept on splitting up into an increasing number of tribes and nations, *though the way of thinking behind each big language group stayed the same,* the groups themselves, like the people who spoke the languages, split up into different speech-kinds, and became so different in course of time that (unless they "learned" it) the folk of one race could not understand the speech of another.

Besides this, just as in the vegetable and animal kingdoms we have race-crossings and race-marriages, we have *"speech-crossings"* and *"speech-marriages"* and as a result, new languages that have inherited the speech-souls of both parents. And languages, like races of men and beasts, die out and are forgotten. They are a part of the race which speaks them: with the race they live or die; they survive or perish. Owing to the fact that when civilization drew a deep breath after the dark "Middle Ages," and started all over again, it based its progress on the dead civilizations of Greece and Rome, these languages have survived—after a curious fashion. Thousands of young men and women painfully learn them in college, in order to forget them as soon as they leave the halls of learning. Their real life lies in the *"roots"* they have furnished the French, Spanish and Italian tongues of to-day.

Modern man gains great advantages from the study of "living" languages. First, *there is a strictly practical gain when travelling in the land in which a language is spoken.* Then, there is the fact that a knowledge of their language makes it possible *to read the great books written by the best brains of the race which speaks the language.* And third, it gives the man who learns it *an insight into the way the brain of the other race works.* It lets him see how the brain-wheels go around, and the little cogs on which they catch.

There is a good deal of truth in the idea that every language you add to those you already know *gives you another self!*

Out of the tangled early trails of language has come the order and beauty of all the living tongues, the result of their Evolution, the sum total of the survival of the tongues best fitted to be spoken by the race using it, and constantly growing as new thoughts bring out new words to express them. The long trail of spoken languages leads from the first pointed finger, accompanied by a grunt, of the Neanderthal Man, to the moral maxims of Confucius, the Arabian Nights, the Gettysburg Address—and beyond!

CHAPTER XXV

GROPING FOR GOD AND FINDING A SNAKE

THE first chapter in the religions of all early peoples is the same for one as for the other. We have seen that even the Neanderthal Man, by the way he buried his dead, showed that somehow, he was dimly groping toward a belief in something bigger, better and more permanent than man himself—something divine, a god!

Primitive religions, before the dawn of history are like a string of the same kind of beads. In other words, when early man first began groping for God,* he groped about in the same way all over the earth. The successors of the Neanderthal Man, the "Reindeer Men," showed the same respect for their dead, and everywhere the custom of laying them piously to rest, together with objects dear to them in life, means some kind of faith in a life beyond the grave, and in a power *stronger* than man.

Groping about for this stronger and higher power began when man started to "think about himself." The Hindoos say: "Only a snake can see a snake's legs," and that is one of the difficulties in explaining the groping of early man for God. The only one who really could explain it (if he could speak) would be early man. But still we may get a fair idea of how he went about it.

The soul-spark of early man was only a very feeble spark of a soul. Like a little boy who has run wild and untaught, early man had to build him a god out of his own mind, and the better the brain that built, the better the god turned out to be. Early man lived in *acting,* not in *thinking.* The more active you are physically the less time or inclination you have to think, so the god-groping was slow work. When he did grope, early man was moved by two big levers: *fear* and *rage.* He treated the god or the gods he had made in his mind just as he would treat some other human being—for he had nothing but human beings to go by.

If he was afraid of him he "prayed" and "made up to him" with

*One distinguished authority has tried to prove that all religion, literally speaking is "based on booze." He claims that religious thought first started in Western Asia with the rendering of divine honors to anything with "an alcoholic kick" in it (the scientific phrase is "the deification of intoxicants"), *and that then religion spread rapidly in all directions!*

176

gifts and sacrifices. If he did not fear him, but still thought he could "get something out of him," he threatened and abused him. It all depended on the particular kind of god or gods he had "made up."*

We do not have to "feel" God *through our senses.* Early man had actually to *feel, see,* or *hear,* his god or gods—and he did. The lightning, the thunder, the moon, the stars, the sun, the physical powers of Nature were gods to him. Some of the early man races had no other god than "evil spirits," like the New-Holland savages of to-day. And, in spite of his dim belief in a hereafter of some kind, early man's whole religion was based on *life not death.* So he gave everything a "life," a "living soul" of its own, and found it possible, in course of time, to collect a strange assortment of gods. He turned all sorts of natural influences into gods or evil spirits: cholera, small-pox, a river-flood, even (as the old Hindoos did) *drum and plow, inanimate objects, made by himself.* Almost anything, in fact, did for a god in the early days before man had a choice of all the many forms of belief we now enjoy, each of which calls itself "the true faith."

Early man also was still in "close touch" with the beasts. Only a few hundreds of thousand years, perhaps, separated him from the great apes, and he often could "talk their language" better than his own. Of course, he thought, "they have a soul just like I do." *And so his gropings led him to beast-gods.* Sometimes he even thought that the soul of his kin went into the spirit of some beast or bird. If you are a Toda, in India to-day, you would not think of eating your tame buffalo: it might be uncle or, maybe, aunty. If you were a Hottentot, however, you would never even be tempted—their god is a caterpillar! Cattle, horses (as spirits of the corn), hawks, fish, goats —there is a tribe of African *goat-worshippers* to this day!—crows, hares, dogs, monkeys and sheep all have come in for early religious honors. And to this day the people of Siam baptize and bury a white elephant as we would a highly respected clergyman, for—*the beast's body might contain the soul of a Buddha!*

Naturally man's *fear,* already mentioned, played a part in this *choice of animal gods.* The more dangerous the beast the more respected and holy it was. The leopard ranked high, and some African tribes still put a man to death for "sacrilege" if he kills a leopard.

---

*In some ways our minds have the same "kinks" which those of the early man did. When our tribal or national chief dies, though we may have been bitterly opposed to all he did and said and thought, we do not "make a god" of him, but we often get quite near doing so. Early man simply went one step further. When the Old Man or chief of his tribe died, he forgot and forgave all his sins. The dead man took on increased strength and importance and—least he return from the land of souls and do some damage—he worshipped after death the owner of the brutal hand which struck him to the ground while alive.

But higher than all, higher than leopard, bear, lion or tiger was the *serpent, the snake.* The snake was what early man, had he had our advantages, would have called: *"Some god!"*

As we know, even the darkened brains of the mammals were able to hold *race memory pictures,* dim traditions of their own past race life, and hand them on to their children. Coming through the Common Ancestor of men and apes, it almost seems as though the mind of early man, traveling dark roads of recollection, *went back to his reptile ancestors—the great snakes, lizards and reptile monsters,* some rare specimens of which may have lingered on into his own day, in Asia or Africa!

Everywhere in the early world—among the Neolithic European and Asian tribes, among the early Dravidians of India and the Malays of Central America—*snakes and serpent-gods were worshipped, usually in connection with the sun! Groping for God had found a snake!* Even to-day (as will be discussed in its proper place) in some parts of the world he clings to the snake-gods his ancestors found. Our own early Indians called the Milky Way "the path of the serpents." The serpent god of the Samoans connects heaven, the sun's house, and earth. The sun and serpent worship of ancient Babylon and Peru, the sun-gods of early Egypt, were given them by Neolithic man. Treading the tangled trails of the world he brought the snake he had found while groping for god to these lands.

The snake's long life and its habit of changing its skin made early man connect it in his thought with a life after death, and the rising of the soul from the dead. The snake stood for strength and power. It was a child of the sun: early man thought of the two together, and the Neolithic peoples, from Egypt to distant Scandinavia, before the Dawn of History, had reached the point where they could make metal images of sun-disks and of sun-"boats" expression religion in ornament. The chiefs and leaders of the tribes boasted that they were children of the great serpent, or children of the sun, or both. Two main ideas in all this early religious groping stand out. The first is the idea of *life*—expressed by snake and sun in all sorts of religious dances and dance-pantomimes.

It seems strange that to-day the most sacred and the most profane ideals seem to meet in the dance. The Aleuts of Kamtschatka, among the lowest savages perhaps, in the world, who have hardly any religious notions of any kind, *do c*arry out a solemn sacred dance, naked, in the snow, with as much devotion as the religious "dancers" in the Cathedral of Seville go through a "sacred dance" the early Christian church inherited from early pagan days, a dance which probably went back to Neolithic times. But Aleuts and altar-boys dance with sincere religious devotion. And on the one hand we have these *sacred dances,* and on the other we have the present-day musical comedy, *the height of the profane!* In the modern dance the holy and what one might call the "unholy meet. For instance, we have sacred (?) "Eurythmic" dances in a *Christian church, in New York, while the "Follies of 1925" are running, a few avenues away!*

Early man did not "mix his dances." His dancing was *all* more or less "religious," because it had to do with the serious business of life. *Life,* for early man as for ourselves, usually began with *birth.*

And, as innocently as the peacock or the ruffled grouse goes through with its mating-dance, early man went through with his. It was a *sun-dance,* for the sun is the lord and inspirer of fertility, it is the sun-god who makes things grow and bear fruit. Dancing itself is one of the things men always have done by "instinct": it is one of the first human "instincts," *borrowed from older forms of animal* life. And this "instinct" man combined with other natural instincts—*with his sincerest religious feelings*—to express in a simple, devout way the great events of his life. All the old nature and life dances of early man would now be called "obscene," though they were not danced in that spirit. They were rude pantomime representations of the relations between the sexes which, before modesty* came into the world, were freer and more "true to life" than pen can paint or word can tell.

Pierre Loti, however, one of the masters of modern French prose, has given us a word-picture of an African *bamboula, a clear yet decent* word-painting of a great religious life and nature dance which he witnessed. We need only transfer it from the Africa of to-day to Neolithic Europe, from black to white "nature worshippers," to have a good idea of what a great sun- and snake-dance was like in the days when Man first "got religion."

"*Anamalis fobil!* howl the *Griots* (the minstrels who play guitars made of snakes' skins), striking their tam-tams, their eyes inflamed, their muscles tense, their body running with sweat.

"And everyone repeats frenetically, clapping their hands: *Anamalis fobil! . . . Anamalis fobil! . . . a translation of the phrase would burn this page!—Anamalis fobil!* the leading-note and the refrain of a devilish song, a song possessed, drunken with ardor and license—the song of the *bamboulas* of spring. . . .

"*Anamalis fobil!* It is the howl of unbridled desire, of negro pith and strength overheated by the sun to torrid hysteria. It is the halleluliah of negro love, the hymn of seduction sung as well by nature, by the air, by the earth, as by the plants, by the perfumes.

"In the *bamboulas* of springtide the young men mingle with the

---

*The idea of modesty formed in the oyster of mental life only too often (*even to-day*) is a compromise: it suggests Mark Twain's description of the man who seeing an immodest dance in Paris blushed and put his hands over his face, but *peeped through his fingers!*

young girls who have just assumed, with great pomp, their nubile costume, and to a mad rhythm, to insensate notes, they all sing, dancing on the sand: *Anamalis fobil!"*

We can see the sun-god's rude stone altar, the great black python fed by priests raising its huge flat head and darting out its forked tongue while the dance of life goes whirling around it!

But we must remember that early man was *sincere* in these indecent religious dance-dramas of his courtship and marriage, these sun-dances in which (as the Australians do in the Corroborree) he did his best to dance "the truth and nothing but the truth" as he knew it.

Yet these early god-seekers'* the Neolithic men, went further than the still simpler folk before them in their search for the divine—and fared worse. The dance the naked Aleuts danced in the snows, with masks hiding their faces so that they could not see the ghosts, *was a dance of life.* It was meant to flatter the ghosts, and cause them to *make the women of the tribe more productive.* But Neolithic Man went further. Flattery was not enough—the ghosts, evil spirits or gods must have more—*they must have sacrifice!*

Sacrifice means giving up the thing you love best or the thing which is most valuable to you. Life was the most valuable thing Neolithic Man had—the lives of his children, the lives of his war-captives. *So lives were sacrificed to the snake- and sun-gods to make them kind!*

*Neolithic Man worked out *three ideas* in his religion which still exists in one or another form, in all religion to-day: *Animism*: the idea that the soul lives after we are dead. *Fetichisms* the worship of *things*, dead, inanimate things, thought to have some magic or miraculous virtue, or a sort of soul. (In this connection there is not much difference between the knuckle-bone of a saint and the greasy "bone and rag and hunk of hair" which is the *gris-gris,* or charm of some negro sorcerer: both are *fetiches*). *Magic*: the influencing of gods by all sorts of ceremonies, incantations and gifts (The unjust rich man who has cheated his fellowmen through the week, and is led by a guilty conscience to put an extra large bill in the collection plate on Sunday, is trying to "make magic" just as much as the African witch-doctor who hangs a new fetich on his witch-pole to ward off evil from the tribe). The *Totem, and Totemism* also grew out of Neolithic Man's confused religious thoughts. He imagined the soul or spirit of some ancestor passed into the body of a certain animal—and it always is the *male* ghost which gets to be a spirit, is only human—and this animal is the kindly spirit that watches over him, and those of his blood, his clan. And all the *animal figures or totems* which represent the family societies and the blood-relationships of early Neolithic Man in Asia and in Europe, the totems of our Indian tribes (which divide them into "wolf clan", "beaver clan", bear clan", etc.) and the Alaskan *totem-poles* we see in our museums come from this *totem* idea of Neolithic Man. And—if you get right down to it the *totem-poles* of the dirty, degraded Alaskan Indians, and the splendid coast-of-arms of the royal, princely and aristocratic families of Europe as their *totems* go—stand on the same level!

The truth of the matter was that Neolithic Man suffered from a diarrhoea of ideas. The Reindeer Men who went before him *did not think to any extent*. They did not need to do so. They did their bit of god-groping, got a hazy idea that there were powers of nature more powerful than man; that the soul lived on after death; and that it was wise to bury the body, *and tie it down well,* so that the soul would not come back to disturb the living. And they seem to have let it go at that.

But the brain of the Neolithic Man was bigger, and when he did begin to think it *turned out so many ideas all at once that he grew confused and uncertain.* But, as even in confusion there must be *leaders,* he soon developed the habit—when it came to trying to establish order in his mixed-up religious thoughts—of "letting George do it," "George" in this case being the *witch-doctor,* the *medicine-man,* the *shaman* or whatever name one chooses to give the *first professional religious man, the first priest.* The priest was a *professional* wonder-worker, a magician, so he *must* know what he was about. If he decided the snake-god must have human sacrifices, well —it was hard to lose Nug, the boy was such a strong, sturdy little fellow, and could shoot further and straighter than any of the ten-year olds of the tribe, but—the *expert in religion had spoken, and there was nothing else to do!* Nug would have to be put to the sacrificial knife.

We must not think that all these first professional men of "the early church" were not *sincere.* They, too, were groping for God, even though they had only found the snake! They were as honest in slaughtering their human sacrifices as the Roman Catholic Torquemada and the Protestant Calvin were, when they had people who did not agree with them as to how God should be worshipped burned at the stake. *Even in Neolithic days the road to hell was paved with good intentions.* And in many cases the first professional priests had a kind of double authority: they were *medicine-men* and *chiefs,* they were *magicians* and *leaders,* they were *both priests and kings.**

And, sincere or insincere—whether they beleved in their "stuff" or went through the ceremonies with tongue in cheek, for we know there must have been, among these professional religious men of early times, some who were *cheats* and *fakers*—their idea of blood sacrifice to please the snake-god and sun-god was carried over from the Primal Dusk into History's Dawn. All over the world sun-

---

*We have so many more religions now than we did when the world was young, that it is hard to give an idea of what this meant to the simple Neolithic tribesman. But if the priest of a tribe were, let us say, a Roman Catholic cardinal, a Protestant bishop, and a Jewish rabbi rolled into one and *President of the United States besides,* we can see his word would have some weight.

and snake-god altars were stained with innocent human blood, and reeked with the black smoke of innocent human bodies long, long after the beginning of civilization.

We cannot help but respect the "Reindeer Men." What little brain they had worked to better purpose. They killed—but they killed their game, they killed to *live*. Their big "family reunions" show only the gnawed bones of horse-steaks, not the pitiable childrens' bones of human sacrifice. But the brains of Neolithic Man—god-seeker though he was—ran wild. He killed his own because the wild fancies of his professional religious men said it was a good thing. He slew for the snake's supposed sake, at seedtime and at harvest. The blood ran red from the altars of the sun-gods in three continents whenever the priestly god directed. Men, women and children passed under the knife of sacrifice because the God-groper, with his jumbled mind full of "half-baked ideas," thought he was doing "the right thing."

And with snake-and sun-worship *ritual* came into the world— *solemn, set ways* and manners of doing things, a whole lot of *exact rules* and regulations, about just how *every least little thing* had to be done when drawing near the god, or worshipping him—*to make it absolutely right.*

But, back of the Neolithic God-gropers stand the religiously easier-going "Reindeer Men." Some of their blood also flows in the veins of the races of to-day. And this blood, perhaps, has made itself felt through the centuries—*for there are still two kinds of God-gropers in the world*—and these two kinds have nothing to do with any particular creed or creeds, for *they represent a state of mind,* and may be found among Catholics and Protestants, among Jews and Mohammedans, in any and every church. One kind in religion are those who have the "Reindeer Man's" way of looking at things; the others are those who have the later Neolithic Man's point of view.

The "Reindeer Man" kind of mind *is all for the simple*: a few big, outstanding facts that matter. Usually it does not bother overmuch about its "soul," and is apt to *live its religion, practically, in the deeds and details of its every-day life.*

The later Neolithic Man kind of mind is strong for *form and ceremony.* It likes *rules* and *regulations,* bells, books and candles, color, lights, incense, "frills." It feels that if a candle has not been "blessed" *in just the right way,* with just the right words and gestures, that, somehow or other, its light is dimmer.

The "Reindeer" mind *thinks the light is the main thing;* the Neolithic mind *must have the "blessing."* Both kinds of religious mind have been responsible for cruel and bloody deeds in history. The *simple* mind, which holds only a few big truths, can be as *fanatic* as the *subtle* mind which divides its big truths into thousandfold detail. *Fanaticism*—being so set on *your own idea* of what is the truth in religion or anything else, that you could almost murder the other fellow who does not agree with you—may occur in either kind of mind. A Calvin could burn as well as a Torquemada.

But *both kinds of mind have achieved great and wonderful things in religion.* The "Reindeer" mind has been more apt to do good practically, without much dilly-dallying with forms and ceremonies. The "Neolithic" mind has given religion romance and beauty, all the lovely rainbow things, miracles and wonders, colors and lights. But —as we have seen in the case of the Neolithic God-gropers—it has always, perhaps, had a leaning toward the more *fantastic, the magical, the spectacular.* And with its feeling for set rules and regulations, *it is less inclined to think for itself,* and more inclined to take the say-so of its medicine-man or priest.

You who read, best know whether your mind in religious things, is a "Reindeer" or a "Neolithic" one. In either case, God-groping no longer leads to snake- and sun-gods who demand human sacrifices. That is one outcome of the Evolution of God-groping. Man first groped for God and found a snake. Now, at least, he no longer finds a snake, and all that a snake means, even though he may not find God!

It is interesting to note that in the days of Neolithic Man *the cornerstones of the first church* was laid. For so we may call the circles or lines of rude stone pillars called "stone henges,"and menhirs, found in England, France, Sweden and Denmark: they probably *were the first memorial stones erected* to express reverence to the sun-god by early men,* the first structures raised "to God."

In other ways—many other ways, as we shall see—later Neolithic Man went far beyond the "Reindeer Men," yet—a groping after God which led to a snake, with religious murder of children, bloody human sacrifice, the burying of living wives and slaves with the dead, and similar horrors due to *beginning to think about too many things all at once,* makes a sad though interesting chapter on human religion. But then no beginnings are perfect—for if they were there could be no Evolution!

* But not *always* were these "stone henges raised to a god." The cannibal Fiji-islanders, when "long pig" appeared oftener on their bill of fare than now, liked to put up a "memorial stone" *for every man he had eaten.* One "large eater" could proudly point to 900 such stones. If he had arranged them in a circle (a cromlech, as circles of the stone pillars are called) they might easily have been mistaken for one of these early church enclosures.

CHAPTER XXVI

MARRIAGES NOT MADE IN HEAVEN

(An Intermission)

NATURE had drawn the caption writer aside after her last "lecture." While the organist (who knew what was in her mind) played a combination of the "Lohengrin" Wedding March and "There'll be a Hot Time in the Old Town To-night," Nature remarked: "I did want to say a few words on 'Marriage in the Early Days,' but it is a hard subject at best, and after three 'addresses' in succession. Anyhow, I must get the subject off my chest, and since I am afraid it may bore my audience, I will unburden myself to you instead. Here goes:

"The early family life was the germ, the original cell out of which marriage evoluted. In the very earliest times, among the dim half-beast, half-human shapes that inhabit the Neanderthal world, 'family' did not mean what 'family' now means. It seems as though in the dark past, when man's sex relations were a matter of 'season,' like those of the animals, that men and women lived and ranged in separate brutish hordes, meeting in the spring-time for mating, which was a pretty promiscuous affair.

"But with the finding of fire, came the light of the little individual fires, 'family fires,' which drew, the individual man and woman he lived with right along and their children, together at a hearth-flame of their own. In the course of time, instinct and custom set up the law that those closely related in blood must not interbreed or intermarry, and so the idea of one 'regular' wife or several 'regular' wives, instead of hap-hazard mating-month wives, developed in a natural way.

"But, in the confusion of early life, other forms of marriage—not made in heaven—also were customary. Sometimes, when there would be a scarcity of women in a tribe or clan, one woman would be the mate (one could hardly call her the 'wife') of a number of men.*

*This form of family association is known as *polyandry*.
And since it might have been hard to tell which was the father of any particular child of these unions, *the descent of the children would be reckoned through the mothers.*

184

"This more or less 'common property' idea lingered on for a long time. Herodotus, for instance, tells us of a Lybian (African) tribe even in his day, that : 'When a Nasamonian first marries, it is the custom of the bride on the first night to lie with all the guests in turn, and each, when he has had intercourse with her, gives her some gifts he has brought from home.' Nor did these Nasamonians think there was anything out of the way about it.

Tradition practically had made the custom sacred! All forms of 'group marriage,' of *orgies* at given times, when the 'lid was taken off,' and the ordinary rules of sex intercourse were forgotten, *go back to these early ideas* and to the religious association of unrestrained sex intercourse and the blessings of fertility.

"Out of the *totem* idea (already mentioned), which identified certain families with certain animals, developed the idea which led away from interbreeding. It taught that *men and women must not marry those of their own totem,* their own clan. An 'eagle' girl must not marry an 'eagle' boy; nor a 'wolf' boy marry a 'wolf' girl; but a 'wolf' boy might marry an 'eagle' girl, and the other way around. These totem systems of blood relationship were worked out by various early peoples in very complicated ways, but they are all based on the same idea. And they all helped to put family life on a *safe and sound basis,* more or less. But it was only a beginning. *For descent reckoned on the mother's side is always the sign of a lower form of tribal life. Not* until the 'patriarchal' system comes in, *when the descent of children* is reckoned according to their father, do we move to a higher, a better family and tribe organization. Out of earliest promiscuity and subsequent polyandry most of the races of the Neolithic times got as far as *polygamy*—the matrimonial possession of several women, and *monogamy*—the 'one-wife for one man' ideal.

"Most of the European peoples which have developed out of the early Neolithic races have settled down, in the course of centuries, to the *ideal of one wife for one man.* A majority of the Oriental races still cling to the *ideal of a number of wives for one man.* But we should remember that *both represent an improvement on what had gone before.*

With the one wife or more, the whole idea of marriage got down to a *personal property basis.* And even that was an improvement. The earlier cave-men who wanted a wife went and *stole* a woman from another tribe. If she did not come along willingly, she was knocked over the head with a maul. And if her 'husband'—in case she had one—'put up a fight'—*he* was knocked over the head as well, unless he got in the first blow himself. But gradually *brides were sold* to prospective bridegrooms. A daughter was an asset—father could dispose of her for cattle, weapons, etc. And the better price she brought the prouder the girl was of herself, and of the husband who was buying her. The 'buyer,' too, liked to have a girl 'bring along' as much personal property in the way of clothes, household goods, etc., as she could. So, seeing that the more 'things' she had the more attractive the primitive girl was to the primitive man, she started collecting as soon as she could. And that's how the romantic little 'linen-showers' and things of the kind, which now weave a rosy wreath of tender sentiment around engagement days got their unromantic start!

"But—there seemed to be no reason why a man who could afford it, in later Neolithic days, should not buy himself three or four wives—if he has the price. Few of the Old Testament patriarchs were satisfied with one better half, and somewhat later King Solomon, as a 'sheik of many harems,' could be compared only to a Turkish sultan before the Great War. Neolithic Man's ideas of right and wrong are the outcome of custom and habit. People through centuries of habit and training accept certain ideas. These ideas pass into their race-soul, their race-life, their race-habits of mind. They are handed on to their children and finally have become absolute standards of right and wrong.

So in Neolithic days the customs of certain races might develop along the line of *one wife,* and the customs of others along the line of *many wives* for the same man. After a time when they had grown far enough apart, and the habit of mind and race custom of two groups of peoples had gotten "set," each would point the finger of scorn at the other and cry, as the case might be: 'Behold this indecent people! Their men marry but *one* wife!' or 'Behold, this indecent people! Their men marry *three* and *four* wives!' And each, from his *own* standpoint of right and wrong, would have been right.

"But—Evolution proves that *monogamy,* the ideal of one wife or mate for one man—*is the highest form of marriage, because it is the form of marriage favored by the most advanced and civilized races.* And only through the *monogamic* marriage—the union of one man with one woman—*could woman have risen to her rightful place in the world to-day.* Wherever we look, we find that where polygamy—the more wives the merrier—is practiced, the races and peoples which practice it are on a lower plane of civilization. And even in Mohammedan countries, where polygamy is allowed by the Koran, the fact is that the great majority of Mohammedans 'cannot afford it.' After all, though 'two may be able to live cheaper than one,' if you have to support *four wives,* the simplest arithmetic proves that it will cost *four times as much* as supporting *one* wife. And, especially in these days, the average Mohammedan has all he can do—like the average white man with one wife—in keeping the home fires burning for a single mate.

"Taking them all in all, later Neolithic times, with all their confusion of religious and moral (?) ideas, 'put over' certain good things, on the foundation of the better forms of marriage.

"Out of the shifting hunting camps and 'annual camp-meeting grounds' of the wild, roving hunters there gradually develop, as men begin to squat down in certain fixed places and stay there—the first villages, and with them the first beginnings of real community life. And it is a real 'community' life. There are, as in modern society, certain families that 'stand out' by reason of blood or wealth, and 'lay down the law' to the rest of the tribe. There are men's clubs' and secret 'clan' and 'blood-brotherhood' societies. The priest-chief is the highest court of appeal. There are 'unwritten laws' about avenging blood injuries, on the basis of 'an eye for an eye, a tooth for a tooth.' There are duties to one's own clan, one's own family. Out of the union of the fighting men of different communities, villages or towns of the small race the race duty, the duty to the 'clans assembled' gets to be the most important. The fighting men of all the tribes 'get together' and out of the town and village chiefs, elect a chief of chiefs and a priest of priests. Courts of the 'race' or 'nation' are formed, and the great families of the villages and towns no longer can settle their private fights among themselves. They have to refer them to the 'race' court, the 'nation's' court. And with this development of the idea that the 'state' or the 'race' of the 'nation' was greater than the tribe or village units that made it up, a thousand and one things developed in man's life. But none of this came to pass until man had definitely settled down to one of the two forms of marriage which still rule the world, and the line of descent of children was reckoned from the father, instead of the mother."

CHAPTER XXVII

AND here, after Nature's "lectures," we get back to pictures again, *real pictures, the first pictures and "paintings" ever fathered by human brains and carried out by human hands!* One of the most interesting things about man's first real pictures is that they run along with man's special way of thinking, the special kind of a *race brain* he has. There is very little that man does that will not "give away" the way he thinks, for his habit of mind creeps into his work and betrays itself.

The most curious thing of all about the first art-works and the first artists who made them is—that *the first real pictures on earth, made by the "Reindeer Men," are better than those the next lot of artists, the Neolithic Men, produce!*

The Reindeer Men" were the first to put their "eoliths," their tools for "anything and everything," to another, not practical use. You can't eat a drawing. It won't keep you warm. You cannot use it for anything, but—the "Reindeer Men" first seem to have discovered that *there was something in life besides eating, drinking and mating.* There was something in themselves, in one or another individual, here and there, that had to come out. There was a need to express beauty. And that is how art came into the early world. It was man's first earnest attempt to express beauty as he saw it.

The "Reindeer" period is *the age of the golden dawn of art.* These first artists the world knew had no brushes or paints, no canvases or easels. They had no paper or drawing-boards. They had only the smooth walls of the caves and caverns in which they lived. They had only the flat surfaces of limestone and bone and ivory—but they supplied all the rest, the ideas and the execution.

Look at their pictures! They were made 20,000 years ago and in the cool, dim caves where they have been discovered—in France, and in Spain—they stand out, fresh and beautiful, on the dark walls where the skillful and loving hands of the artists, whose dust long since has been blown away by the winds of passing centuries, left them.

The outlines of their animal figures—for man in his first artworks, as in all else that he did, took Nature as a model—were "cut in" the rock, and then these outlines were "filled in" with chalk, orcher, charcoal and mineral colors, black and brown. The drawings of these first "Reindeer" artists compare with the sketches of a good artist of to-day. The grazing "Bearded Pony" of the French caverns, the splendid spirited "Great Stag" of the Altamira—It has flung back its great antlers and raised its head, as though uttering a battle-call!—are quivering with life. And the chief who had his cave "fitted up" with the wall-painting of one of the artists of his tribe (for in those days there were usually *but one or two men* who were so gifted *in a whole tribe*—artists were not bred by the dozen!) no doubt took as much pleasure in the handsome red and black "paintings" of his cave "picture-gallery" as any of our multi-millionaires who pay unheard of sums for some "old master."

There are no "old masters," to tell the truth, *as old as these "old masters" of art when the world was young.* And not only were there "drawers" and "painters," there also were "sculptors" and "engravers."

The finest and most beautiful animal figure work is that engraved and chiselled in the bits of smooth stone, ivory and bones on which the "Reindeer" artist did his "smaller jobs."

Look at this bison, "sketched in" on a small, flat bit of limestone. You can tell that the beast was "drawn from life," that it really looked just as it is, with its great hump, and the long horns which rise straight up in the air. And—perhaps it was *the first time on earth than an artist "signed" his name to a bit of work*—off at the left of the stone are a couple of marks which may be *the artist's signature!*

See these two half-size models of bisons—modelled in clay, just as the sculptor of to-day models—found in a "Reindeer" cave in France, in 1921! The hairs of the manes and tails are all carefully "drawn in," with some instrument of bone or wood. And here are reindeer themselves, and horses and the mammoth—the huge beast looking as real as life, drawn on a bit of its own tusk. Even the rhinoceros, fishes, wolves, the wild boar, the great cave-bear and the small brown bear served as models for the clever fingers of earth's first artists.

But the first artists, when it comes to their art, are still more at home with beast than with man. Look at their human figure! Here their figure work is "not so good."

Not one of the human figures wears a stitch of clothing—why should they when they could paint their bodies all sorts of beautiful colors, blue, green, red, white and black, in all sorts of combinations, and the ladies could hang themselves with necklaces of bone or stone beads. But we can see that some of these human figures—though the unknown artist does not "hit off" the human figures as well as that of the beast—are hairless, while others are covered with hair. And this means that while the majority of men were "shedding" their natural body-coat of hair, some still were clinging to it. The female figures in most cases "run to fat," and are far from the "Venus de Milo" ideal. But they do represent and ideal of some kind, and *the stout lady still is regarded as the most beautiful one in many oriental countries,* where beauty is a matter of pounds avoirdupois and is skinfull," rather than "skin deep."

But besides what we might "call straight art"—the big wall-paintings of animals and men which were "cut in" instead of "hung" on the cave-walls of the caverns of chiefs and, probably, the artists themselves, we had a good deal of "ornamental" art. People are beginning to take pride in a tool or a weapon that "looks good," that is beautiful. And so arms and instruments are decorated with simple designs of lines and circles, and the handles of knives and spears are carved into animal shapes.

And that is the art of the "Reindeer Men," *the first art earth knew.* It brought an ideal of beauty—of beauty made by man's own hands—into the world, one that had not been there before. And, strange to say, this simple art of the "Reindeer" folk stands *on a higher art level,* according to authorities of our day, than the art of the later Neolithic Men who followed them, who also had their art and their artists.

The "Reindeer Men's" art is like their religion. It seems to cling to a few simple ideas—but it knows "where it is at." It is an "honest-to-goodness" art. It draws and paints things as they really *are.* It is a "straight art," even if its female figures are horribly fat, like the Bushman's wife of to-day. *But this poor child of Nature,* the "Reindeer Man" went far in his development of the first human ideal of beauty that came to earth. It was probably not born, especially in the case of the "Reindeer Man," of any religious idea—it was just his natural desire to put "something in himself and of himself" into line and color, to make movement and life live again in figure and drawing.

The pretty-colored and lined "Mah-jong counters with which the "People of the Painted Pebbles" played in their forests, during the five thousand years after the Reindeer folk followed the herds their artists loved to draw and model "over the edge of the world," cannot be taken seriously as art. And the next "wave of art," which came in along with the spread of the Neolithic races out of Asia into Europe, was not on a level with that of the simple hunters.

The "Reindeer Man's" wife never hung a kettle over the fire and never cooked up a good stew—she had neither kettle nor pot. But with the Neolithic peoples came *pottery*—in the beginning, pots and pans, and jars and vessels of all sorts of clay, and later metal. And their pottery is ornamented with all sorts of designs and with figure designs. But in a curious sort of way, if we look at the drawings on their pottery, on their knife and dagger-handles and on their "tools," and the things of every kind they used in their lives, we find that the *figures* especially are not as good, not so clear, not so true" to life, and "true to nature," as those of the benighted hunting folk who went before them.

The way in which their brains worked shows itself in their art, just as the way the "Reindeer Men's" worked showed itself in what *they* did. The drawings and designs of the later Neolithic Men are more "fanciful," they are more fantastic, they are full of detail—but they do not "hit you right in the eye" because of their life-like quality and their truth. The "Reindeer" folk, who did not carry their God-groping to the lengths of the later Neolithic people did, took their art as simply and as naturally as their religion. They stuck to a few big, broad ideas—making the beasts they carved and painted "look alive," making their outlines express movement and vigor, making their picture as real a picture of the beast or bird they were picturing as they knew how. The Neolithic Men groped after art along the same lines they had groped for God—and this time they found *detail*. They tried to get in every single, little thing that could be crowded in: *their art over-drew itself,* just as their snake-worship over-leaped the bounds of the sane, and worked out into human sacrifice.

At first, at any rate, the later Neolithic peoples, in spite of the endless amount of detail, *the little nothings,* in their ornamental and carved work, could not show up an art as fine, as straight, as direct as that of the "Reindeer Men." Later on, when the individual Neolithic races developed each an art and a *religion* of its own, the trend to progress turned this first anxious feeling that everything in art depended on detail into other and broader channels. But as a general thing we can take for granted that *the first art on earth, the art of the caves*—the flat, oval stone lamps by the light of whose animal fat dips earth's first artists worked, remain in some of the caves as a pathetic testimony to their industry!—was greater than the art which followed after it.

At the tag-end of the Neolithic Age, as History was dawning, art already has "gone into trade," and "artistic" pottery, copper and bronze vessels, weapons, ornaments, and embroidered skins and mantles were changing hands among all the races as their traders carried the things one people made to another. Art, like everything else had come a long ways from the first necklace of shells or flint-stones that a hairy paw had hung around some dirty, savage neck! It is—*as the picture shows*—almost as "far a cry," if not quite, as from the ivory "Venus of Moellendorf," the statuette of an Austrian lady even older than the "Reindeer" Age to the "Venus de Milo," of the time when Greek sculpture was at its best.

CHAPTER XXVIII

LIFE-REELS OF NEOLITHIC DAYS

THE chief of a Neolithic tribe is making a speech. He is very serious, and talks as much with his hands and arms as with his voice. And the men and women, and tousled-haired children of the tribe all crowd around him. What is he telling them in the forest clearing beneath the green tree-tops? It is simple. He has consulted with the tribal gods and—*they* have decided that since there are enough women in their own tribe, and others can easily be "stolen" from surrounding ones, the old tribal habit of one woman's having a number of mates or husbands—what Science calls polyandry—*will have to go!* Perhaps there are no cheers, for a habit is hard to break, and some of the ten or twelve husbands of an especially attractive wife are sad. But the young men look cheerful, and like most young men in any age or time think that any change is a change for the better. Besides, after all, a wife who is *all* your own is better than a wife in whom you have only a fifth or an eighth interest. And so a new order of things begins as the Neoliths disperse, each to his hut, to "talk over" the new things that have come into their lives.

Huts? Yes, the hut has come to stay. For the forest trees we see are those of a grove, not a great spreading woodland. Outside the grove stretch "farms"—tilled land, in all directions. For the women no longer have to wander weary miles into the forests to find vegetable food. *They plant seed*—one of the things they have brought from far Asian lands—it grows, and the harvest fields, that bear year in year out, tie them and their husbands down to the soil and hold them to a fixed spot; they have a "home", on earth where before they were homeless wanderers. And do we hear a dog barking? We do, for at last Neolithic Man has done what neither the Neanderthal Men or the Reindeer Men were able to do—*he has tamed the wild dog* and heredity, through the centuries, has handed down in the "tame" dog the feeling that they are different from the "wild" ones. It has, owing to change of food and habit, made them look different as well. So now the dog serves man.

Neolithic Maries are "calling the cattle home" as the evening shadows fall—*for man has tamed the wild cattle* as well as the dog which helps drive them to and fro from the pasture. He has tamed —first catching and "coralling" them, making them used to his presence, making them depend on him for food the wild pig and the wild reindeer, the wild horses, oxen and the sheep, for even sheep were not originally tame. There is a hunting-party starting out from the village—the young men hurrying along with dogs straining at the leash—for men still hunt. But once they *had* to hunt. Now that that food is assured without hunting, they hunt half as an amusement.

What are the village sights? First there is a smithy—a little forge at which the smithy is hammering out a copper head for a hunting-spear, while his son blows the charcoal fire to keep it glowing hot. Neolithic Man begins with copper, then comes gold and, finally, bronze. And the things he can make and the quality of his work improve as time goes on.

Who is it standing "out yonder in the cornfield?" It is *the woman with the hoe,* not "the man with the hoe!" For the woman with the hoe came first. All over the earth hoeing the field was looked upon as *woman's work,* by the early races. Woman had strength enough to handle a hoe properly, and man saw to it that she did. But the tamed cattle brought about a change. If we let this picture of a cornfield with a *woman hoeing* between rows of green shoots, fade, and flash on the screen a picture of the *same field a century later,* what do we see? *An ox is pulling the first plow.* For Neolithic Man has learned to make a plow, and to use the strength of his oxen to make it draw its furrows. And since it is beyond a woman's strength to guide the plow and the ox, it has become man's work. *The first furrow plowed in the soil by the first plowshare marked the beginning of every advance which raising woman to a higher level in life meant!*

If we look here and there into the huts we notice that the men who are working in some of them are *potters*—men have discovered the potter's wheel—and are making vessels and pitchers of clay. Others are hammering out bowls of copper. Still others are punching designs in them with little stone tools, and the *eoliths,* the tools they use, are a thousand times better than those of their ancestors. They are of smooth, highly polished stone, with better cutting edges, and instead of all and any kind of tool being used for everything, we find that *all sorts of special tools* are "shaping up," as their owners find they must "think out" some new tool which will just do a certain thing in the work on spear-head or dagger-handle, basin or bowl. A whole number of new things and new ideas are coming into the world in a rush!

At a little distance from the village are some great burial mounds —for man is beginning to bury his dead in an early kind of *family mausoleum or vault*. They contain various rooms, and have an entrance leading inside. Customs differ. Some races have begun to cremate their dead, others still bury them. *Dolmens is the name given* these big "family vaults." And now let us take a look into the big hut where the chief, who is at the same time the tribe's priest and magic-maker, lives. The chief is busy thinking about the next great sun-festival. By rights his little Agg, the boy who is the apple of his eye, should pass under the knife. But as he looks at his hideously painted snake-mask, and the gaudy priestly robe he will have to wear—*and* the glittering knife of sacrifice—he knows that little Agg is safe. The chief-priest is a fairly honest man, as sincere as most men, but there is a limit to all things. And, who knows, *perhaps this whole idea of the sun-god's wanting a human* sacrifice is nonsense! He will hold a small private "board meeting with the sun-god the very next day. And then he will tell his people that the sun-god has appeared to him in a dream, three times in succession, and has laid a *tabu*, a prohibition, on all human sacrifice. Of course some of the men will murmur, for they have lost children of their own. They will say things about its making a difference "whose ox is gored." But the chief is strong. He feels he can dare to carry out his plan, and in one tribe, at any rate, there will be no human sacrifices after he has announced the will of the sun-god, for many a long year.

Let us take a look at the chief's daughter! The poor Neanderthal woman was lucky if she had a string of shells to hang around her neck. But this blond-haired girl has all sorts of bead necklaces, pins and ornaments, though she is squatting on the tramped-earth floor *with never a stool to sit on!* Her little great-great-great-granddaughters will have stools and tables of bronze and wood, but she does not miss furniture because she never has known it. Life is much more secure than in the old days, and she manages to find it pleasant. The young men do not knock the girls of their choice over the head with clubs and drag them off by the hair. They come around in quite a civilized way and "buy them" from father. And father puts a high price on his daughter, both for business reasons and to show how much he thinks of her. The chief's daughter feels very well satisfied. A rich man of a neighboring tribe is paying her father the largest herd of cattle that ever has been paid for a girl in all the tribe's history, and the bride-to-be is correspondingly proud. The fact that she will share her husband's hut with *two other wives* does not worry her at all. It is the custom, and since "everybody is doing it," it *must* be right!

But now come other pictures—scenes in Switzerland, in Scotland, in Ireland—pictures of villages built in the water. Clusters of buildings stand on wooden piles out in the middle of good-sized lakes, their only connection with the shore a long, narrow bridge, and the boats tied to the piles of the single huts. These are the villages of the "Lake-Dwellers," *the most sanitary races of all Neolithic times,* for living over the water, Nature was their plumber, so to speak, and the unsightly refuse-heaps and "kitchen-middens" which grew up around the land villages all went into the water in their case and disappeared.

It is the smaller tribes that live in their houses on stilts in the lakes, the larger ones spread their bigger groups of huts and houses over the European countryside. All this earlier Neolithic life was village life. People and pigs lived together pell-mell, as they still do to-day in some parts of the world. And lake-dwellers and land-dwellers were beginning to wear *clothes as clothes and not as ornaments* since they have learned to weave flax into robes. But the children still had to be called in at dusk out of the wild crab-apple trees (for the apple and other fruit-tree kinds had not yet been "tamed") so that the bears and wolves which prowled around would not catch and eat them.

Any number of things *which are such common-places in our lives that we never give them a thought, were great and rare discoveries the first time man made their acquaintance!* In the days when all crab-apples were wild, there was not a single chicken-run in the world. Away off in the heart of Asia the "wild" roosters—which were not to be tamed until 1,000 years before the birth of Christ, and not till then, begin to start out on the long trail which was to lead their descendants to all the poultry-yards of the world—crowed at sunrise and only waked the jungle-folk. And how many millions of delicious fresh eggs were laid for thousands and thousands of years in Indian forests when the mouths of all the early world would have watered for the savory "hen-fruit" had they known about it! Vermin there was, and the roach was probably keeping pace with man on the long journey down the ages. But Dick Whittington's famous friend and benefactor had not yet arrived on the scene, and if it had might have "gone short," for there were no mice or rats, either, so it would seem. But on the other hand, more and more was added to the life of Neolithic Man, century by century. *With tame cattle milk became a human food,* so much so that even to-day, among certain African primitive tribes, cattle never are slaughtered, and the herding people who own them are content with the milk and butter they give.

Once the potter's wheel had begun to turn, drinking vessels became a matter of course. And the later Neolithic, the Bronze Age men, had all sorts of drinking cups of gold, amber, bronze and even glass, perhaps, as well as drinking-*horns,* often handsomely mounted in metal. They had them while the gorilla-children were still drinking from cocoa-nut and calabash. But—what did these drinking-cups hold? Only the pure water of the spring and well? We fear not, for there seems to be reason to believe that, *somewhere between* 10,000 *and* 3,000 *B.C. early man discovered fermentation and the alcoholic "kick!"* We are apt to think that the temperance question is a comparatively recent one but Temperance has been a "live issue" *for the last* 12,000 *years, perhaps.*

In an early British inland village a huge man, his body attractively painted with bright blue stripes, heavy bracelets of tin shining on his hairy arms, comes staggering out of a hut. Accident—he left the honey in the big clay jar stand too long—has led him to a discovery which will make him look on the bee as a friend and brother for the rest of his life. The other villagers rush up. See them crowd about him! And from his hiccoughed words, as he reels along, waving his arms wildly, they catch a hint as to what he has found. In a moment his hut is crowded. Others lift the magic honey-jar to their mouths, and the happy alcoholic smile rises to their lips. They feel distinctly good, they feel happy. Life is a rosy, beautiful thing. And they go reeling down the street wrapped in a misty cloud of joy. Soon, in every hut of the village, they are making "home-brewed" mead!

Among another people the first barley-beer is brewed. And here, there and everywhere, malt beers and hard ciders, and grape-wines are discovered, used and abused, as the generous grains and fruits yield up the joyous secrets of tipsiness.

Here we have a great reunion of tribes. One of those race-festivals we already have shown. But where is the sober happiness of the "Reindeer Men?" There is a different *spirit* here. The "Reindeer Man" sucked his marrow-bone and washed down his meal with clear water and was content. But in front of each chief in the big circle of "head men" that we see, as the bard—himself "teetering" a bit, perhaps, as he sweeps the strings and begins a wild song of the dead and gone heroes of the race—*stands a huge horn of mead!* It is old mead, it is strong mead, it seems to "go to the spot." For most of the chiefs are smiling. Their smiles show that they do not know why they are smiling but—they are happy. Others are differently affected; they are shedding meady tears into their horns. And still others have what in the vulgar phrase of our day is known as a "fighting jag." Less intoxicated attendants are pulling two chiefs apart, and hastily smuggling their axes and swords out of the way. Yes, the new drinks with a "kick" in them have brought merriment and light-heartedness into the world but *also less pleasant things.*

Some of the chiefs with "fighting jags," who could not "take out" their rage on their fellows will, no doubt, kick and beat "friend wife" when they return home.

In the Bronze Age, drinking makes the round of the whole civilized world. The priest-king drinks in his palace, the tribal chief in his camp. The lake-dweller drinks in his hut, surrounded by water, and the farmer, weaver, miner, everyone drinks as time, place and opportunity permit. From the highest to the lowest, from the Egyptian pharaoh of the "first race" sipping his heavy palm-wine to the French Neolithic stone-cutter growing maudlin over his malt, *the new art of pleasure spread over the earth. The women—always striving for higher and better things,* and not being able to make allowance for the serene joy of the first mellowing stages of drunkenness, *the power of the new-found liquids to drive away care and sorrow,* to make man feel bigger, bolder and happier in their initial stages, *were opposed to it. Too often they could point to broken bones and black and blue bruises* as the net outcome for them of drink's later stages in their men. Priests, too, objected to it for reasons of policy, and unknown sages of the days before writing fought the vice of drunkenness, even before those whose names have come down to us, did, in the Old World and the New. *But all this "hooch" of the early world was still comparatively innocent.*

These drinks all were *fermented drinks,* they were not the stronger, quicker-acting, *destructive distilled liquors* we now know. That kind of "booze" did not dawn on man until the 13th century. Yet, by the beginning of the 19th, the arts of distillation had advanced so far that the gin-keepers of London put up sign-boards inviting every one to: *"get drunk for a penny, dead drunk for two pence,"* and offering *"straw for nothing,"* so that their guests could "sleep it off" undisturbed!

When we look again we can see by the picture shown us that Neolithic Man is near the threshold of History. He is already far, far removed from the simple village life with which he began. Man has found, twisting small tufts of sheep wool between his fingers, that it can be drawn out into a thread. Yarn is first twisted with the fingers, then comes the first rude spindle and—almost before we know it *the first spinning-wheel* is humming, and women spin them garments of wool. A new clothing material and new kinds of clothes are added to the garments of flax and skins they already have. And the *dyes from plants* are used to color these garments, and different "dress" fabrics are woven *on looms.* After weaving, *sewing, knitting and embroidering* come in due course of time. Their stone henge "church buildings" or enclosures grow in size. The handsomely polished flint axe gives way to the bronze sword, and the bronze spear-heads and ornaments which at first were only owned by rich men and chiefs come to be common property in many tribes. To dig out the copper, and even gold and silver they use, *miners, a race to whose toil and skill the world owes a great share of its material progress,* "work" the first mines earth knew, as men find out that "surface" deposits of metal like copper are nothing compared to the rich stores of it hidden underground. And, after copper tin, the "white metal," which we now despise for ornamental use, was found and used to make pretty ornaments for Neolithic necks and wrists, bangles and strings of beads. And bronze, the metal that goes with the greatest development of early man before History and, in fact, takes him over History's threshold, comes to him from the travelers and traders of Atlantis.

The Age of Bronze is the entrance portal of History proper. With the Age of Bronze History, as we usually understand the term, begins. Through the gateway of the Bronze Age we pass from Primal Dusk into History's Dawn. The Bronze Age already *is* History. It is with the end of the Bronze Age that *spoken language passes into written language, speech into record,* that History as we understand it *becomes possible.* But before the vast panorama of the rise and fall of the nations begins to pass before our eyes in the succeeding volumes of this series, we must consider a fascinating and romantic event whose tragedy and romance make it a mile-stone which marks the highest point of progress reached by man as History begins.

It is a tremendous catastrophe, *one that sweeps away a whole section of the known world of the time!* The races which survived it picked up the torch of progress which had fallen from their startled hands, and crossed on over the threshold into the Historic Dawn. With them History begins. With those who perished in the great tragedy which is still echoed by the sacred books and the traditions of all the races that saw and suffered by it, the story of Evolution, *the Evolution of life from atom to the immediate ancestors of modern man may,* in a poetic way, be said to have closed. And that picture of the destruction of "The Lost Continent" is one whose startling romance is based on *a solid underpinning of scientific fact!*

MAN'S ASCENT FROM DARKNESS TO LIGHT*

"The 'history before history' of Europe sounds at first with the murmurs of the primeval wilderness; deep darkness, here and there made darker by spots of dim light along the edges of which are thrown the shadows of strange animal forms. Apes play among the tree-tops, and behind a fleeing drove of wild cattle we see the pursuing hunter, see him only in outline—the First Man!

"But the picture changes; the forest turns into a steppe. In the background gleam the ice-mountains. Over the long stretches of steppe grass droves of mighty mammoths are stampeding; herds of buffaloes, wild oxen and wild horses. Nearer the icebergs reindeer are browsing. And behind all these lurks Man, now a cave-dweller, waiting for a chance to 'get in' a lucky thrust.

Again the picture changes; mammoth and reindeer have vanished. Packs of dogs run through the forest and through the clearing we catch glimpses of mountain lakes, with the fishermen from the lake villages throwing their nets. Sheep and goats are grazing on the open meadows, and in the distance stretch the waving grain fields of the first agriculturists.

"Then this picture also 'flashes out.' Strange traders bring gleaming metals; ruddy copper and yellow bronze. They hold up before the astonished eyes of the simple farmer and fisherfolk gleaming gold and different-colored glass. And right after glass comes iron. We see the arts, the technical crafts, continually develop and increase. Mighty walls and temples arise."

We hear the war-cries of the Egyptians, the Assyrians, the Greeks! The *written record* begins to hand down the stories of the nations— *and the age before history melts into History itself!*

*Robert Forrer: *Urgeschichte der Europear.*

CHAPTER XXIX

THE ROMANCE OF THE LOST CONTINENT

I

A Bird's Eye View of the Bronze Age World

"My own magic powers," said Nature as our machine rose high, high above the world at our feet, "are strong enough to call up from the past a "crust" of dream to spread over the face of the earth and show how it looked in the Age of Bronze.

"Before the picture that tell the Romance of the Lost Continent can be flashed on the screen, we must have the picture of Earth as Earth was when the Lost Continent disappeared. And this map of the world picture, this "crust" of dream, is only the truth, called up out of the past that has gone to make that past *live* for us once more."

We had risen high above the Indian Ocean. Far to the right lay Australia, a continent where early man would keep on being early man until discovered by civilized man, in the days of civilization. With its kangaroos and its naked men of the "throwing-sticks" it had no more to do with our story.

To the left lay Africa, the continent of mystery. Already the ocean rolled above the lost continent of Hellenis which once connected it with South America. But the land-bridge that ran from the Somali coast to the Indian peninsula still was there, and (look at your present-day world-map!) the Balearic Islands off Spain, Corsica, Sardinia, Sicily, the island of Malta—they are the "leavings" of the great land dikes that once connected Africa with Europe.

In all of Africa the tribes of the gorilla-children are swarming. We sweep above the green seas of tropical forest and jungle swamp, but the black tribes still are in the Neanderthal stage and the land is vast: there is no movement of early races. Yet in the North, the Lybian land where the Berbers now live are white races, and in Egypt. Here tribal life is organized in a state. There are walled towns. We see processions of priests moving from the sun-temples. Kings passed by in battle-chariots of bronze. Soldiers march in rank and file. Peasants till the soil. Thousands of years of progress separate them from the black tribes of the African "hunterland." They are white children of the Bronze Age!

"And so it is along the shores of the Mediterranean. Inland, in the inner parts of Europe and on its northern edges we almost can see the story we have told being told again. There still are tribes near the beast-level, slowly working up. There are others a little higher. There are hunters of the Reindeer Man kind living on and with their game. There are tribes that wear copper armor and use battle-axes of finest cutting stone.

For in Neolithic days the long chain of the tribes of man held all kinds of human links that Evolution had not carried up to the big, general level. Some were to move on and up, others were to perish. Before our eyes the life of the inland tribes goes on: the eternal round with its sacred dances to animal-, snake- and sun-gods, its blood and brutality, and growing out of it, civilization. And it is spreading. See, in France, in Central Europe, in Scandinavia, the potters' wheels are turning! The cattle are driven to pasture! The harvests ripen in the fields!

But now look beyond Europe, into Asia! In Asia Minor the lands of the tribes have rounded out into kingdoms. With the things that make up "human society," now as then—laws, order, protection for human life and good—*the trader has come into the world.* All the tribes of Europe and of the Asian world, all the tribes *that have gone ahead,* trade with other tribes. All the races "make" different things, and find different "stuff" in their countries to "work up."

See the caravans! Yes, they are using the *camel* in the lands of Asia Minor and in Egyptian Africa to carry burdens—just as they are using the *horse* to draw the light bronze war-chariots in Egypt and the Mediterranean lands, and the ox to pull the rude carts in middle Europe. Everywhere there is trade, there is "business." From the dark mystery lands of Africa, from the Soudan, the Egyptian trade caravans come back with grain gold, with ostrich feathers, with ivory to be carved into charms and amulets, with the beautiful deep-violet amethysts *we still see gleaming around the mummied necks of Egyptian princesses of long ago!* The leaders of the "trade expedition" are satisfied. They have made a good profit on their woven linen stuffs and other "things of Egypt," and what they have brought back will pass over the Sinai peninsula to Europe. In exchange they will get amber from Scandinavia, copper from France, tin from Britain. Everywhere in Europe and Asia hard obsidian stone, flint stone, passes from land to land, in all its shades of color: green, black, green-white, red-veined. *For though he has passed into the age of metals, man clings to his stone past,* for obsidian makes such wonderful knife-, spear-, sword-blades and arrow-heads. Everywhere the tribes are weaving stuffs and dyeing them, and forging swords, and making necklaces and ornaments, and exchanging their special kind of manufacture for the special kind of thing made by some other people.

And now let us float over the Mediterranean shores. There "men go down to the sea in ships." There is great activity. An old legend says that the first navigators were men of Tyre, who cut a great tree, pushed it into the water, straddled it and set out for unknown lands. But in the age of metals men have begun to build *the first real ships,* and hugging the shore, they move from one land to another and get to know more of each other and of the world. And all the Mediterranean Sea races have *bronze.* They have *bronze armor* and *swords* and *bronze* war-chariots, they have *bronze* doors and gates and *bronze* household utensils. Where did these races that live on the sea-border get their *bronze?*

Rising still higher in the air, and taking in the whole world at a glance, we see Africa quiet, hardly stirring in its tropic forests. But in the African Mediterranean lands, and in Europe and Asia Minor there is great movement. The races are growing in skill, in knowledge, in civilization! They are "rubbing up" against each other in trade. People of all races are traveling in other lands. There is restless activity, *there is continual progress.*

And now, if we look at the vast Asian *hinterland,* we notice another kind of movement there. Not in India or China: they lie apart, "budding" their own special civilizations, *almost "out of touch" with the rest of the world.* But humanity stirs in the vast Central Asian plains across which the "Reindeer Men" long ages before had followed their drifting herds "over the edge of the world." There is a movement there. But it is the *restless stirring of the gibbon-folk,* of the wild Mongol races, the climate of whose land has *changed,* and is driving them on into the warmer and more fruitful regions.

The white races also had come in many successive hordes, out of Asia. But these new outpourings from the great reservoir of humanity are *yellow peoples.* Some tribes are more advanced than others, just as among the Aryan peoples. And we can see them pushing on in their millions, and crowding down upon the people of the world of *bronze.* And that is the world just before History. In Africa, the quiet of *near-stagnation,* except in Egypt and Lybia. Along the Mediterranean and in Europe generally, *progress;* in the Central Asian plains *the milling of the yellow human herd for a great stampede.* But where are the American continents? What of them?

The *bronze* that the Egyptians, the Lybians, the Iberian (Basque) folk of Spain and others use, and the secret of whose "making," the welding of copper and tin, they have given all the "go-ahead" peoples of Europe; this *bronze* is the discovery of a race ahead of every other in civilization. It is a race whose home-land will soon be swept from the earth.

Among the races of the orang-outang strain is one which has left no records, no bones, no fossils, no skeletons, no weapons or armor

—*nothing to* show it ever trod the earth except a legend, few words
in certain tongues, and the discovery of bronze. This race was the
people of Atlantis, the Atlantides. They have vanished, but the great
age of civilization which preceded written history, and which melts
into it, *still takes its name from the metal they gave the world—the
Age of Bronze!*

II

The Secret of the Deep

We were hanging in the air midway between Europe and the
American continent. Below us rolled the long ocean billows of the
restless Atlantic, huge, heaving swells, wave after wave of dark,
fathomless water. And below those green, glassy monutains that
never stop rolling and weaving, as their strange tides move at the dead
moon's pull, lies the secret of the civilization that would make History begin with Atlantis, instead of Egypt and Sumeria, *had we but
its written records!*

Yet the deep, still holds its secret. It *rustles* faintly in the yellow
parchment pages of an old Greek manuscript. It echoes faintly in
the accents of mysterious tongues of unknown origin, Basque and
Berber. It hints silently in the pyramids that link the dead Egypt
and the dead Yucatan of the past. But the eye of Nature sees beneath the waves. She shall call up what is concealed by the Atlantic
deeps.

"When the great reptiles were in the prime of their golden summer-
time," said Nature, pointing to the heaving waters beneath us, "the
Atlantic was cut in two. A continent of solid land, ridged with a
mountain range which the Andes continued down into South America, *ran from the coast of Portugal to Central America.* Then, in
the dim ages in which so many of the great reptile families disappeared, while the angel of the cold drove down from the north,
Earth's white-hot heart burst out into one of its volcanic hemor-
rhages of fire and flame. The face of the world changed amid a rush
of waters, a vomiting of volcanoes, a thunder of upheaval and destruction. When the great outburst was over, instead of an unbroken continent—*an island continent stretched between the Portuguese and the Central American shores.* One great island—Atlantis
—nearly touched the Berber shore of Africa. Another nearly connected the first with Portugal. Still other islands, stretching on within easy distance from the central island of Atlantis, linked it with
Central America. It was an island continent by itself, yet in touch
with Europe, Africa and America.

"We know the beautiful legends of the Old Testament better than
those of the other races. But every race has *its* legend of a garden

of Eden: all the races of white and yellow peoples have their own story of an earthly paradise.

"The earthly paradise of the Mongol races was a green and a flowering wonder-valley high in the Altai Mountains. It was called *Tinter, and there the magic tree of all life drove roots of shining crystal deep down into the bowels of the dark earth, where the demon spirits lived.* The valley of Tinter, where all was eternal spring, peace and beauty, was the Mongol's magic land of longing. The earliest yellow race known to history, the Sumerians, after they built cities in the Mesopotamian plains, still longed for the hidden valley-paradise of their race in the Altai Mountains—*for every race has its garden of Eden. Every race makes its longing for a garden of Eden out of its own heart!* We give the garden a name and a place, *but the garden itself is just our longing for 'something better than the best we have!'*

"Now the Eden-garden of the white races was another garden, an island and not a mountain garden. *It was the great island-paradise of Atlantis,* now buried beneath the salt-sea waves. And it did not become a garden of Eden until it disappeared. *For a true garden of Eden lives only in the heart's longing and not on any map!* It was a garden of glorious palaces, whose golden-bronze walls were shaded by fruit-trees.

"Through its ever fertile fields flowed four great rivers. The paradise lands of Egyptian and Semite, the Greek Islands of the Blest, the Avalon of the Welsh, the Saint Brendan's Island of the Irish, the Portuguese "Island of the Seven Cities," the wonder-islands of High Brazil and Lyonesse—*all the beautiful magic islands of legend which rise up out of the Atlantic and disappear before the sailor's eyes—are reflections of the great 'Lost Continent,'* called up from its bed on the Atlantic mud bottoms as the old story lingers on through the ages.

"And the hopes and longings of the races of Central America, cut off from Atlantis when the end' came, for thousands of years kept green the memory of what was once *their* garden of Eden as well as Europe's, the earthly paradise of the Mayas, the ancient Caribs, and the forefathers of the Incas, just as it was that of the Mediterranean folk of the Age of Bronze.

"At one end of that wonderful island chain we still have left the Canaries, the Azores, the Cape Verd Islands—mountain tops of the buried archipeligo which still rise above the water! At the other are the islands of the Antilles, the islands of the Caribbean Sea. Between them stretches only the Atlantic waste.

"But look with the eye of vision into the great heaving gulf below you!"

III

The City Under the Waves

And seeing with Nature's eyes, I can mark, as the water sees to turn to transparent air beneath my glance, the shadowy outline of the island continent. A great chain of mountains runs through it from east to west. And in one spot, where the Gulf Stream still makes a curve around the under-water coastline, I see the ruins of temples and towers and walls rising on a high plateau. The vast bronze-gold walls which surround its harbors and wharves and the quarters which look on what was once a green and smiling country-side, are green with the thick furze of verdigris which has covered them. But they are walls of bronze, and they surround a great city!

The Atlantic is the ocean of mystery among all the other oceans of the world! It still has its unsounded deeps where a crust skin-deep may be all that separates it from the liquid fires of Earth's glowing heart! And, with the record of the past before us, it is possible that some day another great convulsion of Nature, another vomiting of fire and lava like that which destroyed Martinique, another flinging about of the seas and lands, may bring the drowned continent to light again. It may be flung up suddenly, and when Earth's dead have been counted, and the cost of the damage done mankind figured out, all eyes will be turned to it.

We will see its great "open-air bowls," the "stadiums" as large as those in which the great games of our American universities and colleges are "run off." There the kings of Atlantis (like the kings of the ancient island of Crete, which may have been an Atlantide colony) watched the great bull-fights, bull-fights in which *women matadors* gave great aurochs bulls, huger than any seen in Spanish or Mexican arenas, the death-stroke with the slender bronze blades they held in their white hands. But the marble "boxes," in which the kings of Atlantis sat and looked down on lovely women slaying ferocious beasts are empty. Empty are the tiers where sat the nobles, the craftsmen and the people!

The twentieth century sun will shine down on the great harbors, but only the water-logged spars and timbers of the stout ships which traveled and traded and carried the beautiful things made by the metal-workers of Atlantis to all the African and Mediterranean ports will stick up from the slime and ooze of the harbor basins!

The marble floors of the great priest-colleges, and of the temples to the sun-god, will be littered with the clinging sea-weed of the ages, the shells and mussels of marine animals which have died there. From the cells where the sun-priests, learned and wise, thought thoughts far in advance of their time, will rise the stench of the rotting cuttle-fish which perished in them.

Perhaps it is better that Atlantis never rise again from the sea, with the gold of its temple towers and the shining bronze of its mighty walls rusted with the green scum of the waters, the beauty of its gardens and orchards, its palaces and its pleasure-pavilions gone past recall! No, better that it sleep beneath the restless Atlantic waves which have buried it, to rise, perhaps, only when the last trumpet-call summons all that once was living to rise from its dead bones!

IV

Atlantis, the Glory of the Bronze Age

Atlantis in her prime was the favored land of all the earth. Her people were numerous, happy and contented. Her kings drank deep of the pleasures of life, and her priests were wiser and more powerful than the priests of other lands. Like all the earlier peoples they worshipped the sun-god and the serpent, but we do not know whether or not human sacrifices stained their temple altars. It seems possible that their blood may still flow in the veins of the vanished race of the *Etruscans,* Atlantide colonists, who with bronze chariots, and hosts of footmen with bronze-tipped pikes, fought a losing fight against the early Romans, and vanished from the earth as a nation after their sun-temples had been plundered and the 2,000 bronze statues of their gods had been cast down!

It seems possible that their blood flowed in the veins of the earliest *Egyptians* whose legends said that the race *rose from the Atlantic Ocean* to enter the Nile valley-land. The Etruscans and the early Egyptians are dead races, but—in the living *Basques* of Spain and in the living *Berber* tribes of Africa, the blood of the greatest metalworkers the early world knew, the men who discovered *bronze,* is also supposed to flow to this day. They may be the children's children of the race which lived in the Eden-island of Atlantis.

Another dead and gone race, one which still lived in the days after Columbus had discovered America, was that of the *Guanches,* the original people of the Canary Islands. They were a happy, joyous people before the Spaniards destroyed them with the sword toward the end of the fourteenth century. They loved great public "shows" and athletic games. They worshipped the sun-god, and sacred virgins served in his temples. They embalmed their dead, like the Egyptians, the Etruscans and the Incas of Peru. They were Atlantides cut off from their motherland when the great catastrophe came and they lived on for a time, like a snake's body when its head has been cut off. All that is left of the Guanches, who in the fourteenth century were like the Bronze Age people of the time just before History be-

gins, are a few words of their language—they live only in a few combinations of sounds, like *guantch* "white man" and *Alcorac,* "God,"
which die on the air as soon as they are spoken! But even these few
words show that there is a connection between the tongue they spoke
and the old Berber language and, perhaps, the Basque.

And at the other end of the long, fertile and flourishing island
chain, we also have dead and living races which may be of Atlantide blood. The present Carib Indians are probably descendants
of the Mongol tribes which we saw swarming and milling in the
Central Asian plains, and which flooded across the Asian land-bridge
into North America and on down, *after* the Lost Continent was buried
beneath the sea. But—the ruins of temples, palaces and tremendous
forges still stand, covered with the rank creepers of the tropical forest. Where the snake now nests among the stones, the Atlantide
smiths beat out on their forges the splendid gold and bronze armor of
great kings! And, if not the Aztecs of Mexico and the Incas of
Peru, the races or race-leaders who came before them, the *Maya*
peoples of Yucatan, and the *forefathers of the Incas* handed on the
great secrets of metal-working to the races (often Mongolian or
yellow in origin) which came after them. At the time of the Spanish conquest of the New World the Incas and Aztecs *knew secrets of
metal-working* which died with them as nations, and which never
have been discovered since, especially the secret of a kind of *copper-
steel, a tempered copper, hard beyond anything modern man has
produced!*

Everywhere in Peru and in Mexico, in the home of the early
Caribs and in Yucatan, even in Columbia the pyramid, as in Egypt,
in Etruria (though the great red Etruscan pyramids have not endured the wear of the centuries) *show the ideal of one kind of building belonging to all the peoples of the Atlantide race.*

Is there anything more romantic in the world? Buried fathoms
deep in the cold slime of the Atlantic bottoms lies a golden city! It
held all the best of the world's knowledge! In its buried temples the
sun-worship and serpent-worship of the early world reached its
heights! And wherever its people "colonized" other coasts, they
took their sun-religion, their virgins of the sun, their priesthood,
their metal-working arts, their pyramids, their gift of bronze! Atlantis was a golden island bridge which let Africa, Europe and
America "hold hands," and bade pyramids spring up to be the tombs
of kings and the monuments of its race in two continents. When it
sank into the ocean slime a civilization died, *but it already had handed
on the secret of the arts,* the teachings of its religion and even its
blood to the rest of the world peoples of the Bronze Age. And the
other peoples, their path made clear by the dying, golden gleam of

the city beneath the waves, could cross safely over into the Dawn of History!

v

Before the Skies Fell

The wise priests of Atlantis who read the course of the stars and held the hand of knowledge on Earth's throbbing underground pulse that danger threatened. By day there were distant rumblings as the fire-veins swelled under the earth crust, and the volcanoes of the Atlantide Andes, which had slept for years, began to send up their spirals of white smoke into the air. At night the skies were full of fiery shooting stars. And the messengers of the great college of priests brought word of vast heavings of the ground, and of hills of fire in the far arctic lands of the north.

The priests knew. But the kings thought only of the beautiful women, the choicest and handsomest of every race on earth, who filled their harems. Or their minds were on the great bull-fights, or with the fleets they were leading across the seas to subdue other peoples and add them to their empire.

The priest-college had sent out ships in all directions. In each ship were priests who knew the great secrets of the race: the arts of building, of welding metals, of husbandry, of weapon-forging and jewel-working; the art of making seeds grow, and weaving wool and flax. The black rowers, slaves brought from Africa, bent over the sweeps. The ships sped on into unknown oceans, bearing with them the hope of the wise men of the race. Where they landed, on desolate shores, the naked, painted savages crept down to the beach from their jungles and forests. And they saw that these men were gods —*for to the man who knows nothing the man who knows much is a god*—and the hearth-flame of the Atlantide civilization was lighted in another land.

Perhaps that is the secret the lazy Pacific swells, washing the lonely isles where great ruined monuments of some splendid past still stand, tell. Amid an inferior race the god-like men who came out of the sea, and brought them the arts of life, settled. They were kings and rulers. But, too proud to mingle their blood with that of the savages among whom fate had cast them, the priest kings, in a few generations, after their new subjects had built them splendid temples and palaces, died out.

Like Peruvian Incas and Egyptian Pharaohs, race-pride made them change sister-marriage from *incest* to a *sacred duty*. In a struggle between pride and natural selection the latter must win. And the tribes they had ruled fell back into barbarism again, or were swept away by new human race-floods.

Perhaps that is why the temple stones stand in the lonely Pacific islands of the South Seas, in the Yucatan and Guatemalan jungles, in Colombia, near Bogota, in Peru, near mystic Lake Titicaca, whose bottom is still paved with the golden vessels, the gold-dust and precious stones flung into it century after century before the Spaniards' coming!

Joaquin Miller, "the poet of the Sierras," wrote some fine lines which apply to almost any of these great dead Atlantan cities of the past, buried beneath the tropical jungles:

> "..........a city old, so old
> Its very walls were turned to mold,
>   And stately trees upon it stood.
>
> No history has mentioned it,
>   No map has given it a place;
>   The last dim trace of tribe and race—
> The world's forgetfulness to fit.
>
> It held one structure grand and mossed,
>   Mighty as any castle sung,
>   And old when oldest Ind was young,
> With threshold Christian never crossed,
>
> A temple builded to the sun
>   Along whose sombre altar stone
>   Brown, bleeding virgins has been strown
> Like leaves, where leaves are crisp and dun,
>   In ages ere the Sphynx was born,
>   Or Babylon had birth or morn!

Some of the Atlantide "arks," carrying the priests who held the world's knowledge in brain-pans which were once an ape's, never reached port. Instead of running into a soft, tropical mud-flat, or being flung high on the silver sands of a South Sea beach, they were shattered in the turmoil of the waters and joined their nation at the Atlantic bottom.

Perhaps one of these priest-ships of dead Atlantis was carried by a mysterious current into the tangled purple keep to the Sargasso Sea—a sluggish, half-land of marine mystery, still thought to hide grisly reptile monsters, of the early world, in its hollows.

Suppose we could follow that dead-live current to its slow, slow ending in the Sargasso Sea's very heart. There, hard and fast in a viscid growth so thick that it merely "gives" beneath the feet like spongy soil, we might find, amid the wrecks of all times and nations, the Atlantide vessel, the *oldest ship in the Sargasso Sea*. In the great cabin, shreds of fine linen still clinging to its bones, might sit the skeleton of the priest of Atlantis, the scroll of the *calendar* which the Atlantide sun-worshippers gave the other races of their kin, still held between its bony fingers!

But another swift galley may have carried one of the Atlantide kings to the colony island of Crete. There he would reign until his race and his cities were swept away by the early Greeks, the *half-savage Greeks of Homer's day,* far inferior to the splendid Cretans in civilization, but stronger in number!

One fleet may have made the African coast—there is a great Lybian city, an Atlantide "colony" city, there. A French writer has given us a picture of the tremendous caravan of the Atlantide kings lumbering along through the dense African forests on its way to give Egypt her earliest pharaohs. As the tremendous train of oxen and horses dragging baggage-carts, camels loaded down with gold, fabrics and jewels, the wealth of the Atlantide palaces, the litters with harem women, the guards, the attendants, the camp-followers push through the tropical brush, "the black peoples, among whom the Atlantides took the slaves, their ships carried to the distant lands of the Toltecs, the Mayas and the Caribs hastened up, and through a day even more sinister than the most terrible of nights, followed with moans and cries the endless procession of bronze chariots, sacred elephants, and the great guiding lights which blew out and were relit while the storm-winds raged and the thunders rolled. The whole world seemed breaking up into mud, into night and nothingness!"

THE CATASTROPHE

And Atlantis itself? Its last hour may have come after a golden afternoon, in a sudden night of catastrophe. The priests have been crying "wolf!" for many days, and nothing has happened. What if red stars drop from the skies, what if the volcanoes smoke? Stars have fallen and volcanoes have smoked before—and nothing has come of it! What if the fleets have put out from port, and the kings and their harems and households left for the African coast? "Sufficient unto the day is the evil thereof," the Atlantides cry. The fairest and most skillful of all the women bull-killers, a big blond woman from Gaul (France), is billed for the bull-fight that afternoon! Tomorrow will be time enough to think of packing!

The streets are filled with people, laughing, jostling, talking. Mingled with the Atlantides are traders from distant lands: Scandinavians, Gauls, men from the lake villages, oily traders from Tyre, Babylon and even Nineveh, though it is as yet but a small town. There are men from Asia, there are men from Africa, and not one gives a thought to danger as the golden afternoon declines.

The great inner port of Atlantis is still crowded with ships, and the hard, weather-beaten old sea-dogs laugh all the priests' warnings to scorn. Do you know any sailors, real sailors? They have not changed through the thousands of years. They will believe anything and—they believe nothing! And they do not trust a landsman's knowledge in anything. "The priests? Pooh for the priests!" says a burly old sea-dog, blowing out his lips in a vulgar manner, as he raises a great flagon of wine and waves it toward the volcano smoking to the west of the great wall. "Pooh for the priests! Tidal waves? Waterspouts? We may have a little rough weather, but nothing more.... The whole land-lubberly College of Priests could not make me believe anything else!" As he stands there the rays of the setting sun glistening and sparkling on the silver inlay of his heavy green glass drinking-cup, a gay chorus of sailor voices rings out from the tavern behind him:

> In the "Black Whale" in Ascalon,
>   Three days a man did drink,
> And then fell down from his bench of stone:
>   He could neither talk nor think.
>
> In the "Black Whale," in Ascalon,
>   The host said: "Let him lay,
> He's guzzled more of my good date-wine
>   Than he has the price to pay!"
>
> In the "Black Whale," in Ascalon,
>   The waiters came. The score
> On six big bricks of clay inscribed
>   In to the guest they bore.
>
> In the "Black Whale," in Ascalon,
>   "Alas!" the guest he groaned,
> "At 'The Lamb' in Ninevah, they took
>   The last cent that I owned!"
>
> In the "Black Whale," in Ascalon,
>   The sand-glass stood at four,
> When the "bouncer" black from Nubialand
>   Threw the stranger through the door.
>
> In the "Black Whale," in Ascalon,
>   What prophet says or thinks
> Is all the same, if only he
>   Pays cash for what he drinks!

But even while the merry sailor voices sing their song the gold of the sky pales into spectral gray. Minute by minute this pallor darkens into purple blackness, while from the sea sweeps a vast wind, with a high, curious, moaning sound. A sudden silence has fallen on all the thousands of living human beings—the sailor song is hushed, and laughter, cries and chatter along the squares and wharf-fronts have died away. The moaning voice of the wind rises higher and higher, to a shrill, whining, hysterical note. And then—without warning, comes the crash of the bursting volcanoes! Huge columns of burning lava and blinding flame shoot mile-high into the skies, and in a moment the streets of Atlantis are filled with a panic-stricken mob. Men, women and children flee shrieking into the great temples, into the great halls and barracks that front the squares, to escape the glowing, tingling lava-ash, and the black rain of soot which covers the bronze-gold walls, and the white marbles of the palaces like a pall. But even while gray-black torrents of molten lava are rolling down from the surrounding mountains on the city, comes a new terror.

The tall guards, cased in bronze armor from head to foot, are pushing back the men and women who try to break into the palace entrance with their oak lance-shafts. The kings and their households have fled. The palaces are empty. Their treasures are lumbering through the African forests in cart and on camel-back. But— an order is an order! The captain of the guard, when he left in haste with the body of his men, forgot to relieve these sentinels. And so they still stand off the frantic crowd with their lance-shafts, and defend the entrance to the empty palace while their whole world is falling to pieces around them!

Now, with a tremendous shock, the first earthquake-wave tears apart the great city across its middle! For a moment a vast, terrible abyss opens before thousands of eyes which will never see another sun! In the very bowels of the earth, miles down, as the surface of the ground is torn apart, gleams a great, wonderful and hideous rose of fire, and a hot gust so terrible goes up from it that thousands, breathing in the flame which trembles invisible in the air, fall into the great rose-gleaming fire-pit like singed flies. But the fire-rose of Earth's heart is seen but for a moment! Another fearsome shock and, while palaces and temples crumble on every side, the waters of the Atlantic rush into the gap that splits the island in half—rush in and over. For now, slowly, quietly, calmly, after the two terrific upheavels, like some great flat stone which does not plump at once to the bottom but moves in strange circles down into unknown deeps, *the whole great island of Atlantis sinks—thousands of feet—beneath the waves!*

Fifteen minutes before the sailors were singing their gay tavern catch, the world was bright. Birds trilled, men laughed and talked. *Ten minutes before* the palace guards were still calling "Fall back!" to the mob surging against their crossed lance-shafts. *Five minutes before*—and air and sky were still as death. Not a living soul survived on Atlantis. There was no sound in the air for some moments. Only, had there been eye to see so vast and wonderful a thing, the entire island of Atlantis was drawing its curious descending circles beneath the waves, like a great flat stone, as it moved slowly on down to its final resting-place on the Atlantic bottom, where it lies to-day.

After that the earthquake still tore and harrowed the earth in many lands. Black tempests hung over the seas, and the shores of the Mediterranean were strewn with wrecks. Like a flail the storm battered the caravan of the Atlantide kings, winding its way through the African forests. And then, when a few days had passed, Earth returned to calm and where Atlantis had stood the ocean waters rolled!

That was the great Deluge whose legend is set down in all the early bibles of the world. It is the Deluge of the Old Testament and of the Babylonian sacred books. It was the Deluge mentioned in Plato's "Laws," of the Maya bible, the *Popol-Vuh,* the Deluge of sacred Aztec, Caríb and Hatian tradition, of Greek, Berber and Egyptian legend, for it was so great that it was felt by all the races. And its Atlantide Noahs were the men who dared the raging ocean currents in order to save and carry on the civilization of their race. They are the "men who came from the sea" of all the sacred traditions of the early peoples, who appear to bring back to man his lost Eden-land, his lost earthly gardens of Paradise!

CHAPTER XXX

ROMANCE AND REALITY

THE "Roman of Evolution" tries to clothe the dry bones of scientific fact—for all bones are dry—in the living flesh and blood of fancy. But the pictures which have passed before your eyes are not just "fancy" pictures. The record of the rocks, the story told by the skeletons of reptile, bird and beast, of ape and man, *by the very rocks themselves,* have supplied the facts which Romance has colored.

The great outstanding facts of Evolution cannot be questioned. As a companion volume to the "Romance of Evolution" a learned brother has written a volume which deals with the same subject in a more serious, scientific way. You may wish to study it from another angle. Again, you may not. The "Romance of Evolution" has been written so that the first story ever told, the greatest world-picture ever screened will reach every one. We honor and admire the patient scientists who have brought together, bit by bit, bone by bone, out of the depths of the earth, the material for Nature's glowing, living romance of life.

But the technical language of science is one most of us do not understand. We have a thousand and one duties, cares and interests which take up our time. And yet—we all want to know the one story that is more interesting than any other. We want to know *how* we came to be; *where* we came from; *why* we are as we are. We want a straight, clear story that takes us from the beginning of life up to the beginning of civilization. That story is told in "The Romance of Evolution."

You are not interested in "authorities" perhaps. You want the whole tale pictured for you so that you will "get it." But while "The Romance of Evolution" is the story of Evolution made *live, romantic, colorful,* it is based on God's own *record of the rocks.* Keeping in mind the *big, outstanding facts* that matter, the writer, out of the concentrated study of hundreds of scientific books and theories, has chosen the theories which make Evolution most interesting, which make it a *real* story, a *real* picture. That was the duty he owed you, his readers, who are intelligent enough to know that the story of *life* must be a *live* story!

And so the tale of man—from atom to ape, from ape to human being, from human being to civilized human being, the greatest of all stories, the most fascinating of all pictures, has been presented in *the spirit of life itself!* And the live way of presenting its sequels—for Evolution goes on, is going on through the ages—will be followed. For every part of the great tale of humanity's life is a *live tale,* every picture of humanity's progress is a *living picture!*

BOOK TWO

THE ROMANCE OF HUMAN LIFE
THROUGH THE AGES

BY

FREDERICK H. MARTENS

INTRODUCTION

FROM HISTORY'S DAWN TO MODERN DAYS

IN "The Romance of Evolution," the story of how human life came to be human life already has been told, from the first life-spark of the beginnings of history. History proper carries on that story in its great pictures of the broad tidal waves of race and national life. It shows the flowering and fading of peoples, the rise and fall of empires, just as the "Story of Human Thought and Religion" reveals the *inner* life of Humanity's *soul* and *brain* from the dim past to the present. "The Intimate Romance of History" withdraws the curtain hiding the loves and passions of earth's rulers, passions which often enough have brought about the *downfall of kingdoms and empires.* History and its more intimate romance, religion and human thought, are serials which continue "The Romance of Evolution"— just as the "Romance of the Arts" takes in other serial continuations of the same foundation story. Besides these serials, however, is another, "The Romance of Human Life Through the Ages."

The ideas, the feelings, the emotions of all humankind are always, more or less, a result of the way their *minds work.* Every human, every religious, every mental activity reflects in the *action* of life itself, as in a mirror, the ways races and peoples live their lives. Their way of *feeling* and *expressing* life makes the actual human life of all the ages. And history, in all these divisions, may be compared to *a series of great panoramic pictures.*

These pictures, again, have *thousands of individual scenes.* There are the scenes of actual history itself, which show the struggles between the *nations,* scenes of the rise and fall of empires, on land and on sea. There are scenes of religion in which human thought and belief take shape in *action,* in actual life, sometimes in moments of

I   219

high nobility, at others in tortures and burnings. There are scenes in the *privacy* of royal palaces and *boudoirs,* where historic ambitions, religious convictions, or mere frail human passion set marching thousands in motion to die on distant battlefields or call forth individual tragedies. There are scenes which picture the high moments and glorious fruits of evolution in the *Arts.* And all these scenes, these thousands of *pictures,* are related to each other. In the "Romance of Human Life Through the Ages" we have tried to give pictures of individual lives, shown against the romantic background of History itself. And just as the *background* in a painting makes us understand its *foreground* figures, so the historic background will enable us to understand and enjoy this series of individual glimpses of humanity as the centuries pass.

In presenting the "Romance of Human Life Through the Ages," as in all the other volumes of "The Outline of Knowledge," the aim has been to make the *actual human life* of the past understandable and interesting from the romantic angle. We have tried to make the people of the *past* live again, so that we of the *present* may understand them, share in their joys and sorrows, thrill with their hopes and fears, feel with them in their high moments, and grasp the human pathos of their low ones. We have tried to present actual human beings so that the reader can actually see and feel them *living,* and realize that human nature, in many ways, has changed but little since the first Turanian farmers led their irrigating ditches through the plains of the valley of the Euphrates and the first Pharaohs reigned over Egypt. The *picture* interest, the glow and color of *romance,* the making of human life *human* is what this book aims to do. The works of Flaubert, Daudet, Ebers, Sienkiewiez and many others, historians, writers of memoirs and diaries, and documents of ancient archives have been studied and used. For "The Romance of Human Life Through the Ages" is a series of *living pictures.* And because they are living pictures, because they put *human life itself in motion,* it seems right to speak of them as a great "moving picture" serial, whose story interest, whose *romance interest* has as its soul the *interest of life itself,* which colors its underlying truths with the thousand rainbow colors of fancy.

CHAPTER I

PICTURES OF LIFE IN ANCIENT EGYPT

WE do not know exactly where the early Egyptians, who gradually shaped up out of race mixtures of primitive tribes, came from. But more interesting than speculations as to their origin is the fact that even in the days of the "first kings," we know they were *human beings* with real *human kinks* in their nature. Our Egyptian background of humanity from the time when, perhaps, the Atlantide kings went lumbering with the train of soldiers, slaves and elephants along the dense African forests* to take over the country as the first rulers, to the present day, have been a nation of hard-working farmers. And—a very human quality—they were very well satisfied with the country they lived in, and hated *all foreign ways* and things. The fact that they were farmers was due to one thing: the River Nile. Old Egyptian poets called Egypt *Toshri*, "the red land," after the sandy desert which surrounded the Nile Valley. But the every-day people called Egypt *Kemi*, "the black land." They knew what poets often forget, that man cannot live without food. And without the Nile which gave Egypt her "black" river soil, that nourished the whole country, and from which it was called *Kemi*, "the black land," there would have been no *human* interest, so to speak, in the Egyptian landscape. The Nile, from the very beginning, has been Egypt's life-vein, with great, rich cities at its mouth, and the secret of its source, the springs from which it rises, lost in the mist of legend until our own day.

With the coming of kings who brought with them all sorts of civilized ideas and arts from their vanished island land of Atlantis, the Egyptians probably cut down what remained of the primeval forests which originally had covered the Nile Valley. When we use the word "pioneer" we usually think only of our own American forest-clearers. But every land overgrown with forests that dated back to the days when man ran about with only his self-grown pelt of hair to cover him, had to be cleared by "pioneers." And once the Egyptian "pioneers" had cleared their valley—no doubt they often had to fight the savage black tribes from the African back country to the tune of Ethiopian war-whoops to do so—farming prosperity began.

*See "The Romance of Evolution," Chap. 29.

While the axe of the wood-cutter was busy, camels and goats were brought into the country, and all sorts of art industries started up. In old Egypt the farmer was the backbone of the nation, and was drafted into the army in case of war. For with royalty and a court all the blessings of civilization gradually developed. There were law and lawyers, taxes and duties, government officials and great land-owners, factories and labor questions. In drawing on our store of "pictures" in story form to give us the *feel* of these old humans whom we meet "in the flesh" only in the mummy-cases of our museums, we might first take a peep at some of the professional men and others who helped keep the great wheel of Egyption daily life turning in the Nile Valley.

The Doctors. Outside of the fact that "the breath entering the nose goes to the heart and lungs," the Egyptian doctors do not seem to have known much about their patients. They did understand *purgatives* and *pills,* and seem to have used them liberally for all sorts of troubles, as well as "spells" and "magic" prescriptions for eye and stomach troubles, sores and snake-bites. And they had ointments for keeping away fleas. It is curious to notice that it was as easy to get an "infallible" cure for baldness and prescriptions warrented to "make the hair grow" in ancient Egypt as in modern America. But the early Egyptians were a lucky people in some ways for no signs of gout or syphilis have been discovered among the thousands of Egyptian mummies examined until the 6th century A.D. The mummies prove that circumcision, as with the Jews, was observed, and that flint instruments were used for this and other operations. When you went to the doctor and he prescribed for you you paid him with a ring of gold, silver or bronze. And the doctor's office was in the temple, for the doctor usually was a priest.

One reason the Egyptian doctors were so backward in all that concerned the ills of the poor human body, was that any attempt to *dissect* a corpse, and study the human body at first hand, would have raised a shriek of horror on all sides. The Egyptian *needed his body after he was dead,* and dissection was looked on as a particularly horrible and sacrilegious crime.

PRIEST AND PARASCHITE

In one of the historical novels written by a great Egyptologist, Ebers, we find a delightful situation. A broad-minded Egyptian temple priest who is anxious to learn more about the human body, in order to be better able to cure his fellow-men, makes a bargain with a *paraschite,* an "embalmer." A *paraschite* was regarded as the vilest of the vile and, after he had done his gruesome work, was stoned away from the corpse. This *paraschite* was to provide the priest eager for knowledge with a *human heart* to study and dissect. In return the priest guaranteed to cure his little grand-daughter, who lay

ill of a fever. Dead humanity was a daily incident in the *paraschite's*
life and human hearts as plentiful as cherry-pits in its course. As
he said: "When the dead lie undressed on the wooden bench they all
look alike. The beggar is as quiet as the king's favorite son!" The
corpse of a large, robust higher priest of one of the temples was
lying on "the wooden bench" in the stone embalming room. Beside it
was the body of a dancing-girl, one of the poor creatures who tricked
themselves out with finery in the evenings to lure the youth of Thebes
into extravagance and folly. She had perished of consumption. The
paraschite took out *both* hearts. But he only put *the heart of the poor
dancing-girl back in its body!* The priest had been rich. He had
lived well and fatly, and had known happy days until he had died of
apoplexy. "I will not mutilate the poor girl," thought the *paraschite*.
"She, who had such a hard time of it here on earth, shall know peace
in the other world." But he took the heart of the wealthy priest. After all, he would be rubbed with holy oil and covered with amulets to
protect his soul. And while the doctor-priest, eager to learn something for the benefit of his fellow-men, had a chance to study the
human heart at first hand, the rich priest Rui was buried with pomp
and ceremony, prayers, incense and offerings, his own human heart
neatly replaced by the heart of a *ram!* And every one—unless, possibly Rui in his new place—was satisfied.

From Doctor to Embalmer. From doctor to embalmer and undertaker is a more or less natural move. The underlying idea is the
minds of the Egyptians, to embalm and mummify the bodies of those
dear to them was to prevent their souls from suffering. If the body
and skeleton were left to decay, the soul, slowly, little by little, decayed with them. It was a terrible and long-drawn out agony, so
the Egyptians thought. To save the souls of their loved ones this
awful lingering on in dissolution until the last bone of the body had
moldered away, they made *the flesh incorruptible.* Then the soul
could return from the "blue land" of heaven to inhabit it when ready
to do so. Life repeats itself through the ages. The poor to-day must
content themselves with a cheap wooden coffin. The poor of Egypt,
in the days of the Pharoahs, had to be satisfied with a cheap "mum-
mifying."

Shrine Openers and Burial Trousseaux. The bodies of kings,
priests, nobles and men of wealth were given a "Class A" treatment. For when you went to the City of the Dead, to arrange for a
burial, the "shrine-openers," as the priest-undertakers* were called
(they did not do the embalming work) showed you three life-size
wooden models. You chose the mummy treatment you could afford.

---

*These priests formed a regular "cemtery" guild, and formed regular
"corporations." Each member of a guild had an "interest" in a certain
The first treatment, besides the seventy-day "natron bath" in which

the body was plunged, included the most elaborate additions in the way of perfumes, drugs, costly preservatives, prayers and amulets, and the removal of the soles of the feet and their laying on the breast. This was done so that the sacred floor of the hall of judgment would not be defiled by the dead person when he entered it. The second treatment was cheaper, with fewer perfumes, drugs and prayers. The third—and it was what about four-fifths of the people of Egypt had to be satisfied with—was a simple "pickling in brine."

But in all cases the vital organs—intestines, heart and lungs—were removed and the cavities washed with palm oil wine. The brain was withdrawn bit by bit through the left nostril. There were many, many details, especially in the preparation of the "Class A" mummy, before the last coarse canvas wrapping was sewn up. And, there is something gruesomely coquettish about the gilding, and perfuming and anointing, the jewelry and dresses, the false hair and sandals, and all the toilette accessories that every young mummy got. A young Egyptian girl's *mummy trousseau* was far more elaborate than her bridal one. Around 1000 years B.C., all Egyptian life seemed to turn on death, on observing its ceremonial, giving its main thought to the preservation of the body so that the *Ka,* the soul-double, would find it ready at all times. This thinking of nothing but mummies finally turned Egypt into a mummy herself.

THE PARASCHITE AND THE PRINCESS

In Egypt, where there was an hereditary nobility proud of its birth, *class distinctions,* especially during the *second empire* were rigidly observed. A great Egyptian noble looked down on the common herd with much the same feelings of contempt that a French noble of the eighteenth century felt for the peasants on his estate, or a Russian noble of the early nineteenth century felt for his serfs. Once, in the ancient days, a very lovely Egyptian girl of a noble house, one of the noblest in the kingdom, and even related by blood to the reigning dynasty died. She was given over to the *paraschites* for embalming *at once,* as the custom was. It was night when her slender body, lovely still in death, was brought into the stone dissecting room where a young *paraschite* already had been told to make the necessary incisions and prepare the corpse for the natron bath. Mummy-cases leaned against the gloomy walls, and on smooth polished benches of stone lay bodies covered with cloths. The young *paraschite,* used to the funeral horrors of the place, was sitting on the floor, where sluggish scorpions crawled out from wide cracks

number of mummies, and drew "royalties" on the dead in the shape of "perpetual upkeep" fees, which included prayers and religious ceremonies "Perpetual care" was not included in the price of enbalming and a "lot" had to be paid for separately.

in the pavement, eating his supper, a cake of bread and salt and a few radishes. When the body of the Princess Nourhi had been laid on the slab, and the bearers had gone, the *paraschite* rose, stepped to it and withdrew the white cloth that hid its features. Never had he seen so lovely a face! The black-lashed lids seemed closed on sleeping eyes; the golden-brown cheeks; faintly rose-flushed still, seemed warm with the breath of life. And a sudden love and longing, hitherto unknown to him, surged over the young outcast who so callously plunged the stone Ethiopian knife into the cold flesh of the corpses that came to his hands day by day. This delicate human image of love and beauty could not be dead! She must be dreaming. The *paraschite* knelt beside the body, his knife clattered to the ground.... A few moments later the chief of the "shrine-openers," the priest known as the Inspector of Sacrifices, happened to stop in the doorway of the room as he was passing. One glance, and his voice rang out in a cry that brought all those in the mummy-house rushing to the spot. He had seen the young *paraschite* leaning over the Princess' corpse, his living lips pressed to her cold, dead ones. That his kiss was a *reverent* one, that it only spoke in one brief second all the longing for a something higher and more beautiful, nobler and purer than the wretched conditions of his own despised and dishonored life could give him made no difference. A *paraschite*—the vilest and lowest creature in the land of Egypt,—had dared to desecrate with his ignoble lips those of the dead Princess Nourhi, of the blood of Pharaoh himself! Cries of "Sacrilege!" filled the air. The *paraschite* the following day gasped out his young soul on the stake, beneath the burning Egyptian sun. And after that time, *no noble Egyptian family* ever delivered the body of a young girl to the *paraschites*—that is *at once*. Three days at least had to pass before it was entrusted to them!

The Wisdom of Being a Scribe. There were nearly as many arts, trades and crafts in ancient Egypt as there are in modern America. There were bricklayers and stone-cutters, painters and weavers, tanners, dyers, iron-workers, silver and goldsmiths, jewellers, and miners who dug in the Nubian gold-mines. There was a legend current in the days of the second empire that the *Ka*, the soul double of the Pharaoh Cheops, whose tremendous pyramid had been built by the blood and tears of his people, and whose building left Egypt as though ruined by a war, had to wander restlessly forever, because of the suffering he had caused during his life. And, so the legend said, Cheop's *Ka* tried to win rest by performing good deeds. It was for this reason that one day it appeared to the miners in the Nubian mines, who had but little water to quench their burning thirst, and pointed out to them a spot in which to dig. They did so, and a great spring of clear crystal water gushed out for their relief!

But the best career in Egypt was that of the scribe. Aside from the priestly scribes; the writers, recorders, accountants and what not, who knew the art of writing in the sign language, there were other scribes or "writers" attached to Pharoah's court, or acting as private secretaries and stewards in the houses and palaces of the great nobles, and the monarchs and governors of the provinces. A scribe could rise high in royal and princely favor, and he had wonderful opportunities for making money in underhand ways. But though, according to the general belief of the people, ambition was the scribe's besetting sin, an old Egyptian tale proves that sometimes a scribe had a romantic soul and a heart above figures.

AMON AND THE SCRIBE

Once upon a time a young scribe passing along the highway saw a noble-looking man sitting before a cottage door. And being as wise as an ibis, the young scribe at once felt that he was in the presence of a god. So he stopped, bowed politely, and said that he regretted having neither food nor drink to share with the sitter in order to show his respect. The god Amon—for he was no less—was pleased with the young scribe's courtesy, and asked him what he had on his mind at the moment. The scribe smiled: "I was thinking of the wasteful rich," he said, "who fling away their gold without knowing how or caring why." "Would you not do so if you had the chance?" asked Amon. "Never! Every day I tell myself that wise poverty is better than foolish wealth. No, I never would waste a fortune!"

The god reflected for a moment, then said: "If you are really learned, then write the name Amon in *two* different ways!" The scribe took out his tablet and ink and brush, and in a few minutes he had written the name of Amon on the cottage walls in two ways so neatly that the very creatures deprived of speech stopped to put up a prayer to the god. Amon was content, but put the scribe to still another test. "If you are skilled in figures," he said, "figure out the following business problem for me. If I can get four hen's eggs for one partridge, how many hen's eggs should seven partridges bring me?" The scribe picked up a number of pebbles, arranged them in rows and before the setting of the sun gave the the answer "Twenty-eight hens' eggs!"

Then the god praised him and said: "What riches would you care to have so that you might save and increase them?" So the scribe said he would like to own the cottage and the four acres that went with it. "Very well," answered the god, "it is yours, with all it contains, a bench to sleep on, a mortar to grind your grain, two linen robes, shoes and sheets. But first—do you see the veiled figure in the corner?" The scribe admitted that he did. "If you touch it you will lose all you have!" "It could stand there a thousand years, Your Holiness, before I touched it," answered the scribe. "But tell me," he added, looking through the cottage window, "to whom does that handsome farmhouse over yonder belong?" "You well may say 'handsome,'" answered the god. "The house is big; fifty acres of land go with it, cattle and slaves. Perhaps you would prefer it to the cottage?" The scribe fell at the god's feet. "Is there a man in the world who would not prefer a cheese-cake to a crust of bread?" Amon uttered a magic word of power. At once both stood inside the big farmhouse. "You have a sculptured bed, five tables and six chairs. You have embroided clothes, basins and goblets for wine, an oil-lamp and a litter...." "And that?" asked the scribe, pointing to a figure in the corner covered with a cloth. "If you touch it you lose all you have," replied the god. "I could live ten thousand years without touching it," cried the scribe. "But what is that yonder?" he added, pointing to an immense palace in the midst of the garden.

"That is a royal estate," answered the god. "It is a palace with five hundred acres of ground, a hundred slaves, and hundreds of head of cattle. It is a great estate, but if you think you would be able...." Again the scribe fell at Amon's feet. There were tears in his eyes. "O master!" he cried, "Where is the madman who would choose a mug of beer rather than a barrel of wine?" "Your words are worthy of a wise man," answered the god. He uttered a magic incantation, and they stood inside the palace. "Here you have a dining-room, with divans and gilded seats, and tables encrusted in many-colored woods," said the kindly god. "There is a kitchen with five cooks, a store-room filled with choicest meat, fish and game, and a cellar of the noblest wines. You have a bed-room with a movable platform, that slaves will keep in motion to refresh your slumbers. Your bed is of cedar-wood, and stands on bronze lion's-claws. Yonder is your wardrobe, filled with rich garments of linen and wool. In your chests you will find jeweled rings, chains and bracelets...." Suddenly the scribe pointed to a corner, where stood a figure covered with a veil embroidered in gold thread and purple. "If you touch it your immense fortune will be lost to you," said the god, "for I might as well tell you that in addition to the estate itself you will find ten talents in gold and jewels!"

"O king and lord," cried the young scribe, "let me first of all put up your holy image in this palace, and burn perfumes before it three time a day!" Amon smiled. "Do as you think fit," he said, "but avoid what stands yonder," and he pointed to the figure in the corner. "I would have less brains than a swine if I did not do so!" cried the scribe. "For my part if such be your will, the figure may stand there a hundred thousand years before I touch it. I...." The god smiled once more: "Remember, if you do you lose all!" he said and disappeared.

The young scribe went through his palace from top to bottom. He examined his treasures: the gold was pure, the jewels of the first water. He clapped his hands and slaves came running to serve him. He ate, he drank—the dishes and wines were exquisite. He bathed, and his slaves rubbed him with fragrant oils. He burned perfumes before Amon's statue. The next day, while his servants and slaves fell to the ground before him, he rode through his estate on a bronze chariot. He saw his grain-fields, his olive-woods, his herds of sheep and cattle, his beautiful gardens. "Why should I try to increase my wealth," he thought, "I have more than enough as it is." And then he began to feel bored. That evening, when he turned to burn incense before Amon's statue he could not help glancing at the veiled figure in the corner. "Amon is a good god," he said half aloud to himself, "but then, I did well by him. I wrote his name handsomely on the wall in two styles, I solved his little puzzle in figures for him.... I wonder why he objects to my touching the figure in the corner? After all the whole palace belongs to me, so why should I not touch it...." He went to it and very carefully withdrew the veil. There stood a creature looking something like a young boy and yet not a boy. It had long hair which fell down to its knees, and a charming, gentle face. "What are you?" said the scribe to the figure.

"I am a woman," replied the figure with so sweet and gentle a voice that it pierced the scribe's heart like a Phoenician dagger. "A woman?" thought the scribe. "I learned nothing about women at the priests' college! A woman?" he repeated. "And what are those?" he asked, pointing to her eyes. "Those are my eyes." "Your eyes? How can you see with eyes that the least strong light would destroy?" "My eyes were not made to look with, but for you to look *into* their depths," answered she. The scribe shook his head and then asked: "And what is that?" "That is my mouth." "But you will die of hunger with so small a mouth," said the scribe. "My mouth was not made for eating," she answered, "but for you to kiss!" "Kiss?" murmured the scribe. "That is something else they did not teach me at the priests' school!" "And those?" "Those are my little hands?" "You do well to call them 'little', " cried the scribe. "Why, you could not even lead along a lamb with such weak hands." "My little hands were not made for work." "What for, then?" queried the scribe. "To put around your neck!" "You mean to *grab* me by the *nape* of the neck," said the scribe, for that is how the priests in the school took hold of him when he was to be beaten with rods. "No, not by the nape of the neck," said the figure, "but thus...."

And with these words she made a collar of her hands, clasped them behind his neck, and drew him to her.... At that moment the earth shook. The palace disappeared, with its slaves and servants, cattle, horses and dogs. The green countryside changed into a desert landscape, the olive-groves into the rocks, the wheat-fields into sand. . . The young scribe, when he regained consciousness, found himself in the arms of a woman who had drawn him to her. He realized that he was as poor and wretched as he had been the day before, when he was walking the dusty highway. Yet he did not regret his vanished riches, but praised the god Amon in his heart, *for he had found a woman to love!*

Down on the Farm. History repeats itself. The hard-working farmers of ancient Egypt had the same trouble the farmers have to-day. They could not keep their boys down on the farm, once they had seen Thebes and Memphis or one of the other big Egyptian cities. In the days of the earlier dynasties it was different. Life was more comfortable, and living conditions good, except when kings like Cheops were building pyramids and drafting all the able-bodied men for labor, or when foreign invasion made a levy of all the male strength of the kingdom necessary. The farmer usually rented his farm from some noble, some "over-lord," or direct from Pharaoh (through the latter's stewards), or from some great temple corporation. But he often owned his stock and, once his dues and taxes had been paid, might make out quite well. He had fine, wooly sheep of a valuable breed. His goats grazed on the skimpy herbage on the desert's edge. He had long-horn and short-horn oxen for ploughing and threshing grain. The ordinary beast of burden was the ass. Horses were almost unknown in Egypt before the time of the Hyksos (Shepherd) kings, and then were largely restricted to the upper classes. Geese, ducks, pigeons, quail and cranes were bred in enormous numbers on every Egyptian farm, and the poultry-yard was about the most important part of the farm establishment. There were bees and bee-hives.

The Earliest Incubators known. A great historian also records that goose, duck and hen eggs were hatched out *in incubators* by the poultry-raising farmers of ancient Egypt. Their incubators consisted of lime compartments built in the ground and heated by big stones from three to four hours a day. The eggs lay on straw and were "turned" every six hours; the temperature was regulated by opening and shutting ventilators. There was plenty to occupy the boys on the Egyptian farm once their chores were done. There were the equivalents of our "barn dances," where the young folk met, in the festivities that took place on the holy days of certain gods and goddesses. But the old Egyptians were still so near to old nature-worship practices that behavior at these "barn dances" was by no means as proper as down on the farm to-day. Then, there was hunting of all sorts for the farmer boys. The farmers kept greyhounds and turnspits and other hunting dogs, and even *cats* were trained to catch birds. The country girls, too, had their animal pets, for there were pet gazelles and monkeys in nearly every farm-house (and in the houses of the townsfolk as well). Of course there was a dark as well as a bright side to farm life. Often taxes were unbearable, and the farmer was ground down by tyranny of royal and priestly officials. And the farms of ancient Egypt had their human domestic tragedies just as ours do. Retold from old, old hieroglyphics is the tale of two farmer brothers, one that shows that four thousand years makes but little difference in the passion problems of poor human kind, for we meet similar tales in the columns of our daily newspapers.

THE FARMER BROTHERS

There once lived two brothers, farmers, born of the same father and the same mother. Anapu was the big brother's name, and Bitu was the name of the little one. But Anapu had a house and a wife, while his brother Bitu worked for him. Bitu stitched together the clothes, he walked behind the oxen in the field, he mowed and threshed. For this little brother was a worker. There were few like him to be found. Once, when it came sowing-time, Anapu said to Bitu: "Better get to ploughing, for the land has come out of the water (the Nile flood being over) and the time is ripe!" Then, four days later, while they were ploughing together in the field the big brother said to the small one: "Hurry up, Bitu, and get the seed-corn from the village!" When he got home, Bitu found his brother's wife combing her hair. When he asked her for the seed-corn she told him that she was busy and he should go get it himself. But when he came back loaded down with it (for he was very strong, though small of build) an evil longing enter her heart. She took Bitu by the hand and proposed that they deceive his brother together. This made honest Bitu angry. He reproached her bitterly for her horrible suggestion, but said that he would never mention it to anyone. Then he took up his load and hurried off.

Now Anapu's wife was very much frightened. So she smeared black fat on her body to make herself look as though she had been bruised and beaten, and when Anapu came home in the evening he found her lying in bed, pretending to suffer greatly. She did not rise to pour water over his hands, or to make a light as she did every other evening. "Who spoke to you?" he asked. "No one but your brother Bitu. When he came for the seed-corn, he tried to win me to be untrue to you, and when I refused, he was frightened and beat me black and blue so that I would not dare tell you. But

I must and will tell you, and if you let him live after this, then I shall die. For I know what will happen to me now that I have told you!"

Then rage filled Anapu's heart. He sharpened his knife on the grind-stone, and went and stood behind the barn-door to kill his little brother when he drove home the cattle that night. But the lead cow gave the little brother a warning. He looked in at the stable-door, and saw his big brother's feet, where he stood with his knife in his fist. So the little brother threw down his load on the ground and ran, and after him came the big brother with the knife. Then, as he ran, the little brother called out to the great god Phra: "O lord and master, judge the true and the false!" And the god Phra heard his prayer and suddenly spread a great river between the brothers, full of crocodiles. On the one bank stood the little brother and on the opposite bank the big one. Then Bitu, the little brother called out in the dark: "Wait where you are until dawn. Then I will prove the truth, for nevermore will I return to live with you!" And when the god Phra had risen at dawn the following day, Bitu said to Anapu: "Why would you kill me without hearing my story? Am I not your little brother? Are you not like a father to me? And was not your wife like a mother? When you sent me for the seed-corn she coaxed me to betray you with her. But I see she has told you otherwise." And then Bitu raised his right hand to the skies, swore by the god Phra that he had spoken the truth, drew a knife from his girdle, cut off his right hand above the wrist, and flung it into the river where it was snapped up by the crocodiles. When he had done this he fell to the ground and his soul went to the land of Acacia. But his big brother returned to his house, his head covered with the dust he had strewn on it. There he killed his untruthful wife, flung her body to the dogs, and wept bitterly for the little brother he had lost.

Army Life in Ancient Egypt. Army and navy life, especially army life was *the* life in the adventurous and military days of the "New Empire." From 1500 B.C. to 1225 B.C. the professional soldier played the most important part in national life, and no business, trade or profession offered such chances of adventure, excitement, glory and plunder. Those were the days when it was hard to keep the young Egyptian farmer-boys "down on the farm," once they had seen Memphis and Thebes, had tasted the delights of city life, and listened with glistening eyes to the tales old soldiers told of fighting and looting under the command of "His Holiness" (the official title of the Egyptian Pharaohs, for they were gods as well as kings) Tethmois III or Rameses II, in Syria, Ethiopia, of Mesopotamia. That is the way the wilder boys felt about it, the boys in our days enlist "to see the world." But there were plenty of others who did their best to "dodge" army service. For Egypt was a priest-ridden country. All the priests and all the writers were continually poking fun at the soldiers. They went about ragged, hungry and thirsty. If they escaped the arrows of their enemies, they died worn out by long marches. But take the scribe. He was the clever lad. He entered the temple school, and there was no telling to what position he might not rise if he were bright. He might become a governor's secretary, a court treasurer or steward, a priest. Besides, the Egyptian farmer, though he made a good soldier once he was trained, had the farmer's well-grounded contempt for war. The farmer's life is devoted to *creating*, to making things grow, flourish and increase. War is a *destroyer*. So, when there was a rumor that the recruiting officers were coming to a village, the fellows who did not want to go a-soldiering ran off to the mountains or hid as best they could—when they had a chance. For the village heads worked with the authorities, the great barons, princes and governors whose villages and estates had to furnish their quotas for the army of "His Holiness." Often the young men of military age were tucked away in jail until the quota had been furnished, so that they would be "on hand" when it came time to send them off to the regimental "base."

PHARAOH'S CHARIOTEER

(An Army Boy's Story)

"Here is the ounce of gold to bind the bargain, Enana! We are both of a size. You are in the last company of rookies and you told me you would be on the end file. They'll rout you out at four, while it still is dark. All you need do is to slip on this dark-brown breech-clout, and you'll never show against the side of the shed while I take your place. Think of what the gold means to your family, Enana!" The young lord Thoutmos' peasant foster brother sighed "I'll do it for you not for the gold," he answered, "but I'll take the ounce just the same. Thoth knows my father can use it, what with the taxes. But if anything goes wrong, I'll be the one who'll get cut up by the hip-popotamus-hide whips, not you!" Thoutmos frowned, then his face cleared. "Three months in the hills, and you can show your face in Apu again. I'll write my mother, the Lady Nefer,* and no harm will come to you." Thoutmos, the speaker was the eighteen-year old son of Ameni, Baron of Apu. His two lucky older brothers were already in the army. One was a captain of mounted Asiatic archers, the other a lieutenant in the *Sherdana* (Sardinians) of the Phar-

ular postal service and their postman were called *Fai chat*. Many of their

*The ancient Egyptians were great letter-writers. They had a reg-
letters have come down to us.

aoh's body-guard, the pale foreigners with metal helmets and big swords. But Thoutmos was the boy who had been picked to go into the "church" instead of "the army." It had been a family custom for generations. One boy always went into the Temple of Ammon-Re at Thebes, for it was handy for a great noble family to be represented among the higher priesthood. But ever since he had been old enough to draw his first baby bow, Thoutmos' heart had been set on getting into the army like Nech and Menes. And now—his father was in the capital—he had decided to run away from home to do so. Better to get in as a recruit from one of the Apu villages, than to be packed off to the temple when his father got back. "The five boys and the Great Castle village will keep their mouths shut," Enana went on. "They know you are the right sort, and if things go well they will be five lucky fellows, for you are like your father and never forget a favor done you. The others never have seen you. When you get to Hermopolis they'll shoot you right to the front after about three weeks' drilling. For I heard that Pharaoh has sent messages from Syria to hurry on men to him as soon as possible." Thoutmos' eyes sparkled. "That suits me! To-morrow morning, Enana!" and he was gone.

The next morning when dawn rose. Thoutmos was trudging along with the six hundred who made up the Apu contingent. His first taste of soldiering took some of the rose out of his dream skies. It was tramp, tramp, tramp along the dusty road, at a sort of jog-trot, with ten-minute rests at the end of each hour. Then everyone dropped, panting, till the crack of the sergeants whip brought them to their feet again. Three hot, wearing days, and they were in Hermopolis. Here they drilled a single week. Pharaoh's need was great. He wanted spear-fodder badly. So the sergeants and corporals sweated, and panted and grunted and—though some of them, old veterans of the Syrian wars of Rameses I, shook their heads—the recruits were finally marched in companies to the great courtyard of the House of Weapons of the fortress of Hermopolis, to receive their arms. Usually the distribution of arms was made a festival. Pharaoh or some prince of the blood presided, and there was a good deal of ceremony, ending with a distribution of wine. But this morning the companies filed past the storehouses quickly. Every man had handed out to him his felt cap, his protective oval leather apron, his ox-hide shield, his six-foot spear and dagger—for these rookies were to fill up gaps in a regiment of spearman, and not in a "battle-axe" regiment, whose men were equipped with sword, battle-axe and javelins.

With envious eyes Thoutmos saw endless other companies filing past the great barns where the Director of the Horse was superintending the distribution of the war-chariots (with two horses to each) and the cavalry horses for the black Nubian recruits from the far South. Thoutmos would have liked to have been in the chariot division. He had said something, timidly, about a transfer to the chariots or cavalry that morning to the old sergeant who was in command of the company (the captain and lieutenants were to join them in Memphis), and the latter had growled: "Thank Sakhmi the war-goddess you are in the infantry! The cavalry? How come a naked village boy like you thinks he can get into the cavalry? They are the gentlemen soldiers, they are the fellows who think themselves better than anyone else. You have to be a nobleman's by-blow at least, if you want to be a private in the cavalry ranks! And a charioteer? The chariots are light, they're only wood and leather, and the horses are trained to run like mad. Half the fellows break their arms or legs before they get the knack of handling them. Stick to the good old Egyptian infantry, boy! 'His Holiness' keeps the big *Sherdana* body guards for show, and it has become the fashion to have a Greek regiment or so in the army, though they are no good at all in pursuit, weighed down with their heavy armor. But Pharaoh has his own Egyptian Royal Guard besides the foreigners, and they are infantry! It is the infantry that wins Egypt's battles. Why blast your hide, you numbskull, don't you know you are lucky to be allowed to join the finest branch in the service?" ended the veteran with a sudden bellow of rage. And Thoutmos said no more about an exchange.

Drill in the morning, drill in the evening and march, march, march in between, was the program once they left Memphis, where their officers took them in hand. It was one long nightmare, day after day, as together with thousands of others, Thoutmos crossed the deserts and entered the Syrian land where the Pharaoh Rameses II was camped near Kadesh on the banks of the Orontes.

But when he got there Thoutmos knew the Egyptian manual of arms from the first to the last hieroglyphic. He knew the trumpet signals, he could handle his six-foot spear with ease and agility, he could salute snappily. And this was well, for it was only two days after the arrival of the recruits that the battle was fought. Thoutmos' army education had progressed in other ways. He could roll the dice with any soldier in his company, and his hand was ready when the wine-skin was passed around the camp-fire at night. But he had not forgotten his promise to Enana and had already written home to the Lady Nefert, his mother, to relieve her anxiety as to what had become of him. On the day of the battle the whole camp was in motion at four in the morning. It was to be a surprise attack. While Thoutmos' regiment with others stood drawn up in rank and file, Pharaoh appeared in a litter borne by twenty-four youths of the noblest blood of Egypt. The soldiers sank on their knees and he offered a sacrifice to Menth, the god of war, and Necheb, the goddes of victory, beneath the paling stars. Then his gilt chariot, glittering with gems, the golden-harnessed horses tossing the long ostrich-plumes on their heads, was driven up by the charioteer and Pharaoh, in his coat of mail, on his head the crown of Upper and Lower Egypt, leaped into it. A Memphis boy who stood beside Thoutmos nudged him: "Look, Pharaoh's two best horses, 'Nura' and 'Victory,' are carrying him to battle!" Rameses, after having made his plans as a general, had decided to fight as a private soldier that day. Instead of leading the chariot division, he was going to head his infantry.* And when the foot regiments saw this, and saw Pharaoh's hand raised to beckon them on, a great roar of salute rose from the ranks. "Pharaoh! Pharaoh! Hail! Hail!" they shouted, and with that cry the regiments began to move.

With a tremendous shock the Syrian and Egyptian battle-fronts joined, and the ostrich-plumes of Pharaoh's horses tossed like flecks of foam on the battle-tide of crashing spears and ringing swords.

In his chariot, around which Thoutmos and the men of his regiment were fighting, stood Pharaoh, picking off one Syrian leader after another with his arrows. But suddenly his charioteer, shot through the throat, fell headlong. The fiery horses, unchecked, reared high in the air, and dragging their reins, darted forward trampling down the footmen in their way. Pharaoh was about to be carried directly into the enemy's ranks! It was then that Thoutmos with a shout leaped into the swaying chariot, gathered up the trailing reins, and brought the prancing stallions to a halt. Pharaoh, who had stood like some bronze statue, discharging his arrows as before, while his horses reared and pranced, gave Thoutmos only a curt nod. And with whir and lance and sword, with a ringing of blows on shield and helmet as though a thousand smiths were at work, the battle went on. At last the enemy broke and began to flee, leaving the footman in the rear and Pharaoh's chariot forward in pursuit, Thoutmos guiding the wild horses with a skilled hand. For he had been clever with horses from boyhood on. and when, in the sinking sun, the war-chariots of Egypt followed by the Asiatic and Egyptian cavalry

*There was a good deal of jealousy and feeling among the different branches in the Egyptian army. The charioteers and cavalry (made up of the better-born) despised the farmer infantry, and were hated by the infantry in return. All the Egyptians were jealous of the foreigners: Lybians, Arab lancers, Sardinian and Greek hired soldiers, who drew big pay, and were boastful and arrogant. And Rameses was a clever man. His foreigners made up a small part of his force. He must depend on his own Egyptians to win the battle. Putting himself at the head of the infantry was about the most popular move he could have made.

squadrons dashed past Pharaoh at full speed with high, exultant cries of victory, Thoutmos still held the reins he had handled all day long. But when the great officers of the army, chiefs and nobles crowded about Pharaoh, one of them, with an imperious gesture, held out his hand for the reins. And Thoutmos humbly gave them up to him—for obedience was the first lesson taught in the Egyptian as in other armies—and stepped out of the royal car. And Pharaoh gave him the same curt nod which had greeted his coming as he bent before him, and went off to rejoin his regiment.

But the next day he had his reward. The men of his company were seated gloomily about the ground. Thoutmos' regiment had suffered heavily. Three of the five lads of the Great Castle village of Apu would never return to their fathers' farms. The Memphis boy who had called his attention to the king's horses would never go back to his widowed mother in the city tenement. Even Pharaoh's own wine, which had been distributed among the infantry as a reward for their bravery, failed to cheer the men. They drank it, but with gloomy faces, as though it were sour. And then, suddenly, Thoutmos' captain stepped to his tent-door and called the boy to him. A grey-haired man, he had spent a life-time under arms to rise from the ranks and become a captain of spearman. He could go no further and knew it. So there was a touch of bitterness in his voice when he said: "Youth and luck go together, young fellow! Here is something Pharaoh sent you." Thoutmos took the strip of parchment and read it.

It was a brief military document. It contained no words of praise. But it appointed Thoutmos, private in the first company of the Heliopolis Regiment, Pharaoh's charioteers, in place of the young Count of Thebes, who had fallen in battle. As Pharaoh's charioteer must be a noble, Thoutmos was raised to the nobility, and a barony of ten villages in the Fayoum was assigned to him and his heirs in fee perpetual. He was to report at once to Pharaoh in the royal tent. And while the old captain watched the sudden flush of joy that spread over his face, Thoutmos for a moment was lost in a glorious dream. He was to be Pharaoh's charioteer! He would be a figure in camp and court. He would see his brothers; but he no longer envied them their Asiatic horsemen or their chariot division. There would be more glorious fighting. And then. . . there would be Memphis, Thebes, the lovely court girls and. . ." He saluted his captain snappily: "nothing like being in the army, Sir," he said.

City Life in Old Memphis. Life in Memphis and Thebes, like life in modern cities was of two sorts. First there was the life of those who had to work for a living. An old Egyptian poet has made it look anything but rosy: "The poor blacksmith has to work in the forge-heat. He has paws like a crocodile and is as black as fish-spawn. The metal-workers have to work even at night. The stone-mason must be in the workyard at sunrise, even if his knees and spine break. The barber shaves even at night: he must over-work to fill his belly. The dyer, his fingers smelling like decayed fish, his eyes aching with weariness, never stops renewing pieces of stuff until he is sick of seeing them. The shoemaker's health is that of a dead smelt and he has nothing to eat but his leather." Wages are just enough or not enough to support families. They were usually paid "in kind" (corn, oil, salt meat), and foremen used the stick freely. The ancient Egyptian could have *several* wives, like the Turk, but ordinary, everyday people had about all they could do to support *one* (though this wife, in horrible contrast to our saner ideas, was often a sister or near relative). Yet the Egyptian middle-class and lower-class woman was respected and independent. She married at fifteen and was a grandmother at thirty. The children's clothes cost nothing until puberty—for all they wore was an amulet around their necks. At six or eight they were sent to school, but not for long. Most of them had to start working young to help keep the household going. Shoemakers, carpenters, goldsmiths, curriers, weavers, potters, candymakers (yes, candymakers), perfumers, jewelers', had their shops on the business streets, and on the squares. And, in spite of the pessimistic poet, the Egyptian workman in general had a happy disposition and a tendency to make the best of things. Yet, even in pyramid days, we find the labor strike existing as an institution.

A STONE-MASON'S STRIKE (1250 B. C.)

The people in the streets of Thebes all crane their necks. Something is up! Priests, ordinary citizens, ladies shopping, soldiers—for when the Court is in residence the Main Street of Thebes is as full of soldiers as Sands Street in Brooklyn or Granby Street in Norfolk is of sailors—all turn their heads and stare. Some two hundred stone-masons who have been working on the new buildings of the Temple of Muth are striking.* Why? Because, as they say, "We have no corn, oil, fish or vegetables. We can't work on empty stomachs !" So they are pounding along the streets, their faces and

---

*Strikes were frequent. The workman got their wages in the shape of wheat salt meat, oil and other food on the first of the month. They were expected to make them last until the first of the next month. But they seldom could, with a lot of hungry mouths to feed at home besides their own. About the middle of the month they started *counting every bite*. By the end of the month they were starving. Then they struck. Then workman claimed the scribes, who distributed the food wages, "held out" on them. The scribes claimed the workman wasted the food. Maybe *both* were right. But the fact remains that there was seldom a bit to eat in the workingman's house around the twentieth of the month.

bodies covered with mortar and clay, dragging four frightened-looking scribes, the men they think have robbed them, along with them. They are bound to the palace of the governor of Thebes, who is also the superintendent of all Pharaoh's buildings: Pharaoh had ordered the additions to the Temple of Muth. In the courtyard of the governor's palace the works' superintendent hurries up, with a few policemen, and tries to "soft-soap" the angry workman out of their demands. But their clamoring stomachs make their ears deaf to soft words. "We want food! Unless we eat we die!" they cry, and make such an uproar that the Governor himself comes out to see them. And though they do no know it, this time the workman are in luck. A slave has this moment whispered to the Governor that "Pharaoh himself has just left the palace, and will pass through the street in about ten minutes, with his escort of *Shardena* and body guard!" It would never do for "His Holiness' to run plumb into a riot, a workingman's strike! It would never do for "His Holiness" himself to take a hand and hear the workingman's camplaints. For Pharaoh is generous. A pitiful tale easily moves him to compassion. He would not only give the rascals more than they deserved, but he, the Governor, might get a reprimand or even worse. One never can tell what is in Pharaoh's mind. Anything rather than have "His Holiness" drop in on this strike. So with a smile on his face and a curse in his heart, the Governor calls his steward: "Get them away from here!" he tells him. "Quick! Take them to the granaries! Give them plenty, only get them out of the street! 'His Holiness' himself will be along in a minute, and there is no time to lose!"

And when he tells the hungry crowd of masons to go with the steward, and he will supply all their needs, they crowd around the Governor with grateful cries of thanks and blessing. But the Governor, with one ear cocked for the hoof-beats of Pharaoh's horses, waves them away, and does not breathe freely until the last grimy back has disappeared behind the granary walls. "Now, Thoth be praised," he sighs, "'His Holiness' can come and welcome."

John Barleycorn on the Nile. The "saloon" was a regular institution of Egyptian city life. The Egyptian man in the street (and in the palace, too,) was a friend of John Barleycorn and never objected to a drink. In fact, he drank whenever he had a chance, and the barley-beer he got in the "Beer-House" went by the poetic name of "soap of the throat." Yet even in Ancient Egypt the saloon-keeper was less respected than the other tradesman, and the "Beer House" usually stood in the corner of a dark alley, and did not front on a main street.

"The Face on the Bar-Room Floor." No doubt there were old Egyptian forerunners of that pathetic ballad which was so often

echoed by the walls of American saloons before the Eighteenth Amendment. For a scene from an old Egyptian saloon (based on authentic historic records) is about as "modern" as can be: There was no swinging door. You just went in. And there was no "bar"; but there was everything else. The lime-washed floor was covered with mats. You sat down at a table on a chair or stool. Before you could ask for your particular poison, the waitress hurried up: "Drink yourself into rapture!" was the proper greeting, "What shall it be? It is a good day to enjoy yourself?" And if you had a sense of humor, you answered: "Bring me eighteen cups of wine with your fair hand! I will drink until I am happy, and the straw mat shall be the bed on which I will sleep myself sober!" Along the side of the wall is ranged the *rum*-seller's stock in trade—*rum*-seller because the Egyptians were supposed to have had *shodou*, palm-brandy,—as well as "light wines and beer."

If you were a poor drinking man, your tipple would be millet-beer, barley-beer, iron beer, sweet beer, "perfumed" beer—which would make a hardened toper of today shudder—spiced and hot. But if you had a soul above such a vulgar drink, there was plenty to choose from; you need not go short. In big clay vessels, *amphorae*, with wooden or clay stoppers, smeared over with mud to keep them tightly closed, were wines white, black red and yellow: Mareotis wine, Pelusium wine, Syena wine, "Star of Hourus" wine (a choice brand), heavy wines from Ethiopia and the golden Phoenican wines that came high. All "imported" wines and "domestic" had the vintage-year marked plainly in ink on the clay.

History's First Temperance League and Thieves' Union. The best moral opinion of the times was opposed to drink and drinking. While the old topers in the saloons explained to new saloon recruits that a man who had drunk himself tipsy with wine always fell on his face, while one who intoxicated himself with beer fell on his back, non-drinkers coined proverbs such as "Beware of him, he is a drunkard!" "Beer destroys the young man's soul!" "The drinking man is like an oar torn from the oar-locks: he wabbles from side to side. He is like a chapel without its god, and a house whose beam is shaking." The Egyptian prohibitionist said: "The people in the streets turn from the winebibber in disgust, for he throws mud and hoots at them, until the police come and carry him off to prison to sober up." In fact, the great Pharaoh Rameses II was so alarmed at the evil effect of drinking on the national life that he founded the first *Anti-Alcohol League* known to History, to fight the spread of drunkenness among the ancient Egyptians. We can realize how popular the vice must have been when we see even the *women* of the Egyptian *higher circles* immortalized on the wall-paintings of their tombs in the disgusting act of throwing up their wine! Naturally, the lower class "Beer Houses" and dives were the resort of the "harder" kinds of city Egyptians, as well of soldiers, sailors and—the criminals. For there were plenty of criminals in Egypt, especially in the days of the "New Empire." The *bastinado*, cutting off of the nose, long-term and life-sentences to the Nubian gold mines, and the terrible punishment of *impalement for grave-robbing* did not prevent the thieves of Thebes and Memphis for having their regular "labor unions." The "Chief of Thieves" was the president, and the thieves were regularly enrolled. Those robbed could recover the stolen articles by furnishing a written description of them to the President of the Thieves' Union, and paying one-fourth of the actual value of the things. The most famous thief in Egypt is the one whose story Herodotus has told. It is one that proves the truth of the saying: "Opportunity makes the thief."

THE PRINCESS WHO LOST HER HEART TO A THIEF

The Pharaoh Rhampsinitus, toward the end of a long life, had gotten together such an immense treasure of gold that he called in his master stonemason Thonis, and had him build a great treasure-house of solid blocks of stone, like those used for the pyramids. Now Thonis was an honest man, as men go, but when from Pharaoh's own lips he heard the tale of the gold, dust and bars, bullion and coin, vases, cups and shields, that the treasure-chamber was to hold, something gave way in him. And he kept only his personal slaves busy on one section of the work. When the treasure-house was finished, Thonis had so arranged that one man, by moving a certain stone, could enter the huge hall. The day after the completion of the work the stone-mason gave the slaves who had done the work poisoned wine to drink, and by evening the secret of the hidden entrance was all his own. Thonis never had the courage to use his private entrance to the Pharaoh Rhampsinitus' treasure-house. But on his death-bed, however, he called his sons Suif and Sethos to him, and revealed the secret of the entrance to Pharaoh's golden store-house.

Suif and Sethos were young and enterprising. Soon Psamnis, the royal treasurer, when he came merely as a matter of form, to check up his master's treasures, was shocked to find them steadily growing less. Jars of gold dust, bars of gold bullion, chests of gold pieces had vanished. But where could they have gone? There was no sign of any one having entered the great vault. In fact the intricate system of bolts and bars was known but to two persons, Pharaoh and himself. In despair he hurried to Pharaoh and told him what had happened, and king and treasurer laid their heads together to discover the thief.

First of all, they hid a number of man-traps about the treasure-chests and jars in such a way that a thief was almost certain to be caught. Sure enough when Thonis' boys went about getting rich quickly the next night, poor Sethos was caught in the trap. He could not release himself. Knowing that death was only a matter of hours, and fearing he might betray his brother under torture, he told Suif to cut off his head (so that none could tell who he was), and escape. And, after much discussion and with tears in his eyes, Suif did so. The next morning, Rhampsinitus entered the treasure-house. "Aha," he cried, as he saw a body lying at the end of the vault, "caught at last!" But it was a *headless* body, a body without a name, so to say, and he only added a new mystery to the one he thought he had solved. At home, however's Suif's mother—we know how the Egyptians felt about the bodies of their dead—wailed and lamented. Unless Suif brought home his brother Sethos' body, so that it could be properly embalmed, she would go straight to the palace and tell Pharaoh the whole story. Suif calmed his mother. He promised her that he would bring home Sethos' corpse the next day, and that he should be embalmed as though he were Pharaoh himself.

But Rhampsinitus also knew how the Egyptians felt about the bodies of their dead. He was sure that if he hung up the headless corpse in chains, by the city gate, some one, sooner or later, would come to claim it. Then he could lay hands on the thief. So Sethos swung at the city gate in chains with soldiers on guard to seize any one who might claim him. When Suif saw him he slipped back and before long the soldiers on guard all began to laugh. A countryman, driving to asses with great skins of wine had stopped in front of the gallows. There the neck fastenings of two of his skins had come unloosed, and the wine was running from them. The poor farmer boy seemed to have lost his head. He beat his breast and cried that the wine was going to waste, and he did not know which skin to tie up first. No Egyptian soldier approved of wine going to waste. With their corporal at their head, they all came running, drinking-cups in hands. And before the skins were tied up a good deal of wine had flowed down thirsty soldier throats. The countryman was grateful, but when he began to thank the gallows' guard, they did not hear him. The wine was drugged and they had fallen asleep to the last man. Then, while the shadows of night closed around him, Suif took down his brother's body, loaded it on one of his asses and brought it home.

The rhinoceros-hide whips were busy in the barracks the next morning when Pharaoh found that the dead body on which he had counted had gone to join its head. He raged and tore his hair, and swore by all the gods of Egypt that no thief should get the better if him, by Thoth, no! It was then his daughter Diora had a bright idea. "Let me spend the night in the treasure-chamber, father," said she. "The thief is sure to come again, and I will hold him in conversation. Then, when I am ready, I will seize him by the arm and call out to you. And you can come in with the guards and capture him." This seemed an excellent scheme to Rhamsinitus. That night Diora retired into the treasure-chamber. Outside the door stood twenty men of Pharaoh's guard with drawn swords, while he himself reclined on a couch, ready to leap up the moment he heard his daughter scream. But—though the twenty men with drawn swords waited all night long, though Pharaoh started up from an uneasy nap every hour or so and asked: "Did you hear anything?" not a sound came through the massive stone door of the treasure-chamber.

At last, when morning came, and the whole court was assembled in the great golden hall of the palace, Rhampsinitus high on his throne, Diora entered. And as she came into the room she began to laugh, and all here train of maids and slave-girls laughed with her and the black eunuchs who accompanied her laughed. Even the carved sphynxes of Pharaoh's throne seemed to laugh. And Diora, still laughing said "Father, I met the thief and talked with him, and at last I took hold of his arm and was about to scream when—he was gone, and I found myself holding a dead arm, which he must have cut from a corpse, in my hand!" And once more Diora began to laugh, and then she added: "And I can understand how it is you have lost your treasures in spite of bolts and bars. The thief has a magic key which unlocks even the most solid doors. I am no solid door, father. While I was guarding your treasures last night the thief stole a treasure from me too—he stole by heart!" And Diora rubbed her soft cheek against her father's grizzled one and begged: "Offer the thief my hand in marriage, father, for that is the only way I can recover the heart he stole from me."

And as Diora smiled and coaxed the maid and eunuchs began to laugh again. And soon all Memphis was laughing, even the crocodiles stuck their heads out of the slimy, yellow Nile and laughed. To think that they had set Pharaoh's daughter to catch the thief and he had stolen her heart, just as he had her father's treasures! And the only way to get them back was to take him into the family! For the drums beat and the trumpets blared, and as heralds went through all the streets of Memphis, crying: "Rhampsinitus, by the grace of Amon King of Upper and Lower Egypt, Greeting: Seeing that on the night of the fourth of June, in the year thirteen hundred and twenty-four B.C., a thief who has robbed the royal treasure-house of much gold and many jewels did also steal from our daughter, the Princess Diora her heart and her heart's love, we hereby promise him a full pardon and our daughter's hand if he will return the stolen articles at our royal palace this day. Signed, Rhampsinitus, Pharaoh!"

And the stone-mason's son married the princess, and they lived happily ever afterward, so the story says. When Rhampsinitus died Suif succeeded him on the throne, and it is claimed that *very little was stolen in Egypt during his reign.*

CHAPTER II

AND now we will pass him from these brief glimpses of the life, the real human life of Ancient Egypt, that was the background for all her wonderful civilization, one with which Egypt struggled for the world's empire for hundreds of years, that of Babylon and Assyria.

In old Chaldea and Sumeria, the gloomy Sumerians, a people, probably of yellow Mongol stock, rose from the mud village stage to great walled cities with temples and palaces, where priest-kings ruled and where, as in Egypt, the backbone of the country were the farmers whose irrigation canals dotted the Mesopotamian plain, while all the arts and trades which make life more livable were practiced in the towns. The gloomy Chaldean religion did not hold out much of a future for them. They spent a good deal of time in the temples, but since life after death held out few inducements, they concentrated on making the best of the life they had to live on earth. One of the most romantic pictures of life in old Chaldea throws the figure of the *first reformer* on History's screen.

History's First Reformer. A French Revolution in 4,000 B.C. is what it amounted to! In the great city of Lagash and in the palaces on their estates lived a tyrannical aristocracy of the princes and nobles. They toiled not neither did they spin, though they did fight. But they taxed, and taxed until the farmer was reduced to skin and bones. As soon as the crops were ripe, the tax-collectors and tax-inspectors swarmed out of Largash in crowds. When they had collected the taxes there was not enough left to feed the farmer and his family. And, if the farmer could not make good his taxes, he was sold as a slave to make up the amount due. In the city it was the same. The laborers were ground down in the same cruel way. More and more men of the lower classes became professional thieves, often simply in order to get enough to eat. And when they robbed the dairy-farms of the great nobles' estates of cattle, sheep and asses, and the granaries of the stored corn and wheat and fish-ponds of the temples and were caught, they suffered the most cruel

* To be read in connection with Chapters II and IV of "The History of the world."

and barbarous punishments. At last Uru-ka-gina, a plain, everyday farmer who had been ruined, could stand it no longer. He secretly organized the farmers of the countryside: they got in touch with the city labor leaders and suddenly the flame of rebellion flared up in the land. The nobility, their tax-collectors and guards were put to the sword, and a "labor-government," a "reform government" set up, with Uru-ka-gina as king. But, like most leaders who have led farmer rebellions, he did not last. A good, able, sincere and honest man—a *true* reformer, with nothing but the common good at heart—his farmer-spearman when war broke out with a neighboring kingdom, could not put up the fight the battle-trained nobility had been able to do. History's first reformer died in the flames of his burning capital.

The Babylonian empire succeeded that of the old Sumerians and Arcadians, when Semite tribes invaded Chaldea and conquered and "mixed" with its inhabitants. And under a great lawyer king, Hammurabi—he was the first king known to have worked out a complete code of laws for his country—the city of Babylon in the course of centuries became a decidedly "modern" sort of place.

A New York of Forty Odd Centuries Ago. The old Babylonians had all the "advantages"—with a few exceptions—modern civilization can boast. They had a week of six working days, with a "Sunday," when the folks went to the temple, at its end. The "kids" went to school every day. All the schools were "temple schools," and they learned reading, writing, grammar and history. Just as our school children have to learn the list of the presidents of the United States the little Babylonian school-boys and school-girls— for the classes were "co-educational," with boys and girls sharing the same bench—had to learn the list of the kings of Babylon, back to the Babylonian Deluge. Arithmetic, however, was considered the most important of the "Three R's," *mental* arithmetic. And in museums we find clay "slates" on which the children put the answers to the sums the teacher gave them to do "in their heads." The pathetic smudge of a little Babylonian twelve-year old's thumb has come down the forty centuries which separate it from our day!

The High Cost of Living Four Thousand Years Ago. Arithmetic was the big thing in Babylonian life. For Babylon was the biggest banking and trading country in the ancient world. Babylon (like Phoenicia) was a city of "financiers." One Babylonian banking firm did business under the same firm name without interruption for six hundred years. Balnumahe (a Babylonian Rockerfeller), had the monopoly of several great lines of trade about 2000 B.C. He owned fleets of trading vessels like the Standard Oil, drew rents from tremendous parcels of real estate in the city and suburbs, and was one of the biggest tax-payers in town. They had everything in

Babylon, even artist quarters like Greenwich Village, and asphalt streets, city parks and Libraries, private and public—with catalogues, librarians and attendants. They had courts of justice, judges, lawyers, "halls of record," where real estate deeds were filed, policemen and criminals. Hammurabi, who covered about everything in his Babylonian Code of Laws, even had sections covering doctors' fees. If you were a working man, a *mushkenum*, a doctor could not charge you more than five shekels a visit, but if you belonged to the shopkeeper class, he could hold you up for ten. And the poor "white collar" worker of the days before the white collar was invented had the same trouble he has to-day without his collar to console him. While Balnumahe could hunt up some Asiatic Palm Beach and play African or whatever other species of golf was in vogue in his time, his clerk needed all the mental arithmetic he had learned as a school-boy to figure out how he would pay his month's rent, and feed and clothe his family. There is in existence (Yale Babylonian Seminary) a clay tablet record—more than a million have been dug up and supply the facts we are giving—on which some poor bookkeeper or scribe tried to put down his monthly "budget," with little notes of despair on the margin, notes that show he wondered how in the name of the seven planetary gods he ever was going to strike a balance between "the high cost of living" and the amount of his wages.

Profit-Sharing Between Labor and Capital. Wealth and wealthy men and labor and labor troubles go hand in hand. Yet the Babylonians at times practiced "profit-sharing." There exists an interesting record in which a Babylonian contractor (3000 B.C.) pays a bonus on the profits of a job to all his workmen—*except the bricklayers!* They had been on strike, and so they were shut out from the bonus. But, if strikes were frequent, we also find wealth taking an intelligent interest in the employee. The temples in the big Babylonian cities often owned vast properties, as in Egypt. And, as in Egypt, they had thousands of employees. The Temple of Erech was one which had a regular sick benefit fund, and paid old age pensions, as well as educated its employees' children, and apprenticed them when they were old enough to go to work. The farmers had their "Grange" offices right in town, usually in some temple. And the temples and banks loaned them money to buy blooded cattle or make improvements, taking mortgages on their farms. And when the usual shortage of farm labor developed at harvest time, they supplied "gangs" of laborers to work in the fields.

The Babylonian Business Woman. We think the business woman is a modern development. Not at all. Women of Babylon had every right and privilege man enjoyed. She not only could own and inherit real estate and slaves in her own (not her husband's) name, give promissory notes and go on another woman's (or man's) bond. She also played an equal part in the business life of the banking office and shop, and *she got the same pay in the temples for the same work that men did.* Often women were advanced and promoted over the heads of men: ancient wage-lists prove this past all question.

A PEEP INTO THE BALUMAHE, INC., OFFICES IN ANCIENT BABYLON

The clerks in the enormous Balnumahe Office Building are hard at work, for the great Balnumahe himself came down this morning at 10 o'clock. He had returned unexpectedly from Egypt, where he had been busy arranging an international loan, secured by high per cent mortgages on "His Holiness," the reigning Pharaoh's Nubian-Delta estates. But he was supposed to be hunting hippopotamus as Pharaoh's guest for another week. As soon as Balnumahe came in, he looked into the copper box (it took the place of our wire office-basket), and glanced over the important mail his secretary had laid out for him. Then he clapped his hands. At once Noubta, the bright Babylonian girl who took his "dictation," came in. One after another she put down what he said in *cuneiform,* the wedge-shaped Babylonian script, scratching in each letter with a sharp copper pencil on a tiny tablet of wet, adhesive clay. When they were finished Balnumahe waved a number aside. To these the girl added "Dictated but not read," and signed for him. The remainder he signed himself. Noubta had already turned to put the letters in the small oven in the outer office where they were baked, when Balnumahe recalled her. "There was something I forgot," he said. "Take this!" "This" was a short note addressed to the firm agent in Thebes. It merely directed him to have the yellow-haired Greek slave girl he had bought from the Count of Thebes sent to his country house near Accad at once. Half-apologetically the great Balnumahe added as Noubta wrote: "My wife, Lady Balnumahe, asked me to buy her an attractive slave girl while in Egypt." But black-eyed Noubta, though she bows sedately, knows better. It is an open secret in Babylon that the great Balnumahe's wife will not have a good-looking slave girl in the house. And—she does not even know her husband has a country home near Accad, for it stands in the head bookkeeper's name in the records! Noubta is a bright girl. She may hum: "Does the palmgum lose its flavor on the bed-post overnight?"* as she goes about her work, but she never repeats anything

*The old Babylonians had a great variety of popular songs. But many of them were shameless beyond anything our higher moral standards would allow. They have often brought a blush to the cheek of the scholars translating them from the original clay. Professor Langdon, of Oxford, one of the world's greatest Assyrialogists mentions "the licentious verses" of

in the outer office and she never leaves the baking and sealing of letters, especially private letters, to any one else. Perhaps that is why she is one of the great Balnumahe's favorite secretaries, and draws a big salary for a girl of her age.

Balnumahe soon leaves for luncheon at the Merchant's Club. He will not show up again that day. But work goes on uninterruptedly. Noubta takes the tiny clay letters out of the oven, slips them into little clay envelopes just big enough to hold them (after shaking in sand all around the letter so that it will not stick to its envelope) and closes the envelope flap by pressing Balnumahe's seal down on the wet clay. On the envelope face is the name and address of the person to whom it is sent: the seal is the "return address." The letter for the Thebes agent will go by one of the firm couriers, but the post-office will handle the rest. For the Babylonians had a government, interurban and international postal system, a dead-letter office, a parcel-post division, and express and freight service by caravan and boat. Except the Thebes letter, Noubta has done the mail in *triplicate* (The Thebes letter only in duplicate, for Balnumahe's personal file), which is the rule of the house, for filing.* But Noubta's mind is not really on her work to-day. She is thinking with mixed feelings, of a custom which for all Babylon's "modernism" and apparent civilization, seems repulsive, even insane, to us. It is one which that observing traveller Herodotus has recorded:

SCARLET-LETTER DAY IN ISHTAR'S TEMPLE

Noubta already had consulted five different astrologers and their answers had all been the same. Between the tenth and the twelfth of the month of Thammuz, of this year she must obey the law which decrees that *once* in her lifetime every woman of Babylon, maid, wife or widow, must sit in the Temple of Ishtar and yield herself to the embrace of any stranger whose fancy she may take. The daughters and wives of the great lords came in splendid litters, and numerous servants attended them. But whether they go in silks or in coarse linen, go they must. It is a religious law which cannot be evaded. Well may honest old Herodotus call it "the most disgraceful of Babylonian customs!" Noubta often has passed the great

their love songs. But we must not forget they also had less objectionable "workman's," and, let us hope, more innocent ballads such as a girl like Noubta might sing.

* Business files were kept with the greatest accuracy, and many a Babylonian girl supported an aged mother as a filing clerk. The express men and the boat men who handled freight carried their clay bills-of-lading hung around their necks. As most of them wore only a breech-clout or kirtle of some kind, and the bills-of-lading were about an inch long and three-eighths of an inch thick, this did not worry them.

temple and seen other girls of her own age seated in long rows along the passages marked out between the columns, each wearing a crown of corn on her head and waiting, waiting, waiting. Any stranger, be he who or what he may, thick-lipped Nubian, tipsy Assyrian soldier, fat Phoenician, or haughty contemptuous Greek may pass along the lines, and scan the faces of those seated until his choice is made. Then, if he throw a small silver coin in the girl's lap, and utter the ritual words: "I beseech the goddess Ishtar to favor thee!" she must rise and follow him outside the temple and do his will. No matter how small the silver coin, no woman can refuse it. He is, as Herodotus tells us, "accounted sacred." The girl who is chosen follows the thrower of the first coin. "Those who are endowed with beauty and symetry of shape are soon set free," says the Father of History, "but the deformed are detained a long time, from inability to satisfy the law, for some wait for a space of three or four years!"

Yet, suddenly Noubta smiles. She has thought of a way out. The great Balnumahe has a cousin who is a priest and astrologer in the Temple of Bel-Merodach. And—does she not handle Balnumahe's private mail?—she knows the priest is deeply indebted to his wealthy cousin. A word from Balnumahe and she can arrange to have her time set when she is ninety-two. She bursts into a peal of merry laughter. What a joke on the other priests and on Ishtar herself! . . But now she grows serious again. Some day, not so very far away, she expects to marry. Perhaps the offended goddess. . . But then she remembers some passage in letters from Balnumahe's priestly cousin. "Old traditions must be kept up. . . Silly business of forcing every woman in Babylon to sit in the temple of Ishtar makes us the laughingstock of other nations! . . . Was discussing it with a Memphis priest only last week, and he smiled in that superior way the Egyptians have, and said: 'We do not put *our* women on so low a plane!'" Noubta nods brightly. Her mind is made up. She, for one, is not going to help make the Babylonian women a laughingstock for other nations.

But there are other girls besides "business women" in the great Mesopotamian cities. There is Ila-Azil, for instance, the daughter of a high-priest in Assyrian Ninevah, a girl who moves only in the highest social circles. Yet a great love, as the following tale will show, easily breaks the barriers of the "sheltered life," in antiquity as in our own day.

THE HIGH-PRIEST'S DAUGHTER

Ila-Azil, daughter of the Subai, the high-priest of the goddess Ishtar of Nineveh, lived rather a lonely life in her father's palace. He was a serious old man, taken up with his religious duties. He never lookd at Ila-Azil, and would hardly have recognized her if he saw her, so seldom did they meet. There was a summer-house at the end of the priestly garden. 'It overlooked the neighboring gardens of a modest house that faced on the next street back. In that house lived the young Egyptian Menes. He was an army officer, a captain, whose business it was to buy and send on the Syrian horses regularly, month by month, to Egypt to the great studs of the Houses of the Chariots for the remounts of the cavalry and the chariot-teams. For the Egyptian climate did not agree with horses and the studs had to be renewed continually. Menes often walked in his garden and—Ila-Azil's summer house was thickly latticed so she could watch him at her ease without his being able to her—she had fallen in love with him, though he was a man of a strange race. One day, wearied of her lonely life amid slaves and servants in the great palace, Ila-Azil put on the simple garb of a slaving-maid, slipped into the street and entered Menes' house. Pretending she was a penniless orphan, but at home in all household work, she easily induced the kind-hearted young man to accept her as a servant, and quietly entered on a new life, satisfied merely to be near the man she loved. In her home the slaves waited a full day before telling their master Subai, hoping their young mistress might return. But she did not come back.

Two days before Ila-Azil had left her home, King Sargon had made a triumphal entry into his capital, with the army which had conquered the cities of the Syrian coast. And as he rode in his chariot through the vast crowds that line the streets, his eye had caught sight of a young girl, and even as he looked at her a great longing was born in his heart. A word, and a trusted officer had made it his business to follow and find out who she was, and report to the king. On the morning Ila-Azil left her home, King Sargon stood in one of the great treasure-chambers of his palace. With him were two slaves carrying a stretcher. And on the stretcher Sargon was heaping precious things of all sorts: cups of gold and enamel bracelets, anklets of silver, set with gems, and a great seven-ringed collar of cornaline, lapis-lazuli, blood-red jasper, pearls, agate, sardony rubies and onyx beads. "Take them to Illa-Azil, and say that King Sargon sends them!" he told the officer at his side.

Menes treated Ila-Azil with distant kindness. And when the priest's daughter found that on certain evenings he went out and disappeared for an hour or two, she followed him. She found, to her despair, that in another Egyptian home in Nineveh he paid court to a young Egyptian girl, the child of an old retired jeweler. Meanwhile King Sargon, his brow dark, had listened to the report of his officer: Ila-Azil had disappeared from her father's house, and none knew where she had gone. When the idea came to him that perhaps a love-affair might explain her disappearance, Sargon's face became so terrible, that the officer fell down before him on the stone slabs. But he regained control of himself and said: "Seek her, and see that you find her! For if you do not I swear by the Lady Ishtar of Arbela that you will die in torture!" And soon a sound like thunder rose around the palace. It was the rattle of the chariots darting in every direction to search for the high-priest's daughter.

Sargon, meanwhile went to the palace terrace overlooking the river. There he sat motionless while the hours passed, his heart eaten up with longing. Below him lay the stream, crowded with passing boats, and the whole great city of Nineveh with its temples, palaces and houses. He was its master and the master of all that dwelt in it. But though everywhere men hunted and questioned, no one could give them news of the vanished girl. At last a messenger appeared on the terrace, and reported that Ila-Azil could not be found. King Sargon raised his sceptre, and, in spite of his thick Nubian skull, the messenger fell dead. A second man appeared. His foot touched the body of his comrade stretched out on the pavement. He trembled, for he saw that the king was angry. "Ila-Azil?" asked Sargon without moving. "O Light of the World, all trace of her is lost!" answered the poor wretch, kneeling before the dark shadow on the throne. The shadow raised a granite arm. The heavy metal sceptre fell like a thunderbolt. The second messenger rolled beside the first. A third shared the same fate. But at last the officer found a clue. Menes, whom he visited, told him of having taken in a young girl who gave her name as Mylitta. But she had been in his household only two days and then had vanished. Returning to the palace and keeping out of reach of Sargon's sceptre, the officer told him what he had learned. "Could it have been Ila-Azil?" Sargon said to himself. "Ah, I shall find her if I have to tear up Nineveh stone by stone!"

But Meanwhile Ila-Azil lay worn out and sick with sorrow on a bed in the Egyptian jeweler's house, watched over by the very Egyptian girl upon whom she had spied. They had found her in the garden where she had fainted in her sorrow and despair unable to stand the distress the revelation of Menes' love for another had caused her. The next evening Menes told both girls that King Sargon was searching for Ila-Azil—she had revealed her name and station—but that he would not be apt to find her where she was hidden and they would keep her secret. But one of the jeweler's slaves overheard them talking. Tempted by the hope of rich reward, she hurried to the royal palace. The guards crossing their spears to hold her back, she said she wanted to see King Sargon. "You choose a good moment, old witch!" they said. "King Sargon sits on his terrace like the god of evil. He has just killed three messengers with blows of his sceptre!" But her cries and insistence brought the officer of the day and others to the spot and she was led

I

to the terrace. When she saw the King in the shadows, the old woman flung herself face downward beside the dead messengers. Then rising she cried: "Glory of Assur, I bring you good news!" And when he told her to speak, she informed him the Ila-Azil had been found.

"If you can lead me to her hiding-place, old woman, you may take what gold and gems you can carry out of my treasure chambers," was his answer. Soon the royal chariot, the King himself holding the reins, dashed out of the courtyard. Sargon lashed the horses and the horses and the chariot sped over the the stone pavement with a ring of bronze, while the old woman clung to its side, out of breath. It flew like the wind, and in narrower streets its wheels scraped the walls. At last the old slave told the king to check his steeds. "There is the house! I have left the door open and will mind the horses for you." The King entered the house, strode through the hall and found himself in a room where the two girls were sleeping side by side in the dying lamp-light. He picked up the girl in his powerful arms, and Ila-Azil woke to see the King Sargon's radiant face bending over her. Then, with one leap, the King stood in the chariot. He wound the reins around his middle, and holding Ila-Azil, half dead with terror, to his breast, clucked to his horses, which began to run swiftly toward the palace.

In the palace the high-priest's daughter was surrounded with slaves, and treated with the greatest respect and attention. For when he set her down in the great hall, King Sargon had said: "Have no fear. You rule Sargon and Sargon rules the world!" Day by day the King visited her as though she were a princess of the royal blood, instead of the daughter of a priest. Day by day he pleaded his cause. He was tall, handsome, well proportioned. Egyptian Menes would look like a dwarf beside him. A word from his lips could change the face of the world and the destiny of nations, and his lips were as red as the blood on a sword-blade. His smile had the grace of a terror which nothing could resist. And King Sargon would say to her: "When I saw you from my chariot, Ila-Azil, on the day of my triumph, an unknown longing entered my heart. I have lived alone in this giant palace, surrounded by smiling shadows that call themselves women. They meant no more to me than the figures frescoed on the walls. In vain I brought back from my campaigns the chosen virgins and loveliest women of the countries I had conquered. I flung them aside like flowers after having breathed them for a moment. I was only a king, Ila-Azil, but you have made me a man, you have given me a heart!" Seldom did King Sargon say so much. A word, a nod, a sigh—and his thought was carried as the lightning follows the thunder. But he gave up his majesty for her sake: "But if I do not love you?" Ila-Azil timidly asked.

"When you have lived in this palace, breathing the air of my love, you *will* love me. Dip deep into my treasures! Fling away gold as you choose. Be my wife and my queen. I make you a gift of Assyria, with its priests, its armies, its laborers its innumerable inhabitants, its temples, its cities! Tear it as you would a bit of muslin if you will! I'll find other kingdoms for you, greater, fairer, richer! If the world will not satisfy you, I shall conquer the planets, and unseat the gods! You are the woman I love! Ila-Azil, the priest's daughter, no longer exists!"

And—the woman in Ila-Azil was touched by the tenderness of the King of the world. His love for the young Egyptian was a vain thing, a thing born of her dreams. The love of Sargon was real. A sudden feeling of affection for this man in whom was embodied all the glory and power of the world, who yet had treated her with the respect and the reverence due a princess came over her. She stepped down from the ivory chair in which she was sitting on a raised dais. She drew near the king and smiled at him through tears—and Sargon clasped her to his heart.

CHAPTER III

IN THE LAND OF THE DOUBLE AXES

(Creta)

AGAIN and again, we find human life during the early days a strange combination of high civilization and barbarism. The Egyptian pyramids were the wonder of the world—and the Egyptians wedded their sisters! The Babylonians filed their business letters in triplicate—and their young girls, once a year, had to submit to the chance embrace to the first stranger, no matter of what race, kind or color, in the Temple of Ishtar! The Assyrian kings had vast libraries in their monster palaces—and skinned their prisoners taken in battle alive! In the island of Creta, there was a great and flourishing kingdom (2500 B. C.). Its kings were called "Minos," just as the Egyptian kings were called "Pharaoh."

SAVAGE CRUELTY AND CIVILIZED SANITATION

In great cities, Knossus, Mycenae and others, vast palace and temple ruins have been discovered. They show that every refinement of luxury, even *sanitation,* known to us was an every-day matter to the early Cretans. Wonderful colored frescos adorned their walls, gold and silver, the choicest tinted glasses and faience vases with silver inlay, glazed table-ware, plates and dishes appeared on the tables of King Minos' dining-rooms. The Cretan ladies knew all about tight-lacing, and decollete dresses. They padded their hips and wore flounces. And the castles of the Gothic and Renaissance Ages, even the royal palaces of the sixteenth and seventeenth centuries, so far as sanitary toilet arrangements were concerned, could not compare with the great palace of the Cretan kings at Knossus. There absolutely sanitary toilets with proper wooden seats, the entire closet-room built over a deep, slanting bottom, perpetually flooded with water, have been discovered; just as similar toilets have been found in the ruins of the Roman Emperor Augustus' palace on the Palatine hill. The sanitary flushing of toilets in *modern life* did not make its appearance until the 19*th century!* But—with all their masterful advance, we find the Cretans given up to the worship of cruel gods and human sacrifice. With them as with other great nations of antiquity, civilization and barbarism go hand in hand.

In the days of the Cretan power, the Greek city of Athens had to furnish King Minos every year with a tribute of seven Athenian virgins and seven Athenian youths, who were sacrificed to the sacred bulls of the Cretan arena. For with all their civilization, the Cretans worshipped two cruel deities. One was the Great Mother, a nature goddess, her sign the crossed Double Axes. The other was the monster, half-bull, half-man, known as the Minotaur. And among the youths and virgins brought once a year to Knossus to be sacrificed was a Theseus.*

THE ESCAPE FROM THE LABYRINTH

Gently King Minos' palace guards pushed the Greek girls and youths into the dim, cavernous entrance to the Labyrinth. The Labyrinth was not utterly dark. Everywhere, at distances of about twenty feet apart, a round panel of thick milky-white glass, set in the stone roof, shed a ghostly light on the twisting and winding passages, just enough to let the wanderers in the maze find their way. "If you win out through the passages, Minotaur may spare you!" said the guards encouragingly, but with sly and sinister smiles. For Minotaur (Minotaur was the name given *all* the odd dozen sacred black bulls driven into the white-sanded arena on which the Labyrinth opened on the day of sacrifice) never yet had been known to spare a victim! One reason was because the youths and maids to be sacrificed were annointed with an evil-smelling ointment. This ointment came from the musk-glands of the great cats, leopards and trained lions, which (with an iron railing between) were taught to annoy and harrass the black bulls without doing them an injury. There was little chance of the captives being lost in the maze. Sliding rock doors were so arranged that for all its winding, only one passage was left free. This led to the arena, where the bulls waited. To make sure that no victim would escape, an air-funnel, hidden in the rock, suddenly flung a current of air upon the victims as, blinded by the sudden glare of the sun, they stepped from the dim cavern passages of the Labyrinth out on the arena sands. This air carried to the waiting bulls the scent of their hated enemies. With a sudden rush they at once charged the dazed victims and in a few

---

*The legend of Greek mythology, in which the Greek hero Theseus goes to Creta and slays the legenary monster, the Bull of Minos, the *Minotaur,* may be a poetical account of a *real happening*. It has thus been reconstructed in the following tale. The excavations made at Knossus have proved that a great "labyrinth" or maze of very complicated winding, subterranean corridors, rooms and passages did exist in the great temple-palace.

moments only the gored and trampled bodies remained to show that the sacrifice to Minotaur had been accomplished.

On this occasion the Cretan people who, with King Minos and his court, filled the great amphitheatre from top to bottom, rose in their excitement and shouted their god's name.

As always had been the case before, the Athenian victims, all without any idea of what was in store for them, stepped out on the sands. That is, all save *one*. Some instinct held Theseus back for a moment. And so it came that, still within the cave, he stood as though turned to stone while his unfortunate comrades were slain before his eyes. But he would not give up hope. Turning his back on the white, glaring arena to which his eyes had now become used, he plunged back into the Labyrinth again. Yet—the Cretans could count—thirteen are not fourteen, twice the sacred seven. Already messengers had hurried to the guardian of the Labyrinth. Orders were given to shift the hidden doors of rock. Wherever Theseus now wandered, he could not avoid setting foot on the threshold of the chapel of the Great Mother. Stepping *on*, not *over* that threshold. And above the fatal doorway hung fatal Double Axes. The doorway was only half a man's height and narrow. He would have to squeeze through on hands and knees. And the moment he planted the palms of his hands on any part of the foot-board of the stone inset *chapel floor*, the axes fell. They fell just as his neck was thrust out from the entrance opening, and cut that head off with blades of razor keenness. And the great mother whose statue stood directly opposite, could smile down on the severed head which had rolled to the foot of her altar, while the body to which that head belonged, remained in the doorway in an attitude of humble adoration. It was one of those cruel and subtle refinements in which the ingenious Cretan mind excelled.

Theseus wandered on through the dim, shadowed passages of the Labyrinth with no idea of the fate in store for him. Suddenly a sweet voice came to his ears. He stopped. There was no one in sight, but he realized that some one was speaking on the other side of the stone wall. "Noble stranger," said the voice, "I saw you yesterday, when they brought the captives for the sacrifice to the temple. I could do nothing then to help you. But your gods must have you in their care, for no victim ever yet has escaped the Minotaur. Yet my heart is full of pity for you, and so I shall help you save your life. Listen well to what I say. As you go on you will come, before long, to a narrow entrance which leads into a large room. To pass through it you will have to creep on hands and knees. Now mark well what I say! Before you crawl through the passage, feel with your hand above it, at the height of your head, till you find a bronze knob set in the stone. Turn the knob and a stone panel will slide back. Put your hand into the space behind the panel, and you will find there a metal weight, attached to a five-foot length of strong hempen rope. When you have found it kneel before the entrance passage. Fling the weight through in such a way that it falls just a foot within the outside entrance passage, on the far side. When you do this something will fall from above the far side of the passage, and once it has fallen you can crawl through in safety. You will find me waiting to advise you further."

"As you say so shall I do, unknown friend!" cried the young Athenian. But when he crawled over the threshold of the Great Mother's chapel, and saw the glittering blades that hung above the entrance, blades he had so narrowly missed, he shuddered. When he rose he noticed a white-clad figure standing at the chapel end. Hurrying toward it to express his thanks he suddenly stopped. This was no palace servant, this was no slave. A beautiful girl, with deep violent eyes, and a tender, innocent smile was looking at him. "I am Ariadne," she said in the same sweet voice that had spoken to him through the stone. "But I do not know if I will be Ariadne very long. If my father King Minos and the priests of the Great Mother discover what I have done, I will probably be slain, together with you." And she blushed and hung her head. "No, Ariadne, we will live, not die, together," cried Theseus. He took her in his arms— for he had read her secret in her violet eyes—and for a moment while the stone image of the Great Mother smiled even more kindly, perhaps, than she would have at the gory head, they forgot Creta and Athens, and all the dangers that lay before them. Then Ariadne said: "We can flee from the palace by secret ways known to me! I have gold, and if you can bribe some Greek skipper, we may be miles at sea before our escape is discovered. Yet—the only way out of the chapel of the Great Mother is guarded by the largest and fiercest of the Minotaurs! And, dearest, much as I love you," she added with an adorable smile, while she wrinkled her pretty nose in a disgusted way, "Love can ignore things the Minotaur will not!" But Theseus smiled in return. "The Great Mother shall aid us to overcome the Minotaur," he said as, he picked up one of the glittering axes. "Lead the way to love and freedom!" When the following morning the keepers of the Minotaurs went to look after their sacred charges, they wailed and tore their garments and flung dust on their heads. For the greatest of the Minotaurs, a monster black bull, lay on the stone pavement of the yard without the Great Mother's chapel, his massive head almost severed by a single blow from one of the sacred Double Axes.

Some tale of this kind may underlie the legendary accounts of Theseus and his slaying of the Minotaur that have come down to us. But we cannot end, as we should like to, by saying Theseus and

Ariadne lived happily ever after. Theseus was a frequent rather than a faithful lover. He seems to have abandoned the girl who gave up all for him. Some accounts say that he deserted her and hung himself. Others declare he abandoned her on the Island of Naxos, where she died giving birth to their little babe, which died as well. Then he returned, and was much grieved to learn of her death. But—there are a number of other stories which say that he did not grieve long, but roved and married here, there and everywhere for years to come, sometimes under very discreditable circumstances.

As for the Cretans, their luxurious civilization came to a sudden end about 1500 B.C. They ruled the Greek seas, and for centuries had carried off from the ruder Greek tribes along the coasts the loveliest girls they could surprise and seize. Lovely women were in great demand in Knossus, where they entered the palaces of the king and the rich as slaves. They also were trained for the bull-ring, where girl *matadors* fought and slew bulls of a lesser breed than the holy Minotaurs. They danced in the theaters, they served a thousand and one purposes of luxury and pleasure. But the rude Greeks whom Homer sang finally got tired of seeing their lovely wives and daughters carried off before their eyes, as well as of "maiden tributes" for the Minotaurs. One day they got together, sailed for Knossus and in a sudden rush put the peoples of the great Cretan cities to the sword. They did not return to their ships until the glorious palaces and temples were blazing like monstrous torches. Then, with their minds and hearts at rest, knowing the Cretan ships were destroyed, their cities ruined and their power broken, they dipped their oars in the fire-lit waves and returned to their homes.

CHAPTER IV

GLIMPSES OF HUMAN NATURE FROM OLD SEMITIC LANDS

THE Babylonians were a mixed race, part Chaldean, part Semite. The Assyrians were a pure-breed Semitic race—though toward the end of the empire they were committing race suicide—but when we speak of the Semite races of olden times, we usually have the Hebrews, the Phoenicians and Arabians in mind rather than any others.

The Hebrews. The Hebrews are the people of the Old Testament. This sacred book of their faith, a wonderful collection of legends, prophecies and prayers has largely been taken over by the Christian religion. Among its tales is the story of Abraham, who led his tribe to Egypt (2,000 B.C.?), and one of whose descendants, Joseph, even became prime minister under one of the so-called *Hyksos* or "Shepherd Kings" of the sixteenth dynasty. But when native Egyptian Pharaohs once more descended the throne, (the Theban dynasty, great war lords and builders), the Hebrews were enslaved and, wearying of their efforts to make bricks without straw for the ruling race, managed after considerable difficulty, to make their way back to Palestine. The Bible story of the Exodus is one we can read at any time. It might be of interest to see it told from another angle, an Egyptian one. We have put the tale into the mouth of a supposed solitary survivor of the Passage of the Red Sea.

THE TALE OF MEFRES, THE SWORD-BEARER

"I, Mefres, Sword-Bearer to 'His Holiness' the late Pharaoh Menephres, Child of Osiris, Sun of the World, have here set down, as well as I can recall it, the true tale of the calamities which overtook Egypt toward the end of his reign, and the passage of the Red Sea, which I alone, out of all the host of Egypt, survived. And this account, as I have set it down, I have deposited in the Temple of Ammon-Re, so that others, in days to come, may know how these things came to pass.

"It was one day in the month of *Set.* Pharaoh was driving his chariot along the Nile road near Thebes, attended by his escort, myself included, when two tall old men, Hebrews by the name of Aharon and Mosche, suddenly stepped out into the road like phantoms. The king checked his steeds, which already had flecked the breast of Mosche with foam, and waited. Now this Mosche already had done feats of magic in the palace to induce Pharaoh to let him and his people leave our land. Now he again solemnly begged the king to let them go.

"'Prove the power of your God to me by some miracle,' said Pharaoh, 'and I will grant your request!' And Mosche turned to Aharon and told him to cast his wand into the Nile and bid all the Egyptian waters, the Nile and other streams, our lakes, ponds and reservoirs, even the water in our jars, vases and cups, to turn to blood. And Aharon did so, while we waited with anxiety to see what happened. Only Pharaoh, who had a heart of bronze in his granite chest, smiled scornfully. But when Aharon's wand struck the water, it began to boil and bubble. Red tints appeared in its lemon-colored flood, and soon the whole River Nile had taken on a crimson tinge. It looked like a river of blood rolling in scarlet waves, and broidering its shores with a rosy foam. It seemed as though it were reflecting some great fire or a red sunset sky. But the air was calm. Thebes was not burning, and above the red waters—already flecked by the white bellies of dead fishes—stretched a clear, blue sky. Long, hideous crocodiles clambered out on the river-banks, and huge hippopotami, like blocks of red granite covered with a leprous growth of fungus black, fled through the reeds, raising their tremendous muzzles to the skies, no longer able to breathe in the bloody water. And the canals, the reservoirs and the fish-ponds all had taken on the same color. When we returned to the palace, even the cups which held water were as red as the jaws in which the blood of the altar victims is caught.

"But Pharaoh only said: 'These are magic tricks good enough to frighten the ignorant masses!' And he called for the high-priest of Ammon-Re. And the latter had asked Mosche to return the water to its natural color, so that he could perform the same miracle. Then he stretched out his wand and murmured a few words in a language so old that it was already dead in the days of Menei, the first Egyptian Pharaoh. And the Nile turned as red as blood for him as it had done for Mosche. 'You se,' said Pharaoh, 'my wise men can perform the same miracles you do!' But then, in seven day's time, Mosche performed the miracle of the grasshoppers. This plague was terrible. The horrible creatures covered the whole country by the hundreds of millions. They swarmed in ever increasing multitudes in the houses. Horses, asses, goats, wild with terror, stampeded across the fields, but could not get away from them. In the palace In vain he slew hundreds with his sceptre. In vain we slaughtered the disgusting creatures clustered thickest around Pharaoh himself.

the vile and dirty insects around him. Countless new thousands took the places of the slain. They covered the backs of the sphynxes, the steps of the pyramids, the roofs of the temples. The storks and ibis which first had greeted this unexpected gift of food with delight, took fright and rose in the air with a great flapping of wings and clappering of beaks. And though the high-priest, by murmuring a magic formula, made them disappear and recalled them again to show his power, the second time all his magic could not drive them away. Pharaoh was furious, but to rid himself of the creatures he promised Mosche that the Hebrews should be free to sacrifice to their God in the desert. Then the grasshoppers died and disappeared—but Pharaoh did not keep his word.

"Now Mosche loosed plague after plague on our unhappy country. Finally he took a handful of soot and flung it skyward before Pharaoh's eyes. And a red pest attacked the Egyptians and turned their skin red as fire. And when Pharaoh asked the high-priest of Ammon-Re to show his powers, the old man sadly said: 'To what end? The finger of the Unknown One shows in these wonders. Submit! Our magic is beaten. The sphynx had no word to solve the riddle, and the mystery of the Great Pyramid is an empty nothing!' Then, when Pharaoh still refused to let the Hebrews depart, all the cattle of Egypt died, while the Hebrews lost not a single cow. Then came a plague of locusts which stripped Egypt of vegetation, and left the land as bare as a barn-yard floor. But though, when Pharaoh begged him to, Mosche removed the plague, Pharaoh still would not let him go. Then a hail and a great darkness covered the land. People thought they already were in the tomb, and seated along the temple entrances uttered plaintive cries and tore their garments. And at last on a night of fear and horror, a specter entered every house in Egypt whose door was not marked in red, and every first-born boy in every family died, the first-born of Pharaoh as well as the first-born of the lowest *parischite*. In a distant room of his palace, savage, silent and still obstinate, Pharaoh sat, looking at the boy stretched out on the funeral couch with jackal's feet. And when Mosche appeared on the threshold of the room and repeated his demand, Pharaoh said: 'Go and sacrifice to your God as you wish!'

"But he could not forgive himself for having yielded to the Hebrew prophets. To me he said, one day: 'The bas-reliefs on my palace-walls show me as the invincible Pharaoh, armed with whip and scepter, driving my war-chariot across the bodies of the slain. Yet I have to give in to these two magicians of an unknown people. The gods to whom I have raised temples built to last for all time, do not defend me against the unknown God of this obscure race of slaves. The prestige of my power is gone! and my people murmur!'

"Meanwhile the tribes of the Hebrews already were past the great brazen statue our priests had blessed, and which had the power to stop all escaping slaves in their flight. It did not stop the Hebrews. An immense multitude, their beasts of burden loaded down with the riches they had borrowed from us, they passed on into the desert and out of Egypt. Their tale of sacrificing to the Everlasting God was only a pretext. They were leaving Egypt forever. For the mummy of Joseph, in its painted and gilded case, carried on the shoulders of relays of bearers, went with them. When he heard this Pharaoh fell into a terrible rage. He called out to me to bid the war-chariots be harnessed, and to send for the captains. He buckled his great belt of crocodile-skin around his waist. He bade his charioteer fill the two quivers of his chariot with arrows and javelins. He slipped round his wrist the bronze bracelet which breaks the vibration of the bow-string, and handing me his sword we stepped into his chariot. At once the charioteer leaned forward and spoke to the horses. And we were off at break-neck speed, followed by all the chariots of Thebes.

"Terrible in his fury, Pharaoh drove his horses mercilessly, and after him the six hundred chariots poured with a ring of brass. The infantry came on at a jog-trot, but soon were left far behind. Often Pharaoh had to stop and wait for the host to catch up with him. When this happened he beat against the chariot-front with his fist, stamped his foot and ground his teeth. And he would bend forward and sweep the horizon with his glance trying to catch a glimpse of the fleeting tribes of the Hebrews behind the sand-clouds raised by the desert winds. If I had not calmed and held him back, he would have pushed straight on, at the risk of finding himself alone against a whole nation. We already were in the desert. At great distances clusters of dusty palms would show around some small pond, whose waters our horses would rile and toss about with bleeding nostrils. But Pharaoh, as though he did not feel the fiery heat which the white-hot sky rained down, would give the signal to move on, and all of us, chariots, horsemen and footmen, would take up the pursuit again.

"But a well-trained army moves on more swiftly than a people on the march. At last we could see them, camped along the borders of the Red Sea. And when the tribes saw Pharaoh's golden chariot glittering in the sun, and followed by the war-chariots and the army, they uttered great cries of terror, and cursed their prophet Mosche for leading them astray. Before them was our battle-front: at their backs the sea. But—I saw it with my own eyes—Mosche, standing on a little hill, prayed to his God! And then there took place a miracle which none of our temple priests could have performed. Out of the East came a wind of superhuman violence. It cut into the Red Sea like the blade of some gigantic plough, throwing up to the left and to the right mountain furrows of salty water crowned with crests of foam. Torn apart by the impetuosity of this breath which would have blown away the pyramids like grains of dust, the waters rose straight in the air like liquid walls. Between them they left a broad path that one could follow dry-shod. And at either hand, through their transparence, we could see marine monsters twisting and squirming, terrified at thus being surprised by the light of day in their mysterious deeps.

"The tribes flung themselves into this miraculous passage like a human river flowing between two high banks of green water. Two million human dots speckled the livid sea-bottom of the gulf with dots of moving black, and their feet trod the clay marked only by the imprint of the leviathan's belly. And the terrible wind which blew passed above the heads of the Hebrews, which it would have felled like grain, and by its pressure held back the raging and towering waves. It was the breath of the Eternal cutting the sea in two.

"Terrified by the miracle, we hesitated to follow the Hebrews. But my master, the Pharaoh Meneptha, with the high courage that stopped at nothing, struck his rearing horses with his double-thonged whip. And, his eyes injected with blood, foam on his lips, and roaring like a lion who sees his prey escape him, he forced them to take the road so strangely opened before them.

"Our six hundred war-chariots followed. The last Hebrews already gave themselves up for lost when—we were half-way across— Mosche raised his wand. Then, suddenly, our chariot-wheels rolled from their axles. For an instant there was a terrible mingling of horses, men and wheels, of breaking limbs and splintered wood. I raised my eyes, and saw that the mountains of water that hung miraculously above our heads were falling. The sea closed in on us, rolling together in whirlpools of foam, men, horses and chariots, like straws seized by the eddy of a current. And as I felt myself drawn down into the abyss, I still could see my master, the Pharaoh Meneptha, standing erect in the body of his light car, which still floated on the waves, mad with pride and fury, discharging the last arrows from his quiver at the Hebrews who had reached the opposite shore. And, his arrows gone, he grasped his javelin and—already half-swallowed by the waves—flung it uselessly up toward the Unknown God whom he still defied from the bottom of the abyss!

"An enormous wave rolled two or three times along the shore, and it carried to the bottom the last bits of wreckage. Not a trace remained of Pharaoh's glory or of his men. The same wave must have flung me unconscious on the bank. When I opened my eyes, Miriam, the sister of Aharon, on the opposite bank, was singing in triumph while she beat the tambourine. And all the Hebrew women kept time on drums of wild asses' skin, while from two million throats rose a hymn of deliverance."

The Hebrews' Gift to Humanity. In their national life generally the Hebrews under the Prophets and kings did not differ much from other Oriental Semites. Their kings ate, drank and made merry, fought, maintained harems, harassed a poor agricultural nation with exorbitant taxes for the upkeep of royal courts and the expense of ruinous wars, like other oriental monarchs of their day. The people of Israel farmed, traded and lived their lives much as other people of their day did—with one exception. Other races, as time went on, grew more tolerant of each other's gods. An Egyptian, an Assyrian, a Phoenician, even a Greek and a Roman could agree that Isis, Belit, Ishtar, Astoreth, Aphrodite and Venus were after all, one and the same deity—the nature-goddess of love. And so with other gods. The Hebrews occasionally lapsed. It took the most terrible outcries on the part of great prophets to lead them back from the wanton revels in the groves of Baal to the straight and narrow path. But— Hebrews differed from every other race of the ancient world because they worshipped the one great God. He was not a god developed out of some natural force—the sun, the moon, the elements. He was the Unknown God who created all things. This high and noble idea, the national inheritance of the Hebrews, was the protest against the worship of *many gods* which ruled the rest of the world. And in place of the wild and lustful temple orgies and customs of Babylon, degrading to all moral feeling and woman's rightful claim to respect, the law of Moses *hallowed* marriage. It laid stress on the *holiness* of family life, on children *honoring* their parents. The day of rest was a day of rest for *slave* as well as master, and thus, in a way, embraced *all men* within God's kingdom. The narrowness of Hebrew life, the bitterness of Hebrew intolerance for the ideas and beliefs of others, the continual Hebrew factional strifes and hatreds have not helped the world. But the Hebrew idea of one supreme God and Creator was the Hebrew's greatest gift to humanity.

The Phoenicians. The Phoenicians, whose great cities rose along the middle of the stern shore of the Mediterranean, between Syria on the north and Palestine on the south, were the ancient world's greatest nation of sailors, explorers and traders. They began in a small way. The name of their second greatest city, Sidon, means "Fish-Town," but from villages of fishermen and all the unpleasant associations "Fish-Towns" have for the nostrils of the delicate, Sidon, Tyre, Askalon Byblos, Arvad and other settlements rose to enormous cities, with rich "villa" quarters removed from the smelly "port" streets, where "city kings" and the wealthy merchant princes lived amid the perfumes of Araby, and in a luxury that equalled that of the Pharaohs and the Assyrian kings.

Life in Ancient Tyre. New York, San Francisco or Boston to-day have many points in common with old Tyre. In Tyre and Sidon ground was so valuable that they had "sky-scrapers," office buildings, granaries and store-houses many stories higher than the three and four-story Babylonian house. Along its waterfront, with its shipping offices, its wharves with ships loading and unloading continually, clerks and accountants were busy checking up and noting down. Sailors lounged about in the low grog-shops and other places of amusement of the "Barbary Coasts," and the "Barbary Coasts" of all the Tyrian cities ran wide open day and night, and were busy places. In "Old Tyre" the business of life was transacted and its tenements and lodging-houses held a large working and factory population behind sea-walls a hundred feet high. But on an island half a mile back was New Tyre, and beyond that lay the district of palaces and gardens. The Phoenicians were a greedy, grasping, treacherous race. Their great idea in life was gain. The rich factory-owners, for they manufactured as well as traded, did an enormous foreign and domestic shipping and trading business, and ground down the toilers in their dye-works, glass-factories and weaving establishments. But —any one of the toilers they ground would have been just as good a "grinder" had he gotten the chance! Like the ex-emperor William, the Archduke Frederick of Austria, King George of England, the kings of Tyre dabbled in "business," and were not above making a profit in trade even though they wore a royal crown. The Bible gives us the details of a "deal" between King Hiram of Tyre and King Solomon. The latter had a Red Sea port. He let Hiram build a shipyard there "on joint account," to open the route to India, and the two royal traders divided $8,000,000 as the profits of their first joint trading voyage. The Phoenician religion was cruel, and had many licentious features, and the Phoenicians were hated and despised throughout the ancient world for their greed and dishonesty. Floating coastwise along some Greek island shore a Phoenician trader thought nothing of landing and "picking up" any unfortunate girl who might be down near the water and not have observed his approach. Anything that came to the Phoenician's net he regarded as fish. And a Greek slave girl usually brought a good price in the home market or any other market.

THE TRAGEDY OF IO

The red-haired girl crouching in a corner of the dark cabin of the Phoenician galley turned viciously on the fat, black-bearded Phoenician trader Agama. He had just told her to mount on the bridge, as they were entering the port of Tyre. "What do Tyre or you mean to me!" she exclaimed. He raised his foot and kicked viciously at the heap of cushions on which she sat. She herself was too valuable a bit of "trade goods" to damage: that was the only reason he did not kick her. Instead he turned to the old hag he carried aboard as cook. "Dress her, you old crow!" he said. "If she is not on the bridge in an hour's time, I swear I'll fling your ruddled old carcass overboard!" With that he left the women.

"Lucky girl," said old Banisit enviously. "You will never know the touch of the whip, for Agama expects to sell you for a good round sum. All I am for him is a back for the *bastinado!*" Io sighed. "I shall be a slave," she said with savage despair. "A slave? What more could you ask?" said the old woman. "A girl as pretty as you are is sure to be snapped up for the harem of a high-priest or a prince." "If the man Agama sells me or dares come near me I'll tear his heart out with my nails!" cried Io. "But why, if he be rich and handsome?" asked her companion.

"What has that to do with it! I was not born as you were to be a vile slave in a master's house! My father dwells in a lordly mansion beside the sounding sea. He is one of the first among the rich and powerful Achaeans, the Greeks. One unlucky day I was bathing along a sandy beach on the sea-shore with my maids, far from the eyes of the young men, when a troop of barbarians in ambush among the rocks flung themselves on us like ravishing lions. My maids came out of the water, and fled quick-footed toward the town. But I.... I was ashamed to flee naked before the eyes of men! I tried to escape by swimming. And then the pirates got back in their skiff and laughing they captured me in a net, as one takes a dolphin. O my home land, O dear native town, I shall never see you again!"

"Women must accept what fate gives them," said her old companion. "My mother, too, was a free woman, a Bedouin girl of the land of Pouanit. She was led away a captive when the Syrians defeated her tribe, and sold to the Temple of Ashtoreth in Tyre. She, too, wrung her hands in despair, wept her lost liberty and her beloved deserts. But.... she accustomed herself to a life of servitude!"

"We Achaeans hold that death is better than slavery," answered the girl gloomily. "Agama shall not turn my despair into gold as he hopes. Death will save me from worse!"

But, though she wept, she let the old woman dress her, rub her hair with fragrant oils and, clad in a long, clinging gown of thin green cloth, she climbed the little ladder which led to the quarter-deck, where Agama stood. But charming as she looked, the trader was worried. When she first had been captured she would have thrown herself overboard in her despair, had she not been bound. And now she was gloomily and obstinately defiant. In spite of her piquant white skin and her red-gold hair, she might not make a good impression on possible buyers. But as the vessel drew near the wharf, Io already had attracted the attention of all those on that part of the water-front. And she, who always in her native Argos had been surrounded by an atmosphere of affectionate respect, was suddenly exposed to the impure gaze of thousands of foreign eyes. She could not understand the questions, crude and salty, the humorous obscenities, the base cries of admiration which greeted her presence as she stood on the bridge, the wind outlining every beautiful curve of her slender figure as the thin gown clung to her limbs. But she felt that there was something degrading and humiliating about them. And when she drew nearer and saw the eager staring faces whose glances seemed to draw from her every covering she knew that the hour had come. Never would she watch the white foam curl along the Argive beach again. Never would she see her father or mother, her brothers or sisters. Never would she see the dear home and the beloved town of her girlhood. But neither need she, a free-born Greek, live to be the slave among some one of this swinish race! Agama's eye left her for a moment. He stepped aside to shout back an answer to a question hurled by a friend on shore. And Io seized that moment of inattention. One bound, and she had leaped from the bridge to the deck. Another and she was at the vessel's side. There she stopped. A pile of copper ingots, each weighing at least a hundred pounds, lay there. With the strength of despair she seized one, clutching it firmly to her breast, so firmly that it cut a deep gash in her white bosom. And, as Agama turned, petrified with horror at the profits he saw slipping from his grasp, Io had gained the bulwark. There she stood poised for a moment, like some beautiful statue imagined by Phidias in an inspired hour. And then—headlong, the copper bar pressed to her heart, she flung herself head-long into the deep waters of the harbor. The vessel was hastily brought in and a plank laid. Then divers flashed quickly into the water in an effort to bring back the trader's goods before they were valueless forever. Ten minutes passed before they found the Greek girl. And when they did it was but to let her lie. They could not even make her dead arms release the copper bar they clenched so tightly. Agama, when he heard that she was beyond all hope of bringing to when found, tore his hair and wailed: "These damnable Greeks!" And then, for old Banise had told him what the girl had said: "Death better than slavery? Insane, these Achaeans, all of them! Who would not rather be the most wretched dyer in one of Eschmoun's factories and *alive*—than King of Tyre and food for the fishes?"

The Arabians. There were kings and cities in Arabia as early as 1000 B.C. and there are inscriptions which tell of their paying tribute to the Assyrian kings. But though rich cities and splendid courts rose and flourished, the wild Arab horsemen who often fought in Egyptian, Assyrian and Babylonian armies for pay, lived the wild, free life of the nomad tribesmen in the deserts. They still were leading it when the caravan routes on which the rich cities and their rulers lived changed, and the kings died out and their cities fell into decay. They roamed the sands in tribes with their herds of camels and horses, and lived the life of open-air wanderers, fighting much among themselves. Unlike the Semitic Phoenicians, the Arabs, the Semites of the desert, valued their *honor* above all other things. In the days before Mohammed, the desert had its code of conduct for man and woman. When that code was transgressed came tragedy. Nothing gives a better insight into Arab *character* than the following tale.

THE CHEST

Weddah, son of a chief of the tribe of Yemen Arabs, was one of the noblest-looking young Arab horsemen of his time, just as Om-el-Bondain, the daughter of Abdelasis, chief of the tribe of the Beni Meruan, was the loveliest among desert maidens. From childhood these two had loved each other so greatly that they always were to be found together.

But among the desert Arabs the ancient patriarchal law holds good. A girl's *father* selects her husband, and she is married to her *father's* choice. When Abdelasis married his daughter Om-el-Bondain to Walid Ben Abdelmelek, Weddah lost his reason. After he had gone through long months of mental darkness and despair, he mounted his horse and rode out into the Syrian desert. For he had heard that Walid had set up his tents there, and everywhere he went he asked where he might be found. At first no one could give him any news. But at last, as he was staying as the guest of a desert sheik near a small Syrian village, he was told that Walid had left the black camel-hair tents for the walls and roof of a town-house, and that he was living with his wife in the very village near which he had camped. And the slave girl who waited on Om-el-Bondain was pointed out to him. Soon Weddah managed to make the girl's acquaintance, and after giving her many gifts at last thought he might rely on her to help him. So, one evening, when they met as had been their custom, in a lonely spot, he asked her whether she knew Om-el-Bondain. "Why should I not know her?" answered the girl, seeing that she is my mistress!" "Well, then," Weddah went on, "your mistress happens to be my cousin, and if you will let her know that I am in the neighborhood I am sure the news will please her." "I shall be glad to do so," said the girl. And she ran off to carry the news to Om-el-Bandain. "Are you sure of what you say? Weddah alive?" "I have talked with him myself," answered the slave. "Then hurry and tell him not to leave until I have sent him a message!"

Om-el-Bondain arranged to let Weddah into her house. There she kept him shut up in a cedar chest, and let him out when she thought it safe for them to be together. And when anyone came who might see him, she told him to get into the chest again. Now it happened one day that Walid had a chance to buy a fine pearl. And when he had bought it he gave it to a servant and said: "Take this pearl and bring it to Om-el-Bondain!" The servant took the pearl and brought it to his master's house. But he did not announce himself. He just stepped in, and it happened that Weddah and Om-el-Bondian were caught together at the moment. So the servant, by chance, caught sight of Weddah getting into his chest in Om-el-Bondain's apartment, through a rent in the curtain. Om-el-Bondain took the pearl, but when the servant asked her for a reward because he had brought it to her, she refused, and gave him a severe reprimand. With his heart full of rage and hatred against her, the servant returned to Walid. Him he told what he had seen, and described the cedar chest into which he had watched Weddah getting. "You lie, you mother-less slave, you lie!" cried Walid. And without a moment's delay he rushed home.

There were several chests in Om-el-Bondain's room. But Walid seated himself on the one which held Weddah, and said to Om-el-Bondain: "Give me one of your chests!" "They are all your property, Walid, as I myself am," answered Om-el-Bondain. "Well then," Walid continued, "let me have the one on which I am sitting!" "It is full of things a woman needs," said Om-el-Bondain. "I do not want its *contents,*" answered Walid, "I want the chest itself." It is yours," said Om-el-Bondain with a faint sigh.

At once Walid clapped his hands and had the cedar chest carried out of the room. Then he called two slaves, and told them to dig a pit in the garden, and to dig until water oozed up from the earth. When the pit had been dug, he had the cedar chest carried to its edge. Then he bent down and with his mouth close to the lock said: "I have been told a certain thing concerning you! If it be true, then let every trace of you vanish, let all knowledge of you be buried forever! If it be false, then I do no wrong in burying a cedar chest, for I shall be only burying cedar-wood!" But no answer came from the cedar chest. Then Walid had the chest lowered into the pit, and the pit filled in again with the earth and the stones which had been dug from it. But after that day Om-el-Bondain spent most of her time by that spot in the garden, weeping, until, one day, she was found there dead, her face pressed against the black earth above the cedar chest.

This story of hapless love proves how greatly the desert Arab valued his honor. And both the men involved in this strange tale displayed a chivalrous delicacy with regard to its unfortunate heroine. Walid, her husband, no matter how great his love for his wife, could not leave his servant's report uninvestigated. It is true he could not leave his wife unpunished without losing his honor, his own self-respect and that of his fellowmen. But Walid honored his wife too much to have the chest opened, lest she be put to shame, a shame which he must share. Weddah, on the other hand, also has a knightly soul. He would rather die the terrible death meted out to him than betray the woman whom he worships. But her love is too much for the unfortunate Om-el-Bondain. Pride and self-interest first had prevented her putting anything in the way of Walid's removal and burial of the chest. But once the chest was buried, she could not conceal her despair and, broken-hearted, followed her lover to the grave.

CHAPTER V

OUT OF THE PERSIAN PAST

THE ancient Persians, hardy mountain tribesmen who founded an Asian empire on tne ruins of Babylon, Assyria and Egypt had a great many good points as individual human beings. One of the most "home-like" things about their religion, Zorastrianism (so-called after its founder the prophet Zoroaster), is that a man's *birthday* was counted as a great festival, and much was made of it. For their theory of life was that a man had a man's work to do in the world, and ought to be glad of the chance to do it. And this is the good, healthy philosophy of existence on which our own civilization rests.

What the Persians Were Like. The average Persian of ancient times was stronger and hardier than the ancient Egyptian. A husky mountain farmer, he was used to every kind of hardship, and not cruel and merciless like the Assyrian. He was easy-going and tolerant about the opinions of others and, if anything, a little too quick (the direct opposite to the Egyptian), to take up "foreign" manners and customs. It was good to be a real, dyed-in-the-wool Persian in the old days of the first "Great Kings." Not a Mede, or a member of any one of the conquered races, but a real, Simon-pure Persian. First of all, the inhabitants of Persia proper paid no taxes whatsoever. (Even to-day that is a privilege worth having.) A fine basket of fruit for the king, if he happened to ride into the hill country, some gift of exceptionally good country produce—and the Persian farmer had done his share. And—if you were a member of the tribe to which the king's family belonged, the Ackhaemenians, and lived in the old Persian hill-capital Parsagadae,—whenever the king entered the town after having been absent for a long time, he gave to *every man and woman in it, according to custom, a gold piece*. For the Persian kings, even in the days of their greatest power, never quite forgot that in the beginning they were kings of the "people," rather than of the nobility. The men who counted their court cooks by the hundreds and who moved and lived amid a pomp and splendor beyond that known to any monarch of our times, were recalled to their old democratic simplicity on the day they mounted the throne. For when they were consecrated in the temple of the warrior-goddess in Parsagadae, they solemnly ate a simple old peasant dinner, "down on the farm" dinner of figs and sour milk, to show that they were merely the *first* among a peasant nation. But the Persian King of Kings, though he ate the dinner the plainest among his people ate on the day he ascended the throne, was also the very incarnation of the national soul. It was every Persian's duty to die for him, if necessary, gladly and cheerfully. We have a striking instance of how the common man, the ordinary soldier as well as the greatest noble in the land felt on this head, when the Great King, Xerxes, fled back by ship from Greece to the Asian coast, leaving his beaten armies behind him:

THE SACRIFICE OF THE AEGEAN SEA

It was at Eeion that Xerxes, the Great King, with a small escort of the "Immortals," the soldiers of his guard, and a group of the greatest nobles of the land, left his beaten and fleeing army, and went aboard a Phoenician ship. His eyes were hollow, his cheeks sunken, his beard and dress neglected. The monotonous song the Phoenician rowers sang beat time for his unhappy thoughts, as he lay below deck on his cushions. The greatest army Persia ever had placed in the field had been beaten. His own royal chariots and even the white steeds of the holy Nisaean breeds, sacred to the king, had been stolen by the Greeks. The sky was clouded with grey, and the ships wallowed in the trough of the sea. The melody the rowers sang sounded in broken gasps, their very oars gasped as they dipped into the waves. The sails were reefed. The trireme (a ship with three banks of oars) cracked, as though every one of its planks was about to burst. Xerxes leaped up from his couch, and went on deck. There the storm-winds were tearing greedily at the ship's tackle and clewing, and officers and men, among them several of Xerxes' nephews, were clinging fast to each other. At the helm the steersman tore at his rudder in silent rage.

"Steersman," cried Xerxes, "are we in danger?"

"Yes, Majesty," he answered.

"Have we a chance, steersman?" Xerxes asked, angrily.

"Not the least in the world, Great King, unless this overloaded ship is lightened!"

"Overloaded? Why, I left nearly all my baggage behind!"

"Overloaded with men, Great King!"

The autumn storm raged about the trireme, which moved up and down, to right and left in the sea, and made no headway. In vain the rowers panted among the huge waves that swept over them and across the deck.

"Then I command that these Phoenician rowers be cast into the sea!"

"Who will take the oars then, Majesty? Your Persians cannot row like the Phoenicians. If you throw the Phoenician rowers into the sea we are sure to sink!"

Xerxes straightened his tall figure. "Persians," he cried, "the moment has come for you to show your love for your king! His life depends on you!"

There was not a moment's hesitation among the Persians clustered thickly about the deck. High and low, noble and commoner, fought with each other to be the first to die. They flung themselves at Xerxes' feet in adoration, then ran to the bulwarks, and cast themselves into the sea, man after man, plain soldiers of the Guard in their golden armor, nobles of the court in their long silken robes. And the common soldiers were the first to die, though the nobles followed them. There was no difference in rank and station. What were their lives if only the King be saved? They leaped into the sea on the right and on the left, and when the waves flung their bodies back on deck again, the feet of the few whom Xerxes bade remain with him, thrust them away once more. And the rowers sang their melody as before, while their oars groaned: only now their melody sounded like a funeral dirge. The next morning the storm was over, and the Aeolian coast, the Asian coast, the coast that meant safety for the fugitive king, lay in plain sight. Xerxes landed and gave the steersman of the vessel a wreath of solid gold, a sign of the greatest honor, for had he not saved the Great King's life? And when he had given him the wreath of gold, he called the headsman, and the steersman's head was hewn from his shoulders. For had not he, a Phoenician, caused the death of a hundred Persians? Nor was Xerxes cruel in this. There was a grim logic and justice in his action. A king must reward where reward is due, but a Persian king also swore when he was crowned, to defend and protect his people.

From an Old Sportsman's Writings. An old historical romance by the Greek Xenophon, a famous Athenian soldier, writer and sportsman, gives us glimpses of the *human side* of ancient Persian life. In the "militia," for the Persians had universal military service, the young men had to sleep at night around the public buildings, with their arms at their side. They did not sleep in snug, warm armories, even though it must have been cool at night in the Persian hill towns. "Only the married men were exempt, and did not have to be on duty at night unless special notice was given." And the Persians also anticipated our "Boy Republics" and self-governing camps, where the boys selected their own captains and leaders, for they had the same arrangement.

TEACHING THE YOUNG IDEA HOW TO SHOOT IN ANCIENT PERSIA

Persian boys went to school, as boys did in Babylon, but *arithmetic* was not the leading study: "They gave their time to learning *justice* and *righteousness.*" Severe punishment was handed out to any one convicted of *ingratitude:* the idea being that an *ungrateful* person was likely to forget his duty to God, parents, fatherland and friends. *Shamelessness* came next on the list of offences, and the boys were taught temperance and self-restraint. They brought from home to school their dry bread, "with nasturtium for a relish, and to slake their thirst a drinking-cup to dip in the running stream." And here we have a striking instance of how the lessons learned in youth were not practically applied in later years. For the Persians were as hard-drinking a race as ancient times can show. They never went near a "running stream" to dip a cup in it, if we may believe the historians, once they grew up.

School Precept and Life Practice. And temperance was a word, just a word to them: one of those things one learns in school in order to forget them. The average Persian (especially in later days, when he had grown more "civilized," soft and luxurious) was never happier than when *drinking.* Feasts, carousals, drinking bouts were the *rule* and not the *exception* in Persian life. We need only read the book of Esther in the Bible to know that the Persian kings were no different—when the Great King's birthday or some other festival occasion served as an excuse—from the Assyrian monarchs. In old Assyria, after King Assurbanipal or Sargon had made a triumphant entry into the capital, the royal palace was thrown open to every one in town, high and low. The whole population crowded in and the royal slaves served whatever was called for: beers, wines and plum-brandies. These great festivals lasted for four or five days at a time, until it is no exaggeration to say that the whole city of Nineveh lay in a drunken stupor. From the least, last muleteer and slave, to the highest lords of the land, it was a city of the alcoholic dead. An enemy could have surprised and destroyed it with ease. In the Persian palace, the great feasts seem to have been restricted to more highly-placed guests. The "man in the street" does not appear to have been asked into the royal palace to drink his fill. But he got his fill outside without much difficulty. So much for the boyhood lessons which taught the Persian lad to "dip his drinking-cup in the running stream!" Yet this youthful training had its good effect, nevertheless, and built up a strong, sound body and a healthy constitution. Xenophon, who wrote at a time when the Persians had lost many of their original hardier virtues, and were the most luxurious race of the day, says: "Even to this day signs bear witness to that *ancient* temperance and disci-

pline. It is still considered shameful for a Persian to *spit* in public."
(This natural, decent and sanitary rule which was *inbred* in the
Persian, we in our own more civilized age, must *enforce* with laws
and penalties!), "or wipe the nose, or show signs of wind or be
seen going apart for his natural needs." * As regards wine, Cyrus,
the first great Persian king, had his own sensible ideas with regards
its use in the national army. This is proved by the words of one
of his army speeches: "As for wine, every man must carry just
enough to accustom him to drink water!"

The softness and luxury which crept into Persian life descended
from the royal and princely courts of the great viceroys (satraps)
and governors of the immense provinces of the Persian empire, and
spread among the people. This sufficiently explains their being able,
in spite of many more men and much more gold, to get the better
of the freedom-loving Greeks in their long struggle, their Persian
gold—as gold always does, in every age—sapped the *moral fibre* and
the *civic virtue* of the Greeks. When the time came a small new
tribe of hardy Greek mountaineers, the Macedonians, found it possible to dominate the city Greeks the Persians had vainly tried to
conquer.

---

*A few excerpts from the Cycropedia show the gradual degeneracy
of the ancient Persians from their hardy, ancestral habits. "First they
took only a single meal a day . . . this still is the rule; but begins at the
earliest hour, chosen for breakfast, and eating and drinking goes on till
the last moment the latest reveller would chose for bed. They are not
content with soft rugs and sheets for their beds, they must have carpets
laid under the bed-posts to prevent any *jarring* from the floor. The Persian grandees have invented a new kind of cavalry, who earn their pay as
butlers, cooks, confectioners cupbearers, bathman or flunkeys to serve
at table and remove dishes, serving-men to put their lords to bed, and
help them rise, performers to annoint and rub and make them beautiful."
And the kings took the field with enormous harems and thousands of camp-
followers and baggage-wains.

CHAPTER VI

SOME CURIOUS PHASES OF ANCIENT GREEK LIFE

In order to gain some insight into ancient Greek life it seems best to select from the rich store of information handed down to us, tales which give an idea of the *human* elements in everyday existence in some leading Greek city-states or commonwealths. It is enough to say here that in ancient Greece *monarchy, aristocracy* and *democracy* were all three represented. *Kings* ruled by virtue of hereditary descent from some half-god. Sometimes, as in Sparta, two "kings" were played off against one another by the ruling "Council of Ephors." They had authority only in time of war. Rulers who claimed royal rights, but were more like modern political city "bosses," were the *tyrants*. Besides this, were so-called republics, in which the *aristocracy* or the *democracy* got the upper hand in turn, as the case might be. *Athens* was the greatest among the Greek city-states, and for a time dominated the rest. Then *Sparta,* the great "militarist" state, got the power into her hands, and in turn had to yield it to *Thebes,* and when these greater, and the lesser cities of Greece, had worn themselves out fighting each other, the Macedonians stepped in and became their masters.

I

ATHENS

But the philosophers, generals, politicians and thinkers of Athens, her military and political leaders, her writers, sculptors and other artists, her course in world history are dealt with elsewhere. We will turn here to some of her more curious institutions and customs, the distinctive way in which *human life* expressed itself in "the violet-crowned city."

THE FAMOUS "IMMORALITY LAW" TEST CASE OF PHRYNE

Phryne, who lived in the 4th century B.C. was a *hetaera*.* She

*Ancient Greeks have the doubtful merit of having introduced into *human life* the *hetaerae*—prostitutes, not "mistresses,"—"the most brilliant and gifted members of their class known in history." The great difference between these women and those of their kind in the ancient Orient, was that in the Orient the professional harlot was neither socially

plied her trade in pleasure-loving Athens, was one of the most famous courtesans antiquity ever produced. A Boeotian small-town girl, born in Thespias, she only smiled when the other Athenian courtesans refused to call her by her right name, Mnesarete, but nicknamed her "Phryne" or "The Toad" instead, because of her dark complexion. She could afford to smile. For her extraordinary beauty had brought her so vast an amount of wealth that—she offered to rebuild the walls of the city of Thebes, the capital of her native Boeotia, in all their enormous circumference (Alexander The Great had destroyed them in the year 336), if the words: "Destroyed by Alexander, restored by Phryne the courtesan!" were engraved on them in a prominent place. But the city fathers of that ruined town did not accept her offer. Perhaps they felt that the walls whose huge blocks had shaped themselves in obedience to the pure and noble music of Amphion's lyre, would crumble for shame were they to be restored with a courtesan's ill-gotten gold! Phryne did, however, inspire two great works of ancient art. One day at the great festival of the sea-god Poseidon at Eleusis, she laid aside her garments, let down her hair and stepped into the sea in the sight of the people. Apelles, the great painter, who was in the crowd, was seized with inspiration at the sight by this vision of loveliness, and the idea of his great picture of Aphrodite Anadyomene was born. Phryne sat as its model. Praxiteles also was inspired to carve so wonderful a statue of this mercenary heartbreaker that it was placed beside his statue of Aphrodite in the latter's temple. What gives Phryne's famous trial before the Athenian supreme court, the Areopagus, a special historic and human interest, is the fact that it *established the triumph of the Greek hetaerae over the law of the land!* It deprived virtuous women of their only advantage, and opened the door to general moral laxity.

nor legally recognized, unless she were a religious prostitute, who exercised her profession in connection with the worship and religious services of the temples. In Oriental countries the trend was for girls, especially slaves, to be brought up or trained to make a livelihood through abuse of sexual instinct. Or else in Egypt, Assyria, Babylon, Persia, the religious worship of nature gods and goddesses made the temples centers of vice, and drew in those who felt a natural vocation for sensual indulgence as a religious duty. In ancient Greece, *the religious idea was not so pronounced.* But this was more a "money-making" scheme and the worship of Aphrodite a mere excuse for sexual excess. Though the Temple of Aphrodite in Corinth maintained a huge staff of common prostitutes for the accommodation of the sailors of the great "port town." Temple prostitutes were common in the Greek cities of Asia Minor, but they were looked down upon in Greece. With one striking exception— the *hetaerae.* In utter variance to modern ideas, the houses of prostitution were state monopolies in the Greek cities, which derived a revenue that may well be called "dirty money" from this polluted source. The city of Miletus, in particular, was noted for its famous *hetaerae.*

Before this famous "Immorality Test Case" the Law had taken a stern attitude toward the *hetaerae,* and had not indulged their caprices at the expense of society's decent members.

An Archon was one of the highest and most respected officials of the Athenian city government. But Phryne snapped her fingers at archons. According to one version of the tale the Archon Dicepholos was a miser. His nephew Nicias, on the other hand, was a graceless prodigal. Since Nicias was free with his money (which he borrowed at high interest to fling away on his pleasures), he naturally stood high in Phryne's good graces. What happened? Uncle Dicepholos bought in nephew Nicias' promissory notes from the money-lenders, and obtained a judgment against him. But when he was about to be arrested, Phryne was impudent enough to have the city police sent to make the arrest soundly beaten by her stalwart slaves, while Nicias, happy at his escape, mockingly crowned the bust of his Uncle Dicepholos, which stood in the marketplace, with a wreath of violets before entering Phryne's house to feast there.

Dicepholos promptly revenged himself. He called together the Areopagus, the highest court of Athens, and Phryne was cited to appear. But the wily courtesan caught the elderly miser in a trap. He himself went to her home to enjoy the satisfaction of handing her the summons. But once there, the wily courtesan ensnared his heart with her coquetries until the elderly magistrate, babbling that she was fairer than any Aphrodite Praxiteles ever had chiseled, fell at her feet and with tears in his eyes begged her to love him. This was the moment for which Phryne had waited. At a sign, Nicias and a number of witnesses concealed behind a curtain entered, and found the respectable magistrate in this compromising position. Of course, this was enough to ensure Dicepholos' dropping the case so far as he was concerned, and the case was quashed.

A far more serious offense, however, was the accusation (probably only too well founded) that Phryne had profaned the holy Eleusian Mysteries, the secret religious ceremonies of an especially pure and lofty kind, in which all the virtuous married women of Athens took part. And here, so low had the morality of an Athenian supreme court sunk, we find that the just complaint of the party of "decency" suffered a most complete defeat. Phryne was defended by a young lawyer and personal friend, Hyperides, but he poured out his eloquence in vain. The stony hearts of his justly indignant judges remained unmoved. But then her wily lawyer stepped up to Phryne, and with an eloquent, noble gesture, as though to say: "Can beauty such as this be guilty of wrong-doing?" rent her robe, and disclosed her lovely bosom. And the judges on whom his pleading had made no impression, were so moved that they acquitted her at once. The sentence was a death-blow to the cause of virtue and morality in Athens. And Phryne's weak judges, alas, that showed Athens was faring ill, that it already was to "hastening ills a prey." Their verdict proved it a land where a prostitute could acquire enough wealth to rebuild the walls of great cities, and only had to display her charms to be excused from crimes against society and the state. A state whose chief magistrates could not rise above the appeal of feminine beauty for justice' sake, had become one of those lands where "wealth accumulates and men decay."

But we also find the life of the *hetaerae* has its more romantic and less criminal aspects. Aspasia, a great "politician" in skirts, is more properly considered with Pericles, the partner of her heart and politics. But, from an earlier day, we have a tale which gives us a view of the *hetaerae* life.

THE GOLDEN CHAIN

Plangon the Milesian was one of the most fashionable Athenian *hetaerae* in her time. Her loveliness and charm moved the hearts even of old and morose men, and she was constantly surrounded by pontiffs, archons, generals, satraps, men about town and young sons of noble families. At night her adorers poured fragrant oils and essences on her marble door-step, and in the mornings her threshold was so covered with flowers that they had to be swept away before the door could be opened. Plangon, however, was very particular in the choice of her friends. Only the richest were admitted to her intimacy. An archon lasted eight days, a high-priest fifteen. One had to be a king, a Persian satrap of a Greek tyrant to last out the end of the month as her guest. Once she had stripped them of their fortunes, her erstwhile friends were thrown out of the door, like fowls which have been plucked for the pot.

And then, suddenly, Plangon changed her mode of life completely. All admirers were turned away. She dismissed the great Persian satrap Pharnabazus, although she had plundered him of the revenues of only a single province. And the depraved "gay world" of Athens was shocked at what in its depravity it called an "ignoble and monstrous virtue." But Plangon had fallen in love with Ctesias, of Samos, young sculptor, and he with her. She had determined to reform, and become an honest woman and already rosy dreams of respectability, even a possible crossing of the thresholds which her profession had closed to her began to fill her soul. And then, a bevy of her old companions called on her one day and maliciously told her that—her Ctesias had been the lover of one of the most notorious of their sisterhood, Bacchides of Samos. Plangon fainted on hearing the news. She had thought she was Ctesias' first love, and could not overcome her despair at what she considered his deception. When next she saw him she reproached him bitterly, even going so far as to tell her two giant red-haired Scythian porters to throw him out of the house. But while they hesitated a moment, for sometimes in the past their mistress had been known to change her mind after giving this order, Ctesias pleaded so earnestly for forgiveness, that Plangon half relented. Yet only half, for she said to him in the most cutting tone: "Fetch me Bacchis' golden chain, and I will believe you really love me! Otherwise never darken my door again!"

Bacchides of Samos, among the *hetaerae* of that famous island city, was an ant among crickets. Whenever she had plucked some king of Asia Minor, some great Persian lord or some rich Athenian landowner, she took the gold of which she had deprived him, and had it melted down into massive links. These she added to her famous chain. It was not a slender gold chain such as one passes around one's neck two or three times. It was a chain heavier than those which fettered the slaves in the mines. It was a chain like an anchor-chain, made of great links of pure gold, and already several yards long. For Bacchides was looking forward to the rainy days of old age, when her admirers, frightened away by a new wrinkle or a gray hair, would take their vows of affection and the coin with which they weighed them to younger competitors. Bacchides loved her chain. It meant to her that when the autumn days were at hand, she could retire to some small town and, detaching a link or so every year, live out her life in peace and quiet, leaving enough to pay for her funeral expenses and to build a small chapel to Aphrodite the Protectress. About the most impossible thing in the world was asking Bacchides of Samos for her golden chain—with any prospect of getting it.

But Ctesias was deeply in love. He at once sailed for Samos, and when he landed went straight to Bacchides' house. There he gave his last gold-pieces to the old negress he had known in happier days, and begged her to tell Bacchides that some one who had greatly loved her in the past wished to speak to her. Bacchides smiled. Life had given her a cynical outlook on love. "There is only one person in the world who ever really loved me," said she, "and that was Ctesias of Colophon." "And that is the very man who wishes to see you," answered the slave. When Ctesias entered he at once flung himself at Bacchides' feet. "Bacchides, I must die," he cried in tones of despair, "you alone can save me. But when I tell you how, you will think I have escaped from the mad-house at Anticyrus! Yet I shall ask you, nevertheless. I *must* have your golden chain!" With surprise Bacchides listened to Ctesias' story, and when he had finished his head dropped on her feet and the tears flowed from his eyes. For a moment Bacchides sat in silence.

She saw her dream of a decent and restful old age vanish. She saw herself buried as a public charge, the little shrine she had meant to found dissolve in thin air. She saw ahead long dreary years of wretchedness and slavery, the hard toil which is doubly hard to the aged who have neither toiled nor spun. But Bacchides of Samos still loved Ctesias. She leaned over the broken-hearted boy and stroked his hair. "You shall have my chain. Take it back to your angry love, and sometimes spare a thought for Bacchides of Samos, to whom you once swore to be true your life long!" And, though he felt like a thief, Ctesias did as she told him. When his bearers set down the cedar chest in Plangon's house in Athens, he drew out the huge chain with an effort, and said: "And now must I be thrown out of the house by your Scythians?" Then Plangon, weeping bitterly, accused herself of having a hard heart and a jealous disposition. She freely forgave her lover and they were duly wedded that evening before the constituted temple authorities. But Plangon was too noble to deprive the unfortunate Bacchides of her chain. Once more Ctesias made the trip to Samos to return it to its owner, and with him he took two pearls of wonderful size and lustre. These, with a grateful note from Plangon, were her thanks. And having duly reformed, and being happily married, there is every reason to believe that Plangon lived as happily as any of the inhabitants of Athens, with her Ctesias. And poor Bacchides could look forward with renewed serenity to a decent old age and a proper burial.

II

SPARTA

Sparta the land of iron men and iron money—for the Spartans were forbidden by law to trade, or to have gold or silver in their possession—conquered golden Athens (405 B.C.). But it was in turn ruined and brought low by the very wealth, the gold and silver which the capture of Athens and the empire over Greece brought it. In a way it is not to be surprising, for Solon, the rigid old sage who provided the cast-iron laws which the Spartans formerly observed, had managed to create living conditions among the Spartans which made *human life* as uncomfortable and uninviting as can be imagined. Let us consider a few of these laws—and thank heaven we are not ancient Spartans! It is true that another sage, Anarcharsis, laughed at Solon for thinking that the dishonesty and greed of his countrymen could be restrained by written laws, but Solon wrote them just the same.

Some Penalties of Being Born an Ancient Spartan. Solon, as sometimes happens in politics in these days, came to power because both sides were mistaken in him. The rich voted for him because he was wealthy; the poor because he was honest. He surprised them both and neither rich nor poor were pleased with his surprises. There were no "conscientious objectors" in ancient Sparta after Solon's day. For he made a law which severely punished any one *who did not take sides,* one way or the other, *in any internal troubles.* If you joined a rebellion and your party lost out, however, it did not matter so much, for you would have been punished just as severely if you had remained neutral. This law gave an armed rebellion all the fascination of a game of chance.

His laws covering women were very curious. A man taken in adultery could be slain on the spot, and his slayer went scot-free. But a successful attempt on the virtue of a free woman was merely punished by a fine. There was no such thing as "changing fashions" in walking about, feasting, dressing or mourning where women were concerned. Solon had covered all such things in his laws, which allowed every woman *three dresses,* no more! Solon's laws also decided what was "unbecoming" and immodest and Spartan women dressed accordingly. Lycurgus was another great Spartan lawgiver who helped to make life unpleasant for his fellow-citizens. He arranged that every one, rich and poor, had to eat together at community tables. "You shall not spend your lives at home, lying on costly couches at splendid tables (though where they were to get them when it took a yoke of oxen to move a hundred dollars worth of Spartan money, the gods of Greece only know!) delivering yourselves into the hands of tradesmen and cooks, to fatten yourselves in corners, like greedy brutes, and ruin not only your minds but your bodies. Thus enfeebled with indulgence and excess, you would stand in need of much sleep, warm bathing and freedom from work—as much care and attendance as if you were continually sick." This, according to Lycurgus, was what eating at home with the family led to. When this law was first passed, the richer Spartans were so indignant that they stoned Lycurgus and he had to run through the streets for his life. A young son of wealth even beat out one of his eyes with a stick. But Lycurgus, when the people, ashamed of their violence, confirmed his laws, made a friend of the wild young fellow who had deprived him of half his eyesight, and turned him into a steady, sober-minded Spartan citizen. Girls and boys in Sparta were brought up from infancy by a strict course of physical training. To what lengths theoretical law-making will lead a lawmaker when he has the interest of the state in mind, and forgets that those who make up the state are *individual human beings,* is shown by two of Lycurgus' laws. They are laws which any civilized land to-day would reject with horror. The whole inwardness of marriage in Sparta was the raising of strong healthy children, preferably as many boys as possible for army use. And with this idea in mind, Lycurgus passed laws which make it perfectly honorable and proper for a man to give the use of his wife to others when he saw fit, so that children might be born of such unions. And again, the state examined the new-born child. If it were strong and healthy it was "passed," to go through the unhappy childhood of a Spartan boy, and learn to smile while the stolen fox (the boys in training stole all the meat they could lay hands on, and only were punished when "found out") was clawing out his bowels beneath his cloak. Children that did not look promising to the board of infant examiners, poor puny, sickly little ones, however, were quietly dropped down a deep gulley. In Sparta only the physically fit survived. Yet the crude and hard life they led, their concentration on war and fighting to the exclusion of all else, finally enabled the Spartans to get the better of the Athenians. And the virtues of courage, manliness and a high mind which the Spartan discipline gave, are shown at their best in one of the greatest and last of the Spartan leaders, Cleomenes. At the battle of Leuctra (371 B.C.) the Spartan army had gone down in defeat, and the Spartans had lost the overlordship of Greece to the Thebans who had whipped them. But long after the death of Alexander the Great, King Cleomenes, a man who had every virtue and none of the vices of his race, tried to raise Sparta from its level of decay. He tried to introduce reforms within and without. But he was beaten in the battle of Sellasia (222 B.C.), and when he fled to Alexandria in Egypt, where the Egyptian King Ptolemy granted him a refuge, was basely murdered there by his royal host.

Sparta never recovered her old power after Cleomenes' death, but in the earlier days of the Roman empire the old war-like spirit led many Spartans to enroll themselves in the legions, and fight there, when Rome was the only country left for which a Greek could fight with any hope of success.

III

THEBES

The Boeotians were the real "farmer-folk" of ancient Greece. They were, not altogether justly, regarded as the dullest and most stupid of mankind, and the Athenian used the word "Boeotian" as a term of contempt. To call a man a "Boeotian" in Athens was an insult. Yet Boeotia produced some famous men, among them the great poet Pindar, and Plutarch the historian, and at the battle of Luectra, the heavy-armed Boeotian infantry, which had a well-deserved reputation, defeated the Spartans and for a short time Thebes, the Boeotian capital, gave its orders to the rest of Greece. At the same time, so great was Sparta's fame, even in her decline,

I

that it was said that the Boeotians, when they whipped the Spartans (who had taught them the art of war), acted like schoolboys who had beaten their teacher. A race of farmers and shepherds, an idyl of the countryside might best give an idea of their nature. One of the most charming Greek tales of this kind is located in the land of Phrygia, in Asia Minor, but it suits the Boeotian character so well, that we will tell it here.

THE STORY OF PHILEMON AND BAUCIS

If, in the very days the battle of Luectra was fought, you had been wandering in the neighborhood of a certain hill near Tyanea, the shepherd who tended his goats there would be sure to have shown you the linden tree and the oak tree which stood side by side on a hill, enclosed in a low wall of field stones. For with the trees went a tale which had been handed down in the land from the olden days. It is a story so *human*, so true to the best in life, even to-day, that though the fact that the old Greek god Zeus plays a prominent part in it, and performs a miracle which we know could not have taken place, it still has all the charm a true tale of human love holds for all whose hearts respond to its appeal.

On the Phrygian hill we have mentioned there once stood a small cottage with a thatched roof. In it lived Philemon and Baucis, a farmer pair, husband and wife. They had wedded when young, and grown old together, without noticing it. They had happy dispositions and contented minds. The kindly soil supplied all their modest wants, and they were more content in their poverty than many a prince with his riches. One night, while they slept peacefully in bed, for they went to bed with the sun as a rule, there came a knocking at the door. It was the god Zeus and his son Hermes, who were knocking, disguised as weary travellers. They already had knocked at the doors of all the houses in the village which lay but a mile away. But they had found none of the people who lived there hospitable enough to take them in. Philemon and Baucis, however, welcomed them heartily, and made them sit down on a bench to rest. Then, while her husband built a fire of brush and faggots, Baucis hung a small kettle over the flames.

Then, while her guests were washing their hands and faces in bowls of beech-wood, she set the table with her trembling old hands, propping up one leg, which was shorter than the other, with a bit of slate, and put olives, cornel berries preserved in vinegar, radishes and cheese, with eggs lightly toasted in the hot ashes, on the table. Dishes of earthenware with wooden cups were set out, and then the hot, savory stew was put on the table, smoking in a large wooden bowl. With true friendliness and good will, the guests were urged to eat, and to drink the home-made country wine that went with the meal, and for dessert apples and wild honey were pressed upon the disguised gods.

And Zeus and Hermes, who appreciated the goodness of heart of the simple kindly old couple, ate as though their meal tasted better than the divine nectar and ambrosia they enjoyed on Mount Olympus. But suddenly Baucis trembled with terror. She had noticed that the wine in the earthen pitcher renewed itself as fast as it was emptied. Nudging Philemon she whispered that they were entertaining gods for guests, and the aged pair fell on their poor old knees and begged forgiveness because they had no better fare to offer such divine beings. Then, filled with eagerness to treat these gods who had stooped to break a fast beneath their roof, properly, both the old folks thought of their one old goose. They would kill and roast it for the gods. Awkwardly they began to chase it around the room. But the goose, which had been treated as a pet for the past ten years, thought they had gone mad. Fluttering and squawking, it scrambled and flew about, and at last took shelter between the gods themselves. And Zeus, laughing, said: "It has chosen its protectors wisely, so it shall not die!" Then he continued:

"The mean and churlish louts who lived in the village below made a great mistake when they turned us away. Come to the door!" And as the Darby and Joan of ancient Greece, full of awe, stepped out on their threshold, there where the village had stood, was a great lake. The gods had been so shocked by the inhospitality shown them that they had sunk the churlish village under water, fathoms deep. "But you," said Zeus, as he gazed on the aged pair with a kindly smile, "you shall be rewarded." So he led them a little way from their cottage, to another hill and bade them look. And before their wondering eyes, the tiny peasant hut changed into a glorious temple. Proud columns of white marble took the place of the wooden corner-posts, the yellow thatch grew into a spreading roof of gilded cedar beams, the hard earth floors turned into a smooth marble pavement, and instead of the weather-beaten wooden door, that tottered on its hinges, magnificent gates of bronze, inlaid and carved with golden ornaments, swung open before their eyes as though to invite them in.

"And now," said Zeus, "you kind, good people, ask whatever favor you wish of me. It shall be granted!" Then Philemon looked in Baucis' eyes and Baucis looked in his. Without a word each read the other's thought. And Philemon said: "O Lord of the Skies, we ask that we may continue to dwell here as priests and guardians of your shrine as long as we live and . . ." then he hesitated a moment, as though fearing to ask too much. "We have passed all the days of our life here in peace and concord, happy in our love. When our time has come let the same hour take us both from life. I would not live to see Baucis' grave, nor would I wish her to have to lay me in mine!" And Zeus granted the prayer which asked so little and yet meant so much to him who made it. As long as they lived Philemon and Baucis were the guardians and keepers of the holy shrine.

And one day, when they had swept out the marble floor in the morning, and stood for a moment resting on the topmost step, drinking in the sweet morning air, Baucis as she looked at Philemon, saw that he was changing and putting forth leaves. And Philemon, looking at Baucis, saw that she was changing in a like manner. But it was a change without pain. It was as though a new and different life, one that held vague promises of rest and quiet content and an untasted happiness had entered into them. As a leafy crown began to spread above their heads, each said to the other, "Farewell, farewell!" and then the bark closed over their mouths. Zeus had kept his word, and neither Philemon nor Baucis knew unhappiness in their passing from human life. Neither had to feel the pangs and heart-breaks that human creatures feel when one beloved takes the dark road before them. And long, long after Greece was only a trifling province of the great Roman empire, the goat-herd of Tyanea, in whose family and village the story had been handed down for centuries, would show the two trees, the oak and the linden, into which Philemon and Baucis had been changed by the kindly power of Zeus.

IV

THE ISLES OF GREECE

But the spirit of Boeotian and Phrygian shepherds and farmers, like the militarism of Sparta, or the luxury of Athens, does not reflect all of the many human facets in the character of the ancient Greeks. It would take a thousand tales to do justice to them, tales of Miletus and of Sicilian Syracuse, of Samos, the home of Bacchides, tales of the Greek cities of Italy, tales of the Greek cities of Asia Minor. Yet, before we leave ancient Greece for ancient Rome, two stories shall give us other *human* glimpses of the Greek mind. The first is a tale of one of "the isles of Greece" that Byron sang. It proves that an old Greek city "boss" could deceive himself as easily as any of us deceive ourselves to-day. The other, a tale from the Greek kingdom of Lydia, in Asia Minor, proves how the ideas of a well-bred Persian woman with regard to propriety differed from Greek viewpoints.

THE THREE FLAGONS OF POLYCRATES

We can get a good idea of the character of Polycrates, tyrant of the island city of Samos (535-513 B.C.), by the fact that Anacreaon, the Greek poet who wrote the most charming, passionate and tender verses in praise of wine and wine-drinking known and who, according to one report, poetically choked to death on a grape-seed, was his most intimate friend. Polycrates made Samos so hot for the great and good philosopher Pythagoras, on the other hand, that the latter had to flee for his life to escape his tyranny. Polycrates, after ruling in splendor (he was the greatest pirate on the high seas known to his age, by the way) and building a magnificent palace, a great mole, an aqueduct and a temple to Hera, was coaxed to the Lydian mainland by the Persian satrap Croetes by the lure of easy gold. He found instead the wooden cross on which the Persian crucified him as a common sea-robber. The following tale has a moral. We shall not tell what it is, however, but leave it to the reader to discover it for himself.

One day the tyrant Polycrates ordered three sealed bottles containing three rare wines of different kinds, the costliest and most precious in the world, to be brought him. A slave obediently hastened off to obey his command, and returned with a flagon of polished black stone, a flagon of yellow gold, and a flagon of transparent crystal. (Now when the three flagons had been filled in Polycrates' cellar, the forgetful bottler had poured the same everyday red wine of Samos, that appeared on Polycrates' table day by day, into each of the three bottles.) Polycrates looked at the flagon of polished black stone and moved his eyebrows. Then he broke the gypsum seal and sniffed the wine. "This flagon," he said, "is of base material, and the odor of the wine it contains does not appeal to me!"

He raised the flagon of yellow gold and admired it. Then, having unsealed it, he said: "This wine is bound to be inferior to its beautiful container, richly adorned with jewelled grapes and chased golden leaves." And he pushed it away.

Then he took up the third flagon, of transparent crystal, and held it up against the sun. The crimson wine leaped and glowed. Polycrates broke the seal, filled his cup with wine, and drank it at a single draught. "Ah," said he, as he wiped his lips, *"that* was the best wine I ever tasted in my life!" Then, setting down his cup on the table it struck against the crystal flagon, and the latter fell to the marble floor and was shattered to bits.

V

ASIAN GREECE

A Tragedy of Different Points of View. The Lydian Greeks, until conquered by the Persian King Cyrus the Great, were a strong and powerful nation, whose capital was the city of Sardis, built on a river whose sands were rich in gold. Its last king, Croesus, was accounted the richest king on earth in his day, and if we want to imply that a man is rich beyond the dreams of avarice we still say, "He is as rich as Croesus." The Asian Greeks were a luxurious race, and at the court of Sardis Asiatic luxury and Greek civilization were mingled. In the tale which follows, a man in a moment of human weakness, does something innocent in itself, but which seals his death-warrant. It offers us a contrast between two viewpoints. First there is the Greek one. The Greek admired beauty for its own sake. He admired it with an artist's soul. And he wanted others to share his admiration, and his enjoyment of it. But, the personal charms of an *oriental* woman of high rank were guarded by her with a jealousy of which the Greek soul had no idea. It was a matter of honor for a Persian princess to be invisible to any but her husband. The conflict between these two ideas brings about the tragedy of Candaulus and Gyges, and is one that has been told in story, poem and even in opera. We have followed freely the tale as told by Théophile Gautier. It is supposed to have happened before the Persians added Lydia to their empire.

THE RING OF GYGES

Crowds lined the streets of Sardis. King Candaulus of Lydia was marrying, not a Greek, but the daughter of the Persian satrap Megabazus of Bactria. Her name was Nyssia, and rumor said she was the most beautiful girl in all Asia. Rumor said so—for the Persians did not share the Greek ideas on the subject of modesty. The young athletes of Greece thought it no shame to let their oil-glistening bodies shine in the stadium sun. The virgins of Sparta danced unveiled before the altars of Diana. But the maidens of Persepolis, Ecbatana and Bactria held bodily purity even higher than purity of soul. They looked on the freedom with which Greek manners and customs indulged the pleasure of the eye as gross and objectionable. No decent woman, in their opinion, allowed a man to see more than the tip of her foot, peeping out from below her long tunic. But the fame of Nyssia's beauty—perhaps the slaves who served her in the bath were responsible—had spread all over Lydia, and finally reached the ears of King Candaulus. The fair daughters of the great Greek families of noble blood, the *hetaerae* of Athens, Miletus, Samos and Cyprus, the handsome slave girls from the banks of the Indus, the blonde maids brought at high cost from the misty lands of Gaul, had been careful never to breathe Nyssia's name to Candaulus. But—Candaulus had heard it.

At all events, the report of her beauty became a legend, a myth, to which every one added according to his fancy. And now that the wedding procession came down the long street, the crowds expected to see their new queen face to face. Gyges, the captain of King Candaulus' guard, rode in advance of his men, heavily armored horsemen on white steeds of noble race. Then came boys in rose-colored tunics, embroidered in silver. They played the nuptial hymn on their ivory lyres with a short bow. After them followed the big-muscled slaves who were bearing the wedding gifts, gifts of every kind on hand-litters: heaped gold and silver vessels, rich stuffs, vases and art objects, perfumes, bracelets and collars. Then supported by twenty-four Ethiopians, came the great ivory and gold statute of Hercules, King Candaulus' ancestor, followed by other statues. A file of splendidly caparisoned camels and dromedaries then swung along, musicians playing cymbals and timpani on their necks, and carrying the gilded poles, the cordage and the stuffs of the tent the young queen would use on hunting parties and voyages. But the people paid less attention than usual to this rich display. They were waiting for Nyssia to appear.

At last Candaulus himself drove up in a splendid chariot drawn by four magnificent horses and, after him, came the daughter of Megabazus. She was carried on the back of an enormous elephant whose tusks and trunk were banded with rings of silver, while strings of enormous pearls were wound about his legs. A sort of platform rested on the costly Persian rug which covered the beast's back. It had a railing of gold and semi-precious stones, and on it sat the young queen, literally blazing with jewels, which almost hid her garments. But a long veil of saffron-colored stuff hid her face from sight, and she seemed annoyed by the gaze of so many thousands of eyes even through her veil, since from time to time she signed the slave-girl behind her to drop her parasol of ostrich plumes to screen her better from the crowd. In vain Candaulus had begged her to show her face in public, if only on this one solemn occasion. The young barbarian girl had refused to pay her people the tribute of allowing them to see her beauty. The popular disappointment was general, but there was nothing to be done about it. The Sardians returned home as wise as they had been before regarding Nyssia's charms.

Now Nyssia was very, very beautiful. A Phidias would have done murder to have had the chance to chisel her in ivory and gold. An Appelles would have slain himself in despair, had he seen and not been allowed to paint her. The reader would have to assemble all his loveliest and dearest memories of flowers, perfumes, music and sunlight, and mingle them with the ideas called up with all the visions and images of what is most graceful and charming on earth, to form an idea of Nyssia's face and figure. And King Candaulus, the only mortal who had a right to enjoy this marvelous beauty, a loveliness whose like he had not known existed, was filled with a delirium of possession, as the priest is with the spirit of his god. His happiness bordered on ecstasy, his love on madness. At times his very felicity frightened him. Who was he to own such a treasure? How dare he guard for himself the living reality of which every ideal lover, sculptor or poet ever had dreamed? He held in his arms all the visions of their dearest hopes, desires and despairs! And what was he? Just a wretched little king of Lydia, with a few cedar chests filled with pearls, a few cisterns filled with gold pieces, and thirty or forty thousand slaves purchased or taken in war!

His happiness was too much for Candaulus. He almost wished Nyssia were less timid and shrinking, for to be the sole admirer of a beauty like hers began to weigh on him. This lovely woman's barbarian modesty made her refuse to raise her veil for any other than himself. He would have liked to have seen her ride unveiled through the streets of Sardis, so that the people, mad with admiration, would fling themselves beneath the silver wheels of her chariot to be crushed by them, like the Indian fanatics before their idol's car. "Alas," he cried, "I am the only worshipper of an unknown goddess, and have no way of spreading her religion over all the earth!" In Candaulus the enthusiasm of the artist had destroyed the jealousy of the lover. Had he married some beautiful Greek of Athens or Corinth, he would have had the first sculptors of his court model her. And, in a land where the most virtuous women took pride in serving as the model for a famous statue, his wife would have rejoiced. Nyssia, like an obedient wife, lent herself to his caprices. She would let him deck her as a Bacchante or a Nymph, or stand with her golden hair flowing in a shell of mother-of-pearl, while he sat lost in thought admiring her. But she would soon tire of being a model. Then she would mention, in a cold and disdainful manner, that such amusements were unworthy of a king's dignity and contrary to the holy laws of marriage. "It is thus," she would declare, as, draped to the eyes, she retired to the mysterious recesses of her own apartments, "that a mistress is treated, and not a virtuous woman of noble blood!" And the time came when Candaulus could no longer keep his wife's loveliness to himself. He needed some one in whom to confide. He felt he must tell some one about it. So one day he drew his captain of the guard, Gyges, aside and led him to a lonely palace court. There he said to him:

"What would you do if you were a diver, and had drawn from the ocean's green bosom a perfect pearl, of incomparable whiteness and beauty, a pearl beyond all price?"

Gyges, somewhat surprised by this sudden query, answered: "I would put it in a box of cedar plated with bronze, and then I would hide it in a desert spot under a rock. From time to time, when I was sure no one could see me, I would go to look at my precious jewel and watch the colors of the sky mingle with its pearly tints!"

But Candaulus cried enthusiastically: "If I had such a jewel, I would have it set in my crown so that all could see it flashing in the clear sunlight. I would glory in its radiance, and would smile with pride when people said: 'No king of Babylon or Assyria ever owned as fair a pearl as Candaulus, the descendant of Hercules, King of Sardis and Lydia.' Compared with Candaulus, Midas, who could change all things to gold, was a beggar-man!"

Gyges listened with astonishment to the king's passionate and poetic outburst, trying to grasp its hidden meaning. Then Candaulus told him that he was a diver who had fished up out of humanity's sea of the commonplace and the incomplete that radiant pearl—Nyssia! For a time he had been jealous, but now when he thought of her divine and harmonious beauty, he longed for some other soul on earth to share his delight. He longed for some friend who would echo his cries of admiration. "Gyges, you must be that friend!" he added. And with these words Candaulus suddenly disappeared in a secret passage.

Gyges left the court filled with the statues of the king's ancestors deep in thought. He shook his head, perplexed, for he did not share his master's point of view. The following day Candaulus returned to the subject of their previous conversation. Could she have heard his ardent praise of her beauty, perhaps Nyssia would have forgiven her husband's lack of reserve. Suddenly Candaulus cried: "By Hercules, Gyges,"—for Gyges had listened to him with some constraint—"I think you do not believe me! You think I am boasting! But you shall be convinced. If once you see Nyssia in all the white radiance of her loveliness, with no officious concealments, no jealous draperies, as nature modelled her in a moment of inspiration, you will know I speak the truth! To-night I shall hide you in a corner of our nuptial apartment . . . and you shall see her!"

"My lord, think what you ask of me," answered the young officer, firmly but respectfully. "Do not force your humble slave to commit an action so contrary to what is right. I fully believe Nyssia to be the most beautiful of women, and you the happiest of husbands and lovers. Your ancestor Hercules, for all his conquests, never found a woman to compare with your queen. But give up a whim unworthy of you! . . ."

Yet Candaulus argued and pleaded till Gyges said: "What you compel me to do is wrong. And . . . you promise to bear me no ill will yourself, but suppose Nyssia discovers the sacrilege of which I am guilty? Who will protect me from her vengeful anger?"

"I did not know you were so careful and prudent by nature," said Candaulus, with a slightly contemptuous smile. "But do not worry. I will hide you so that Nyssia will never know any other eye but mine has seen her." Gyges, reluctantly, fearing to make further objections, agreed to do as Candaulus wished. Then the king, taking his hand, told him that Nyssia was walking at the moment in the palace gardens. It was their opportunity to carry out their plan. The King led Gyges to the nuptial apartment. Then he manipulated the intricate system of metal rings which controlled the many bolts of the great double doors—for this was before locks had been invented!—and ordering Gyges to stand against the wall, turned the door back upon him. The door hid the young captain completely, but through a small space left free for the play of the metal bolts, he had a clear view of the whole interior of the room. He saw the royal couch, magnificently chiseled and curtained, facing the door, the altar to the household gods, the black statues holding torches which lined the cedar-panelled walls at regular distances. He saw chairs, chests and coffers, the wooden pegs from which hung Candaulus' garments, and the bench of ivory on which Nyssia laid her robes. "As a rule I retire first," Candaulus said, "and leave the door open as you see it. Then Nyssia, who usually has some order to give her women, or some other odd or end to attend to, follows. One by one, as though it were an effort to do so, she lets fall on this ivory bench the draperies and tunics which envelop her during the day like its bandages do a mummy . . . and you will be able to see, Gyges, that I have not said a word too much about her beauty! When she moves from the bench to the bed, that is the moment during which you must make your escape! But walk as though you were walking on eggs, hold your breath, and go as swiftly as possible. The feeble ray of the one lamp still lit does not reach the threshold of the door . . . And now, back to your hiding-place for night will soon be here!" And Candaulus disappeared, leaving Gyges hidden behind the door.

Gyges was far from being happy. He was not without delicacy. It was disagreeable to him to *steal* a favor for which he would willingly have paid with his life. There was something distasteful to him in Candaulus' attitude in the matter. Poor Candaulus was an artist and a poet, Gyges was merely a plain soldier. But his sense of the fitness of things was offended. And . . . Gyges was afraid. On horseback, in his war-chariot, he would have dared any foe but . . . he was afraid to peep at a lovely woman through a crack in the door. And he had a sudden dreadful thought. Young King Candaulus' head had not been strong enough to withstand Nyssia's superhuman beauty. Suppose he in turn went mad from love of her? . . . It was at that moment that King Candaulus entered the chamber, and Gyges heard him whisper softly but distinctly: "Patience, my poor Gyges, Nyssia will soon come!"

And when Gyges heard her light footsteps draw near, now that he was in for it, he made up his mind not to lose a single bit of the charming spectacle which his royal master had offered him. After all, one cannot expect a young captain of twenty-five to show the self-control of a white-haired philosopher. And step by step, while Gyges watched, Nyssia leisurely disrobed. When at last, with nonchalant grace, she was about to undo the girdle which held her tunic, her last remaining garment, Gyges' heart beat with such violence that he thought for a moment he would lose consciousness. For an instant Nyssia hesitated, then letting the garment fall, the white poem of her divine form appeared in all its splendor like the statue of a goddess unveiled in the temple on its day of inauguration. And Gyges realized that Candaulus, who smiled with proud satisfaction, had not even begun to do justice to the daughter of Mezagabus. But Nyssia's green eyes could see in the dark. Her back to the door, she moved to the royal couch. Then, for a second only, she turned before taking her place by her royal husband's side . . . and her own green eyes, piercing the shadows like those of a cat or tiger, saw a flaming eye regarding her through one of the cracks in the door!

A cry like that the doe utters when, dreaming peacefully beneath the leaves, an arrow pierces her side, was about to leap from Nyssia's throat. But she had the will power to suppress it. She stretched herself out by the side of Candaulus, cold and livid as a serpent, the violets of death on her cheeks and lips, but not one of her muscles trembled, and soon her deep, regular breathing seemed to show that Morpheus had strewn his poppy-juice on her lids. But Nyssia had guessed all, and understood what had happened.

She lay wide awake through the long hours of that night. She never had felt a deep love for her husband. But she had for him the serene tenderness every good woman feels for her husband. The Grecian liberty of his manners had often offended her. His ideas of modesty were the very opposite of her own, but now her very soul had been wounded, she seemed to herself sullied and dishonored. She felt deeply that she had not deserved the insult her husband had put on her. And now she would have preferred death to one of his caresses. For he had insulted her beyond pardon. After such an effront she felt for him only mortal hatred and deep contempt. She slipped from her couch at early dawn. But though she had her slaves empty one silver bucket of water after another over her shoulders in the bath, she knew that all the water in the world would not wash away the pollution of Gyges' glance. For she was a barbarian, and the barbarians, men as well as women, considered it a great and irreparable dishonor to be seen unclothed by another. While great tears rolled down Nyssia's cheeks she deplored her fate. Her body, which she had tried to make a mansion of a pure and noble soul, had been made a subject of idle talk, "Why did the gods grant me the fatal gift of beauty?" she cried. "Why am I not the wife of some humble mountain shepherd, whose manners are honest and simple? He would not have hidden another shepherd like himself on the threshold of his cabin to profane his humble happiness!" At last, her resolution taken, she regained mastery of herself and dried her tears.

No doubt her scruples were exaggerated. After all, her virtue had not suffered by Candaulus' foolish act. Nor had his motive in doing what he did been a base one. But bodily modesty among the oriental peoples was carried to an excess which the Greeks could not understand. When a man wished to *speak* to Nyssia in Mezagabus's Bactrian palace, he spoke with head bowed down, and two euneuchs, daggers down, stood ready to sheath their blades in his heart if he dared to raise his head while speaking to the princess. To a woman thus brought up, Candaulus' action was a mortal injury. It was not merely a blameworthy action deserving of reproof. Two men lived who had seen her unveiled: *one* of them must die. King Candaulus, the following day, was satisfied with the impression Nyssia had made on his captain of the guard. He even warned Gyges not to fall in love with the queen, and spoke of himself as a man who was the sole owner of the manuscript copy of a lovely poem, a few lines of which he had permitted Gyges to read. But . . . no sooner had the king left Gyges than a woman whose face was hidden by her veil in barbarian fashion glided from behind the column where she had hidden while they talked, and touching the young captain on the shoulder, signed for him to follow her.

Suddenly, he knew not how, Gyges found himself in Nyssia's apartments, and she herself, her lovely shoulders uncovered, her dress in disorder—for of what use was it to hide what Gyges' eyes already had seen?—stepped up to him and said:

"Do not lie! Do not excuse yourself! Have the honesty and the courage to admit your crime! I saw you and know all. Candaulus himself hid you behind my door. But I am no light Greek woman, ready to submit to the impure fancies of artists and voluptaries! There are two men, of whom *one* is one too many on earth!

One must disappear. If he does not die then I cannot go on living. It shall be you or Candaulus, as you choose. Kill him, avenge me, and your murder will give you my hand and the Lydian throne! But make up your mind without delay, for the light of two of the four eyes in which my nudity had been reflected must be extinguished before night."

Nyssia's terrible alternative surprised and shocked Gyges. He was a loyal servant of his royal master, who always had treated him with confidence and kindness. But in vain he pleaded his cause. He begged and implored Nyssia to abandon her decision. He implored her to pardon the king. "Forget an injury of which no one knows, and which will remain buried in shadow and silence! King Candaulus loves and admires you. His very fault was due to an excess of love!" But Nyssia was not to be moved: "Kill or die," she said, "I will wait until you decide which to do!" So at last Gyges, with a sigh, declared: "If blood must flow, then rather let it flow from other veins than my own." But while he said this with all the frankness of antiquity, he was moved by nobler motives which he did not mention. He had fallen deeply in love with Nyssia, and the thought that Candaulus should continue to posses her, was insupportable to him. And the knowledge that Nyssia herself had stretched out her hand to him up the steps of the royal throne made him forget that Candaulus was his master and benefactor.

Nyssia drew from her bosom a Bactrian dagger, its jade handle inset with golden circles. "The time," she said, coldly, "will be when he sleeps. See to it that he never wakes again!" Gyges listened in a daze. He could not understand such resolution in a woman who could not make up her mind to raise her veil. "Hide where you hid before," she added. "I will disrobe. I will lie down, and when I signal that Candaulus is sleeping, do not hesitate and see that your hand does not tremble! And now, lest you change your mind, I shall take charge of you until the fatal hour arrives!" She whistled in a certain manner and four hideous brown slaves appeared. Their arms were bunched with muscles, knots of muscle like the trunk of an oak. They had huge, protruding lips, and gold nose-rings. A few Bactrian words, and they seized Gyges and carried him off with them. To Nyssia the murder she had proposed seemed a sacred duty. Among the Persians and other barbarians any man who surprised a woman unclothed was put to death.

The queen thought herself within her rights. Only, since she had been dishonored in secret, she avenged herself as well as she could. When night came Nyssia herself led Gyges from the corner of the palace where the olive-skinned dwarves had mounted guard over him to the door he knew so well. Not a word was spoken. The daughter of Mezagabus took a savage delight in making the very means chosen by the Lydian king to gratify his caprice serve the purposes of her revenge. "Remember, it will be vain to try to escape," she said. At the slightest move of the sort I will waken Candaulus, and you can try to explain what you are doing in our room in the night, dagger in hand. Besides, my Bactrian mutes are guarding every exit of the palace with orders to slay you if you appear. Remember that I will make you King of Lydia and . . . that I will love you if you avenge me!"

Candaulus came. And this night Nyssia poured him a cup of black Samian wine mingled with honey from Hymettus, in which she had mingled a heavy sleeping potion. But the young king had a strong head, and the sleeping draught did not take effect at once. When Nyssia was taking off her jewels her nervous fingers broke the fastening of a bracelet of amber beads crusted with gold. As they rolled on the floor, each bead seemed to Gyges to fall like a drop of molten lead falling into the water. And when Nyssia laid aside her last tunic, it seemed to him like the white bier-cloth used to cover the bodies of the dead. At last Nyssia gave Gyges the sign. And she gave him a look—tender, so appealing, so filled with languor and intoxicating promise that Gyges, fascinated and maddened, darted from his hiding-place, crossed the chamber with a single bound, and plunged the Bactrian dagger into the heart of the descendant of Hercules to its hilt. Nyssia's injured modesty was avenged!

The Sardians, indignant at Candaulus' death, were half inclined to revolt, but the Oracle of Delphi having declared itself in Gyges' favor (he had sent its priests a large number of silver vases and six great jars full of gold), the new king kept his seat on the Lydian throne. He reigned for many years and lived happily but . . . he never showed his wife to any one! He knew only too well what it would have meant.

CHAPTER VII

SOME PICTURES FROM THE AGE OF ALEXANDER

FROM before the days of Xerxes down to the defeat of the armies of the Greek city-states by King Philip of Macedon, Greeks and Persians had been struggling. The Greeks fought more with steel, the Persians with gold. Each people called the other "barbarians." And, in their way of looking at everything they were as far apart as the poles. Even so adaptable a man as Alcibiades, the gifted, showy, dangerous Athenian politician, who knew no god but self, when he lived as an exile and a traitor at the court of a Persian satrap, secretly despised the man whose bribes he had accepted. In their simplest ideas of right and wrong, decency and decorum, the Greeks and Persians—as the preceding story has shown—could not agree. And this difference of opinion, ran through the lives of each people.

Alexander the Great (356 B.C.—323 B.C.) was the first man who, once he had conquered the Persians, and held the Persian empire in the hollow of his hand, tried to turn Greeks and Persians, Westerners (Occidentals) and Easterners (Orientals) into one people who could, at least in some of the chief things of life, meet on a common "platform." And Alexander failed.

Why East and West Cannot Meet on a Common Ground. In all human life through the ages there seems to be this one great dividing line between East and West which cannot be crossed. By individuals, yes, but not by peoples. Alexander's generals, who divide the lands of the East among themselves after he died, in a few generations had turned into Oriental monarchs. The Romans who took up the fight of the West against the East conquered but did not "mix" with the Orientals until the empire began to decay. Then out of a mixture of Eastern and Western ideas and races, the hybrid Byzantine empire, half-oriental, half-occidental, was developed, only to be conquered in turn by the wholly Oriental race of the Turks. When King Philip of Macedon defeated the army of the Greek city-states at Cheronae, he made Macedon the leader in Greece, and once his son Alexander had destroyed Thebes and leveled its walls, Macedon ruled the West. There does not seem to be any connection between the Persian girl who married a Lydian king, and Alexander the Great—and yet there is. For the story we have just told of her and her husband Candaulus, sums up the whole difference between the Greeks and the Persians (each race called the other "barbarians"), between East and West. There are all sorts of fundamental things in life—ideas of right and wrong, for instance, which we share with oriental peoples. But—Western peoples (Occidental peoples) and Eastern peoples (Oriental peoples), from the beginning of history, have had different ways of *understanding* fundamental facts. The *humanity* of Eastern and Western races, the *human beings* who make up the races, always have looked at life from absolutely different angles—and if you carry an angle far enough it gets very far away indeed from its starting-point. The story of Nyssia and her outraged modesty, for which only death could atone, is no idle tale. Nothing shows more *clearly* how differently East and West looked, and still look, at everything in life.

Alexander's Great Human Thought. The great thing that Alexander the Great did in a *human way*, was to try to introduce the idea of *sinking race differences in race union* into human life. After he had conquered the Persian empire, he attempted to "merge" his Macedonians and Greeks and his Persian and other Oriental races into *one* people. He would have failed, no doubt, even had he lived, for East and West do not seem, in a big way, to be able to meet on a common ground of life. In the world to-day one *key* to the difference is that throughout the Orient (in spite of the fact that Western ideas have brought about a more liberal standpoint in Turkey, perhaps), woman is placed on a *low,* purely *physical* plane *which Western thought will not tolerate.* The harem ideal: woman as a jealously guarded, soulless servant of man's pleasures, still obtains. But Alexander the Great, and the generals who divided his empire did introduce new thoughts and new ideas into the Oriental life of their time. They represent the first working-out of ideas of racial and political *union* in a big way in ancient history. In certain ages, ages of militarism and conquest, army life seems to stand out above all other.

A Soldier Breeding Ground. In Alexander's day Macedonia and the Greek states were much like Sweden in the days of its conqueror King Charles XII (1682 A.D.—1718 A.D.). The old home country, Macedon or Sweden, was just a breeding-ground for soldiers. Its one great product was recruits, the young blood of the land, exported in great batches to whatever foreign country in which the king was waging war as spear—or cannon-fodder. All the human *life of activity* of Macedonia and of Sweden, in the days of King Alexander and King Charles, centered on breeding, feeding, equipping, training and shipping men to the army. From the government standpoint the farmer and city worker married to produce human material to fill the depleted ranks of infantry and cavalry regiments. That was their duty. So, army life, being the outstanding form of human life lived in Alexander's day, it may be interesting to see what it was like.

When Armies Fought for Kings. Kingship nowadays is a poor thing. Royalty is a shadow. Armies to-day are "national" armies. They may be led to slaughter under false pretences. They may be "propagandad" into wars, but it has to be on "national" grounds. The pretexts at least must be patriotic ones which affect the whole nation involved. In Alexander's time war, almost everywhere, was the one great business of life. And a king *was* a king. Royalty was still more or less a divine institution: kings claimed descent from gods or half-gods, and were regarded with an amount of reverence of which we can hardly form an idea. And when a really great king, like Alexander, came into the world—he roused enthusiasm among his people. At that, to return to Charles XII of Sweden, Alexander's subjects were mentally more independent than Charles' Swedes. The Greeks of antiquity were natural-born critics: and the Macedonians, though not so polished as the Greeks of the great cities, still were Greeks. Charles XII, many centuries later, could make demands on his people with which the Macedonians never would have complied. Alexander claimed to be divine, even during his life-time, but there were many among his host who took his claims to godship with a grain of salt. Charles XII based all his rights on the divinity of his kingship: that he was an absolute ruler by the grace of God. And he could bleed a devoted and loyal country to death because, in all his mad, fantastic struggle for empire, he suffered every hardship his soldiers endured. In this manner Alexander, too, swayed the hearts of his men.

At the Macedonian Front. After the battle of the Granicus, where the Persians suffered their first great defeat, the loot of Asia began to find its way back to Macedonian cities and villages. And after that Olympias, Alexander's mother, who headed the "home government" during his absence, never had any difficulty in raising recruits. The lands of Thrace and Thessaly (lately added to Macedonia), were full of hardy, half-civilized horsemen. And especially after Issus, where the horsemen of the Thessalian cavalry had the biggest share in the plunder of Darius' camp at Damascus—gold, women and wine, letters of the "Oh, boy, you should have seen! . . ." variety began to find their way to the Thessalian villages. And Alexander's cavalry came in of themselves. Plutarch says of Issus: "This first gave the Macedonians such a taste of Persian wealth and women and barbaric splendor of living, that they were ready to pursue and follow upon it with all the eagerness of hounds upon a scent."

The Golden Rewards of War. That this had a bad effect on army discipline was shown by the luxury, idleness and dissipation which invaded the ranks. The officers set the example: Hagnon the Teian wore silver nails in his shoes. Leonatus employed several camels just to bring him powder out of Egypt to use when he wrestled. Philotas had special hunting-nets, a hundred furlongs long, made for his sporting needs. Instead of plain oil, the soldiers of the rank and file used precious ointments when they bathed, and ordinary pike-men of the Phalanx carried slaves about with them to wait on them and rub them down. But on the other hand, Alexander kept his men pretty much on the go all the time. Their great debauches and festivals alternated with periods of terrible hardship and desperate fighting. We will let an old veteran of the Phalanx, who spent a wild army youth in Asia, was one of the mutineers in the great revolt, and fought his last fight as one of the Eumenes' Argyraspids, talk. After Alexander's death, his generals Eumenes and Antigonus fell out, and old Parmio was one of Eumenes' veteran pikemen of Argyraspids (Silver-Shields) of the dead king. When the rest of the veterans, after defeating Antigonus in a great battle, "sold out" their leader because they feared to lose their baggage, old Parmio was disgusted. He had been canny enough, during his golden Asian years of loot and plunder not to fling away all he had gained. Some of his spoil always had found its way back to the sister who still lived on the little home farm in the Thracian hills. And while his comrades were still discussing the traitorous exchange of their general for their baggage, Parmio set out and made his way back to his native place. There he could spend his remaining days telling the village lads what a race of pygmies had torn dead Alexander's royal mantle to pieces, and were quarreling as to who should have the most strips.

AN OLD ARGYRASPID'S TALE

"You call this a hot summer, Leontus?" the old Argyraspid said one evening, as he sat on a bench beneath the great village oak, with a number of the village shepherd boys lying around him in the grass. "Why, boy, you have no idea of what heat is! You should have been along with us when we were marching through the Gedrosian* deserts, those terrible wastes which seemed to stretch to eternity.

"Wherever we looked nothing but sand, sand, sand. I remember we had been pushing on through the desert only a week when, one morning, our captain gave a cry of joy and pointed ahead of us.

* The desert country known today as Beluchistan.

We all stopped and looked. And then we cheered, for on the edge of the desert rose the green tops of cypress trees, and the white shimmering columns and roofs of buildings. And then, suddenly as though a wind had blown it away, the delightful picture had disappeared. The man next me in the ranks cried out as he clenched his fist and shook it at the horizon: "To think we must die like this! Where are our hills where the grapes grow, our benches outside the town gates where one could chat while looking down on the sea!" "Silence, you old dog," said the captain. "At least let us die in peace, and forget your cursed bench before the town gate!" The whole army stretched along in one long endless line, beneath the glowing red sky, horsemen and footmen. The horses hung their foam-dripping heads, and now and again men or horses would fall, and the rest would pass them as though they were not there. By noon the dust rose like little air-bubbles in the water. It settled in the pores of the skin, and singed them. And the women who followed the army—some with children, some without, Lesbian and Milesian dancers, courtesans out of Egypt, strumpets from the Syrian towns—they fell from the sutler-wagons and lay dying about the sand like flies. Night always came suddenly. It fell like a terror, and brought no rest. Instead of a red-hot sun, white-hot stars gleamed in the skies. Here and there soldiers, driven by their intolerable thirst, sunk to the baggage-wains to which the horses were tied. They would cut some poor beast's jugular vein with their short sword, then drop down with it, and let the spouting blood run into their parched throats!"

"Once—could fate have played us a more hideous trick?—there must have been a cloud-burst in the distant northern hills. A great flood of water, mountain high, was carried far out into the desert. Men, women and children, camp-fires, weapons, wagons, sleepers and tents, all were carried away. And, as swiftly as it had come the flood was gone. The best we could do was to drink what water we could wring from our wet garments. Many a man flung himself eagerly on the drowned, licking up the precious drops of moisture from their clothes and bodies. We Silver-Shields marched with Alexander's pages, the handsome boys they called the 'Noble Youths,' all drawn from the best families in the old country. They were not as tough as we pikemen and went fast, for all they rode and we went afoot. They fell from their horses and died, with a last call of 'Mother' as their breaking eyes saw the white roofs of Aegie or Pallaè, or the green hills where their father's mountain castle stood. Gradually all order went by the board. We simply staggered along, each for himself, men falling noiselessly and unnoticed as we went. Behind us the soft drift-sand followed like some stealthy, noiseless undertaker, and buried men and horses, camels, mules and dogs, helmets, bows and spears, the golden and jeweled spoils of India, as soon as we had passed."

"But Alexander! Never will earth see his like again. These two-penny generals that use Alexander's old veterans to pull the golden chestnut of their cheap royalty out of the fire for them—bah! I know them all. Second-hand ware, boys! Kings? Why, every Macedonian was a king in Asia in Alexander's day! I was a king! And while the generals were hanging their heads and dying like the rest of us, only Alexander held himself upright on his horse. Yes, he suffered, but he would not give in. He would not show it. He defied the sun and the sky. And as he rode along with his Pages, rolling in their saddles, the hired soldiers of the other races raised themselves from the sands where they lay dying, and gasped: "Save us, Alexander, if you are the son of god! Save us! Save us!"

"Was Alexander the son of God? I do not know. Some say he was and others deny it. But I never knew a man so like a god, so raised above all other men by his pride and his will. And—for all I shouted and cursed him as loudly as any other pikeman in the great mutiny—he *was* a god for the soldier. These little kings who are tearing his great purple mantle of empire to pieces between them compare to him as dung-hill cocks do to an eagle. My old Captain Charmides—he was killed when we stormed Aornus, that Indian mountain fort that stands on a rock so high above the river Indus— my old Captain Charmides used to say, when we talked about the camp-fire: 'Is Alexander a god? I do not know. But where he rides with us the kings and princes fall on their knees, the dust of battle rises, blood flows in rivers, and the riches of the earth pour into our empty hands! From the Hellespont to the Indian Ocean humanity in its millions writhes like worms beneath his feet. His name wakens terror. He is as irresistible as the plague. Did not Darius, the King of Kings, flee from him to the very utmost end of his empire to be slain by a horse-boy? Light and darkness, cold and heat do not exist for him. Time stands still for him. All the life of the world hangs on his breath. And we are part of Alexander, part of his kingship, of his glory! If he be a god we are part of his godship. I have served under Philip his father. He was a great king. I do not know if Alexander be divine, but he is more than human. And he comes nearer being the god of a soldier's dream than any mortal that ever lived!' "

"Never will I forget when at last we found water—toward the end of our desert march. Ha, how they drank and died by the thousands, the foreign hirelings, the new recruits, who had not learned what a veteran learns out of his bitter experience of hardship. And Alexander did what a mere man could not have done. The first cupful that came to us from weary miles in advance had been sent back to him post-haste. A man brought it on a dying horse. In a small earthen bottle. And Alexander looked at us—looked at his pikemen, his pages, his generals, all around him. Our faces were mad with desire, with greed, with hatred even. For we did hate him at that moment. We grudged him that swallow of water beyond everything in the world. Even the Page who had brought it and who had sunk down on the sand, looked at him with a curse in his eyes, for all that he was the King. And Alexander glanced around at all of us, smiled with his split lips and—poured out the water on the burning sand at his feet, while we flung ourselves forward with a cry of horror! Do you wonder I look down at all of them—Ptolemy, crafty Antigonus, bold Seleucus, all these heirs who trembled at the sight of his seal on an order when he lived!" And in the silence which followed the shepherd lads who lay in the grass saw glowing visions of battle and plunder, the forbidden joys of rich Asian cities . . . They forgot the horrors of the desert march. And, after all, old Parmio lived in the past. Life was tame in the hills, with only the goats to look after. And why settle down with one of the village girls, when the whole mysterious East was there to explore? . . . Why not take service with Antiochus or Seleucus or with the king at Pellaè?

"When I filed through the great hall of the great palace in Babylon—for every soldier of the army, man for man, was allowed to file past to bid Alexander farewell as he lay on his death-bed, unable to speak, and only his eyes, those great eyes that used to dart flame in battle, alive—I know that we had come to the end of things. What happened after could be of small account to any one of his veterans. For the great days had passed with the man who made them!"

The Wedding at Susa. Alexander's grand schemes for making Greeks and Persians one race, his own marriages with Persian princesses, one the daughter of Darius, his making his generals and officers marry the daughters of the Persian nobles and satraps, his even compelling thirty thousand or more of the men in the ranks to take Persian wives, bore but little fruit. East remained East and West, West. But owing to him Greek art and literature became known in the East and after he died the Greek kingdoms formed in Western Asia lasted for centuries. When he celebrated his wedding with the lovely Persian Roxana, he had sworn to pay all his soldiers' debts. So one day before the festivities began, great tables were set up in the camp streets, and slaves by the hundred dragged sacks full of gold coin from the palace. First the Macedonians thought it was a trick: the king only wanted to find out which among them were the spendthrifts and wastrels. But heralds cried out, "Come one, come all, ye heroes of Macedon! Tell the paymasters what you owe, and to whom you owe it, and they will pay as you direct, according to the king's command!" Then they crowded around the tables.

After Alexander's death in the kingdom founded in Asia by the *diadochi*, the "generals," Greek culture, Greek art and Greek science were introduced and flourished until the days of the Roman conquest of Asia. And Alexander's own city, Alexandria, the city born of his dream of uniting the spirits of the East and the West in one soul, was the center of Greek civilization and learning until it fell to the Arabs whom Mohammed's call sent swarming out of their deserts bent on the conquest of the world in his name.

CHAPTER VIII

ROME AND CARTHAGE

WHEN the Romans began they started out as a primitive race of mountain farmers with walled towns in the hills. Gradually they drove out the Etruscans, who were the lords of Italy before them and—at once settled down to the cultivation of war and politics. For one of the most interesting things about the average ancient Roman is the fact he was a natural-born fighter and politician. From the time the Romans dropped their kings (245 B.C.) and established a republic, to the days when monarchy came back with Augustus in the shape of an absolute emperor, the great *human* interest in Roman life—outside of the life and death struggle with Carthage (a Phoenician colony which had inherited the wealth and power of ancient Tyre and Sidon), was war and politics. But the details of *practical* politics, past or present, while of interest to those directly concerned, have few romantic angles. The struggle between the *plebeians,* the poorer classes of Rome, and the *patricians,* the Roman aristocracy of blood and wealth, which rose to an imperial climax and then worked out in decline and fall, would often suggest comparison with European political conditions today.

But, no matter how they might disagree with regard to home politics, the Romans were united when it came to getting the better of the rest of the world and making it obey them. By the year 268 B.C. the legions, made up of solid Roman citizens, had conquered all of Italy, including the Greek coast cities, which had tried to hang on to their independence.

Range Life and Plantation Life in Ancient Italy. The taking over of all Italy made the state richer: the Romans, in these days of civic honesty, before men began to feel that they must grow rich at any cost, even at the expense of the *nation,* set aside great territories as national property: nor was it possible for their "oil reserves" and other national property to be so administered that, let us say, the Carthaginian navy could benefit thereby. A large number of *patrician* and *plebeian* families, however, grew wealthy in a perfectly legitimate way by buying in tracts of land, and buying farm-land and pasture land. These big plantations were cultivated by the slaves which were cheap in times of war. The slaves formed large "families," as the Romans called them, and were in charge of an overseer. The life was something like that on the big Southern plantations before Civil War days. When necessary, "free labor" was hired in the nearest town to help get in the harvest. It seems odd to think that in Italy in those days were immense "ranges" of pasture land, where "cattle barons" and "sheep kings" with Latin names ran immense herds of sheep and cattle. How many Western range-riders suspect that before Caesar was born, Campanian cowboys followed a primitive Roman "chuck-wagon on the round-up," and that at evening the Nubian cook called out in the tongue the college boy learns to forget at Yale or Princeton: "Come and get it or I'll throw it away!" And it is quite possible that many of the Roman sheep-herders were Basques, for Iberian (Spanish) slingers were a feature in all Carthaginian armies, and were often captured and sent to Rome to be sold in the slave market. But when, in 268 B.C. the Romans began to coin silver money, it meant that they were going to make a bid for the world's commerce, and that meant war with Carthage.

Rome and Carthage. The Romans were ready to die in battle with their wounds all "in front," for the spreading of Roman power and— and trade. After they had obtained possession of Italian mainland, they found themselves that they would have to destroy their great Semitic trade rival, Carthage, before the Roman *trader* could do business with the rest of the world. Carthage was a great city-state, on the North African coast. Its walls stood on an island of fertile land hedged around with deserts, and it owned far-flung colonies, was mistress of Spain and Sicily, and was stretching out its feelers in other directions. It was the leading sea-power, and if Roman commerce was to make headway, Carthage would have to go.

In this struggle Rome represented the spirit and the civilization of the West, Carthage that of the East, and under different circumstances, and waged by different nations, it was a struggle similar to that begun when the Persian King, Darius, first attempted to subdue the Greeks. A great French romanticist has given us some wonderfully authentic glimpses of *human* life in ancient Carthage.

A DAY IN A CARTHAGINIAN GENERAL'S LIFE

The Greek, Lybian, Gaulish, Balearic and other Carthaginian mercenaries had not beeen paid for months. So they had mutinied, and killing and driving away their Carthaginian superior officers, were now camped at a short distance from the great walled city of Utica, which had sent urgent messages for help to Carthage. There was no public money in the treasury, and the rich who made up the

Grand Council did not feel inclined to dig down into their own pockets to make up the arrears of pay for the twenty-four thousand barbarians they had been putting off with promises. The great Hamilcar, their best general, was absent in Spain. So now that the city was threatened by the mutineers, they handed over the command to Hanno, their next best soldier. Hanno was clever, cunning and merciless to all the Africans and other peoples of Carthage. He was a true Carthaginian, and almost as wealthy as the Barca family, whose head Hamilcar was.

Spurred on by terror, all the Carthaginian citizens grew brave. The rich were out beneath the walls at cock-crow turning up their tunics and going through the pike-manual. One night, when Hanno had made all his preparations he sent his soldiers and elephants across the gulf of Carthage on rafts, and the following morning came within sight of the barbarian camp. The Carthaginian army at once moved to the attack. First came the Sacred Legion. The Sacred Legion was the crack cavalry corps of ancient Carthage. It was made up of young patricians, the tallest that could be found. They wore armor of golden scales and rode tremendous horses, with manes, tails and ears docked, which carried silver horns on their frontlets to make them look like a rhinocerus. Among the squadrons of the Sacred Legion ran youths wearing small helmets and balancing a javelin with a cord in each hand. After them came the long pikes of the heavy infantry. All these traders and merchants had loaded themselves down with as many weapons as possible. Some had a lance, a mace, a hatchet, a club and two swords. The darts stood out from others like a porcupine's quills, and their arms stuck out of corselets covered with plates of horn or metal placques. Behind the infantry came the great chariots holding the war-machines, drawn by long strings of mules and oxen.

As the army spread out the captains, hot and panting, ran from left to right, giving orders and dressing the ranks. Members of the Grand Council who held commands had come wearing purple mantles. The magnificent fringes of these mantles got tangled in the laces of their high boots. Their faces painted bright and red shone under enormous helmets topped by figures of Phoenician gods. They had big shields, rimmed with ivory and set with jewels, and to look at them one would have said that they were suns passing above a wall of bronze.

But the Carthaginians maneuvered so clumsily that the rebel mercenaries sarcastically invited them to sit down. They called out to them that in a few minutes they would empty their fat bellies, dust the gilding from the skins, and make them drink iron. In the camp of the Mercenaries a strip of green cloth rose before the leader's tent, the signal for battle. The Carthaginian army replied with a great noise of trumpets, cymbals, tympani and flutes made of asses bones. A Balearic slinger stepped out in front of the ranks of the mutineers, and ivory shield split, and the two armies struck in the shock of battle.

The Greek mercenaries, thrusting their spear-points into the nostrils of the Carthaginian horses, made them rear back on their masters. The Punic (Phoenician, *i.e.*, Carthaginian) footmen, striking straight down with their long swords, exposed their left sides. Then the Barbarians, breaking their ranks, put them to the sword. The Carthaginian companies began to give way. Hanno's great litter with its large crystal pendants, which had been tossing among the Carthaginian soldiery, suddenly disappeared. The Mercenaries thought the battle won. They already had commenced to raise the song of victory when Hanno himself was upon them, mounted on an elephant's back. He was bare-headed beneath a parasol of Byssus* which a slave held over him. A collar of blue stones flapped up and down on the flowers embroidered on his black tunic, and diamond armlets covered his arms. In one hand he brandished a very long pike, which spread out at its end like a lotus, and shone more brightly than a mirror. And as he appeared, behind him, a terrific and threatening figure above the dust-clouds that rolled along the battle-field, the Mercenaries saw bearing down on them in one long, tremendous line, all the elephants of Carthage. They were huge beasts with gilded tusks. They were covered with bronze armor, their ears were painted blue, and on their backs, above the housings of scarlet cloth, swayed leather towers, each containing three archers with their large bows drawn. Many of the soldiers had dropped their arms, thinking the battle over. They had broken ranks, and stood in disorder, filled with terror.

And, already, from the towers javelins, leaden balls and arrows were falling among them. Some of the Greeks, in order to climb up, clutched the fringes of the scarlet elephant-cloths. Their hands were cut off at the wrist with curved swords, and they fell back on the spears waiting to receive them. Their pikes, too weak to withstand the black animal torrent, snapped. The elephants mowed down the companies as a herd of wild boar tramples the grain. As they passed through the camp the great brutes tore up the tent-stakes, and upset the tents with their bronze-plated chests. Those of the Mercenaries who were not slain took to flight, and hid in the gullys of near-by hills. Hanno, leaving his victorious army without the gates, then entered Utica with a small escort. As soon

---

* Byssus was an extremely fine and valuable kind of salt-water silk, made of the delicate thread-like filaments, or "beards," which fringe certain mussel shells.

as he had received the salutations of the city notables, he had himself led to the bath and called for his cooks.

Three hours later he was still plunged in the oil of cinnamon with which the great marble basin in which he was seated had been filled. While he bathed he ate. Spread out before him on an ox-hide were peacock tongues seasoned with honey. Near him stood his Greek physician, motionless in a long yellow robe. From time to time he gave orders to reheat the bath while two young lads, bent over the steps of the basin, massaged the general's legs. But Hanno did not let the care of his body interfere with his duty toward the state. He was dictating a letter to the Grand Council, and since prisoners had been taken, he was searching his brain for some terrible punishment to deal out to them.

"Wait," he cried to the slave who stood before him, . . . writing in the hollow of his hand. "Bring them in here! I want to see what they look like!" From the back of the hall chamber, filled with a whitish steam, where the torches cast a red light, three Mercenaries were thrust forward: a Greek from Samos, a Spartiate and a Cappadocian. "Write as follows," Hanno continued:

"Rejoice, O Light of the Baals! Your *suffete* (the two *suffetes* were the mayors or "city kings" of Carthage) has exterminated the hungry dogs! Blessed be the Republic! Order prayers to be said. . . . Here he caught sight of the captives, and burst out into laughter: "Aha, you brave mutineers! You are not singing so loudly today. Well, do you recognize me? What has become of your swords? You are terrible fellows, aren't you?" And he acted as though he wished to hide, as though he were terrified: "You insisted on having horses, women, dogs, estates, high offices, no doubt, and priesthoods! Well, I'll see that you get them! You shall be married to virgin gallows. Your back pay? It shall be poured into your mouths in ingots of melted lead! And I'll see that you get up in the world, way up, up amid the clouds, so that you will be near the eagles!"

The three Barbarian mercenaries, hairy and ragged, looked at him without understanding a word of what he said. Wounded on the knees, they had been lassoed with cords, and great chains hung from their wrists, and trailed along the ground. Hanno was indignant to see them so passive.

"Down on your knees, you dogs! You jackals! Dirt! Vermin! What? You do not answer? See that they are skinned alive! No, not now, in a little while when I can see it done!"

He panted like a hippopotamus, rolling his eyes. The perfumed oil washed about as he moved his heavy body, and clinging to the scales of his skin, made him look rosy in the torch-light. Then he went on with his interrupted letter:

"During four days we suffered greatly from the sun. We lost our mules in passing the river Macar. In spite of their position, the extraordinary courage . . . "Ah, Demonades," he suddenly roared, "how I suffer! Have the bricks reheated! See that they are red hot!" There was a noise of stoking. The incense burned more thickly in the large basins. The naked masseurs, sweating like sponges, crushed a paste made of cheese, sulphur, black wine, the milk of bitches, myrrh, galbanum and styrax on Hanno's joints. A raging thirst seemed to devour him, but the yellow-gowned physician would not indulge it. Instead he held out to him a golden cup filled with a steaming viper-broth.

"Drink," said he, "so that the strength of serpents, born of the sun, may enter into the marrow of your bones! And take courage, Oh, Reflection of the gods! You know, of course, that a priest of Eschmoun is studying the cruel stars which circle around the Dog-star, and which are the cause of your malady. They are paling like the scales of your skin, and you will not die of your disease."

"Yes, yes, that's so, isn't it?" repeated the general—"I shall not die, shall I?" And from his purple lips came a sigh more nauseous than one corpse might have exhaled. Two coals of fire seemed to gleam in place of eyes in his face, for he had lost his eye-brows. A great fold of rough skin hung from his forehead. His ears had begun to grow larger, spreading out from his head. The deep wrinkles which formed half-circles around his nostrils gave him a strange and terrifying appearance. He looked like some savage beast. His unnatural voice seemed like a beast's roaring. He said:

"Do you think you are right, Demonades? In fact, a number of my ulcers have closed. I feel stronger. See, how heartily I eat!" And less because he was hungry than in order to show he spoke the truth, and to prove to himself that he felt well, he began to clear away the cheese-cakes, the boned fish, the oysters, the eggs, truffles, and small birds roasted on sticks, which were spread out in front of him. And while he glanced at the prisoners he enjoyed the thought of their sufferings in advance. But again his rage overpowered him.

"Ah, you traitors! You low, scurvy wretches! You insulted me, me your general! Your services, the price of your blood, you said? Bah!" Then, speaking to himself, he added: "They all shall die! Not one shall be sold! It would be best to take them all to Carthage to suffer there. I fear, though, I did not bring along enough chains. Here, you! Write: Send me . . . How many prisoners are there? Find out from Muthumbal! Go, and see that their hands are cut off and brought to me in baskets!"

Suddenly wild cries sounded above Hanno's voice, and the clatter of the dishes set down around him. And pealing out on the night came the trumpeting of the elephants, as though the battle had re-commenced. A tremendous tumult broke out around the city. Hanno had his battle to win all over again, for the Mercenaries had re-formed, had turned the elephants on their own ranks by a clever trick, and were crushing the Carthaginians beneath the walls of Utica. The inhabitants, fearing the barbarians, would not open the gates for them.

Hanno, as Flaubert has painted him, is a real Carthaginian type, a genuine *human* if not a *humane one*. For the Carthaginians were cruel by nature, like the Phoenicians, the Assyrians and other Semite races. Yet Carthage produced two men equal to the greatest of the Romans, Hamilcar and Hannibal.

A NAVY BOY'S LIFE ABOARD A ROMAN "BATTLE-WAGON"

AT the very beginning of the struggle between Rome and Carthage, the Romans, who were "land-lubbers," realized that unless they ac-quired sea-legs they would not get very far toward realizing their dream of empire. The Carthaginian Navy counted hundreds of splendidly armed ships with trained crews. The Romans had neither. But a kindly storm had flung a great Carthaginian *quinquereme,* a "five-bencher," a war-galley with five banks of rowers, on the sand beach at Latium. And with this crack vessel as a model, the Romans set up a Hog Island, and opened Navy recruiting stations in Rome and other cities. And young Septimus Nepos, who was only seven-teen, but big for his age, managed to get into the Navy by advancing his age a couple of years, (as has been done in later ages). And as soon as he had passed his physical examination he was sent off with a squad of other recruits under a petty officer to the Navy train-ing camp at Latium, to be whipped into shape for work at sea.

Latium was a busy, busy place. The Roman government had de-cided to build nothing but quinqueremes, five big war-galleys with five banks of oars, almost exclusively, and only a few triremes, three-banked vessels. Workmen were busy day and night. Nor were they working at top-notch wages, while the Navy boys and marines were drawing the ancient Roman equivalent of thirty dollars a month. The Roman idea in those earlier and patriotic days was that a war was a *national* undertaking. Every one, so to speak, was "conscripted," by the government. Later on came the days of great government con-tracts and the division of huge profits by both capital and labor, while the soldiers and sailors still fought gaily for their month's pay. But when Rome's first great fleet was built, there was no idea of per-sonal profit involved. It was a *national* matter. The war with Carthage was a *national* war. And, perhaps, all worked with greater zeal knowing that the burden of war fell on all alike. Shipyards, sheds, dry-docks, parade-grounds and arsenals covered the whole landscape around Latium. And there Septimus, with thousands of others, was put to drilling, after he had been assigned to a "deck" division.

It cannot be said that he disliked Navy life. Daily drill was tiresome, of course, but there were several "leave" evenings a week, and there was plenty to interest a sailor on leave in the town which had rapidly grown up on the outskirts of the great naval camp. For it was a great camp.

The government was building one hundred quinqueremes in all, and twenty triremes and a hundred quinqueremes meant crews, all told, of twenty thousand men. Later, during the same war, the Roman and Carthaginian fleets fought with hundreds of ships, and as many as one hundred and fifty thousand men on each side at times. The "four-striper," or navy captain of Roman days was called the Trierarch. He was the captain of the ship, and he had his navigating officer, and his lieutenants. The crew, under petty officers, was divided into oarsmen, sailors, and marines. But—the marine was the *important* arm on a Roman ship! For the Roman marine was a regular soldier, who fought with sea-legs on a wooden deck instead of with land-legs on the firm ground. Septimus regretted sometimes that he had not gotten into the marine corps, for the marines were rather inclined to look down on the sailors. Will it seem strange to the reader to learn that in the saloons of the camp town, over the brown barley-beer or the red Falernian wine, sailors and marines often came to blows over the merits of their respective branches, and that the Trierarchs often held summary courts-martial on the newly-laid deck-planks of their handsome vessels? Yet Septimus was thankful he had not been drafted as a "rower," and he could laugh at the fellows who sat perched up on the high scaffolds, benches just like those they would sit at abroad ship, learning to row *on land!*

Before two months had passed the Consul C. Cornelius put to sea, amid a great deal of cheering and hurrahing, with seventeen of the new ships. But the cheering was a little early, for after a week had passed, came the news that he had been surprised and captured with his whole squadron by the Carthaginian admiral. A gloom fell over the whole camp. But C. Dullius, the *plebeian* consul, who was very popular with the ordinary seamen of the fleet, arrived in camp the next day, and at once gave orders to "hoist oars" and get under way. A few days only, and the Roman fleet ran into the Carthaginians near Mylæ, off the west coast of Palermo. The trumpets signalled abroad both fleets, the ships drew up into line of battle and Dullius attacked without delay. Septimus belonged to one of the "crow-crews." The *corvii,* "crows," as the Romans called them, were a little invention which won the battle for them. They were grappling-engines thirty-six feet long, and four broad. At one end was an oblong hole which let them turn freely around a strong pole-beam twenty-four feet high, fixed near the ship's prow. At the other end was a strong rope. It passed over a sheaf at the head of the pole. As Septimus' battle-wagon, "The Remus"—which Dullius had selected for his flag-ship—drew near the Carthaginian admiral's galley, Septimus with the rest of the boys who held the rope of the "crow," gave a yell and suddenly let go. The big draw-bridge, with a thud that jarred the ship dropped on the Carthaginian deck, and the strong, sharp spike on its under side, shaped like a crow's beak, caught in the planks and held it there. And with a great shout of "Gangway, gangway! the Roman marines, who had been drawn up on the deck in column formation, rushed across the bridge and fell on the Carthaginians. And with them, for the "crow-crews" had begged for the privilege, and been granted it, of taking part in the hand-to-hand fighting, ran Septimus and the rest of the bridge-droppers, with their short swords drawn. The Carthaginian admiral-ship was a galley of tremendous size. A splendidly carved and gilded vessel of *seven* banks of oars it had once belonged to King Pyrrhus. But seven was not a lucky number for the Carthaginians that day. The Roman boarders, marines and sailors, fought just as though they were fighting ashore, and in a short time King Pyrrhus' *septireme* was theirs, its commander a prisoner, and its crew slain or captured. The same thing happened everywhere. The Carthaginians lost thousands of men and half their ships, and the rest beat the waves to foam with their oars in headlong flight for Sardinia. The great sea-fight of Mylae, which the Romans won by fighting at sea as though they were fighting on land, instead of trying to out-maneuver or outsail their foes filled every Roman with pride. For a time the Navy was the only thing that counted in Rome, and sailor-boys like Septimus, when they marched in the great victory procession at Rome, found that nothing was too good for the heroes of the great fight. Admiral Dullius was the guest of honor at one great public banquet after another, and was escorted home from festivals with torch-light processions and bands of flute players walking on ahead. With the other lads of the fleet Septimus came in for his share of appreciation. His navy clothes were a key that unlocked all hearts and all purses. Every one wanted to buy him a drink and, sad to say, for great victories often have these little after-effects on the individual human units who win them, Septimus acquired a taste for red Falernian which never left him. But walking or reeling through the streets of Rome, he was a *hero*. The eyes of Roman maids of good family would soften as they gazed on Septimus staggering along under a greater load of Falernian than his system could accommodate. They would sigh and say: "What a pity! But, after all, the poor boy must have some relaxation after fighting so heroically, and daring death by drowning and the sword to save us! We must not judge him too harshly!" And girls who did not belong to good Roman families—and there were many of them in the streets of Rome—would fling their arms about his neck, kiss him enthusiastically, and make clear that they loved him for his own sake alone.

In due time Septimus returned to duty. When four years later, he again came to Rome, after the sea-battle of Ecnomus, the *Rostrata,* the big victory column ornamented with the metal beaks of the Carthaginian ships taken at Mylae, was still standing in the Forum, and he had become a chief petty officer. But—the Romans had grown used to naval victories and to sailors. Hardly anyone even turned their heads to look at Septimus and when, yielding to temptation, he drank deep of the wine when it was red in a tavern, and reeled out into the street, there was no pity in the feminine eyes which gazed at him. Instead, one young girl who was passing said to another: "There's another drunken sailor from the fleet. It is perfectly disgusting. The *aediles* ought to see it that they are kept off the streets!"

After all, human nature is much the same in every age.

THE SACRIFICE TO MOLOCH

After Hanno's defeat and others which followed, the Mercenaries made things so hot for the Carthaginians that, though they had sent for the great Hamilcar, and he had come from distant Spain—practically a personal estate of the great Barca family—they were besieged in their own home town. Hamilcar had defeated the Barbarians with great slaughter, and had crucified them by the hundreds, but now thousands of African tribesmen, even negroes from the interior, swelled their ranks, and Hamilcar had been obliged to retire behind the walls of Carthage. And there, gradually, the food gave out. The Carthaginians began to die like flies of starvation. The soldiers on the walls had hardly enough strength to beat back the assaults. In the streets many devoured the unburied corpses which lay about, while others drank henbane, which turned them mad, and flinging themselves on those passing, tried to tear them to pieces. It was then that the priests of Moloch called for a great sacrifice to the god.

Hidden away in a secret chamber of Hamilcar's great palace was his son Hannibal, whom he had brought from Spain, unknown to any one in the city. The first-born sons of both great and small must be sacrificed to Moloch, the Grand Counsel decreed. But Hamilcar had made up his mind that Hannibal, the hope of his race, the pride of his name, should not share the fate of the rest. Moloch would have to do without him. And as soon as he knew that the black-robed priests had started their house to house round, to take over the first-born sons of every house-holder of Carthage, he hurried to the room of his daughter, who had the boy in charge. He sent for the Superintendent of his Slaves. "Giddenem," he cried, "find a slave boy eight or nine years old, with black hair and a broad forehead and bring him here! Make haste!" Then he turned to his son. With one hand he seized the boy, with the other tore a strip from a garment which trailed from a stool. Then he tied little Hannibal's feet and hands, and stuffed the remainder of the strip into his mouth for a gag. This done he hid him under a bull-hide couch, throwing a large drapery over it. As Hamilcar stood gnawing his lips Giddenem entered with a boy. He was a wretched little creature, thin, yet swollen-looking. His skin was a dirty gray, the color of the foul rags that hung about him. His head was sunk between his shoulders, and with the back of his hand he wiped away the flies which clustered around his eyes.

"How can they mistake him for my son?" thought Hamilcar. "And there is no time to look for another." Hamilcar glanced at Giddenem, and felt like strangling him. "Go!" he cried, and the Master of the slaves fled. But the moment after the Superintendent of the Household scratched at the door, and whispered that the priests of Moloch had come. Hamilcar began to pace the room like a madman. Suddenly he stopped, and plunged his hand into a porphyry vase which still held some clear water. Then, like a slave merchant, though he shrank from touching him, he began to wash the boy Giddemen had brought him, and to rub his neck and chest with fragrant oils. From the pegs on the walls he took down two squares of purple, hung one over his back, and one across his chest, tying them together with a girdle that had a diamond clasp. He poured perfume on his head, flung a collar of electrum around his neck, and on his feet put his daughter's own sandals. The child, dazed and pleased with this unexpected splendor, clapped his little hands and jumped with joy. But Hamilcar, opening the door, dragged him with him, holding him so tightly that tears drove away his happy smiles. As he crossed the court a plaintive, supplicating voice cried: "Master, O master! . . . I am his father!" Hamilcar kept on, but the other followed and lightly, timidly touching his elbow, faltered: "Mercy! Have mercy! . . . Will you? . . ." He could not go on, and Hamilcar surprised by the depth of his grief stopped. He never had thought—so great was the gulf which separated him from the slave—that they could have anything in common. His grief even seemed a kind of outrage. It seemed like an invasion of his privileges. He gave the hapless father a look colder and heavier than a blow from a headman's axe, and as the

I

slave fell unconscious in the dust at his feet, stepped over him and continued on his way.

When he reached the great palace hall, where stood the three priests of Moloch in their black gowns, he suddenly began tearing his garments and crying: "Ah, my little Hannibal! My poor little Hannibal! My consolation! My hope! My life! Take me with you and kill me too." And as he tore his face with his nails, and howled like a hired mourner at a funeral, the priests of Moloch were surprised to see that the great Hamilcar had so soft a heart. They came near being moved themselves. But suddenly, on the threshold of the hall, appeared a pale, terrible figure with open arms which cried: "My child!" With one leap Hamilcar was upon him, and covering his mouth with his hand, he cried more loudly still: "It is the old man who has brought him up! He has always called him his child! This is driving him mad! Enough, go!" And pushing the three priests and their victim before him, he closed the door on them with a thrust of his foot. As for the slave, he had him sent the best there was in the kitchen: a loin of goat, beans and preserved grenadines. And the poor wretch, who had eaten nothing for days, fell on the victuals and devoured them, while his tears dropped in the plates.

When Hamilcar returned and unbound the child, the angry boy bit his hand to the bone, but his father only caressed him, and after a time he fell asleep. When it was darkest night, Hamilcar took him, still sleeping, in his arms, and softly and without a torch descended the stairs which led to the water-side of the palace. Passing into the great store-house he stopped to take a jar of raisins and another of pure water. Then he pressed a hidden spring, a stone statue moved noiselessly aside at the end of the hall, and closed behind him as he walked through a long passage to the secret chamber with its underground outlet on the beach. In this hidden cave, where stood the jewel-covered statue of the ancestor of the Barcas, Aletes, the boy woke and smiled in the light of the torch his father now lit. And Hamilcar, now that he was at last unobserved, hugged him to his breast, and weeping and laughing at the same time, called him endearing names, and covered his face with kisses. And little Hannibal, frightened by this terrible tenderness, said not a word.

In the great square of Khamon stood the huge brazen statue of Moloch, surrounded by his priests, and by all the people of Carthage, rich and poor, high and low, and clad in their best to do honor to the god. Between the giant legs of the image burned a great fire of aloe, cedar and laurel wood. The tips of his long wings already glowed red-hot in the flames, and the ointments which had been poured over him ran like perspiration down his brazen limbs. The bronze hands, with movable fingers, at the ends of his unnaturally long arms, let down and raised by chains running across his shoulders, were extended palm outward, toward the child victims who, covered with black veils, had been herded together in a group before them. After some short acts of ceremony, the people of Carthage held their breaths. The first human sacrifice *must* be a voluntary one. Through the lanes left open in the throng, crowded men who cast pearls, golden cups and vases, the richest and most splendid things they owned, into the red-hot belly of Moloch—for the priests had drawn aside the bronze plate which closed it. But this was not enough. At last a man pale and hideous with terror staggered forward. Before him he pushed a little child. And then all could see a small, black object in the bronze hand of the colossus. Slowly the idol raised its arm, and the hand deposited what it held in the red, glowing cavern in its body. The priests leaned forward and burst out into a wild chant, praising the joys of death and sacrifice. And as the smoke rose up and blew away from the statue of Moloch in great spirals, it looked as though the child had been carried off in a cloud. Then, one after another, the victims—their hands were tied, their eyes were bandaged, they could hear and see nothing—were raised as the bronze arms worked faster and faster. As soon as the merciless hands lifted one to the edge of the opening, he disappeared as a drop of water does on a red-hot stovelid, and a small white cloud rose from the red glow, while a fine shower of ashes dropped through the grating of the idol's cavernous belly to increase the pile rising between his giant legs. When the fourteenth boy victim was reached Hamilcar made a great gesture of horror, then stood motionless as before. By the time night fell a madness had seized the mob. Women crowded to the iron hands and pushed the weeping and shrieking children who clung to their skirts into them. Fathers flung the toys of their dead into the furnace, henbane drinkers danced crazily around the statue, and men drew knives and fought with each other without knowing why. At last the priests of Moloch ended the ceremony by seizing hands full of the gray ashes and flinging them into the air in all directions, so that the whole city might benefit by the sacrifice.

THE MAN WHO DIED OF FRACTIONAL GEOMETRY

War does not spare even those farthest removed from it in thought or deed. Archimedes (212-207 B.C.), was the greatest mathematician and inventor of antiquity. A friend of King Hiero of Sicily, he was far too interested in writing essays on squaring the circle, why floating bodies floated, and what made conoids and spheroids act, as they did, to bother with love, war, politics or anything else. His idea of a graceful gift to King Gelo, who succeeded his father

Hiero as king when the latter died, was a little treatise entitled *Psammites* or "The Sand Reckoner," which showed the exact number of grains of sand it would take to fill a sphere the size of the world. To Archimedes figures held all the world's romance and beauty. A proposition in plane geometry had the effect on him a beautiful flower or a radiant gem has on ordinary persons. Finding the quadrature of a parabola gave him the same sensations others derive from a kiss from lips beloved. King Gelo, however, who had thrown over the Romans in favor of the Carthaginians, and was besieged in Syracuse, his capital, was more interested in war machinery which would keep the Romans out of his city than in Sand Reckoners. He came to Archimedes for help. The great mathematician remonstrated gently "O king," he said, "such things are really beneath the dignity of pure science! But, if you insist very insistently—I will design some trifles of the sort for you. But you must not ask me to make a *written* record of them. I would not have posterity know that I stooped to such things!" As soon as Archimedes' trifles, as he had called his engines of war, got into action, the Romans realized that it had been a mistake not to have coaxed him to Rome in the days of old King Hiero, who had been their friend. For they did terrible execution in the Roman ranks, made the siege last three years longer, and nearly lost them the city. One of the most dreadful of the devices Archimedes tossed off in an idle moment as a favor to his king was the terrible "Burner." The Roman ships lay in the water within bow-shot of the towering walls of Syracuse. Suddenly, one day, without any apparent cause they flamed up to the skies, hulls, masts and figure-heads, cordage, tackle and sails! Many sailors were burned to death, many others rushing from their bunks, where they had been drowsing away the hot Sicilian noon-hour, flung themselves into the sea where (it is well-known that most sailors cannot swim), most of them drowned. Archimedes had simply had his "Burners" rightly placed, and the terrific heat engendered by concentrating the sun's rays in combinations of burning glasses had destroyed the Roman fleet. After that, duty outside the walls became doubly hard on sunny days. Marcellus, the Roman general, might be writing in his tent, when suddenly he would leap into the air with a cry of pain, and clap his hand to his arm. And while the canvas began to flame in the spot where the "Burner" had sent in its ray of concentrated sun-power, he would rush out to have the angry wound on his arm dressed. It must have been a common sight about the Roman camp for a sentry calmly walking his beat, suddenly to find himself aflame, and running like a living torch toward the nearest pond.

Archimedes might have given modern inventors many a happy hint. For King Hiero he once made a small mechanical device by which the king merely had to turn a handle, to make a large and heavily loaded ship move in the harbor. He founded the science of hydrostatics or water-measurement, and might be called the Father of the Water-Meter. It came about by chance. King Hiero had given a leading Syracusan goldsmith an order to make him a new golden crown. The crown, a handsome thing of its kind, was duly delivered but—somehow, though it looked very fine and felt heavy in the hand, Hiero felt there was something not just right about it. He knew that all is not gold that glitters and, besides, he knew the goldsmith. But there seemed no way of proving that the goldsmith had increased his legitimate profits by using silver alloy. So Hiero asked Archimedes to give the matter his attention. Archimedes thought about it hard and long, but in vain until, one day, he stepped into a public bath.* The tub was full, and as he got in the bulk of his body displaced an equal amount of water, and it began to flow over the top on the marble floor. When he saw this Archimedes gave one leap, was out of the bath. He did not wait for his clothes, he did not wait for anything. Out of the building he flew, and the people of Syracuse stopped open-mouthed to see the most famous mathematician of his age dashing madly along the street in the direction of his home, naked as a new-born babe, crying "Eureka! Eureka! I have found it! I have found it!" His one idea was to get to his study and figure out his discovery. The next day he went to King Hiero:

"Your goldsmith is a clever man," said he. "He knew that the *weight* of the crown must be right. But he used silver and other alloys which are lighter than gold, so he had to make the *volume* of the crown larger. Now the level of water in a vessel rises when a solid is placed in it, in exact proportion to the volume or size of the object put in the water. And your goldsmith should be hung. For I have measured your crown, and its exact weight in gold separately in two different vessels filled with water, and the rascal's thievery is proved by the difference in the overflow."

Once Archimedes had made King Gelo's war-engines for him, he turned back to his more important work. For he was so taken up with his mathematical studies that he would forget to eat and to wash. And when, once a week at least, his servants with gentle violence plucked him out of his nest of papyrus covered with figures in which he worked, to give him his weekly bath, he would keep right on drawing geometrical figures, spirals and cylinders, in the

* The story is that Archimedes came to stray into the public bath by mistake, having been attracted by a quaint geometrical design engraved over the entrance, and wishing to ask those in charge about it. Before he could even frame his question the bath attendants rushed up, and dragged him to the bath, and he stepped into it mechanically, and without thinking.

oil with which they anointed his body. As to the "playthings of war," as he called them, which he made for Gelo, great historians have given us an idea of what they could do.

Some of these engines shot off immense masses of stone with such force that they killed the Roman rank and file "in heaps." Other machines thrust out great poles to which tremendous weights were attached, over the Roman ships, and then let the weights crash down on them. Others, again, ended in a kind of iron hand or crane's beak. They would pick a ship up by the prow, set it on end, and then plunge it to the bottom of the sea. A special form of this engine lifted the Roman galleys to a tremendous height in the air, and shook them as a terrier does a rat, until all the crew had been "spilled" out, to be smashed in their fall, before dashing the vessel against the rocks. Short range and long range engines, all had been thought out by Archimedes. They did so much damage that the Romans "seeing that indefinite mischiefs overwhelmed them, began to think they were fighting the gods." In fact, Marcellus might never have taken Syracuse, had he not surprised a lonely tower and thus secured a foothold.

Archimedes was in his study when the end came. While the Roman legionary armies were putting the Syracusans to the sword, and the blood was running in through the streets, he did not even know the city had been taken. It may have been eleven-thirty in the morning, when a small party of Roman "doughboys" broke into the great mathematician's work-room. His breakfast, untouched, stood on the table, for Archimedes had forgotten all about it. His mind was far, far away. He was hunting a delightful parabolic segment through the tangled jungles of calculation, and was lost to the world. The moment the Romans saw him they knew who he was. And it might as well be said that they had but little use for him. To them he was not an innocent old gentleman, to whom Rome, Carthage and Syracuse were fantastic figures, and to whom only science was real. They did not know that he was a gentle, kindly soul, who had innocently drawn the plans of his terrible machines to oblige the son of an old friend—and get rid of him. To the boys with the short swords he was a fiend, a demon magician, a blood-thirsty monster. But Marcellus had issued an army order that he should be spared. So one of the soldiers, who would much rather have given him the point of his spear, jabbed Archimedes with the butt end and said: "You are under arrest, you old villain! Step lively! Come along!" Archimedes' segment was just within his grasp. Naturally, he was annoyed. Confound people, they always were coming in and bothering him at the wrong moment. "Get away!" he cried, pushing back the man, who had stepped closer to him: "Don't you see I am busy!" All the Roman soldiers' eyes grew bright. This was just what they wanted. The corporal nodded. And at the very moment when Archimedes, with a little chuckle of triumph, grasped the parabolic segment he had been chasing so long, he felt a cold, intolerable chill in his breast. Looking up with an amiable smile he died, not even knowing he was dying, as the short Roman broadsword pierced him through and through. "Killed while resisting arrest," said the corporal softly, and with great satisfaction. "I guess the old son-of-a-gun won't burn up any more Roman boys during *this* war!"

Marcellus was very much put out by Archimedes' death. He called the soldier who had killed him as a murderer. But the whole squad testified before a military court that Archimedes refused to go with them when summoned to do so in the politest way. He even had attacked them, so that they had no choice but to kill him in self-defence. Antiquity does not give us a more *human* picture than this: a great man of science, a simple, gentle, amiable soul dies at the hands of other men, decent, honest fellows, too, in their way, because of one of those misconceptions which in every age have led men to hate fellow-men who were really undeserving of their hatred.

HANNIBAL'S HEART-STORY

Without question the most compelling and romantic personality of the time of the Punic Wars was the great Hannibal himself. Here we are concerned with him only as a *human* being. As such he towers head and shoulders even above the great Romans of his day, and the Eastern kings with whom he had to do seem like pygmies compared to him. In general, history does not give us much insight into his *private* life. For though only a private person, a great noble of Carthage, Hannibal's career made his life almost altogether a public one. In early years he had married a noble Spanish lady named Imilke, who inherited rich silver mines near Castulo on the Guadalquiver, her home town. But it seems that they had no children, and it is believed, especially since she never accompanied him into the field, that she died young. In paying a just tribute to Hannibal's moderation in all things, one historian praises him because: "He never ate lying down, and never drank more than a pint (*sextarius*) of wine at a meal. And among the many captured women of his camps he observed a chastity which, as every one said, proved he had not been born in Africa."

And yet—though we can but glimpse it dimly through the mists that shroud so much of the more *human* side of the past—there was a love romance in Hannibal's life. This man, who seemed to live for war alone, who was the idol of his soldiers, comprising all the tribes of earth—Spaniards, Gauls, Iberians, Numidians, Africans,

Carthaginians, Italians and others—had a tenderer side to his nature. The tale has come down the ages that the steely heart of Hannibal, unmoved by the most beautiful Roman maidens his wild Numidians drove into camp on their raids; that Hannibal, whose eyes never showed a gleam of interest in faces and figures which roused the admiration of his oldest captains, met *one* girl whom he could not resist. A small-town girl she was, the bright, pretty daughter of an unimportant citizen of the little Apulian city of Salapia, near the ocean. Roman historians imply that she was not even a "good girl." But, be that as it may, Hannibal loved her. Their idyll is supposed to have occurred between the years 210 and 216 B.C. In the ancient days, especially where a soldier was concerned, an affair of this kind was not considered objectionable, as it would be in our own times, whose moral standards are so much higher. The fact that the girl and the soldier truly loved each other was held to cover many other sins. And it seems hard to grudge this man of giant visions and giant accomplishments, who suffered the loss of one hope after another his whole life long, this one violet-crowned and sun-gilded interlude of love in his life-round of hopeless struggle! Hannibal had sworn by all he held holy to his father Hamilcar and his gods, never to give up the struggle against Rome. He saw Carthage fall, had to wander, and, a stranger and an outlaw, was driven from the court of one oriental king to another as the merciless arm of Rome stretched out to seize him. Still the greatest general of his day, he won victories for the monarchs who befriended him, with the careless ease of a juggler who performs some trifling trick of parlor-magic. When it came to war, and the ranging of footmen, horsemen and elephants on the chess-board of battle, Hannibal even smiled at things sacred, at omens, signs and the like. In the ordinary affairs of life, and in the extraordinary ones, no doubt the gods knew best. But when it came to war? . . . . When he had taken charge of the armies of King Prusias of Bythnia the priests declared on the eve of a battle, that the examination of the cattle slaughtered as a sacrifice were "unfavorable." And when the King, alarmed, thought that it might better to put off the battle, Hannibal, full of amused impatience, cried out: "Would you take the word of a piece of calf's liver before that of your old general?"

The lives of the great men of all times, who, without being kings, have yet influenced the destinies of nations, is full of tragic ends. And yet it is a question whether there is any more tragic than that of Hannibal. He survived the destruction of his native land. Then he served King Antiochus of Syria as an admiral—but the Romans demanded his surrender. He moved on. In Armenia he is supposed to have laid out King Artaxerxes' capital for him—but the

Romans demanded his surrender. He moved on. And at the court of King Prusias of Bythnia it seemed as though the old eagle of Carthage might at last find a perch on which to rest his weary wings. But, in due time—the Romans demanded his surrender. And the contemptible Prusias, an ignoble soul, given up to low pleasures, betrayed the man who had served him so well.

Hannibal lived in a castle the King of Bythnia had given him, near Lybissa. Like a wise old soldier he had seen to it that it had various exits, some of them secret. But the king's spies knew where they were. Hannibal, as the king's commander-in-chief, always had a guard of honor camped around the castle. But one day his page came to him and said that the guard had been changed, and that an unusual number of soldiers had appeared. Looking down from a window, the old hero saw that every exit, even the secret ones, were already guarded. He needed no more to know that Rome at last check-mated him. But the man who had so nearly ridden in triumph through the gates of Rome was not the one to walk through them, a Roman prisoner. Calmly he called down a curse on the head of Prusias and his kingdom, for the hospitality he had betrayed (it was a curse that was fulfilled). Then seating himself at his table, he had wine brought, and prepared the fatal cup with the poison he always carried about him.

Perhaps at that last moment, as he sat there, betrayed and abandoned, the sunray which fell through the slitted castle window and set the golden motes dancing above the cup he was about to drain, brought back the sunlit days of Salapia, the days of love and happiness, that had passed as swift as a dream. Let us hope that this one golden memory of his life came back to cheer the old hero. Let us hope the memory of the smiles and kisses of the little Lucanian girl, the girl whom he had loved with all his heart amid the rattle of steel and the clash of armor, whom he had loved with a love which, perhaps, he had never given the high-born Spanish lady who brought him her silver mines as a dower, took away the bitterness of the poisoned cup he drained!

CHAPTER IX

A ROMAN OF THE CONQUEST

AFTER the fall of Carthage came the age of Roman conquest. Gradually, one by one, all the kingdoms of the East fell into Roman hands. And with these kingdoms their wealth. With wealth came luxury, and moral and social decay. The patriotic code of the older Roman days which put *country first*, and *self last* was forgotten. The new idea was to get rich quick and, if necessary, at the public expense. The struggle between the classes, the rich and the poor, grew more intense. Strong men—Marius, Sulla, Lucullus, Caesar, Pompey, Crassus, Anthony—representing different parties and different principles, dominate the courts, the magistracy, the senate. The Roman army was turned into an instrument of private political ambitions. The Roman people were bribed and fed into voting as the party leaders wished. The personal romances and political ambitions of most of the great men of these times will be considered elsewhere. But, though it is not a romantic age, we find one figure which, strange to say, is romantic in a queer, pathetic way. Is it possible for a *usurer,* one of the greatest usurers known to all times, *to be romantic?* We shall see.

The Money-Madness in Rome. Rome, during the Asian conquest, grew as fast as New York toward the middle of the nineteenth century. It contained an enormous population of "freemen," Roman citizens high and low, whose one idea was to make money fast (and in many cases spend it as fast as it was made), and another huge population of slaves. And with nobles, merchants, landowners and traders all borrowing and investing money, trying to increase their capital in various ways, it was a golden age of the unromantic race of money-lenders.

Political life had become absolutely corrupt. Political offices were all a matter of bribery and corruption. One great modern historian, Ferrero, has compared Caesar—up to a certain point in his career—to a New York Tammany Hall boss. And the money-lenders, after a time, came to have everything and everybody in their hands, and to control the state. When we read Shakespeare's noble tragedy we get the idea that Brutus, for instance, was a lover of freedom. Not at all. Brutus was a politician and a lover of himself. He was one of the most stony-hearted usurers of his day, and would sell out a widow with six children and one cow without batting an eyelid. Pompey, the great military leader, the chief of the aristocratic party, the general of the Roman Senate, also was a money-lender at usurious rates. Only, he preferred high class clients. After he had plundered the East of its riches, he loaned money at usurious rates to a flock of little ruined kings. There actually came a time when the whole Roman state, from Julius Caesar to the least little Roman shop-keeper, was in the power of a small group of money-lenders, some of noble others of plebian birth.

A ROMAN MONEY-LENDER'S ROMANCE

Marcus Licinius Crassus (115-53 B.C.) was not born in the back room of a pawn-broking establishment. He was a young man of good family. But—a taste of military service in the war against the slaves has filled his soul with a longing for military glory which, in later years, was to be the direct cause of his death. Crassus was a born financier. He had the soul of a Shylock, but a strange, romantic desire to be a hero went hand in hand with his greed for golden gains. Crassus was a highly respectable man in private life. His morals were excellent. He loved his family. He was orderly and industrious. He was the last man in the world one would have suspected of romantic longings. And yet—he cherished them. Crassus loaned money to any one and every one—provided the interest was high enough. As a lawyer he would take any case, no matter how vile—provided the fee was large enough. Like many natural-born financiers, he was not a good mingler with the crowd. Aristocratic Pompey, who did not give the well-known tinker's slam what the people thought of him, was always greeted with cheers when he appeared on the streets of Rome. But poor Crassus, though he gave splendid "free" banquets, at which the people were fed without charge by the thousand, got little thanks for it. He was the kind of man who would make another a gift of a golden goblet with a large gesture of generosity, but would be pitiless when it came to non-payment of interest and extension of time on notes due, and liens and mortgages and all such things. Crassus' one idea was to get hold of money and to keep it. Once he suddenly began to pay marked attention to one of the Vestal Virgins, a lady named Licinia. Aha, you think, we have come to the romance of this life of sordid gain! Not at all. Crassus pretended a love he did not feel for the Vestal Virgin because—she had a valuable plot of land in one of the suburbs of Rome, and he was anxious to get hold of it at a low price. So well established was his personal virtue, that when a scoundrel by name of Plotinus had him impeached, judge and jury at once commenced to laugh when the case was presented. Crassus' avarice, so to say, immediately acquitted him of bad moral principles, and he kept after poor Licinia until she had sold him *her* land at *his* figure.

The general Lucullus' conquests in Asia had given new activity to building, real-estate speculation and investment in Rome and Crassus was the man who could always furnish the cash money, for a consideration, to those who needed it. Crassus bought a tremendous number of Oriental slaves as soon as they grew cheap. He selected among them all those who were skillful engineers, architects and master-masons, and set up a kind of school where they taught large classes of young slave apprentices. The services of the apprentice builders Crassus then *rented* out to the small contractors who were too poor to buy slaves on their own account. In those days fires were very frequent in Rome, where most of the houses were built of wood. Crassus' clever financial brain hit upon a great scheme. There was no *city fire department*. He organized a little fire department of his own; a first-class squad of fire fighters, regular firemen, among his slaves. All over town he had his look-out men. But—Crassus' fire department was *Crassus'* fire departments. It was not there to *put out fires for other people*. When a fire broke out, the "look-out man" hurried to the fire-house. At once the firemen rushed to the spot. But with them went one of Crassus' clerks. While the firemen stood ready with the hose, the unfortunate owner of the burning building had a chance to sell it quickly—at Crassus' price. Nine times out of ten he did. And then the private fire department went into action with a will and put out the fire. Usually Crassus picked up a few good bargains in neighboring houses threatened by the flames. In this way he became one of the largest real estate and house-owners in Rome. But all the tremendous wealth he gradually accumulated left him unsatisfied. Strange to say, this man whose heart missed a beat if he got twenty-eight instead of thirty per cent return on an investment, could not master the *romantic* desire to be a great *military* hero. The man who would have you in to dinner and feast you splendidly one day, but would strip your clothes from your back the next if you could not pay what you owed him, yearned to conquer golden kingdoms of the Orient, like Sulla, Lucullus and Pompey. The man who turned his tenants out in the street the very hour their rent was not paid, could forget his account books in radiant visions in which he saw himself riding as Consul at the head of the legions, while terrified enemies scurried to cover in all directions.

It was easy for a man with Crassus' wealth to become Consul in Rome in his day. He even, in the interests of business, became one of the *triumvirs,* the *three* men who shared the power of the state.

The Consulate he shared twice with Pompey. But—he was eager to gain glory on his *own* account. The fact is that a burning thirst for adventure, for the vain and fleeting thing known as military glory was Crassus' romantic will-o'-the-wisp. In spite of his money-grubbing and money-grabbing, at sixty he was still full of the spirit which makes a boy in a machine-shop stop suddenly at his lathe— and see the whole great West open up before him, vast plains, countless herds of cattle and towering mountains, himself the hero of a desperate fight against rustlers who are robbing a fair young girl rancher of her little herd of cows. He beats the "two-gun" man to the draw, he sees the smoke still curling from the end of his Smith and Wesson—and suddenly, he is back in his dull actual life again. Crassus, at the bottom of his ignoble money-lending soul was like that— and the fact makes him history's one romantic money-lender.

In the year 164 B.C. Crassus at last saw his life's ambition realized. The man of usury and extortion, of fire sales and legalized plunder, with the first *denarius* he had earned still in his possession, started out to realize his boyhood dream. With seven legions of infantry and 5,000 cavalry, with all the pomp and circumstance of war, glittering in armor, the purple mantle of a commanding general floating from his shoulders, with the tubas and *bucinas* blowing, he rode at the head of the legionaries who swung down the road to Ostia to embark for the "Persian" War, the war against the Parthians. For he was to be the hero of that war. He expected to return to Rome as great a conqueror as Pompey or any of the rest. The grey-haired money-lender who seized the widow's earthern drinking-vessel, and cast her out into the streets with her starving little ones when she could not pay the rent was off chasing his rainbow dream as happy as a boy who has just finished reading "Treasure Island."

The details of that war are a matter of history. It is enough to say that after some skirmishes Crassus settled down in Syria to wait for spring, and showed that his eye still was keen for the main chance by plundering the temple at Jerusalem of its treasures. In the spring of 63 B.C. he marched into Persia, now the kingdom of the Parthians, a fighting race of hardy horsemen. The Parthians laid waste the country everywhere, and retreated before him, luring him further and further from his base of supplies. But Crassus was chasing his dream, he was living his romance. One great battle and glory would be his! Unfortunately, Crassus was not a man whom other men yearned to die for. His soldiers had not "taken" to their general. They were weary and discouraged when, on the banks of a little stream, the Parthians at last surrounded them with immense forces of their light armored cavalry. And this cavalry fought a long-distance fight. They began systematically to bury the Roman army beneath a rain of arrows, and great trains of camels were continually in motion bringing up new supplies of arrows for their mounted archers.

When the Romans charged, the Parthians retreated, and then renewed their bombardment. One Roman division caved in. Suddenly, out of a great dust-cloud, Crassus saw a Parthian detachment gallop by—they carried the head of his son on a lance! Then, too, Crassus' army was largely made up of young recruits (the only good Roman army was with Caesar in Gaul), and its officers were the gilded youth of Rome: the two did not hit off well. The Romans held the field, but when a retreat was decided upon, the army fell apart. The soldiers, when a herald came from the Parthian general suggesting that Crassus treat for surrender, said they would mutiny if he did not meet the Parthians, and settle the details. Crassus then knew the end had come.

And, let us give the old usurer credit. All his life long he had been hard with others. Now he showed he himself could stand the gaff. He knew if he rode out to meet the *surena,* the Parthian commander, that he was riding to his death; that he would be slain. What did he do? He called together his officers, told them that he knew he was riding into an ambush, but that he preferred to have the Parthians kill him rather than his own men. And knowing he was doomed, far from Rome, his family, his great palace, with the mountains of Armenia showing dim and blue in the distance, he rode off with his little escort and was killed as he had forseen. A remnant of his fine army succeeded in reaching Syria, the rest of his men were slain or captured. King Hyrodes of Parthia, with his court and most of the people of Seleucia, his capital, were at the theater, where a Greek tragedy was being performed. The actor was just reciting a tale of tragic death when the *surena's* messenger entered and flung the gory head of Crassus on the stage. Thus ended the romantic dream of conquest, glory, and a great triumphal procession through the Roman Forum, of the most romantic money-lender history has known.

CHAPTER X

FROM AUGUSTUS TO AUGUSTULUS

It is a long, confused tale, that of the degeneration and downfall of Rome. The story of Rome's decline belongs to history. After Caesar's death the struggle as to which *one* man was to rule Rome, narrowed down to one between Antony and Octavius Augustus, Caesar's nephew. Antony, a "wandering husband," lost. Augustus became Rome's first emperor. He represented the victory of autocracy over democracy. In spite of all the conquests still to come, in spite of Rome's military glory and greatness, its decay had already begun. There were three great causes for that decay: the moral breakdown of the Romans; the coming of Christianity; and the flooding of the empire by great hordes of Barbarian tribes, which continued for centuries. From this period of decline, which begins with the first Roman emperor, Augustus, and ends with that of Augustulus, "little Augustus" (29 B.C. to 476 A.D.) we have three groups of scenes to illustrate some of the more romantic aspects of life as it was lived. The first may help to give an idea of Roman society under the earlier emperors (and social conditions do not improve under the later ones). Another is devoted to the martyrs whose blood was the seed of the Christian faith. A third, retold from the extended romance of a great historical novelist, attempts to show the differences between the brutal, yet candid and trustful Barbarian soul, and the subtle, treacherous soul of the decadent Roman. With it is a tale which shows that even great Attila had to learn that "hell hath no fury like a woman scorned."

I

Do Unto Others

Nero, the royal madman and voluptuary, sat looking out at burning Rome beneath the great columned portico-room of his Golden House. There was not much furniture in it, for the emperor feared assassins. In the back of the hall, gates of gilded bronze opened on a marble cage. In it were two lions from the Lybian desert. Nero called them his "kittens," but these "kittens" lapped human blood instead of milk. Suddenly the emperor turned his face, reddened with wine and the glow of the flames, to a slave. "Pallas," he cried, "Rome is burning! Down in the streets with you, and spread the tale that the Christians set it afire!"

"No, Master," answered the slave, "I cannot do that!" Nero could not believe his ears.

"Do you not know that the Christians are magicians! They live like rats far down beneath the burial vaults. All Rome rests on the Christians. I have thought of having the Tiber river led into the passages, to drown them, or of breaking down the walls of the sewers and smothering the catacombs in filth. They foretell the downfall of Rome, only they call Rome Babel. Ah, the Capitol has just caught! Hurry out, Pallas, and let Rome know the Christians did it!"

"I cannot do so," answered Pallas, "for it is not true."

Nero rose. He smiled. "If you will not go down into the city, then you will have to play with the "kittens," he said. He opened the gates of gilded bronze and pushed Pallas into the court of the lions' cage. "I know that my Redeemer liveth!" said Pallas, and knelt in prayer while the emperor turned to a second slave. "Alexander, down into the streets with you, and say the Christians have set fire to Rome!"

"No," answered Alexander, "I am a Christian!"

"Have I not power to destroy you?"

"Only if the God on high permit you to."

"What, do you not fear death? Lentulus, bring a light! I shall set your clothes afire, so that we can see whether or not you will burn. I will set fire to your hair and your beard! But first you shall be soaked in oil and naphtha. You shall be covered with pitch and tar. Then we shall find out whether you can live forever."

Lentulus rushed in: "The city is in revolt! Flee, Nero!"

"Why should I flee? Bring a torch for this slave!"

"The Spanish legions have mutinied! They have proclaimed Galba emperor!"

"Galba? Galba? Well, then, let us flee. But how?"

"Through the catacombs!"

"No, that is where the Christians live. They will kill me."

"They kill no man," said Alexander.

"Not even their enemies?"

"They pray for their enemies."

"Then they are insane—all the better!"

The Christians were gathered together in one of the crypts of the catacombs. They were discussing the burning of Rome. "The Lord avenges the destruction of Jerusalem," said one, "but hark, are there not footsteps coming this way?"

"Some one is in the passage."

"It is one of the brethren."

"No, for he did not stop to kneel at the cross."

"Then it is one of Caesar's spies or hangmen."

Nero appeared. He was dirty and tattered, and a handkerchief was wound around his forehead. When he drew near the Christians he mistook them for Greeks because of the white mantles they wore. He grew more composed and said:

"Are you Greeks?"

"We are neither Jews nor Greeks, neither Barbarians or Romans, neither servants or masters, we are all brothers in Christ. Welcome, brother!"

"It is Nero, the wild beast!" cried Alexander, who was among the faithful. The emperor recognized his runaway slave. In his terror he fell on his knees.

"Do not kill me!" he cried. "I am only a poor stone-cutter who has lost his way in the passages. Show me the path that leads out of the catacombs. Must I go to the right or to the left?"

"Do you know me?" asked Alexander.

"Alexander," replied the Emperor.

"Yes, the slave whom you meant to burn, I am he."

"Mercy! Do not take my life!"

"Stand up, Caesar. Your life is in God's hand!"

"You will help me?"

"You shall have a guide."

"Tell me only whether to keep to the right or to the left. Then I can help myself."

"Keep to the left."

"Perhaps you are lying to me?"

"That I cannot do. You see, that is the difference between us."

"Why should you not lie? It is what I would have done."

"Keep to the left!"

Nero, convinced, moved on in the direction given. But after taking a few steps he stopped and turned around:

"Ugh, you vile slaves, now I can manage for myself."

The next day, hunted and tracked to his lair, the imperial wild beast, after shedding many unmanly tears, managed to plunge the dagger into his breast—after all, it was better than being whipped to death in the Forum!

II

A Little Alexandrian Holiday

The Alexandrians, more especially the youth of Alexandria, had insulted the "divine" Caesar Caracalla, the Roman emperor, as he sat in the great Stadium watching the combats of the gladiators. They had hissed him. And—verses ridiculing him and his mother had been brought him by his spies. "We will give the youth of

Alexandria a little holiday," said Caracalla, "that they, or, rather, their *parents*"—he added with a sinister smile—"will remember!" And he called for the prefect Zminis, an Egyptian base of soul and happiest when carrying out some bloody order.

The next day the imperial heralds rode through the streets of Alexandria. They invited the Alexandrian youth to gather in the arena of the Stadium. There the divine Caracalla would address them and—each of them would receive a gift from the emperor's generous hand. So the youth of Alexandria, moved more by curiosity than by the promise of the gift, assembled by the thousand and unsuspectingly poured into the enormous amphitheater. Zminis hurried to his master to report. "When the amphitheater is filled," said Caracalla, "I will go to the Temple of Separis. I will have a fine view from the roof and will see whether you carry out your orders properly. Now send for the soldiers at once. And should any of them shrink from their work, tell them they shall have the plundering of the Canopian Street, where all the rich jewelers' and goldsmiths' shops stand side by side." Soon Macrinus, the Praetorian prefect, the general of the Pretorian guards, announced the glad tidings to his soldiers, drawn up in rank and file before the Temple of Serapis, and his words were greeted with loud cheers.

All the male youth of Alexandria was by now assembled in the Stadium arena. Many thousand strong were these happy, careless boys, and the whole great arena was crowded. But meanwhile, the Emperor's Macedonian Phalanx, and the Praetorian companies also had filed in, and filled the passages that ran along the lowest tier of arena seats, and had drawn up in all the ground entrances that led into it. Above them, the great tiers of seats gradually grew black with other men. From his place on the roof of the Temple of Separis, Caracalla saw with a pleased smile that carpenters were securing the great exit door of the arena from the outside with tremendous beams. Suddenly the prefect Zminis rode up on a long-legged horse, out of one of the arena gates, into the small space left, at the head of several squads of Numidian cavalry. He waved his hand, a tuba blew seven long, mournful notes, and then—the massacre began!

A few hours later, how that scene was changed! Where, head on head, the whole enormous arena had been filled with thousands of handsome, upstanding young figures, full of life and joyous expectation, like some huge, flower-basket full of blossoms, there now stretched a sea of blood and corpses. The Alexandrian boys had been talking, laughing and even singing together when, as the tuba gave the signal, the black Ethiopian and brown Numidian archers ranged along the benches usually filled by the audience at the chariot-races had risen. Drawing their bows, they had commenced to rain their merciless arrows down on the unprotected and unarmed throngs of boys on the arena sands. At the same time from all the inner doors that opened on the stadium ground the men of the Phalanx and the Praetorians had stormed out with lances felled and swords drawn, to begin the bloody slaughter which ended only with the death of the last young Alexandrian. The radiant flower-basket of humanity now looked like a cornfield beaten down by a storm. Caracalla, who smiled with satisfaction as he saw the horrible work progress, had a poetical strain in his mad soul. It seemed to him as though a storm wind had torn thousands of straight branches and thousands of metal leaves from the crown of some giant tree his eyes could not see, and had flung them into the arena. And they had whirled down as though on a cornfield, and beaten it into the ground. But this hail of branches and leaves was a hail of lances and arrows, and each of the broken ears of corn was a young, blooming life!

The massacre was over. The Emperor had disappeared from his post of observation. Soon the tubas sounded again. Caracalla, in a splendid chariot, surrounded by courtiers and officers, appeared before the Stadium. He entered it and in a few moments stood in the imperial box. There he gloated over his work. It had been a real holiday. He had taken his revenge for the hisses of a few hot-heads, for two lines of scurrilous verse! They would not be so quick to insult his divinity another time. He had given Alexandria a little holiday its citizens would not so soon forget. And he smiled when cries of agony mingled with roars of laughter and brutal oaths rose from the Caponic Street nearby, where his brave soldiers were plundering the rich goldsmith shops, and putting to the sword the men, women and children they met on their way.

III

Before the Theater

Family life in high Roman society under the empire? It was not always edifying when the paid poisoner was a recognized institution. It was in the days of the Emperor Caligula, cruel as a tiger and mad as a March hare. It was early in the afternoon. In his splendid marble palace home, Claudias Balbo, a wealthy patrician, is entertaining his wife's friend, young Lentulus. Lentulus is one of the handsomest and most profligate of the gilded youth of Rome. The two men are rolling the dice. "Play, play," growled Balbo, to his friend, who shakes the ivory dice-box with a far-away look in his eyes, "you are absent-minded." "Perhaps" answers young Lentulus, carelessly. He is thinking of Balbo's wife, the fair Julia, whom he is to escort to the Coliseum that afternoon to see the gladitorial games. A new batch of Barbarian prisoners have come from the front. It will be great sport to watch them kill each other. And he shakes and casts as though he does not much care whether he wins or loses.

Julia enters in all the splendor of gems and rich silks. Her black hair is covered with a blond wig—the blond hair of the Teuton Barbarians is the rage in Rome at the moment. Her lips and cheeks are heavily rouged, her eyebrows tinctured to match her wig. "Why is Lentulus sitting here at dice with you when he is to take me to the Coliseum?" she asks. "He is at liberty to go now, for all of me," says Balbo in an indifferent tone of voice, yet with a stealthy side-glance full of hatred. And suddenly: "Nothing would please me better than to see both of you go—and not come back." "You can get rid of me easily enough," answers Julia, with a cynical smile, "if you will give me my money. But I will not agree to a divorce unless you pay the 200,000 *sesterces of my dower*." The door of the atrium, the antechamber, closes on them. "Your divorce, your Lentulus, you demon," murmurs Balbo, "we shall see." He calls his secretary. "Follow them, Galba," he hisses. "Take old Locusta, the poison-mixer along, and when they return see that the wine is ready for them. After to-night's supper, Venus be praised, I will be able to marry Agrippina without it costing me a fortune!" Meanwhile, as the house-door closed on the two outside, Lentulus turned to Julia: "Did you prepare the mushrooms Balbo is to eat to-night?" he asked. "No," said Julia, with a smile, "but Locusta did, and she knows her business!"

IV

THE TEMPTATION OF SEVERINIUS

It was a great splendid room in which Messalina, the Empress, pleaded with the young Christian whose manly beauty had caught her eye. But it showed the aftermath of an imperial orgy. The Emperor Claudius, Messalina's husband, was stretched out in a drunken stupor on the mosaic floor, snoring with mouth wide open. Near him was extended the form of Rome's wealthiest senator. Beside them lay the golden goblets that had slipped from their grasp. But they were deaf to the ardent voice of the dissolute Empress, as she feverishly tried to break down the silent resistance Severinius opposed to her blandishments.

"After each of our kisses we will offer a pair of doves to Venus! ....I shall have them brought from Sicily and the Aegean shore, thousands and thousands of doves! You shall drink the wines of Latinum from golden cups and eat the pheasants of Samos from dishes of silver! . . "

Then exasperated by the Christian's silence, she cried: "Slaves shall rub you with ointments! Soft music shall lull our intoxication!.... Yes, I will put Caesar's golden crown on your brow! You shall see, Severinius! . ." And she laid a caressing hand on his arm. Gently Severinius repulsed her. She hardly noticed it. Even when she flung herself on him and covered his face with kisses, he repulsed her, though he trembled, for she was very beautiful. Then he began to repeat to her the sacred words which tell us that the thoughts and actions of earthly life should be pure, to prepare the soul for the eternal joy in the paradise of the blessed. But Messalina listened to him without understanding. Suddenly interrupting him she cried violently: "Do not talk to me in empty words, like the poets and elocutionists! Talk to me of love!"

"I do talk to you of love, Augusta," answered Severinius gently, without raising his eyes. "For He spoke only words of love. He blessed the crowds that came to listen to Him, and told them to love each other, since such was the wish of His Father, who is out Father. Even on the cross he murmured 'Love ye one another!' He taught the lesson of love and pity, Augusta...."

She tossed her head with the brusque movement of some wild beast in despair and the crown of roses she wore dropped to the ground. Severinius fell back in affright before the strange, menacing light in her eyes. She spoke in a dead voice that seemed to come from unknown depths, one in which agony and authority were mingled:

"Talk to me of love!" she said.

And this little phrase, so short, so simple, so tender, in the surroundings of Messalina's imperial palace, whose atmosphere was one of crime, debauchery, madness, horror, and beauty, this simple phrase seemed to express the desire of all humanity, longing for love. But Severinius turned away his head. His glance fell on the drunken Caesar stretched out on the mosaic floor, his tunic soiled, his hair in disorder, his mouth dribbling saliva as he snored. And when Messalina once more wound her arms around him Severinius thrust her from him sternly. And this time, when she broke out into tears like a little child, and the crystal drops ran down between her fingers, as she held her face buried in her hands, he saw the vision of his approaching death.

Suddenly the Empress looked at him: "Why do you repulse me?" asked she. "Why do you hate me?"

"I do not hate you, Augusta," answered the young Christian. "I do not hate you, for you are beautiful, so beautiful that one longs to be turned into dust, to be trampled by your feet!" And Messalina, thinking that at last he was yielding, smiled triumphantly.

"You shall go clad in robes made of the silks of Bylbus, and you shall have the perfumes of Capua with which to perfume yourself.... You shall wear chains of pearls and emeralds...."

She pointed to the drunken senator who lay on the floor, not far from the Emperor Claudius, the companion of his orgies: "I shall have the gold, the 300,000 sesterces which fills *his* treasure-chests poured into your own coffers!.... I will have a circus of massive gold built at the foot of the Esquiline hill. You and I alone have the right to enter it. There the rhapsodists and the mimes shall perform the adventures of the daughter of Calliope for us only to see. Think of our promenades through the silent garden walks!.... I will lay my head on your breast, and from time to time you will stoop to receive my kisses, supporting yourself on a magnificent cane, like that of Queen Hecuba in the poet Euripides' tragedy...."

Severinius knelt before Messalina. But he did not look at her. He saw only the glorious vision of paradise, and in his ears sounded the voice of the Master as he spoke on the Mount. When he rose his eyes were calm, and he answered with gentle firmness:

"My father, O Messalina, was one of the decurions who carried the body of the great Augustus to his grave. He was a brave soldier and left his bones to molder in the land of the Gauls. All my forbears have fought and died for Rome!.... Augusta, let me go, so that their souls may rest in peace!"

"Come closer!" commanded the Empress. Severinius obeyed. She seized his toga, while her eyes devoured the handsome youth who asked only to leave her. "Stay!" she cried. "Stay with me!...." Severinius felt his senses reel for a moment. So near was she and so lovely. But he regained control of himself: "Have the doors opened for me!.... I must go!.... I must rejoin my Master, the Master whom I serve, so that the true word may be spread abroad to disperse the sickness of men's souls!.... And as he spoke he was suddenly filled with celestial happiness. He felt himself caught up in a cloud of bliss. With flaming enthusiasm he spoke of his chaste and tender love for Coelerina, his young betrothed. He told Messalina how they looked forward to a life of Christian labor and usefulness far from Rome, on the banks of the Lake of Genesareth, in Joppa, Antioch!

Messalina suddenly uttered a cry of rage. Leaping from her seat she dug her fingers in the young man's shoulder.

"Of whom are you speaking?" she demanded.

"Of the woman who will eat my bread and share my roof-tree, Augusta," he answered. And the shadow of life's reality so weighed on him that he felt ready to burst into sobs.

"You have already given her the iron wedding-ring?"

"I have given her my life," he replied.

"Your life is not worth much at this moment," said Messalina with sinister humor.

"That God only knows!"

"Which God?"

"The only God!"

Messalina shrugged her shoulders. For a moment she spared a contemptuous thought to this Galilean sect which was trying to spread the religion of its "Only God." Then her eyes darted infernal fires. She released Severinius' shoulder, and once more flung herself with such a mad tenderness on the young Christian, clinging to him and covering his face with kisses, that the unfortunate youth had to exert all his strength to rid himself of her embrace. This time he pushed her from him so violently that she stumbled against the body of the snoring Claudius, and had to cling to a column for support. And then she said, in a terrible voice:

"You do not want the kisses of an Empress?" The unfortunate victim cried: "Augusta.... let me go, and may God reward you!"

"No. I wish you to suffer. You have refused what I have asked! I shall refuse what you ask!"

And suddenly Severinius thought of the sufferings of the Crucified. He was ashamed of his weakness. His speech grew firm.

"Augusta, greatness should be paired with kindness! Those who do evil never rise from their dust...."

"I will have you dressed in a leather jacket and forced to beg in the streets like a priest of Bellona!"

"And I will put a crown of thorns on my head to suffer as He did!"

"You shall be thrust into a beggar-woman's rags, and made to sell honey-cakes at the Saturnalia, while the crowds hoot you!...."

"That will not break my spirit, Augusta! I shall think of Jesus of Nazareth who endured the insults of the Hebrews, and the sneers of the Sanhedrim, with a reed for a scepter!...."

"I will sell you to a publican of the Saburra, where the Italiotes will spit in your face!"

"May heaven's will be done!"

"And I will accuse you of having been one of Charea's men, the men who murdered Caligula, so that Caligula's old Argyraspids will tear you to pieces. I will have the sinews of your ankles cut and then you shall be forced to dance!"

Her voice was bitter with hatred, and Severinius looked at her sadly. He knew now that death was his portion. He felt the shadows closing around him, while Messalina shrieked:

"Slaves shall drive you through the streets of Rome with whips! You shall be shod with wooden sandals, for your feet are unworthy of touching the ground! You shall be crucified at the Sestertium, where the criminals suffer death. While you are dying, at night, you will hear the sorcerers of Praeneste laughing around you. They will tear out your nails, and the witches will suck the blood from your veins as you perish!...."

But Severinius smiled a smile which already was not of this world.

He saw the heavens opening before him, and with an ironic majesty he defied the mad woman before him:

"Have me beaten through the streets, Augusta.... I am content. I shall kneel to pray to my god, and your chariot-wheels may pass over my body as His did over the body of your father. But grant me one favor. Do not have me crucified at the Sesterium. I come of honest folk, and I would not wish to have my blood flow where such infamous blood has been poured out...."

"Your prayer is granted. You shall not be crucified. You shall merely be crushed beneath one of the twelve shields which protect the majesty of Rome in the temple of Mars," she sneered. Then, in a last endeavor to overcome his obstinate resistance to her will, she once more flung herself upon him. But this time Severinius cast her away so rudely—making the sign of the cross, as though repulsing Satan—that she struck her face against a porcelain vase as she fell on her knees, and the blood flowed. When she rose she tore at the string of the golden bell suspended above her couch. A slave entered the room:

"Strike, strike!" she cried. Her shrill laughter seemed a continuation of the tinkling bell. Her haggard eyes were filled with a distant vision of death and desolation. Her teeth chattered. And again she cried: "Strike, strike! And with his dying breath let him suffer the last infamy! What, he would refuse an Empress's love! Strike!"

The *dispensator* (the slave executioner, who "dispensed" death) approached Severinius. "Kneel!" he said to him.

"I only kneel to God, the servants of God and to my betrothed," answered the young Roman.

Then the slave, picking up the sword lying on the ground beside the drunken senator whom Messalina had pointed out, dealt Severinius a brutal chest-blow. A vague plaint came from his lips, followed by the dull noise of his fall, which made the gold and silver ornaments on the canopy of Messalina's couch clash and tinkle. It seemed as though some damned soul were singing in triumph because of the crime just committed.

Messalina, sitting on her couch, with her head in her hands, was still laughing her mad and evil laughter. From time to time, without raising her head, she repeated "Strike, strike!"

Suddenly she rose. She hastened to take from behind the great statue of Saturn the old, yellowed skeleton which the Emperor Claudius liked to put near him at the table at the beginning of an orgy. "Because it is a good thing for men to see that they don't amount to much," he would say. Dragging the skeleton along by one bony arm, the Empress approached Severinius' inanimate body. "Now I am satisfied! See, that is what you shall be for a long, long time, for having refused the love of Messalina!" And, dropping the skeleton, her fury taking a sudden new turn, she ran and pulled the bell-string eleven times. A group of special guards appeared Pointing to the *dispensator* she called to their leader: "Take away this reptile, and slay him with tortures!" Then, sinking back on her couch Messalina began to weep bitterly, while the Emperor Claudius' skeleton, lying across its drunken owner's body, fixed her with its shadowy eye-holes, and silently seemed to sneer at her tears.

CHAPTER XI

A QUARTET OF MARTYRS

From the time of Nero who turned the Christian brethren of his day into torches by fastening them to high stakes, soaking them with oil and setting fire to them, to the legalization of Christianity by the Emperor Gallienus (261 A. D.), persecution raged and martyrs* were plentiful. Hundreds and thousands of devoted men and women died for their faith rather than acknowledge the "divinity" of the Roman emperors. Not that the Roman emperors, looking at it from their side, did not have a "case." For Christianity, with the exception of Islam and Buddhism the most *democratic* faith in the world, was undermining the imperial authority and creating a state within the state. These questions are matters of history, but as the sufferings of martyrs reflect some of the most *human* and interesting features of the rise of Christianity, they have been considered in the following group of tales.

I

THE MARTYR UNMARTYRED

We are in the great Coliseum at Rome,** in the days of Nero and our scene is retold from the Polish novelist's famous romance "Quo Vadis." Our martyr, in this instance, is a fictitious character, yet all that happened to her may really have occurred. There had been delightful days of Christian-baiting for the Roman crowd. One day famished dogs, huge Molossian hounds and Irish wolf-dogs were led into the arena and the Roman holiday and ended with the ravenous creatures' snatching bloody members of human bodies from one another, while the odor of blood and torn entrails that rose from the squirming mass of dogs and Christian martyrs overpowered the Arabian perfumes with which the great circus had been drenched by Nero's order. The next day another batch of martyrs was crushed by the lions. A third day, and still other Christians were nailed to

---

* The various martyrologies, the books that tell the tales of the Christian martyrs, contain many stories which are evidently fictitious, while others, again, may be accepted as true.

** See "The Romance of Architecture," Chapter 7.

big wooden crosses, to linger through long hours of agony. And, in the evening, along the great avenue of the gardens of Nero's Golden House, covered with straw and soaked in oil, hundreds of Nazarenes, as they were called, were set alight by the slaves, who ran from one to another, as the street-lighters used to run from one lamp-post to another in our cities, before electricity took the place of gas. Then, amid this double row of flaming torches, Nero, with a drunken crew of courtiers and women, drove his chariot hiccoughing a ribald song. But for the martyr who was not martyred we must return to the Coliseum. This time Nero had thought out a novelty in the way of a cruel death. Lygia, the Christian girl, enters the arena—naked, bound with ropes to the back of a huge German auroch, the enormous shaggy bull of the primitive Teuton forests. And with this Christian maid, a princess in her own land, her giant slave Ursus has been thrust into the ring. When he recognizes his mistress he rushes forward and seizes the auroch by the horns. The minutes seem to lengthen into hours, while the people hold their breaths and gasp as the man's face, neck and arms grow purple! He is trying to twist the great brute's head. The crack of the aurochs' neck-bone as he sinks on the sand, comes as a relief. Ursus undoes the cruel ropes. He picks up the lovely, alabaster-white figure of the young Christian girl and—the mob goes wild! Degenerate, blood-thirsty, ready with the *turned-down thumb that means death,* as pitiless a mob as the world has ever known, these thousands of debased Romans are touched. The slave looks like a father. And the fathers among the crowd, as the slave holds out the girl with a dumb gesture of appeal to Nero, as though begging for mercy, think that he is a father too. Pity sweeps over them. It melts their hearts. And all, hooting, howling, stamping, turn to Nero's imperial box. He *must* grant mercy. Nero has been yearning to see the girl's white body slashed to ribbons by the bull's horns. But the cowardly emperor fears to offend his wild beast subjects, who contrary to all his expectations have turned on him and have grown pitiful, and human. Reluctantly, his bloated and wine-swollen hateful face, the Emperor turns *up* his thumb—Lygia is saved in the nick of time!

For the benefit of those who do not know the great Sienkiewicz's romance of ancient Rome, be it said that after her marriage to her lover, duly blessed by a Christian priest, she settles down to a happy future with the man she loves. Nougues, a French composer, has written an effective spectacular opera to the story of "Quo Vadis," in which the scene just described occurs. *Where Lygia May Still Be Seen To-day.* Since the operatic stage makes a poor circus ring, the auroch is supposed to be killed behind the scenes. But Ursus comes out to hold up Lygia to Nero. One of the reasons, perhaps, why the famous Austrian *prima donna* Maria Jeritza made such a success in the part of Lygia when the opera was first given in Vienna, was because her slim and golden type of beauty aroused the sympathy of the whole audience. We can imagine how different an effect would have been produced had the strong-arm man who held her up offered Nero one of those *large prime donne* who weigh two hundred and fifty or sixty pounds. Perhaps, if the original Lygia had been a very stout girl, all those Romans whose eyes filled with tears at the sight of her slim, girlish loveliness, would have turned *down* their thumbs without a moment's hesitation, for even to-day beauty moves the heart to pity where sheer bulk only awakens disgust.

II

A MARTYR FROM CONVICTION

The tale of St. Barbara of Nicomedia is one of those which have to be taken with a grain of salt, for in his "Lives of the Saints," the Rev. S. Baring-Gould declares that "the real locality of her passion was in the brain of the inventor of the legend."

Dioscorus, a wealthy and noble Greek, had a daughter named Barbara. And so lovely was Barbara in face and form, that he built a high tower and shut her up in it, so that no man might see her and "she might be kept out of mischief." But when he had selected a husband for Barbara to marry, she upset him by declaring she meant to dedicate her virginity to Christ. "She had become a Christian." Dioscorus put off further discussion of the subject to go on a journey. Could she have a bath constructed in the tower basement for her amusement while he was gone? asked Barbara. Yes, with *two* windows. But no sooner had her father departed, than Barbara coaxed the masons to make *three*. Dioscorus went, leaving strict orders to cut the windows high in the wall, so that no "impudent and forward youth might look in while Barbara was splashing in her bath." And on his return he found *three* windows instead of *two*, and his daughter used them to explain to him the mystery of the Trinity. Dioscorus, shocked at her disobedience and her attempt to lecture her own father—for he was one of those men who believed that the motto of every well-behaved child should be: "Ask dad, he knows!"—drew his sword to put her to death. But suddenly the rock of Barbara's tower-chamber opened, received her into its bosom, and left Dioscorus furiously beating its flinty surface with his blade.

The obliging rock had passed Barbara out into the mountains, where two goat-herds saw her. One goat-herd being "a good fellow, told a lie and said he had not seen her anywhere." The other, a graceless rascal, pointed his finger in the direction she had taken. Soon her father Dioscorus found her. We are told that he kicked, beat and drew her by the hair before the chief Roman magistrate. The latter tried to get her sacrificed to the Roman gods. But Barbara, even when stripped and beaten until her sides were raw refused. In prison the Saviour appeared to her and healed all her wounds. The next day her sides "were torn with iron combs, and her head was hammered." But she still remained steadfast. Then, when, to shame her, Marcian the magistrate ordered her to be led naked around the town, she prayed and at once a gown fell from heaven and covered her. So Marcian, giving up the attempt to wean her away from her faith, had her head chopped off by the sword. If this tale were true, we should be only too glad to believe that two flashes of lightning at once reduced Barbara's father Dioscorus and Marcian the magistrate to little heaps of ashes. They surely deserved such a fate!

Why Good Emperors Destroyed Christians. This tale is an example of the "fictitious" martyr story. It should be remembered that even "good" emperors persecuted the Christians because neglect of the temple service was supposed to enrage the gods and bring down drought, pestilence and every other disaster on the empire. It was with the mistaken idea of protecting the people he loved that the virtuous Emperor Marcus Aurelius (161 A. D.), for instance, did them to death.

III

MYRRHINE, THE MARTYR BY MISTAKE

Poor little Myrrhine is not altogether a sympathetic heroine for a story. We would shrink from her in these days, for she was a little Corinthian temple *hetaera* in the reign of the Emperor Domitius. Her story, however, is historically true, and a romantic instance of truth being stranger than fiction. Myrrhine, fully convicted that her life as she led it in the service of the goddess Aphrodite was a notably religious and proper one, laughed and danced her happy way through the golden Crecian days, until she met a certain Theoctenus. Theoctenus, an educated and wealthy young Corinthian, became her lover and in due time—for the Christian doctrines, in spite of all the emperors could do was gaining new converts daily—became a Christian. And then, one day, the persecution broke out in Corinth. There were street riots. Theoctenus was killed by the Roman soldiers, and the villa he occupied with Myrrhine was searched. There copies of the Gospels were found, and poor Myrrhine was at once arrested as a Christian. Now Myrrhine and Theoctenus never had discussed religion. Perhaps her lover, knowing she was a sincere little creature, shrank from taking up with her a faith that preached a morality so different from that of the goddess Aphrodite. Perhaps he meant to save her soul at some later date. At any rate, Myrrhine had not taken kindly to the one or two Christian assemblies, the gatherings of the faithful, which she had attended. She had been quite frank about it, and Theoctenus' friends regarded her as an out and out pagan, which she was. But—the books had been found in her villa, and hence she *must* be a Christian, declared the authorities. And Myrrhine, whose belief in Aphrodite as the *only* goddess never had wavered, was led out with a group of her non-fellow Christians to be slaughtered. The victim of a ridiculous mistake, of official red tape, she went to her death the same little courtesan, the same little slave of the temple and its worshipers she always had been.

And now comes what is at once the most pathetic and grotesque portion of her story. The Christians who had been rounded up for execution were killed in various and terrible ways, for variety's sake, on a terrace called Temenos, near Corinth, fringed with olive-trees. Some were crucified, others were shot to death with arrows. Womens' arms and legs were tied to great tree-branches which had been pulled down by cables. Suddenly released, these branches tore their victims limb from limb. But Myrrhine was lucky—she was merely to be beheaded. Near her stood the Christian bishop Onesimus. Often he had grieved to think that this little pagan soul would not listen to his teachings. The headsman drew near, balancing his heavy sword in his hand and then Myrrhine uttered her first and last word since she had come from the prison. Sadly she had watched the horrors going on about her. And it did seem hard to her that she must suffer as the Christians did, without receiving their reward. Then, as the headsman raised his blade Onesimus heard her murmur: "Oh, Virgin Mother!"

It was purely a mechancial exclamation. In her happier days she had used it under any sudden stress of emotion, when she was surprised, overjoyed or terrified. How could the good bishop know for a moment that she was calling on the goddess *Isis—the Virgin Mother of the Egyptian cult?* A radiant smile lit his features. At last, thought he, this obstinate little heathen soul has seen the light! And, his heart rejoicing in the eleventh-hour conversion, he raised his hands and blessed her as her girlish head fell at a single blow of the executioner's sword. The Christian brothers and sisters who watched, hidden among the crowd, saw their bishop's actions. They knew that at the last moment Myrrhine had become one of the elect. They rejoiced that she had suffered martyrdom for the true faith. And she was laid piously away with the other Christian martyrs and her tomb marked by a stone bearing her name.

A thousand years later, the Provencal bishop Guillaume-Guiges de Bocfozel, a good soldier and a passionate huntsman, one of the French nobles who went on the Crusade which took Constantinople from the Greeks and set up a short-lived Latin empire of Constantinople in its place, was in Corinth. And there this good man, who had gained much gold by plundering the cities of the Greek heretics, and who spent liberally for the holy bones of early Christian saints and martyrs, was shown an old tomb—it was Myrrhine's. It contained the relics of a very holy martyr, he was told. The tomb was opened, the frail bones and the severed skull of the little Corinthian priestess of Aphrodite were duly found. The Bishop Guillaume died before the relics could be transported to his Cathedral Church of Riez in Provence. And, the chapter of his diocese, wishing to be sure that the relics were what they were said to be before they were exposed in the church, sent one of their number to make a personal investigation. At the end of a year the investigator returned with them. Yes, indeed, Myrrhine's bones were beyond doubt those of a pious Christian, a well-known saint, martyred by the pagan Romans, the daughter of a king of Corinth. And, reverently placed in a rich golden shrine, they were added to the Cathedral treasures. And the next Bishop of Riez, Bertrand de Sennelier, left money so that a candle might be kept burning night and day before the shrine, because seeing that this princess, martyred by the pagans, came from a land of sunlight, she must have loved the light!

A Martyr of the Noblest Kind. A martyr who embodies all that is fine and glorious in the idea of martyrdom—suffering death for one's belief—was the rich and noble young Perpetua, left a widow with an infant child at her breast. It was in the year 202 A. D. that the Emperor Severus had issued an edict, forbidding any of his subjects to become Christians or Jews. Soon the persecutions began in Roman Africa, and twenty-two year-old Perpetua was one of the first in the city of Carthage (which had been rebuilt as a Roman city) to be flung in a foul dungeon, amid the insults of the soldiers who dragged her there. But when her child was brought to her she said: "The prison has become a palace to me!"

IV

THE VISION OF PERPETUA

It was in her black and fetid prison cell that the noble Perpetua had a vision, which foretold her what her fate would be. When her brother came to see where she was confined, Perpetua said:

"There was a ladder of gold reaching up to heaven. It was so narrow only one person could ascend it at a time. Around it were swords, lances and hooks, to tear the flesh of those who climbed. And a great dragon lay at the foot of the ladder to keep the righteous from going up. But I trod on the monster's head, and when I reached the top of the ladder, I stood in a great garden. There the Shepherd was milking his ewes, with thousand of white-clad forms about him. He welcomed me and gave me a bit of cheese, which I received with hands joined and ate, while those in the white robes said: 'Amen!' Then I awoke with a sweet taste in my mouth!"

And Perpetua's vision was realized. She was called before the court and refused to sacrifice to the "divine" emperor. The day for the execution was set. Then the authorities wanted to dress the Christian women who were to suffer in *yellow gowns*. This was an old custom, handed down from the days of the Carthaginians. At their sacrifices to Moloch the male priests wore black robes and the priestesses of Ceres yellow ones. But Perpetua said: "It was to escape these heathen observations that we suffer death, and since we die to escape them it is not right to force them on us in our last hours!" It is difficult under any circumstances to force a woman to wear anything she has decided not to wear. The authorities allowed the women to go to the amphitheater without forcing the yellow robes on them.

There the men were exposed to furious and hunger-maddened lions, bears and leopards. The women, many of them, were tossed by furious bulls. But Perpetua found a happier death. With tears in her eyes she kissed her babe for the last time and bade her companions farewell. Then she stepped out on the sands where a band of brutal and hardened gladiators were drawn up to give their victims the death-stroke.

The gladiator who stepped up to Perpetua was a young boy, not yet skilled in the vicious art of his craft and, perhaps, not yet as brutalized and degenerate as his companions. He blushed as his inexperienced hands raised the sword to kill the poor girl who stood before him. And seeing his awkwardness and confusion Perpetua, with a heavenly smile leaned forward, and grasping his sword firmly in her hand, she so directed it that it pierced her heart. And she knew, as the cold steel entered her shrinking flesh, that she had set her foot on the first rung of the golden ladder she had seen in her vision!

CHAPTER XII

GLIMPSES OF THE INDIAN AND CHINESE SOUL

LET us turn for a moment from imperial Rome to the far East, where in two great lands, with teeming millions of inhabitants, the cycles of life run on almost unnoticed by the Roman world.

India, a land divided up into many states whose kings or *rajahs* war against each other, worship the strange and monstrous gods of Brahminism. It lives a life almost entirely apart from the rest of the ancient world until the Age of Alexander the Great. When we gaze at India's distant past through the colorful lens of its rich literature we have a confused picture. Towered cities and castles, gilded temples flash in the sun. Wild beasts roam in vast tropical forests. Fantastic and cruel idols are worshipped by millions with monstrous rites. Tremendous battles trample down the rice-fields with charges of hundreds of mailed elephants. Demons, mad hermits, jewels, gold and pearls, silks and costly stuffs, lovely women and sacred cows, all are mingled in a confused and colorful medley. Yet from it we may disentangle some *human* facts.

Brahma and Buddha. The whole ancient *social* system of the Hindus is based on *caste*. It is a system which endures to our day. There are four main divisions. First come the nobles or warriors. Second the priests or *Brahmins,* third, the peasants and traders, fourth the Sudras, men of non-Aryan descent, and below these are the classes of the *pariahs,* the lowest outcasts of humanity, the vilest of the vile among the native races, whose very *shadow,* falling on the man above him means defilement.

Again, we have Buddhism, which teaches that perfect peace can come only by eluding *life* and *love*. The *human* element in this olden Hindoo life is represented in the two tales which follow. The first shows the low moral plane of the Brahmin gods, and the irreverence with which the Hindoo, like the Greek, sometimes treated them. The other tale aims to give *human* reactions to the nobler Buddhist faith, showing the beauty of a charity which embraces the lowest of human beings.

THE MAN WHO BECAME A GOD

Once there were two young fellows, a weaver and a carpenter, who were such good friends that they worked in the same shop, slept in the same bed and could not bear to be separated a single hour. Now one day there was a great festival in the holy city of Benares, in which they lived. The two friends were shoving along through the crowd of the townspeople and the thousands of dancers, musicians and actors who had streamed in from the surrounding country, when a procession came down the principal street. Every one stood on tiptoe, and climbed on roofs and trees in order not to miss anything, and among the climbers were our two friends.

And there, in the procession, rode a beautiful princess on an elephant, surrounded by chamberlains and eunuchs. She wore only a long golden veil which revealed the slender charm of her form, and her face was as sweetly rounded and delicate as a lotus-blossom. One would not have dared to touch it with one's finger, for fear of doing it some harm. Her lips were red, her eyes were long-lidded and melting, her brows were like twin grape-tendrils, and her skin like the crescent moon. Over her brow her black hair lay like a garden. No sooner had the princess passed, however, her lovely face lost amid tossing parasols and waving aigrettes, than the poor weaver fell from his tree as though stricken by some sudden poison.

The carpenter carried him into the nearest house. A physician promptly appeared, but soon had to confess that he did not know what to make of the case. There lay the youth, his eyes closed, pale and without emotion. At last, when the physician had gone and the carpenter, tears in his eyes, was softly speaking to his friend, trying to recall him to consciousness, the weaver opened his eyes:

"What happened to you? What is the matter?" cried the carpenter.

"If you are truly my friend," answered the weaver, "then gather the wood for my funeral pyre and pile it up. For I want to leave this life. If ever I have hurt your feelings I beg your forgiveness. I did so heedlessly and without thinking, for you have been very dear to me."

The carpenter clasped his hands together and the tears ran down his cheeks: "But at least let me know what it is all about?" he cried. "If you tell me I may find a way to help you!"

The weaver shook his head: "No," said he, "I am past all help. My sufferings would only be increased. The blessed release which death would bring would be postponed!"

"Well, if you intend to die then I will bear you company," said the carpenter, "but before I go I must confess I would like to know why I am dying!"

Then the weaver closed his eyes, drew a deep breath and said very gently: "Well, my friend, if you must know, I will tell you. Do you remember the princess we saw riding on the elephant? I had no sooner seen her face than this fever overtook me. Lay your hand on my forehead. Do you notice how it burns? And yet my teeth are chattering with frost. I cannot endure such torture. The holy god whose banner shows a crocodile, the god of love, has afflicted me with his curse!"

Then the carpenter's face broadened in a happy grin. "If that is all that troubles you, dear friend, I can help you," he said.

"How are you going to help me? Her palace is surrounded by guards. She has a thousand servants. No one can gain admittance to her but the winds of the air."

The carpenter was silent for a moment. Then he rose and said: "Your wish is already granted! You shall see your love this very night!"

Taking his friend by the arm, he led him through side streets back to their home. Here he at once set to work. He took a big piece of wood and shaped it into a large eagle. Besides that he made two human arms, a mace or club, a lotus-flower and a crown of wood. The bird could be set in motion with the elbows. When he had finished the carpenter seated the weaver on the bird, and gave him the symbols he had carved—they were the symbols of the great god Vishnu—and said:

"There you are, dear friend! At midnight the princess will be in her bedroom, on the highest terrace of her palace. Set this bird in motion with your elbows and fly high. When the princess hears you coming through the air and sees that you carry the sacred symbols of Vishnu, she will take you for Vishnu himself. And not even a princess will refuse to listen to words of love from a god."

The happy weaver could hardly wait for midnight to come. No sooner had he taken his seat on the eagle than he felt completely cured of his chills and fever. And on the stroke of midnight he flew out of the window. He flew up above all the houses and palaces in Benares, and enjoyed his flying so much that he circled around twice instead of once. But then he let himself down on the terrace of the princess' palace. The princess, who had heard the rustling of the great wings, had jumped out of bed, and was not a little frightened when the bird lit on her terrace, and a man with a diadem descended from its back. The weaver did not leave her much time to be frightened, however. Though his own knees trembled, he stepped up to her and said: "At last I find you, lovely one! For your sake I have left my paradise island in the Milky Sea, and have come to win your love!" The princess, poor girl, saw the weaver's diadem and his *four* arms. Folding her arms she said with deep humility and respect: "Oh, great Vishnu, how is it that you have honored my unworthiness with your favor?" "Because of your beauty," answered the weaver-god. "Your beauty makes you the equal of the gods. Tell me you will be mine!" Then the princess answered: "Ask my father for my hand. I know he will not hesitate a moment to give it to you." But this did not suit the weaver. "No, my beloved," he answered, "no human being, aside from yourself, is worthy of the honor of seeing me. And much less speaking to me. I am a god! So be my bride according to the *Gandharwa* rite*! Otherwise I shall curse you and yours, and reduce the whole palace to ashes!"

And with that he left his eagle on the terrace and led the princess trembling with pride and happiness to think she was beloved by a god, into her bower. Before the dawn broke he once more flew away, before anyone had seen him. And every night after that he came and went. During the day he slept and continued to talk to his beloved in his dreams and thus he lived an uninterrupted round of happiness, hardly knowing that the world about him still existed. But one day as her slave girl went to waken her mistress in the morning, and bent over her, the latter, still asleep, suddenly put her arms around her neck, and, her eyes closed, whispered: "Oh, beloved!" When the slave-girl, startled, drew back, and the princess awakened by her movement opened her eyes, she blushed a rosy red and was much confused.

Now, as a slave-girl will, this one told one of her companions of the strange occurrence. Soon the rumor that the princess had a lover spread through the entire palace and reached the ears of the king her father. He turned pale and at once went to the queen. "Go to our daughter," he said, "and investigate this matter!" And the queen hurried to her daughter's apartments, looked at her with a mother's eye, and cried: "Wretched girl, what have you been up to? Whom have you admitted to your privacy?" But when the princess kneeled at her mother's feet and told her all that had happened, the queen was radiant with joy. She at once hurried back to her husband: "We are blessed beyond all other mortals! It is the god Vishnu himself who visits our daughter at night!" And when he heard these joyful tidings the king's face also glowed with joyful pleasure. But he did not wish to commit himself too soon. So he only remarked: "Let us stand at the palace window to-night and see him when he arrives." And at midnight, when the king and queen were hidden behind the window and waited with beating hearts, Vishnu's eagle came rustling up with the weaver. And when the royal pair saw the diadem, the four arms and the mace, all doubt left their hearts. The king almost danced with joy. "There is no one on earth can stand against me," he cried, "now that Vishnu's sacred self visits our child! With his aid I shall be first among kings. The whole earth shall be subject to me. To-morrow morning at the latest I will gather my armies, war on the other monarchs and subdue them!"

---

* The *Gandharwa* rite was a form of marriage for which only the consent of the two lovers concerned was necessary.

And he was as good as his word. But the enormous number of his enemies soon drove him back on all sides, and surrounded him and his city with a hedge of soldiers and war-elephants. So in his dire need the king went to his daughter and said to her: "When the god Vishnu comes to see you to-night, speak to him, and ask him how much longer he expects to look on while his father-in-law is being destroyed by his enemies?" And the princess spoke to the weaver as her father had told her to do. But the weaver only laughed: "Is that all he wants? I'll soon put an end to his enemies! Why do you suppose I carry my sacred battle-maul?"

But he did nothing, and his enemies drew their lines closer and closer about the city of Benares. They had destroyed his other cities and laid waste his fields, and at last he was hemmed in in his fortress-palace, while the enemy prepared to storm it. So for the last time he told his daughter to beg the god to aid him. He also gave her all sorts of presents, camphor and musk, and rich perfumes, silken garments, flowers and beverages, to give to the god. And the weaver thought to himself: "To-morrow the fortress will be taken. And if it falls I am sure to be slain." So with the first ray of dawn he mounted his eagle and shot high up into the air, waiting for the enemy army to form for battle. "Then," thought he, "I will drop down on them, and they will be so frightened that they are sure to run away."

But while he was circling about in the air, the real god Vishnu up in the skies saw him. So he called his eagle, the genuine *Garuda*, king of all the birds, and said: "I have seen this human creature for weeks flying around in my shape on a bird in your shape! What shall we do about it?" "Most holy Vishnu," replied the *Garuda*, "it seems very likely that this man will soon be struck by an arrow and fall to earth. In that case what becomes of your own fame and holiness? People are sure to say: 'We have shot down Vishnu and his eagle from the skies!'" The god reflected a moment. "True, true," he said, at last, "we cannot let matters go that far. But what are we to do?" The eagle sighed: "There is but one thing left to do," he answered, "and that is to help this sly youth. Do you enter into his body while I enter that of his wooden bird, so that the enemy may be destroyed. If this is done our own glory is increased." And the god Vishnu followed the *Garuda's* advice. He entered the body of the weaver and the *Garuda* passed into that of the wooden bird. As soon as the sun rose the enemy soldiers were burned up by a breath of fire which came from the heaven above them. Then the King of Benares were indeed more powerful than the other kings of earth, and they all paid tribute to him. As for the weaver, he appeared as a suitor for the princess' hand and (once the king had learned the truth), was accepted by her, and their nuptials solemnly celebrated in the largest temple of Benares. In an old attic of the palace he kept the relics of his courting days, the wooden eagle, and the symbols of Vishnu. But he flew no more by night. In the first place he felt no inclinations to do so, and besides his wife had the key to the attic.

VASAVADATTA

In the town of Mattura in Bengal there once lived a most beautiful courtesan known as Vasavadatta, who conceived a violent passion for a young man named Upapusta, a wealthy merchant's son, the first time she saw him. So she sent her servant to tell him that she would be glad to receive him in her house. But Upapusta did not visit her. He was chaste and very pious, observing the law, and living a holy life according to Buddha's teaching. Hence he despised the woman's love and would have none of it.

Not long after, Vasavadatta, because of a crime, was hailed into court, and condemned to lose her hands, feet, ears and nose. She was led to the burial ground, and the judgment was carried out. Then she was left to die on the spot where she had suffered.

She still was living, and her faithful servant was driving off the flies with a fan, so that her lost moments need not be troubled by them, when a youth drew near. He did not seem to be led by curiosity, but walked humbly along, a boy holding a parasol above his head. When Vasavadatta's servant saw that it was young Upapusta, she hurriedly collected the chopped-off members of her mistress and hid them beneath her mantle. When Upapusta had come quite close to Vasavadatta, he looked in silence at her whose beauty had glowed like a pearl through the whole city, and the courtesan recognized the man she had loved, and said in a failing voice:

"Upapusta, when my body was adorned with gold and silks and fragrant with essences, it was as beautiful as that of the love goddess. Then I waited your coming in vain. When I was lovely and excited desire, you did not come. Upapusta, Upapusta, why do you seek me now, when my bleeding, mutilated body is an object of horror and disgust?"

Then Upapusta replied in a gentle voice: "Vasavadatta, in the swift days of your beauty my senses were not snared by vain appearances. Already then I saw you with the eye of vision as you now are! I did not kiss your body as a vessel of lust. But do not mourn the beauty you have lost. In truth you have lost nothing. Do not weep for the shadows of pleasure which escape you, let life's evil dream vanish! All earthly joys are like the reflection of the moon in the water. You suffered because you desired too much. Long no more, be kind to yourself, and cling no more to life—you see how poor a thing it is! I love you, Vasavadatta, as Buddha bids us love our fellow creatures. Depart in peace!"

The courtesan listened to his words, and since she recognized their truth she died without earthly longing and departed this world in blessedness !

China, like India, was a land that lay apart from the life-currents of the rest of the ancient world. It was a land of fantastic splendors and abject poverties. Feudal kings, as in India, waged battle against each other or lolled on silken cushions in the perfumed hush of luxurious harems where singing-girls and tiny-footed favorites beguiled their purple hours of leisure. The tales which follow give us a glimpse of the secretive, demon-haunted Mongolian soul, one that still, like every other human soul no matter what the color of its earthly envelope, is subject to the great fundamental laws of love and life.

Chinese Soul Pictures. The tale of Yang Gui Fee, from China's feudal days is the delicate and imaginative romance of an enduring passion. It echoes with a perfume of peonies and a chime of pagoda-bells, the great world-truth that love is ever the same throughout all the earth. And it illustrates the belief of the Chinese in magicians, sorcerers, spells and incantations. Our second tale gives us a gripping glimpse of the demon influences which haunt the soul of the yellow man. Haunting shadows, whose leafy fingers are without the strength to seize and strangle, deal death.

THE VOW OF YANG GUI FEE

It was whispered at the Court of the Emperor Ming Huang, of the Tang Dynasty, that in the great peony-gardens of the imperial palace not a flower dared bloom unless the emperor's favorite wife, the lovely Yang Gui Fee, had granted it permission. For so great was her beauty, and so powerful her charm, that for a kind glance of her slitted eyes, not only the peonies, but every other living thing about the Court hastened to do her will, from the Divine Son of the Sun to the lowest scullions in the imperial kitchens. Yet when Yang Gui Fee brought her cousin Ho Loo to Court she did an ill thing. He was a wild drinker, boastful, insolent and overbearing. He soon succeeded in offending the people as well as the nobles. And, one fine day, the whole city rose in revolt, the army joined them, and the Emperor Ming Huang, with his Court and a few companies of faithful palace guards, had to flee to the mountains.

And there, in the midst of a desolate mountain pass, the palace guards, who blamed all their misfortunes on Yang Gui Fee and her cousin, mutinied. Ho Loo was torn from his horse, and cut to pieces by the indignant soldiers. But still they were not satisfied. With loud demands for her surrender they swarmed about the imperial litters and cried: "If Yang Gui Fee is allowed to live we are all dead men, for she will never forget or forgive the slaying of her cousin!" Through the terrified eunuchs who clustered around the great palanquins with their curtains of yellow silk strode the tall form of the Emperor. Yang Gui Fee had flung herself into his arms, and he had sworn that she should not die. But the guards had forgotten their reverence for the Son of Heaven. Then, while their wild cries drowned the sound of his voice, and while his back was turned, one of the eunuchs suddenly clapped his hand over the lovely Yang Gui Fee's mouth. He dragged her from among the other women and, a few moments later, she was hanging from the gnarled branch of a nearby pear-tree. When they learned that she was dead the rage of the soldiers calmed. And, as soon as the news of it spread to the capital that the lovely Yang Gui Fee was no more, the rebellion died as suddenly as it had sprung up. Ming Huang returned to his ancestral palace.

But in vain he tried to forget his dead favorite. The great halls of the palace seemed empty without her, though they were crowded with courtiers. He never crossed the threshold of his harem, for the fragrance that rose in those halls of pleasure clutched at his heart. It was the sweetness which had clung to Yang Gui Fee when she drew near him! He could not bear to walk in the peony gardens where the white, scarlet and golden blooms had opened to the silver sound of her laughter. So when one of his eunuchs told him that a certain magician named Yang Chee Wu has the power to call back the souls of the dead, the Emperor sent for him.

And that very evening, while the Emperor sat and watched him, for they were alone in an inner room, the magician burned magic herbs and murmured incantations until, suddenly, his soul left its body to wander off and searched for Yan Gui Fee. First the magician's soul descended to the under world, where the shadows of the dead are gathered. But the shadow of Yang Gui Fee was not there. Then he ascended to the highest heaven, where the Sun, the Moon and the stars make their eternal rounds, and the vastness of space is filled with spirits. But the spirit of Yang Gui Fee was not there. So he returned and told this to the Emperor. But the Son of Heaven was angry and said: "Sorcerer, sorcerer, your skin shall be drawn from your body inch by inch unless you bring me news of Yang Gui Fee! No one as beautiful as she was could have been without a soul. And no soul disappears into space without leaving a trace!"

Then the magician, who valued his skin and did not want to lose it piece-meal, said: "There is a spot on the world's rim, between mountain and valley, where the souls of the blessed live in silent clefts in the rock. I will see whether Yang Gui Fee is there." And again he burned strange herbs and murmured incantations. And again his body grew rigid as though in death, and his soul roamed in space. And when he came to the rim of the world one of the blessed spirits said to him: "Yang Gui Fee is not here! But you will find her in the island paradise in the midst of the Yellow-Dragon Sea. It floats on the waves invisible to human eyes, and many spirits live in the palace of white jade and water-crystal that rises on it." So the magician took his way to the island paradise.

And there, in a great garden, where jade-flowers and coral-trees cast exquisite fragrance on the air, a serving-maid asked him whom he sought. "I am looking for Yang Gui Fee," said the soul of the magician, "for I bear a message to her from one whom she loved on earth." Then the serving-maid bade him follow her. She led him to a high tower of white porcelain, and when he had ascended to its topmost story she drew a curtain. There sat Yang Gui Fee on a throne. She was even lovelier than she had been on earth, and she wore a head-dress of emeralds and her robe was trimmed with yellow swan's down. But there were lines of sorrow on her rosy forehead. And she said to the magician:

"Well do I know that the heart of the Emperor yearns for me. Yet for me no path leads back to the world of men! Many ages ago, when both he and I were blessed spirits, Ming Huang and I loved each other. And, though I knew that some day a grinning eunuch would hang me from a wild pear-tree, I took an earthly form and followed him. Then once, as we stood on the palace terrace gazing up at the two twin stars, the Spinner and the Herd-boy, who loved each other as we do, he swore to be true to me through the ages. And he took a ring from his hand and broke it in two. One half he gave me and the other half he kept himself. Take back my half to the Emperor and tell him not to grieve. Tell him to remember his vow, for we shall be united again in a few years' time!"

And when he returned with the ring and the message, the Emperor Ming Huang rewarded the magician splendidly. But after that the realities of life seemed a dream to him. And when the eunuchs drew back the curtains of his royal couch one morning, they found that his soul had gone to rejoin that of Yang Gui Fee in the white jade palace in the Yellow-Dragon Sea. He lay as though sleeping and there was a smile on his lips.

SHADOW-MAGIC

Once upon a time, in the days of the early emperors, there was a strong and savage robber by the name of Yuan-Tzan. So fierce and so terrible was he that no one dared oppose him. Courage gleamed in his eyes like two radiant lance-points, and such was the power of their glances that they pierced the shields of his enemies.

Now one day Yuan-Tzan surprised a merchant in the forest, just as the poor man was counting his gold-pieces in the shadow of a great chestnut-tree. Yuan-Tzan stabbed him to death with his dagger, then sat himself down in the shade of the same tree to count the murdered man's gold. But the blood of the man who had been slain flowed down to the roots of the tree and entered them. And the shadow of the chestnut-tree grew cooler and cooler until at last Yuan-Tzan felt as though an icy bier-cloth had been flung over him. Surprised, the robber looked up. And he saw that the leaves of the chestnut-tree had turned black. And all the five-fold black chestnut-leaves stretched themselves out like the five fingers of as many black hands to seize him. Then Yuan-Tzan realized that the murdered man's soul had entered into the tree with his blood. He jumped up and ran off a few steps. Then he turned around and began to mock the tree, saying it had turned black with rage. "You are held fast to the ground by your roots," cried the robber, "and cannot do me any harm!" And then, satisfied with himself, he went home, lay down and fell asleep.

But in the middle of a dream of all the gold he had robbed from the merchant, Yuan-Tzan woke, shaking with frost. Again he felt as though a wet, icy bier-cloth had been flung over him. The moon shone brightly into the room. And there, in the moonlight, Yuan-Tzan saw on the white-washed wall against his bed the sharply-outlined shadow of a great five-fold chestnut leaf. It seemed painted there in black ink.

And for the first time in his life, Yuan-Tzan was afraid. He leaped up from his bed and ran out of the house.

But once outside, he clenched his fist and cursed with rage and once again mocked the chestnut-tree. "No matter what happens you will never see your gold again!" he shouted. And once more he sat down in the bright moonlight to count his gold pieces. But no sooner had he begun, than his body was once more shaken with a chill and the black shadow of a chestnut-tree fell on the heap of gold, although there was no chestnut-tree to be seen for miles around. And Yuan-Tzan jumped up and ran away, leaving the gold lying on the ground.

After that Yuan-Tzan lived a restless life. He robbed many jewels, much silver, a quantity of silken garments. But he never again stole gold from anyone. And he kept carefully away from all chestnut-trees.

Then, one night, he fell asleep under the wall of a burned-down house. The cold chill woke him. Again he felt as though the icy bier-cloth had been flung over him. And when he sat up and rubbed his eyes, he saw on the ruined wall the great black shadow of a chestnut-tree. And from one branch of the shadow-tree hung the shadow-corpse of a young girl swinging in the wind. And Yuan-

Tzan jumped up and ran all night long, until the dawn began to show and the first song of the birds floated through the woods on the fragrance of the forest like the newly-formed ice-crystals on the surface of the water. And then a young girl came along the forest path. She was clad in white, and was so very lovely that Yuan-Tzan forgot everything else and followed her. When the girl noticed this, she began to blush and then to run. Her hurrying feet, however, did not raise a grain of dust as she ran along, and her delicate body did not cast a shadow. At a little distance she stopped, looked back at Yuan-Tzan, and nodded at him in a hardly noticeable manner. Yuan-Tzan followed her. She drew him toward a wood of chestnut-trees, but when he saw this Yuan-Tzan stopped and would not follow. When the girl noticed it she took another path, and led him to a grove of young birch trees, not far from a village. Yuan-Tzan did not fear any human beings, for he trusted in his tremendous strength. Nor did the young birch trees alarm him. They had delicate, white stems and small bright leaves that curled as a child's hair does. And under the whitest and most delicate of all the birch-trees, the young girl stopped, and received the robber with an entrancing smile.

Yuan-Tzan stepped up to her and was about to put his arms around her. But, suddenly, the girl's eyes turned angrily, and she began to call for help so loudly that the peasants in the nearby village heard her. Yet Yuan-Tzan, who feared no man, tried to force her lips to meet his own. Then the girl flung herself down on the ground. Yuan-Tzan stooped to pick her up. But—as he stretched out his arms for her, her body suddenly turned quite flat and black and lay on the ground, a shadow-body which he could not grasp. Then Yuan-Tzan saw that it was the shadow-corpse of the girl who had been hung. And he realized that the chestnut-tree on which she had hung herself had to obey her ghost!

Yuan-Tzan's legs grew so still with fright that he could not make a move, though the peasants from the village already crowded around him with their knives drawn. Yet none of them dared come too near the terrible robber, who held his dagger, engraved with dragon-lines, in his hand. Then as Yuan-Tzan stood there, wildly brandishing his dagger, he was suddenly shaken by a chill, as though some one had flung an icy bier-cloth over him. He looked at the ground and saw the tiny shadow-dots cast by the little birch-leaves grow larger and larger, and divide into the five divisions of the chestnut-leaf. And he watched with surprise the small white birch-leaves, which curled as a child's hair does, into great five-fold chestnut-leaves, like black fingers about to seize him.

He realized that the chestnut-tree had changed its form to lure him to it. And suddenly his heart was so stricken with terror that he dropped his sharp dagger engraved with the dragon-lines, and buried his face in his hands. And when he saw this, one of the peasants thrust his knife into Yuan-Tzan's neck from behind and killed him.

CHAPTER XIII

BARBARIANS YELLOW AND WHITE

Out of the barren, brooding deserts of northwestern China, out of the fearsome Mongolian deserts there swept down upon the dying Roman empire, in the fifth century, a Barbarian flood more hideous and terrifying than any other. The Mongol Huns were more like a deadly plague of hideous yellow locusts, locusts whose bite was death, than human beings. In countless hordes, riding the raw flesh in which they lived soft under their wooden saddles, they flooded Europe under Attila, their king.

A Yellow Alexander. Attila was a yellow, water-drinking Alexander. He boasted that no grass ever grew where Hunnish horse-hoofs had trodden. But though he slaughtered the Goths and the Greek emperor paid him tribute, he was defeated in a great battle at Chalons (451 A.D.). Had it not been for that defeat which the Romans and the other Barbarians gave the Huns, the *yellow* instead of the *white* Indo-European race might have inherited Europe and controlled its destinies! The next year when about to send the dice of empire rolling across the battle-field once more, Attila died by a woman's hand.

ILDICO'S NEEDLE

Two of the guests hurrying to King Attila's wooden palace on the Hungarian plain were riding together along the West bank of the Danube river one morning. One was the Roman Orestes. The other, a Barbarian, a Rugian, came from the coast of the Eastern Sea. His name was Edeko, and he was one of Attila's vassals. "Why are you riding to the wedding?" said Orestes. "Because I dare not stay away," was the answer. "My case exactly," said the Roman, "and I suppose Attila's new bride, the Burgundian king's daughter, did not dare say no when he demanded her in marriage." Edeko nodded. "What a man of mystery Attila is," he said. "All Attila tells is that he comes out of the East. My own people claim that the Huns are the children of warlocks and witches, born in the Asian deserts. When any one asks Attila what he is, he answered, 'The scourge of God!' He founds no empire and builds no cities, but he rules all empires and destroys all cities."

"But Ildico, the Burgundian princess, whom Attila is marrying is a Christian, is she not?"

"Yes, but that does not trouble Attila. He has no religion."

"But he must have, if he calls himself 'The Scourge of God,' and insists that he has found the sword of the god of war."

"Forms are a matter of indifference to him. His prime minister Onegesius is a Greek and a Christian. . . ."

"What a man! Instead of settling down in Rome or Constantinople, he picks out a sandy waste."

"He likes it because it resembles the steppes of his Eastern homeland. The ground, the birds, the grasses are the same. He feels at home!"

Two days later, Orestes and Edeko came to Attila's city of tents. Outside, enormous herds of pigs, sheep, goats and cattle were grazing, living food for this great horde of yellow savages who could not produce. In the tented alleys of the town swarmed thousands of men small in size, bandy-legged, and with broad shoulders. They wore rat-skin mantles and their legs were wound around with rags. At the entrance of the first tent-street, Attila's son, Prince Ellak stepped forward to meet the distinguished guests with an interpreter. They were led into the House of Guests.

"Is that a prince and are those human beings?" said Orestes to Edeko. "The one is a horse-trader and the rest are rats," replied the Rugian.

"There are figures such as only a drunkard's mad dreams could imagine! Why, they have no faces, these Huns! Their eyes are holes, their mouth is a slit! They have a nose like a skull's, and ears like pitcher handles!"

"Yet—the Roman legions run away from these half-naked savages, who have neither armor nor shield!"

"At any rate, they will not conquer the world this year." And the two men followed Prince Ellak, who had heard and understood every word they had said, though he acted as though he knew no Latin.

Beside Attila's palace proper stood the House of the Women. It was filled with the rich plunder of nations. There were golden and silver articles and vessels. There were hangings of silk and velvet. There were Roman chairs and tables, Greek vases, Gaulish weapons and woven Gothic goods. It looked like a robber's cave and it was.

Ildico, the handsome Burgundian girl, stood at a window, lost in thought. She had been willing to accept Attila's hand, for the sombre and majestic dwarf had fascinated and bewitched her. But— she had thought to be his wife and queen. Not until this morning had she learned that she would not share his throne, but merely be shut up with the rest of his harem in the House of the Women.

Attila's favorite concubine, the Kirghiz Cercas, who was stitching Ildico's bridal veil with mocking smiles, had taken pleasure in explaining all this to her Burgundian rival that morning. And Ildico had not friends in the palace, and it was impossible for her to appeal to the stranger princes.

As she stitched, Cercas sang a melancholy song of her far Eastern home:

Lion-tracks the tiger lure,
  Siddi Khur, Siddi Khur!
On the steppe he trails his spoor,
  Urgan, Khalgan, Kossegheel
Claws of copper, teeth of steel,
  Dalai-Nor, Dalai-Nor!
Trail him, you shall know his law,
Trail him, you shall feel his paw,
Trail him, and come back no more,
  Dalai-Nor!

At last Ildico seemed to have made up her mind. "Will you lend me a needle?" she said, "I want to sew." And she borrowed from Cercas the largest needle the Kirghiz had. But instead of sewing she hid it in the bosom of her dress. A hideous dwarf, Attila's court jester, now suddenly appeared in the door, quickly thrust a note into Cercas' hand, and was gone. And when Cercas had read the note she changed color. She was so filled with rage that for a moment she could not speak. Then, at last she gasped:

"Ildico, you have made a friend! Here in this room! . . . here, on your breast!" And the Kirghiz girl flung herself on the Burgundian maiden, embraced her and commenced to weep and laugh at the same time.

"Give me back the needle, the fine big needle I loaned you! I must sharpen it with emery! I must dip it into my special little bottle of smelling-salts. And then—we will sew up the tiger's mouth together, you and I! Then he will bite no more. *Siddi Khur! Siddi Khur!*

"Let me read your letter," Ildico interrupted her.

"You don't know the language. I will tell you what it says. He— our lord and master Attila—is making ready to marry again. He is preparing to marry Honoria, the daughter of the Emperor Valens! And this time he has sworn to burn us all. That is what he calls giving us honorable burial!"

Ildico pressed Cercas' hand. "Sharpen the needle, but give it back to me," she said.

In the great banqueting hall of Attila's palace the whole company of princes, soldiers and envoys rose to their feet. A curtain at the back of the room had been drawn. It disclosed a raised platform. On the platform on a seat sat a small, undersized man. There was a table in front of him, and on the table stood a wooden goblet. At a sign from his minister Onegesius, who watched his master's face, they seated themselves once more. Attila never winked an eye. He did not greet them. He acted as though they were not there at all; as though he were alone in the hall. But there was more than mere pride in his attitude. And the guests looked at him with deep respect. Finally, he raised his wooden goblet to his lips and then the wine flowed in golden and silver drinking-vessels on the guests' tables, while Attila smiled. He liked to see those about him yield to the influence of wine while he drank water from his wooden goblet. After a time the great Attila rose from his seat and crossed to a lounge or divan that also stood on the platform. There he stretched himself out. Yet, as he lay there with his eyes fixed on the ceiling, he still was imposing.

"But what of the wedding and the bride?" Orestes asked one of the Huns.

"We do not even *mention* our women. Do you think we would *show* them?" was the answer.

The drinking went on until the guests were far gone in liquor. Suddenly flames rose on all sides, and the hall was filled with smoke. The guests all staggered to their feet. Sobered in an instant, they cried out and started to flee. But Onegesius beat on the table with his staff, and the Huns present burst out laughing. It was a wedding jest. A few tons of hay had been set afire outside the building. When quiet once more reigned Attila was gone. He had left the building by a panel-door during the confusion. The interrupted wedding feast continued till dawn.

At sunrise, the Roman Orestes was still sitting with a prince of the Avars over his wine-cups. The appearance of the great banquet hall was indescribable, and outside it most of the guests were dancing madly around a great fire. "What a wedding!" said the Roman. "Yes—I should have liked to have spoken to that strange man!"

"Attila does not like to grant interviews," replied the Avar. "Why should men meet to lie to each other," he says. "He is not without sparks of humanity. He does not believe in shedding blood needlessly, and does not revenge himself on a beaten foe."

"Is he religious? Does he fear death?"

"He swears by his sword. To him death is only the gate to his true home. That is why he lives on earth as though he were a guest or a traveller!"

"Just like a Christian! It is strange that he showed such respect to Pope Leo in Rome! But what is the matter? . . ."

A terrible howling sounded outside. It seemed to come from the palace, and then spread throughout the immense Hunnish camp. Half a million men were howling, and the wave of their grief flooded the air with terror. The guests still at the table hurried out. All the Huns were dancing about madly, slashing their faces with knives. Edeko, hurrying up, seized Orestes by the hand and dragged him through the crowd.

"Attila, the Lord be praised, is dead!"

"Dead? Then Ildico killed him!"

"No, she was sitting by the corpse, heavily veiled and weeping."

"She must have done it!"

"Yes, no doubt! But these savages are so conceited that they do not believe Attila could have been killed by a mortal hand. We must hurry to Rome with the news. The man's fortune is made who gets there first with it!"

Strange to say the acquaintance Orestes and Edeko had formed was renewed by their sons, but under different circumstances. Edeko's son was the great Barbarian chieftain Odovakas. And Orestes' son was the last Roman Emperor, Romulus Augustus. And the son of Edeko dethroned the son of Orestes.

The Men of Ultima Thule. With all the gold in the world and all the scum of the earth floating into Rome in one great turbid tide for centuries, with the continued struggle between the rich and poor, with the continual breaking down of the national *morale* by luxury and wrong living, came the hosts of barbarian nations. Wild, savage, primitive tribes of every kind descended from the northern European plains, the dim, cold Scandinavian lands—*Ultima Thule,* as they were called—and the western plains of Asia. They came— and though for centuries the superior discipline of the Roman legions held them back, in the end they conquered. When the Romans began to fill the ranks of the legions with barbarian hired soldiers they marked out the beginning of the end of their empire. When a nation no longer can fight her own battles, when she has to depend on savage auxiliaries to make up for her own race degeneracy and dearth of manpower she is treading the last downward steps of an empire's downward road. Let us give a few pictures of human contacts in a purely *human relation* to show the difference between the Roman and the Barbarian soul.

Race Souls That Did Not Meet. Like the Greek and the Persian, there was something about the race souls of Roman and Barbarian that prevented any deeper understanding until long after the fall of the empire. The continual merging of all races in Rome and its provinces, then the "world's melting-pot," and the growth of settling down; the rise of the barbarian kingdoms of the Franks, the Lombards, the Anglo-Saxons in Britain; the Vandals and Visegoths and the Goths on the ruins of the Roman empire; all brought about a change. And in this separation between Roman and Barbarian, to some extent, religion played a part. Gradually Christianity was accepted by the Barbarians, but—they chose a form of Christianity the Latin Church regarded as a heresy, Adrianism. Arius, a Libyan in the fifth century A.D., held that Christ was "perfect God, only begotten." A cry of mingled horror and approval went up when he began teaching this doctrine. Great was the rejoicing among the orthodox when Arins died in a public toilet in Constantinople (336 A.D.) and the place and the manner of his death were regarded as a judgment of God. In innumerable churches Christian bishops cursed one another in turns. It had been taken up by the majority of Germanic Barbarian tribes of the great migrations—Goths, Vandals, Suebi, Burgundians and Langobardians. It died out before the growth of Medieval Catholicism. But it was an added cause of bitterness between the Romans, who held to the Nicene doctrine. and the Barbarians, who were Arians.

THE CENTURION WAALIA AND THE PRINCESS PLACIDIA

When the young centurion Waalia had seen Galla Placidia, the Emperor Honorius' young sister, pass in haughty state, carried in her litter by four Nubian porters, he did not know that the meeting was one which would affect his whole life. The Emperor Honorius frivoled away his time in childish amusements in his palace at Ravenna. The Vandal general Stilicho reigned for him in Rome. And Waalia, the son of a Goth in the Roman service, who had died in battle for Rome, was honored by Stilicho's confidence. He had just returned from a successful secret mission to Alaric, King of the Goths. In the modest suburb across the Tiber, Waalia rented a small house, for when in Rome he lived with his sister. Their mother had been a young Roman girl in whose veins, in those days of debauchery and decadence, there may have flowed patrician, or even imperial blood. Waalia, blonde, tall and strong, had inherited his father's barbarian soul, passionate and violent, a prey to strong emotions. He had begun soldiering early, and having attracted Stilicho's notice in battle, had been rapidly promoted. Salvina took more after her mother. She was dark, and sweet and gentle by nature. Waalia did not trouble his head about religion, but Salvina was Christian. Waalia was ambitious. When he came home after his report to Stilicho and his vision of Galla Placida, Salvina set about preparing the evening meal, happy to see her brother back again. But Waalia sat and dreamed the dream of every ambitious Barbarian. He dreamed he was clad in the consular toga, like Stilicho. He dreamed he was treading beneath the marble and gold roof of the Palatine Palace, while the soldiers cheered him. For Rome fell ever to the strongest sword, the clearest head. And with this dream he associated Galla Placidia, the haughty beauty whose glance, when he had stared her in the face, had swept over him as though he were not there. And he knew then that he loved her, that he must win her!

And, softened, perhaps, by his own love, he listened sympathetically when little Salvina confessed that she had a sweetheart. He was a Syrian, she said, named Cherilus. He was a skilfull jeweler, and had a shop and good custom among the rich Roman ladies, because of his fine goldsmith work. But of course her brother must approve. Might she love Cherilus? "I thought that perhaps because he was only an artisan, and not a soldier, you might be angry," she smiled. Waalia would rather have given her to a soldier, some brother centurion. But he smiled and said: "Who can command love? Happy are those who love and are loved in return. Yes, you shall have your jeweler." Then his thoughts went back to Galla Placidia.

Little did he know the soul of the woman he loved. Galla Placidia, at eighteen, was already skilled in the arts of mixing poisons, learned from her confidential eunuch Chrysogonus. She was betrothed to Stilicho's son, but hated the proud master of the empire. Stilicho was a Vandal, and Aryan. She was orthodox, hand and glove in a conspiracy to destroy the Vandal's life and power. Cold in spite of her loveliness, she had but one aim—to become Empress of Rome. To accomplish it Stilicho must go. And so she conspired with the Catholic bishops in the shadows of the basilicas. The hand of power was to wash the head of religion. Stilicho was to be blackened in the young emperor's mind, invited to Ravenna, and there treacherously killed.

But Stilicho, having promoted him to be perfect of a cohort in the Palace Guard, sent Waalia to Ravenna. There following instructions, the young centurion soon taught the weak Honorius to like him. The Emperor soon made him his inseparable companion. Weak, cowardly, suspicious, Honorius had a soul tainted with secret hatreds. The imperial palace, with its rich marbles, was magnificent. Its mosaic floors were covered with sand yellow as gold, which fleets of ships brought specially from Asia. Beneath the high, vaulted roofs, fountains of water, perfumed with rare essences, flung their cooling jets and kept the atmosphere ever fresh and fragrant. The gardens were vast. There were great lakes in them for sham naval battles, and a special *stadium* where the Emperor amused himself giving chariot races, with the charioteers wearing his colors. His two great interests in life were his dog-kennels and his poultry-yards. His peacocks, his golden pheasants, his hens and pullets knew his voice, and he was followed everywhere by the great Arab grey-hounds sent him by a Bithynian proconsul. And when his former favorites murmured, the Emperor Honorius answered by raising Waalia to the dignity of captain and chief of his own special guard. These guardsmen were known as the "Protectors." They wore golden armor and white tunics. In fact, so great became Waalia's influence at court, exerted in favor of his master Stilicho, that Galla Placidia was alarmed. She set out from Rome with a numerous escort to visit her brother and undermine the centurion in his favor.

Great was Waalia's emotion when, one day, he found Honorius showing his sister his poultry-yard. Thousands of birds, Colchian pheasants, spotted Numidian guinea fowl, pigeons, white doves, merles, nightingales, finches, sang and flew about beneath the silver wires of a veritable palace. In the middle was a great pool, in which swam beautiful fish. Honorius, amid his courtiers, was feeding a little white hen of which he was especially fond, when Placidia appeared. He presented Waalia to her and recommended him to her as one of his best friends. She gave Waalia a kindly glance, and he trembled beneath her regard.

And from that day forward she began to spin a net of dark intrigue around the young captain of the guard. For him she always had a limpid and subtly promising smile which set his soldier blood boiling. She made it plain that she was favorably inclined toward him. She spoke to him sometimes, in her silver voice. Her words were unimportant, but her tone was alluring. She saw to it that a vague rumor spread that the bravest young soldier in the empire might well aspire to the command Stilicho held. It was not said in as many words, of course, yet that was the rumor's sense. And Waalia, with those about him flattering and lying, gradually lost the natural hostility and alertness which were made the strength of his nature. Besides, he did not think of Stilicho, or the empire. He thought only of Galla Placidia. She had become his whole life.

And with a thousand caresses the treacherous princess taught her brother the Emperor Honorius to mistrust Stilicho, and to hate him. She made the weakling believe himself a hero and a statesman. In his ignoble soul he did secretly hate Stilicho because the latter was a great man—who humored him. Galla Placidia induced him to set off on a personal tour of inspection of the legions near Ravenna, to show his independence and lead the all-powerful minister to take some rash step. And when the perfidious girl entrusted herself in gracious words to Waalia during her brother's absence from Ravenna, love blinded him. He forgot his duties to Stilicho. Now that her brother had gone, he saw the princess often in the great halls of the imperial palace or under its porticoes of rose-colored marbles. She drew from him—from his candid Barbarian soul, all faith where it trusted—every detail of his intimate life, of his hard years as a soldier, his love for his little sister Salvina. And Waalia himself was surprised to find that his love was so fine, tender and strong a thing. Even Galla Placidia's associates in the web of intrigue she was spinning could not tell whether or no she loved the soldier. Her eunuch Chrysogonus was disturbed. He feared the feminine weakness which becomes intoxicated with the fragrance of roses, the sound of wind and sea, the enervating heat of the sun, or the sudden outbreak of violence of a man's passion. But, unexpectedly, came news that in the camp at Patavium the legions had mutinied. Cowardly Honorius had fled at once, but Waalia told the princess that Stilicho would be in Ravenna within two or three days, to put down the revolt. "Then," said he, "is the time to have him killed, for you have made me see that his death is necessary to the safety of the divine emperor!" But that same day, when his love drove him to some yearning hints, she said: "I am mistress neither of my body nor of my life, for I am an emperor's daughter. I often wish I had been some little plebeian girl . . ." She said this with a candid and innocent virgin's smile. And then she lowered her head and whispered: "Come to-night to the gate of the imperial palace, in the gardens, near the women's quarters! A slave will let you in at dusk!" Mad with joy, Waalia saw her move on through the gardens with her splendid train.

And that night Galla Placidia did meet him, and Waalia poured out his passion. And the Princess, in spite of the cold and vague smile with which she listened, even began to catch fire when he covered her hand with kisses. But when Waalia, trembling, his eyes tortured, his face glowing, stretched out his arms to take her, Galla Placidia regained her self-possession. The moment she felt his ardent sigh pass the length of her body along her robe of thin silk, she was once more the princess. She pushed away his face with the flat palms of her hands, and in pretended confusion, bade him leave her. Then he asked her to prove his love, to bid him do something, anything so that he might show it. And she asked Stilicho's death. "Would you kill him?" she asked. "To gain you I would slay Honorius himself among his soldiers and eunuchs and put his diadem around your forehead," he answered. And then he leaped forward and brutally seized Galla Placidia in his arms, while his lips sought hers. This was the moment for which she had waited.

Her cry rang out. "Chrysogonus! . . . help! . . ."

Suddenly turning on Waalia, Galla Placidia, as she sat on her couch and tried to arrange her disordered hair, cried in her rage. "You vile soldier, you vile barbarian, you slave! Did you think I am a courtesan?" And Waalia, seeing he had been duped, that all she had wanted was to use and fling him aside, answered with a pride and haughtiness equal to her own: "And you, did you think I am an assassin, like your Byzantine eunuchs?"

But Chrysogonus, who had been on the alert, had alarmed the palace. Soldiers were hurrying up. Waalia drew his sword and turned to her: "Galla Placidia," he said, "I still want you, to punish you, and therefore I shall yet make you mine, like a slave, though I have to set the Roman empire ablaze to do so!" Then he escaped through a window.

Events now crowded on each other. Stilicho came to Ravenna, was received with honeyed words and flatteries and foully murdered. And when Waalia reached Rome, he found his sister Salvina lying in her blood in their little home. It was the vengeance of Placidia, who had sent Chrysogonus and some hired assassins to do the bloody deed. Waalia rode post-haste to Alaric, King of the Goths, and the latter was persuaded to attack this Rome which, like a fruit overripe, was ready to fall into his hands. He laid siege to the imperial city. But Galla Placidia had returned to Rome. While Alaric and Honorius exchanged letters that came to nothing, she had to watch the Goths put up a senator, Attalus, and make him a shadow-emperor—to rule for them. She only smiled, and set about to making Ataulf, Alaric's brother, fall madly in love with her. He represented Alaric and was in and out of Rome often. And when Waalia told Ataulf that she was vile, with a courtesan's soul, and the murderer of his little sister, Ataulf drew his sword, and the two chiefs were separated with difficulty. And Galla Placidia continued to intrigue. She pretended to be on the point of yielding to Ataulf as she had been to Waalia. She so maneuvered that Alaric made his triumphal entry into the city as a professed Christian. He wished to avoid bloodshed. Alaric gave great games at the Coliseum. Then, as he had arranged with the Princess, Ataulf, when the Gothic soldiers and the Roman people had gathered for the games, struck a blow at Waalia. He induced his brother to bid the many who under Waalia's leadership cried that Rome should be sacked to disarm and retire. At once a bloody battle began. But Waalia's men, among whom were many Franks, Goths and Herculians, held their own in the first struggle against the Goths. Ataulf was wounded. And in the silence which fell, while more Gothic soldiers were brought up, Waalia turned to Alaric and from his place on the blood-stained arena sands cried:

"Are you content, Alaric? The Christian priests to baptize you can now pour our blood over your brow instead of water. . . . Once it was different. Once you were another. Your name inspired terror from the sea to the Danube and the Carpathians. To-day which of your enemies fears you? What will your young sons say when they know you have sacrificed the best of your soldiers for the amusement of a people who cheer us as though we were vile gladiators? Shame on you! Shame on your people! Shame on your sons!"

His words were the echo of Alaric's own thoughts. "By the Christ and my own ancestors," he said, stretching out his hand from the great imperial box, "you are right! Let this battle end. Retire to your tents and go in peace. You have done enough for your glory to-day, Waalia!" And the struggle was over, and the princess' plan to have Waalia destroyed had failed. The Emperor Attalus reigned in Rome, beneath the wing of the Goths, outside the city. And Galla Placidia had led Ataulf to the point where he was ready to murder his brother Alaric. Waalia had retired to the Apennines, but when he heard that Alaric had broken with the treacherous Romans and was again besieging Rome, he hurried to the Gothic camp. And Galla Placidia began to tremble when, in Rome itself, while the Barbarians camped without, the slaves, and workingmen rose in revolt, and their bloody assaults weakened the few faithful legions which guarded the palace of Septimus Severus on the Aventine hill. And one night, the slaves opened the gates and let in the savage hordes of Alaric's soldiery. This time Rome was to be put to the sack. But we will pass by the scenes of terror, of murder, violation and madness, to follow Waalia. The Goths did not reach the Palace of Septimus Severus during the night. At dawn Galla Placidia, in her chamber, heard a sword strike against the porphery pavement of the entrance to the women's wing of the palace. It must be Ataulf, thought she. He was the only one among the Barbarians who knew this passage to the women's wing. He had come to save her from violence. He would defend her with his sword. Twice, boldly, she called his name, "Ataulf, Ataulf!"

Doors clanged. A warrior suddenly appeared under the Corinthian doorway. He wore the dyed purple furs and the open bronze helmet with aurochs' horns of a Gothic chief. His eyes pierced the shadows. It was Waalia. Galla Placidia shivered, and suppressed a cry of despair. She had thought him dead and gone, and there he stood as savagely handsome as ever, though his hard face was crossed with scars, black with smoke and reddened by flames. She was afraid. And standing on the threshold, drawing in the air fragrant with perfumes, he said in a terrible voice:

"So here you are, Galla Placidia, here you are at last!" And then he laughed. He had extorted the name of the palace from a slave. He had wandered long after finding it, through its vast halls. But now he had reached his goal. He recalled all the wretchedness, the disdains, the outrages, Galla Placidia had made him suffer. He recalled the foul murder of little Salvina. And his hour of revenge seemed to him the sweetest in his life. So he laughed in a savage way, while the torch he held in his hand dripped drops of flaming resin on the mosaic floor.

Then he let his arms and his helmet fall crashing to the floor. His arms crossed, he enjoyed Galla Placidia's terror, the fear he inspired. He said:

"Greetings to you, greetings, Galla Placidia! Greetings, beautiful empress! . . . Soul of Rome—is not that what they used to call you?—here I am! I promised you in Ravenna, in the little room filled with fragrant odors where you lured me to deceive and humiliate me, and to hand me over to your butchers, that we should meet again! I promised you I would be avenged! I promised you that I would take you as one takes a painted and mitred courtesan amid the clamor of conquest! I keep my promise!"

He went on:

"Do you remember Ravenna? Perhaps not, the "Soul of Rome," as the people used to cry when you swept by in your litter through the streets, is so lying and so forgetful. But I see again the great gardens, facing the Adriatic. I see the palace porticoes strewn with their golden sand, the statues and the fountains playing in the marble peristyles. I see the great dining-rooms where we feasted and drank. I see the vast halls wainscoted with gold. I see the young Emperor's poultry-yard, he presented me to you amid the crowd of courtiers, eunuchs and soldiers. . . . And I see you again . . . I hear the vile voices of your fellow-plotters, Olympius and Heraclianus, Stilicho's murderers. I listened to them because I loved you, Galla Placidia, and you wanted me to do so. Cursed hours! I blush when I think of them! You were laughing up your sleeve at me. You *acted* love with the cunning of a virgin and a courtesan combined. You prepared the traps into which I fell. Often since then, have I thought that my madness caused Stilicho's death as much as your treachery. The destinies of the Roman empire have been tangled with the fate of an obscure centurion of Gothic birth. But . . . the past is past! You are in my power. We are in conquered Rome, not in Ravenna, puppets in the hands of vile courtiers. Rome is dying at last, after its many crimes against men and the gods! . . ." Again Waalia laughed. And then Galla Placidia, forgetting her haughtiness, her dignity, her pride as an emperor's sister, lowered herself to plead for mercy.

"Have mercy, have mercy, Waalia! I was led astray by the advice of the eunuchs! I was only a girl of eighteen, little more than a child! I regret the past! Waalia! Oh, have mercy on me!"

She kneeled before him and wept. But Waalia thought of his little sister Salvina, lying dead and outraged by the assassins Galla Placidia had sent, in their little home in the Transtiber Quarter. And his heart hardened.

"Did you show mercy to my sister Salvina, a blameless child who had never harmed a soul? Ha, I recognized your murderous hand that evening when I found her dead in the little Roman home of which I had told you, when you seemed interested in the little details of my life! Her fate shall be your fate!" He leaped toward Galla Placidia, and seized her brutally by the wrists, while the haughty patrician girl uttered a loud cry of terror. "You shall be mine!" he cried as he lifted her and carried her toward the adjoining room. And . . . Galla Placidia, the "Soul of Rome," the sister of the Emperor Honorius, had to submit to Barbarian outrage. . . .

Suddenly a tremendous shock was heard. Lightning had struck the statue of the satyr Marsyas in the Forum. The palace of Domitius Severus trembled to its foundations. Waalia, his revenge and hatred satisfied, turned to the emperor's sister: "Galla Placidia," he said, as though he were giving an order to a slave, "Pour me some wine in one of those golden cups. I am thirsty!" And like a slave Galla Placidia rose submissively choking down a sob. "Hurry, slave!" Waalia, repeated, with growing anger. "Pour wine for Waalia your master! . . . Pour, Galla Placidia, pour! . . ." He pointed to the golden cups on the ebony sideboard and stamped his foot.

Galla Placidia trembled, and now her own hatred leaped into flame. For her eye had lit on one cup, of gold and enamel steeped in poisons by the Byzantine eunuchs. She seized it, filled it with wine and held it out with a trembling hand to Waalia. He mocked her:

"You will have to do a slave's work better if you think to escape the whip," he said. "Think of your own slaves!" He raised the cup to his lips and with a wild laugh cried: "To the destruction of Rome! To the end of the empire! To Barbarian glory!"

But as the wine ran down his throat, the golden cup slipped from his hand. He felt the poison he had drunk burning his entrails. He straightened up, pressed his giant fists against his chest as though to strangle the pain within him, tried to resist death. In vain. With a dull crash he fell to the floor. His body shook with a few spasms. Twice he tried to rise, and then all passed from his consciousness and his features grew cold in death.

A few feet away, Galla Placidia, asked ardently: "Tell me, tell me what is the matter with you, Oh, Waalia, my master?" And when she felt sure he was dead, she uttered a great cry of joy:

"To Barbarian glory!" she cried scornfully, while with one foot on the Goth's corpse, unclothed and triumphant, she raised another cup—not a poisoned one—to the Roman skies in triumph.

Galla Placidia escaped from the palace with her faithful eunuch. Good fortune threw her into Ataulf hands, and when the Goths, with a tremendous train of baggage-carts laden with the spoils of Rome marched away, she was carried in one of them. Alaric, the Gothic king died of a mysterious disease not long after. Did Ataulf poison him as he and Galla Placidia once had planned? Who knows? But later, when the Goths had definitely established themselves in Gaul (France), the wedding of Ataulf and Galla Placidia was splendidly celebrated in the city of Narbonne, the capital of the new kingdom. Olympiodorus, a historian who lived at the time has told us of it:

"A hall was decorated in the Roman manner in the house of Ingenuus, one of the leading citizens of the town. The place of honor was reserved for Galla Placidia, while Ataulf, in a Roman toga, sat beside her. Fifty handsome youths clad in silk, slaves he had given her, then advanced, each holding two cups in his hands, one full of gold pieces, the other of jewels. They were part of the spoils that the Goths had taken from Rome. And Priscus Attalus—*who had been a Roman emperor for a brief time,* was glad to act as a minstrel, and sing a wedding hymn composed in their honor."

Rome never recovered from Alaric's sack. Toward the middle of the fifth century the Vandals completed her destruction. A few hastily murdered emperors followed, and the last Roman Emeperor of the West was Augustulus, which means "little Augustus," as he was contemptuously called. He was lucky enough to have the bloodstained Roman purple taken from him, and to be allowed to retire to private life as an ordinary individual. He was given an income of six thousand gold pieces a year, and the comfortable castle of Lucullus, in Campania, in which to live. While the Greek Emperor of the West, Zeno, took over the "title" of Roman emperor, Odoacar, the Barbarian chief, who had "put out" Augustulus, really governed Italy under the title of "Patrician."

What Came Out of the Melting Pot. Out of the mixture of races, of civilizations, creeds and customs, Greek, Roman, Oriental, Christian and Barbarian, Italy too, became one of the Barbarian kingdoms, but with a difference. The Christian popes of Rome grew more and more powerful. They built up a *Church empire* which took the place of the Roman empire. And in the centuries that follow the triple-crowned successors of Augustus (and of Nero and Caracalla, at times), though they carried on the work of civilization, also tried to rule the world. With the pomp and splendor of great worldly monarchs, the popes dictated the law to Christianity. In splendid robes, covered with jewels, the proud successors of the humble barefoot Galilean fisherman, the Apostle Peter, dispensed crowns and kingdoms to obedient princes and laid the curse of excommunication on those who did not obey.

CHAPTER XIV

HUMAN DOCUMENTS OF BYZANTIUM

(The Greek Empire)

THOUGH the Roman empire, the empire of the *West,* had ended with Augustulus, the "Greek" empire, the empire of the *East,* whose capital was Byzantium (as Constantinople and the Asian lands of the Greek empire were called in the Middle Ages), survived. Established by Constantine the Great, a Christian ruler (330 A. D.) it lasted till it was taken by the Turks in 1453 A. D. It inherited the civilization of ancient Rome. It was greatest under Justinian, the husband of the infamous Theodora, and for nearly a thousand years was Western civilization's *last frontier* against Asiatic barbarism.

The Byzantine Soul. The Byzantines taught the Barbarian world law, government and administration. It handed on the *imperial* ideal—which produced the medieval "Holy Roman Empire" of the Teuton kings—to Charlemagne, the first medieval emperor. But it was a base, corrupt and abject soul for all that. The Byzantine Greeks on the whole, were a cowardly, treacherous and fanatic race. Their rulers were cruel tyrants. And yet this weak race, by diplomatic intrigue, the use of hardy hired soldiers, Bulgarians, Northmen, Isaurians, Armenians and others, and the secret of fighting with liquid fire, long staved off its fall. The tales which followed gave us respectively three sides of Byzantine character. First, a look into the dark and evil spirit which ruled Justinian's court, the empress-prostitute Theodora, and of court life. Secondly, the spirit of the the terrible religious fanaticism which, for the shade of meaning expressed by omitting an *i* in a single word, would make a woman turn on her lover and without hesitation have him murdered.

THE ROSE OF DEATH

Aistulf, the handsome young Gothic chief, had climbed to the top of the roof of the well in his friend Agothecles' garden, the better to watch the Empress Theodora, the wife of the Emperor Justinian, pass on her way to St. Sophia's church. He had seen the detachments of Scholarians and of the Vangarian Bodyguards pass. He had seen the Empress' women pass, and now the imperial baldachin, the canopy carried above the Empress' head, came swaying along. Before it walked eight little maids of patrician blood, carrying flowers, while eight others rang little silver bells they had in their hands. After them came boy flute-players, dressed in sky-blue. The baldachin, made of pure silver, was topped by a great crown of flowers. Before it chamberlains spread broad strips of purple cloth, taking them up as soon as the Empress had passed. The chair of state in which she was carried had come from the treasure of Gelimer, the Vandal King of Carthage, and with him had been captured by the great general Belisarius. The jewels with which it was covered shot rainbow gleams in the sun. Theodora sat upright, her two arms resting on the arms of the chair, and nodded her diademed head in greeting on every side. For a moment it seemed to Agathon that she glanced at the figure of his Gothic friend, up on the well-top, and then the canopy had passed. After it mounted life guards followed with swords drawn. "Look out, there, my fine guardsman, your horse's hoof hurts as much as though it were not gilded!" Agathon called out suddenly. And then turning to his friend, who had climbed down from his perch, he added: "What follows is of interest only to the mob!"

He pointed to a slim, brown man who, at the tail-end of the procession, took one handful after another of silver pennies out of a chest on the back of a gentle little white horse, and flung them right and left to the multitude. And as Aistulf, still absorbed by visions of imperial beauty he had that moment seen pass, kept his place for a moment, the man who was flinging out the silver pennies came abreast of him. As he did so, he suddenly stretched out his hand above the hands of the people, smiled and handed Aistulf a rose. The Goth gazed with perplexity. Never had he seen a rose so beautiful. It was dark red in color, almost black, like caked blood. "Give this rose to one of the palace watchmen at the South Gate to-day, at the tenth hour, and it will make your fortune!" whispered the man.

As he sat down, a few moments later, at his friend Agathon's hospitable table, one of the latter's servant boys brought in the rose, which Aistulf had carelessly let drop, in a tall Egyptian vase of glimmering glass, and set it beside him. Agathon laughed. "Why," he cried, "the little rascal has a better idea of the value of the flower than you have. Did you not know that the man who gave it to you was one of Theodora's messengers?"

"A messenger of Theodora . . . to me?" stammered Aistulf, paling to the lips. "Long before she became Justinian's wife," said Agathon. "Theodora lived with a friend of mine in a charming villa here in Byzantium. Roses like this one grow only in that villa garden, nowhere else in the city. When some youth takes the Empress' fancy she sends him one of these roses. So you have the good luck to be expected in the palace to-day. "But"—Agathon continued slowly—"though the rose opens every entrance to the palace, I do not know that it opens any exit. It is said that the fish and the eels of the Bosphorus see things we do not see."

"And what do they see?" asked Aistulf. "The eels and the fishes see blood-stained sacks whose mouths have been sewn up," answered Agathon. But Aistulf shook his head and smiled. That evening his steps led him gradually and half unconsciously to the South Gate of the palace. A troop of giant Herculian mercenaries was just entering, and he entered with them. In the great hall he offered the rose to a man who seemed on guard at a door with an expectant look. But the Herculian only laughed, and flung his rose on the ground. "Do you take me for a girl?" He·asked. Aistulf struck the man in the face with his fist, and in a moment the place was in an uproar. Aistulf had almost killed a fat eunuch, whose duty it was to see that no noise disturbed the Emperor, when a tremendous voice asked: "What's going on here?" and Clothaire, the commander of the body-guard, pushed his way through the crowd of soldiers, ushers, eunuchs and litter-bearers. He helped Aistulf to rise, and commenced to question him. But the latter only pointed to his rose, which had lost half its petals. And Clothaire, who knew the Empress, understood. "How did the donkey happen to stray in here?" he muttered. Then, turning suddenly to those who crowded around, he shouted, "Off with you!" And as all fled he drew a small earthen vessel from his girdle and put it to Aistulf's lips. Aistulf drank thirstily.

"What under the sun possessed you to come galloping up here with your bit of thistle?" he asked. "This gate leads to the Emperor and not—not where you wish to go." He led Aistulf to a narrow passage and called to a man who came forward to meet them: "Here you, chamberlain, this donkey who belongs over on your side! He has nearly been killed by my guards. Better take a look at the thing he carries!" The chamberlain gave a glance at the rose, and bowed for Aistulf to follow him. They passed through many chambers, some dark, some illuminated. They passed through gardens where their steps crunched pebbled ways, and the fragrance of opening blossoms rose gratefully to Aistulf's nostrils. Everywhere they passed hurrying boys, aproned slave-girls, eunuchs with yellow bonnets, watchman, chamberlains, negroes, and all grinned when they caught sight of Aistulf and his rose. But he did not see them. At last he heard the rustle of silken robes. Eyes looked at his from behind fans glittering with jewels. And on he was led to a door.

He found himself in a grotto of what seemed to be rosy, shimmering quartz. Costly cushions were heaped in a corner, half concealed by the splashing jets of a fountain whose drops glittered in all the colors of the rainbow as they caught the light. And then Aistulf caught sight of Theodora. As she yielded herself to his arms he forgot all else. . . .

"It is time for you to go," said Theodora, at last. She clapped her hands and Aistulf, trembling, his whole heart on his lips, cried: "Will I see you again?" As he spoke the small brown man of the procession, the bearer of the rose, stood before them. He crossed his hands over his breast and bowed with a smile. And Aistulf felt ashamed in the presence of this man who knew his secret. He would liked to have killed him. Already, since Theodora did not reply, he had bowed his head to pass through the door which the brown man had pointed out to him, when Theodora's voice, in a gentle whisper breathed one word—"Aistulf!" And "Come again tomorrow!" she said, as he turned around to her. But at that very moment he turned, a negro slave's long sharp knife was driven home in his back, its point coming out of his chest. Aistulf fell forward on his face with a slight gurgling sound. The slave, straddling his corpse, leaned over and wiped the blade of his dagger on the youth's long blond hair. And a drop of blood fell on a dark-red rose petal at its feet, a petal of the rose that had led Aistulf into the arms of Theodora—and of death.

THE DIFFERENCE OF AN "I"

In the imperial box, the great ladies of Byzantium were chatting as they watched the races. It was a day of terrible heat, and the great awning spread above the box did not protect them from the humidity. Even on the face of the Empress Theodora, wife of His Serene Majesty, the Emperor Romanus Lecapenus, beads of perspiration showed beneath the embroidered stuff of the diadem, and ran down beneath the bunches of pearls which hid her ears. Behind her, the court ladies chatted:

"How well the eunuchs look in their new robes!"

"It is said that the imperial secretary has been carried to the skies by the angel host, to take his place among the blessed spirits." Then, in a lower tone of voice: "He is at Proti! The monks are watching him, and his eyes have been put out!"

"What are these Russian Varangians like, who came last week?"

"Brute Barbarians! Their chief, when he was threatened with the imperial displeasure of Byzantine (ships were plundered off their coasts), put his hand to his nose with an insulting gesture. He may yet pay dearly for that insult."

At this point a commotion took place in the Hippodrome. One of the Barbarian warriors of the envoy's band had risen from his place and was shaking his fist at a charioteer. The daughter of a provincial governor, newly come to Court, was delighted to explain what it was all about. She knew the tongue of these Barbarians, the Russians, and laughed as she translated what their warrior said:

"He is quarreling with one of the Blue party, because he struck a comrade in the back. Think of it! He is calling him all sorts of names. What madness, to take the part of some low wretch who means nothing to any one. He says, 'You have not a spark of honor?'"

"What does that word 'honor' mean?" asked one of the other ladies.

"Well, we have no word that expresses its meaning exactly," replied the governor's daughter. But listen. He is making a speech: This is what he is saying:

"You do not know me! I am Sviatoslav, the son of Iaroslav. I dare you to stand up to me face to face. I'll let you have a sword and I'll take a stick. I fear no one. When I walk through the woods, the birds in the clouds tremble! All of you are cowards. You shoot flame from a distance through tubes, but I despise you, you and your comrades, your soldiers and your sailors, your counts and your dukes, and. . ." Suddenly the governor's daughter stopped, and her face grew very red. "Why do you stop? He is keeping right on!" said those about her. "And now he is turning toward The Imperial Omnipotence, toward the Emperor Romanus himself! "I can no longer understand what he is saying," stammered the girl, in great confusion. But while the tall, handsome blond Barbarian continued his violent harangue, his eyes afire with rage, the lovely Epiphania, the wife of the commander of the legion of the Imperial guards, known as the "Scholarian," watched him with a strange smile.

On his way back to the palace where the Russian ambassadors were lodged, Sviatoslav, the son of Iaroslav, was in a good humor again. After all, the Blue was not such a bad fellow. His comrades had excused him, and they had settled their differences over a pot of wine. But as he went along the street, an old woman plucked his sleeve. "Off with you, old witch!" he cried. "I know all about it. Some one has sent for me. But I'll not go with you!"

"But this is a very great lady, Illustrious One, a very beautiful lady!"

"Off with you to your tavern, and tell whoever sent you to find some other victim!"

"We do not live in a tavern, but in a great palace," said the hag. "Are you afraid to follow me?"

"Certainly! Swords—as many as you like! But not dagger-blows in the back—as they are the fashion in your city. Off with you! But—wait a bit.... Describe this marvel who wants to see me!"

While the Byzantine woman murmured to him in a low tone of

voice, he listened, then laughed briefly. Finally he said: "You have not mentioned her husband."

"He is an army officer of high standing. He is a friend of His Imperial Majesty. He is the Lord Christodoulus, who commands the Scholarians."

"Some eunuch, I suppose, one of those who put on your Emperor's red shoes for him?"

"No, he is a hero. Last year he killed four Russians with his own hand."

"That is not true," answered the other, half drawing his sword, which flashed against the leather of its sheath. But the old woman did not budge.

Suddenly calm, Sviatoslav said with an account in which eagerness, submission and irony were strangely mingled:

"Will I have a chance to meet this braggard?"

"Not to-day, but you will not regret his absence."

"Very well, then. I will meet you this evening, before the Church of St. Irene." The old woman, when he appeared a few hours later, led him through various streets. Suddenly, in a windowless stretch of wall, a door opened. They entered and it closed behind them.

"Where are we, dog of Tsarigrad?" murmured Sviatoslav. But the hag had disappeared. The Barbarian found himself in a great hall. In the dim moonlight he could see that it was hung with rich and heavy stuffs, and that a soldier must have been there a few hours before. For on the floor lay a handsome dagger. Then he recalled something the old hag had said. The Master of the Scholarians had gathered a picked body of his horsemen, and had ridden off to the East wall with them. No one knew why. As he stood there one of the shadows along the wall moved. A kind of phantom approached the young man. He could only make out a long, trailing robe, and smell a wave of exquisite fragrance which came to his nostrils. The figure motioned him to be silent and to follow, which he did.

They passed along the gallery which gave on gardens where dogs howled at the moon, then through a narrow corridor to the right, and finally the adventurer's foot touched the first step of a flight of stairs. He stepped up two steps, then stopped. The stones seemed hollow! Were they the entrance to some subterranean prison? Strange tales were told in Constantinople of underground prisons where captives were kept without nourishment, in the icy mud, eaten up by vermin, and chained in positions of torture till they brayed like asses. Sviatoslav's lips tightened, and he struck the steps with his sword. The dull echo reassured him, and in a few minutes more he had stepped into a room. Epiphania—for it was she who had been his guide—dropped her long trailing mantle and looked at him with a smile. And Sviatoslav saw that she was very beautiful.....

Sviatoslav came more than once to Epiphania's palace. They were happy in their love, at last. And, one morning Epiphania, pointing to the cross on his chest, said: "How glad I am to think that you are of my faith! My last scruples disappeared yesterday morning when I saw the cross you wore."

"Ah, yes! It was a gift from a Greek."

"A Byzantine?"

"No, he was a monk from Trapezunt. He came to my village on the Dneiper at the time when the salmon run. First, when he talked, I yawned like the rest. But in time his words moved me. I understood that your God must be greater than our Peroun, for your emperor, though he is a coward, is more powerful than our chief. So I went into the water, accepted baptism, and this jewel, and now take the communion before I enter battle. Only my comrades, who have remained pagans, mock me and pretend that I worship a dead man, because Jesus was laid in the sepulchre. I already have slain three warriors because of this. Yet they keep on laughing. Askold, especially, the old chief. He hates me because years ago he and my father fell out about a bear during a hunt. The dog of an idolater! But they made him the head of the embassy, and I must leave with him tomorrow."

"And you will leave me?"

"I have no other choice!"

"Stay! Do you remember how Askold insulted the Emperor when you were presented at Court? The insult was not forgotten. The Emperor has decided that his injured majesty must be avenged. Two strong detachments of Scholarians have been sent out. One, headed by Christodoulos, is waiting in ambush on the road to Adrianople. The other stationed further East. There are no other roads your embassy can take. The Scholarian companies are numerous and disciplined. The man you hate will fall into their hands, and not survive the night!"

Sviatoslav hesitated. Then, slowly, to convince himself, he said: "The plot is well-laid. Askold will take the eastern road.... He will perish in the ambuscade.... All the better!...." But suddenly he gave a great cry: "Impossible! Dmitri, of my own village, is one of his escort. He is a lad who saved my life. Give me my sword, I must give the alarm!"

"You will die!"

"Maybe."

"You will compromise me."

"Dmitri comes from my own village."

Epiphania knew that one cannot reason with a madman or with a
I

simple soul—obsessed by one idea. She struck a silver bell of Persian workmanship and said to the old woman who raised the curtain: "Run quickly and fetch me Paracletos, the scribe!"

A youth of nineteen, with pale cheeks and a bulbous nose came in with his parchment roll, and fell on his knees before his mistress, while he squinted at the Slavonian.

"My friend," said Epiphania, "this stranger will often come to the palace of Christodoulos. You are both nearly of an age. You must be friends and drink as comrades." A flash of rage crossed the young Byzantine's face. But he did not disobey his mistress' command. He drank, as did Sviatoslav. Then Epiphania said: "You are a clever lad and can imitate any handwriting. Write an order addressed to the captain of the Scholarians in ambush on the eastern road. They are to abandon their post, and rejoin Christodoulos' troop, on the road to Adrianople."

"I will obey, Excelentissima.... and, what signature?"

"Sign the name of the Master Christodoulos."

Leaping up, the boy let his writing materials fall to the ground.

"Never," he cried. "It is a crime! It means death! Have mercy, my body is weak and I fear the tortures!"

Epiphania smiled: "Then do not resist. You may as well know that the draught you drank was a magic philtre. If I command, Astoreth will rend your vitals as though with tears of molten copper, and you would tear out your entrails to relieve yourself."

The superstitious scribe's boy face grew convulsed with terror.

"Calm yourself," said his mistress. "Your hand must not tremble. Use the proper forms and—you are to carry the message yourself! I expect you to be intelligent, discreet and diligent. If you fail you will be punished by the powers I shall release within yourself."

The poor wretch withdrew, terrified, taking his papyrus roll with him. Sviatoslav laughed loudly. And Epiphania said: "You will rouse the servants!" She added: "Besides, the hour of parting is near. You yourself wish it. So return to the frozen north with your hateful master, Askold!"

But now Sviatoslav, his heart filled with gratitude since his honor was assured by Dmitri's salvation, had no thought of going. "No, no," he murmured, "I will stay! I have not the heart to leave you here in Tsarigrad all alone, since you have saved Dmitri's life!" Sure of her victory, Epiphania said very gently: "Come back tomorrow evening at twilight. Perhaps there will be news then in the city of the emperors."

"Greeting, old sheep!" he cried to Epiphania's confidant, the following evening. "But . . . the curtains are all raised. Are you not afraid we may be seen?" The old woman grinned. "Lord Sviatoslav, such precautions are no longer necessary," she answered.

A Nubian slave whom they met, cast herself at the Slavonian's feet as he passed. And behind the curtain of the Saracen doorway to her room Epiphania embraced him. And then he saw that the room was filled with a profusion of coffers and chests, from which had been taken a number of robes, tunics and vestments, all black or purple. "But why all the clothes?" he cried gaily. "And your collar?" he added, "what had become of it?"

"His Imperial Majesty severely blamed the Master Christodoulos' stupid blunder. The counter-order carried by Paracletos left the eastern road open and—the Barbarians escaped. Christodoulos, being without excuse, was at once condemned to death for treason to the state. My friend, I am a widow. More and more am I aware now that the heavenly powers approve of my weakness for you. For they favor my plans. In a few months you shall have the command of the Scholarian legion, and shall unite yourself to me by a legitimate marriage.

"For a time you will have to retire to a country villa I have in Asia, near Chalcedon. I will give you intelligent servants. They will hide you and change your appearance. Let your hair grow, and shorten your long moustachios and your scalp-lock. You must lose your tanned skin, your Barbarian awkwardness, and your harsh accent. When you return to the Emperor's Court, I shall be the only one who possibly could recognize you. And meanwhile, I will have smoothed the way for you. My relatives are powerful, very powerful, and the patriarch himself is my confessor. Besides, your bravery, your noble manner, and your military experience are in your favor. With my treasures, and they are immense, you shall hire a good number of the folk of your villages as fighting-men. The Emperor, who plans to make war on the Emir of Alappo and the Bulgarians, will be glad to see them, and the Russian Vangarians and their chief will be well rewarded."

Sviatoslav listened as though in a dream.

"But why stop at Master of a Vangarian legion?" Epiphania went on. Some moonless night, by the grave of God, a slave whom we have bought leaves a door unlocked. A gag is clapped on an imperial mouth, a dagger-thrust is delivered, and a sack dropped in the Propontus.—That is how emperors are made—and unmade!"

Putting her hand in a casket she drew out a pearl diadem:

"Put it on! It becomes you, Barbarian. Be haughty! Stand erect! Would you be able in the imperial gallery, above the Hippodrome, standing among the great officers of the crown, to put out your hand and bless the Roman people? Try it!"

She took his right hand and stretching it out, made it trace the form of the cross in the proper way, while both, together, said:

"In the name of the Father, in the name of the Son...."

The Sviatoslav interrupted her. He wanted to change the formula, and add a word of his very own.

"The Son, Christ, is it not....? The monk often called on His name, but he always added another word. Christ!.... Christ!.... I cannot recall it. Ah, Christ . . . Homo . . . Homo*i*ousian!"*

But Epiphania, no sooner had he uttered the word, with a cry of horror, shrank back from him against the wall. There she stood, her arms out-flung as though crucified against the brocade tapestry.

"Homo*i*ousian? Unfortunate wretch! Your apostle was a heretic! You are blinded by false doctrines! Alas, the heavenly protection I thought rested on us was a snare of Satan! We are marching straight to the abyss with the evil one for a guide!"

"Homo*i*ousian . . . "

"Homoöusian! That is what you must say, my friend! The three persons of the Trinity are not only *alike* in their nature. All three possess the same nature. The Redeemer, just like the Creator, must be honored with the ineffable title of Homoöusian!

"Homoiousian! *But that is just what I said!* cried Sviatoslav. "Woe, woe on us!" Epiphania continued. "You are a heretic! I would rather have seen you a heathen, like Askold. You are a rebel, a traitor to the faith, an accursed and corrupted child of the infamous Arius!"

"Do not insult that worthy man, whom the good monk I knew so greatly admired, and who was formerly persecuted by the wicked!" said her lover.

"Enough, Sviatoslav!" Epiphania resumed. "Tomorrow.... No, this very minute, we must hurry to the patriarch. He will receive your confession, impose penances on you! You shall kiss his feet, and in a penitential robe you shall pray heaven to forgive us...."

"What a stupid jest, Epiphania," said Sviatoslav. "I cannot be bothered with your changing words and phrases. First you offer me your hand, with an advantageous position, and even the empire itself. Then you change your mind, scold me and treat me like a slave! What, kneel in a cell, put on a hempen shirt, drink water, pray and kiss a priest's slipper? Let others do it! Hunt up your scribe for such work! As for me, I shall return to the Dnieper!"

Again the Byzantine found herself opposed by the obstinacy of a simple soul. She made no further attempt to move him. She only

* It was the difference of the *one little* letter "i" in the word expressing the Saviour's nature which men's religious fanaticism, while "Arianism" was a live issue, caused untold murder, torture, hatred, blood-shed, death and suffering. The followers of Arius, called the Saviour Homo*i*ousian "of like substance as the Father." The orthodox Niceans said: Homoöusian, "of the same substance as the Father." Oceans of Christian blood, rivers of Christian tears flowed because of one letter's difference in a word.

asked him when he meant to leave Constantinople, and when he answered the following day at dawn, she said: "You stay at the Archangel Tavern, do you not? And it has no garden which runs down to the sea?" "No," said Sviatoslav, "it lies in the midst of other streets." A thousand conflicting emotions struggled in Epiphania's dark, treacherous and fanatic soul. Chief among them was her hatred for this miscreant who refused to understand and obey. And there was her own urgent need to make her peace with the church—if necessary by means of a bloody sacrifice, for the contamination of having loved—she shuddered again—*an Arian!* The two young people parted without another word.

Sviatoslav was slain the next morning—Epiphania had hastened to betray him to the Emperor Romanus' vengeance—in the courtyard of his inn. He was to have been brought to the palace of the Blachernae to be tortured, but he was not one of the sort who are taken alive in battle. And many dead Scholarians lay beside him when a sword-blade at last found the way to his heart. For a time his head, stuck on a pike, was to be seen near the imperial palace of Chalce. Then one day the pike, loosened by rain, bent forward and the head rolled to the ground. There a youth in a scribe's brown tunic seized it by a long blond lock, slapped its bloodied cheeks, and flung it into a nearby sewer opening.

Epiphania, it was rumored, became the mistress of the Emperor. She had many masses said for Christodoulos, but none for the Russian. Only, at the bottom of a small cedar chest, exquisitely perfumed, the Byzantine kept hidden, under an old mantle, an almost shapeless crucifix and some fragments of a sword-blade. Epiphania died suddenly, at an Easter service, while the Gospel according to St. John was being read. One chronicler has stated that she was on the point of marrying the Emperor Romanus Lecapenus when Theodora, his wife, finding it out, had her poisoned in a sacramental wafer. At least, having taken the communion, she died in a state of grace!

CHAPTER XV

THE Arabians remained a hidden people in their sandy deserts until the seventh century. Then they burst out and a raging tide of religious enthusiasm carried them out to convert the East to Islam, the faith of the camel-driver Prophet Mohammed, by the might of the sword. Their waves of fighting fanatics swept over Persia, Egypt, Syria, Palestine and Asia Minor, they flooded into India, swept over Spain and were dashed back in France by the Christian hosts under Charles Martel (732 A.D.). The faith of the Prophet in turn set fire to the Mongols and Turks. They left their Central Asian steppes late in the eleventh century and as the Arabs slackened in their fighting zeal these new converts—to Islam all races and colors are alike if only they believe in Allah and the Prophet—carried the Moslem standards into battle. And in the fifteenth century the Ottomans, a Turkish race, take Constantinople, the "city of Constantine," and change its name from Byzantium, as it was known when the capital of the Greek empire, to Istamboul or Stamboul.

The Spirit of Islam. Some phases of the spirit of Islam are developed in the stories which follow. Our first tale, whose time is shortly after Mohammed's death, gives us something of the feeling of the *swiftness* of the Mohammedan conquest. And it shows the *whole-hearted* way in which the followers of the Prophet made the convert—no matter *why* he became one—one of themselves. It also shows how a difference in religion may tragically affect two ordinary human lives. The tale is one of a fine, poetic nature whose weakness in the hands of an ambitious woman brings ruin. It reveals too, the *knightly* character of the Saracen, the Arab of the desert in the days of the conquest. The oriental, the Mohammedan, places woman on a low level. He claims she has no soul. But there always have been exceptions to this rule. Some Mohammedans have loved or love only *one* woman, just as some Christians have loved or love *many*. A *shiek* is an Arab tribal chieftain. But every *shiek* is not a "shiek"—always or invariably. There are sons of Connecticut, New York, and California who show that they deny woman a soul just like sons of the Sahara. The third points a moral which applies in any age and to men of any race or faith: that wealth does not necessarily mean happiness, and that gold cannot bribe death. In the fourth we have a tale which reveals the spirit of Islam at its best. It is the spirit of "no compromise." The Hindoo priests offer the Mohammedan sultan great sums to spare their idol. But he is fighting for a principle. It is his mission in life, so he thinks, to destroy idols, and establish the worship of *one* god. And—his sticking to his principles is rewarded by the discovery, in the idol, of far greater wealth than he would have gained by giving them up.

JONAS AND EUDOCEA

Damascus had fallen to the wild desert Arabs. The fanatic horsemen of Khaled and Abu Obedeih, the Arab generals, had forced a surrender. But the Greeks had fought bravely. They had been led by Thomas, a Greek noble—who had married the daughter of the Emperor Heraclius—and it was owing to his valor that the Christians of Damascus had obtained favorable terms. All those who wished to leave their houses and their pleasant gardens where the fountains played, could do so. They could take with them whatever they chose to carry away, and for three days the Moslems promised that they should not be pursued.

The caravan of the exiles gathered in a green meadow near the city. There camels and asses were laden with the silver plate, jewels and costly stuffs of the fugitives. And the brave Thomas, who led the hapless band, had a train of more than three hundred mules, laden with the wardrobe of the Emperor Heraclius, bale upon bale of costly silk and gold brocade. The exiles were mostly folk used to the soft life of palaces. Now, from pride, patriotism or religion, they were giving up their homes forever. But the Emperor's daughter, who dearly loved her husband, set the example of endurance to her own band of maidens and to the rest. Though tears came to many an eye as it turned back to look at the flowery banks of the river, and the green palm-trees that rose among Damascus' white roofs, the caravan pushed on bravely toward the mountains that lay in a blue haze beyond the desert they must cross.

Among those who had followed the wife of Thomas into exile was Eudocea. Eudocea had lost the love of her heart in a strange way. She loved a young nobleman of Damascus, named Jonas. But her parents would not hear of him and, in despair—it was during the siege—the two lovers planned to elope. Jonas, riding carefully out of the gate one night, and hoping to escape the Arab patrols, fell into their hands. He had only time to shout a word of warning to Eudocea, and see her turn her horse's head and flee back to the city, which she entered in safety.

Khaled, the stern Arab general, listened to Jonas' pitiful story.

But Khaled's business, as he saw it, was to make converts for his faith. The love adventures of young Greek noblemen, fortunate or otherwise, did not interest him. "Accept Islam," he cried, "and you shall have your bride when Damascus falls into our hands! Otherwise. . . ." He pointed to a giant negro who stood ready with a huge scimitar within his tent. Jonas was young. He waited to live. He wanted to clasp Eudocea in his arms. He accepted Islam. When the city was taken he hurried to Eudocea's convent—there she had shut herself up to become a nun, for she thought he had been put to death—and pleaded with her. But Eudocea, when she found out that Jonas had become a renegade, and had renounced his faith, shrank from him in horror. She at once joined the caravan of Thomas, and placed herself under the protection of his wife. And Khaled, to whom Jonas appealed, could do nothing. But Khaled regretted the agreement with the enemy. Knowing this, Jonas told him that, although the caravan of the Damascan fugitives had now been gone for three days, the time during which they were not to be pursued, he guaranteed it still could be taken. And he offered to lead Khaled through by secret short-cuts to the mountains where they might be caught.

Khaled's heart was filled with joy. He clapped Jonas on the back, called together four thousand horsemen, and set out. First they rode over the desert plains. It was easy to follow the route of the fugitives. The foot-prints of mules and camels, articles flung carelessly aside, and an occasional dead body, showed the road they had taken. At last their tracks led into the gorges of the Lebanon mountains, and there were lost. The Moslem horsemen began to grumble. They were weary and now they would never catch their victims. "Have patience," cried Jonas, for he was bound to find his Eudocea.

"They will be caught in the mountains. They cannot escape us now!" The Arabs rested only to pray. They rode along the towering mountain rims, where their horses' hoofs struck sparks from the flinty soil with every step. But they did not find the fleeing caravan. The horses cast their shoes, and battered their hoofs, so the men dismounted and led them along. The soles of their boots, shod with iron, broke from the leather uppers. Their clothes hung from them in tatters, and their food gave out. Even Khaled, who would suffer almost anything out of hatred for the infidels, began to lose courage. But Jonas showed him fresh tracks; the caravan must be near. Yet a bit of news gleaned from a farmer boy perplexed them.

The Emperor Heraclius feared that the fugitives, if they poured into Antioch, might alarm the people and lame the defense of that great city. So he had sent messengers to tell Thomas to march along the sea-shore toward Constantinople. And—only a single mountain lay between Khaled and the large armies Heraclius had sent against him. After a night of storm and stress, his scouts sought out Khaled in his tent at early dawn. Yielding to their pleas, he mounted his steed and rode with them to a nearby mountain top. There he looked down at the valley below his feet and gave a cry of joy.

The valley bottom was a long green meadow, dotted with flowers, through which ran a crystal—clear stream. Tents dotted the meadow, and its grass was bright with embroidered robes and silks spread out to dry in the sun. The people of the caravan were taking their ease. A few guards stood before the large tent which, Khaled thought, probably sheltered Thomas and his wife. But most of these poor Damascene exiles were stretched out in the cool grass by the river-bank, sleeping after the exertions of the last night of storm. Others were drinking their morning coffee. As for Jonas, who had joined Khaled, his eye looked for one only among all those gathered in the valley-ground. He did not see her.

Khaled arranged his horsemen in four squadrons. Then, when all was ready, he charged down on the unsuspecting Christians with the cry of "Allah and the Prophet!" Thomas, who marshalled the fighting-men of his band, flung himself into the thick of the battle, and did his duty as a brave man and a soldier, but Khaled, in a hand to hand fight, struck off his head with a scimitar, and with his death resistance ended. While the battle raged one division of the Arabs had gained the middle of the encampment to capture the women. They, poor souls, had gathered around Thomas' tent and under the leadership of his wife, fought off the Moslems like men. The Emperor's daughter was very beautiful. She rode a horse, like an Amazon, was dressed in splendid garments and wore a diadem of jewels. She fought so bravely, in fact, that she was near being slain by an Arab horseman. His captain, however, seized the man's arm, and Thomas' wife surrendered.

Poor Jonas! Was he a better Moslem than he had been a Christian? How can we tell when the veil of the centuries lies between our inquiring mind and the hot, love-sick heart which had betrayed! His love was a consuming fire. He had not hesitated to give up the delights of the Golden Sion for the chance of winning Eudocea. He would, no doubt, have resigned Mohammed's paradise quite as readily to have her smile on him again, to have her yield her lips as she had done at their stolen moonlight meetings in the shadows of Damascus' wall, while the Arabs camped outside them. His one thought, amid the carnage of battle had been Eudocea. He ran hastily among the overturned tents, he trampled the bodies of the slain, he burst through groups of fighters who gazed after him in astonishment. At last he found her. But in Damascus she had repulsed him with horror—her lover who had betrayed his Lord. (The fact that he had in his heart set her *above* the Lord and all the powers of heaven did not move her!) Now she saw in him only a monster. She pointed to the bodies of the dead and dying that littered the field. She swore she never would be his, and rising tried to flee. In vain Jonas struggled and pleaded with her. Only after a violent struggle could he force her to the ground and make her a prisoner. Then she offered no further resistance, but sat quietly on the grass beside him. Jonas thought she would relent. He renewed his passionate entreaties and used every argument a lover's ingenuity could devise to reconquer the heart he had lost. Eudocea listened with averted head, while slow tears gathered in her eyes and ran down her cheeks. And then, watching her chance, and before Jonas could stop her, she drew a dagger and thrust it into her breast. To his outbursts of grief, his Moslem comrades only answered: "It was written in the book of fate that this woman's leaf of life should flutter down from the Sidrah-tree at the moment it did. But Allah, though it was his will that you never should possess her, may have greater blessings in store for you." And Khaled, moved by his distress, made him a gift of the Emperor Heraclius' daughter. She should be his unless her father sent to beg her release. Then, with the loot of the Christian camp packed on mules and driven before them, the Arabs hastened to regain Damascus. On the second day of their return march a great dust-cloud made them think an army was moving against them. But it was merely the train of a venerable Greek bishop. He had come in the Emperor's name to ransom his daughter. Khaled returned her to the bishop without a ransom: "Take the girl," he cried. "I want her father, and all her father had. Never will I rest until not one foot of land is left him!"

Jonas was given his choice among the captive maidens to make up for his loss of Heraclius' daughter. But—be it told, the loss of Heraclius' daughter had been no loss! The evening when Khaled had first sent her to his tent, Jonas, who had known her well enough in happier days, bowed when two of Khaled's men led her in and left her standing before him. And when she raised white arms and tear-filled eyes in supplication he hastened to reassure her.

"You have nothing to fear from me, Lady," he said. "While you are in my care—and it is better that you are in my hands than in others—you shall be treated as a sister. "And"—he hesitated—"if you can find it in your heart to say a prayer for the unhappiest man on earth, I will be grateful!" For Jonas' desire had turned from all earthly brides. He fought bravely for his new faith on every occasion. He was always in the front rank in every battle and, at last, he was fortunate enough to die instantly of an arrow which pierced his breast at Yermouk.

Alawkedi, a pious *imam* of Bagdad, relates that after Jonas' death he appeared in a vision to Rafi Ibn Omeirah, his old commander. He was treading a flowery meadow in rich robes and in golden sandals. And he told Rafi that Allah, to reward his faithful service, had given him seventy of the black-eyed *houris* of his paradise, each lovelier than the sun and the moon. "Such is the reward," added the pious *imam* "of the man who dies a martyr to the faith!"

But we would rather believe that Rafi Ibn Omeirah's vision came to him one night after he had indulged in *hasheesha,* the herb of joy. To us it seems far, far more probable that when Jonas lay stricken on the battle-field and the tumult and the shouting died on his ear, that he saw a vision. It reflected no black-eyed houris' smiles. They saw instead Eudocea. She leaned over the golden battlements of the heaven of the Christ, like a blessed damosel. And her blue eyes were smiling, with the smile she had given him in Damascus, before the world had changed. Her lips opened and he knew she was calling his name. She was his once more, all his! And with that consciousness all the years of Jonas' renegade life among the Moslems, all thought of Allah and his Prophet dropped away from him. Suddenly he knew that the faith he had abjured was the only one. It was bound up with all his memories of his mother and his love for Eudocea. And as he died with a whispered "Christ is risen!" on his lips, he heard the rustle of angel wings, he seemed to be caught up by angel hands. And the heavens, where Eudocea waited to greet him, opened in glory before his breaking eyes.

A SARACEN'S LOVE

Abdulasis, son of the Arab Emir Mousa—who completed the Moslem conquest of Spain that the bold raider Tarik had begun—though brave, was a dreamer and a poet. When he had established himself in his palace in Seville, the Moorish law gave him right to a hundred Christian virgins, "fifty rich and fifty poor," to place in his harem. But Abdulasis was a poet and a dreamer. Though an Arab he was one of those men who love but one woman. Ninety and nine of the girls brought him he married to his companion-at-arms. He chose one for himself, but only as a matter of form, for that girl he did not see. It was not until wandering one night among the fountained gardens of aloes and pomegranates, breathing the perfume of the jasmines and roses, that he came by chance on one of the women of his harem who sat on a marble bench, her head buried in her hands, weeping bitterly beneath a moon made for lover's dreams.

Abdulasis' heart was moved by her tears. He loosed her hands and looked into her beautiful eyes. "Why do you grieve, lady?" he asked. "Why should I not grieve?" she answered at length, between broken sobs. "I am Egilona, once wife of Don Roderick the Goth and Queen of Spain!" Abdulasis' heart stood still. Now that he had looked into her eyes he knew he loved her. He knew there was no other woman on earth for him. But—so distinguished a captive was one who would have to be sent to the Khaliff at Damascus. It might be fatal to keep her in his harem. And yet—no one knew her identity. Abdulasis dared the risk. Thenceforward Egilona was a queen again, queen of the Moslem Emir's heart.

A whole section of the palace was set aside for her use. She had her own train of slaves, eunuchs and attendants. Abdulasis' own guards kept watch before the silken hangings of her apartments with scimitars drawn. She was served like the Khaliff's wife herself. When she rode through the streets, deeply veiled, the silver bells with which the housings of her white horse were hung warned all men to fling themselves on the ground until she had passed. And— Abdulasis made the muezzins who called the hours of prayer from the minarets couple her name with that of Allah and the Prophet in a blessing!

But when his father Musa had left Abdulasis to rule in Seville, he had left with him a watchdog in the shape of his kinsman and adviser Ayub. Ayub was an old man whose one aim in life was the advancement of Islam. He watched Abdulasis gradually forget his duties in his devouring love for Egilona, and at last he spoke to him: "My lord and cousin," he said, "you are flinging away your kingdom for the sake of a slave, a mere woman, a Christian. She is a witch, for you spend your time dreaming of her when you should be reviewing your soldiers or attending to the business of state. Do you think, when reports of your indulgence of her every whim reach the Khaliff that you will continue to be the Emir of Abdulasia? Put her away before it is too late!" But Abdulasis, his face dark with rage, merely pushed Ayub aside, flung himself into his saddle and galloped off.

And the long delicious days of rapture went on as though they never were to end. Abdulasis gave up every hour to the beautiful Egilona. In the cool shadows of the gardens of the Alcazar, the fortress-palace of Seville, where the fresh breath of the mountain air stirred the fragrance of the flowers, he never left her side. They floated on the waters of the Guadilquiver at night, in a silver barge. The red glare of torches fell on the rippling waters, and the night breeze filled the perfumed sails and they were alone with love, for the negro mutes who made up the crew and attendants could not tell what they might see. And in the glorious halls of the palace itself, and the glow and splendor of golden and many-colored arabesque walls, Abdulasis and Egilona would forget the chess-board over which they sat to look into each other's eyes, while the fountains glittering jets of water fell back musically into their great marble basin with a shower of snowy foam.

Long might their happiness have endured, had Egilona been content with love alone. But Egilona, though she loved the Moorish Emir, loved ambition more. She could not forget that once she had been Queen of Spain. And one day she told Abdulasis the tale of her life. Egilona had been a Moor, daughter of the Moslem King of Algiers. A mere girl, she had set out in a splendid galley to sail to the land of the young prince to whom she had been betrothed, the King of Tunis' son. But her galley was cast ashore by a storm on the Spanish coast. As the vessel grounded in the foaming surf, the Moors of her suite formed around their Princess with swords drawn. For from the nearby village the Gothic fishermen poured down to the beach to gather in what the sea had cast up to them. But—the village *alcalde* interfered when he learned the rank of those shipwrecked. There was peace between the Goths and the princes of the African coast at the time. Egilona and her turbaned followers were brought to Don Roderick's court in Toledo as honored guests. And, once he had seen her, the heart of the young king was so captivated by her charms that, forgetting all else, he determined to marry her. Egilona was ready to exchange the devotion of a lover handsome and royal for the affection of a young prince she had never seen. She compared the restricted life behind harem walls with the freedom and splendor of the court of Spain's last Gothic King. And she accepted Christianity without a murmur and married him. But Don Roderick soon yielded to a fatal passion for one of the new queen's maidens, Florinda, daughter of Count Julian. He betrayed her trustful innocence. When the poor girl awoke to the fact of her dishonor, she wrote her father and told him what had happened and he in turn betrayed his master and the Gothic kingdom of Spain to the Arabs, in revenge.

Egilona during the great battle fought on the shores of the Guadalete, between the Christian Goths and Moslem Arabs, rested in the gay silken tents of a separate camp far behind the battle-line. There she waited with the women of the court, to welcome her victorious husband. But suddenly the bright pavilions were trampled down by the terrible rush of the fleeing thousands of Gothic soldiers. With a few devoted guards she had managed to make good her escape with the wild war-cry of the Arabs sounding in her ears.

"And Roderick?" asked Abdulasis. "When Count Julian's men turned on their own comrades, he flung himself into the river. And while she was turning his white horse toward the other bank, the unfortunate Florinda, clad like an Amazon, rode down to the water's edge, and fitting a bow to an arrow, pierced the heart of the man who had dishonored her." "Ah," cried Egilona, while her eyes filled with tears, "why did I marry Don Roderick? Had it not been for me he might have wedded Florinda, instead of making her the victim of his guilty passion. Then all my misfortunes would not have happened. But Abdulasis leaped from his cushions. "Do not regret the crown you have lost," he cried. "You shall be my wife according to the prophet's law. You shall reign a queen in fact if not in name!" And he married Egilona with pomp and ceremony, though Ayub mourned his rash step in sackcloth and ashes.

But Egilona's ambition was not yet satisfied, though Abdulasis consulted her in all the affairs of government. For the hearts of some women never are content until their eyes close in death. One day, while they were sitting together in the glorious chamber of the Alcazar called the "Sultan's Hall," Egilona drew from beneath her mantle a circlet of gold, and held it up before her husband's eyes. "It is the crown of Roderick the Goth," she said. "It is the crown you should wear, Abdulasis! Never will you be a real ruler until you wear the crown," she went on. "Why be content to remain Emir of Abdulasis when you can be King of all Spain?" And, though he at first refused, Abdulasis, whose heart was like wax in Egilona's white fingers, at last consented to wear the royal circlet. First he wore it only in private, in the halls and gardens of the Alcazar. But, even before he rode out with it gleaming around his white turban through the streets of Seville, the rumor had grown and spread that Abdulasis was become half a Christian. "The Emir had turned Christian!" The word spread from mouth to mouth among the Moslems. It ran like wild-fire through the bazaars and the streets. And the people began to look darkly on the Emir when he rode out of the palace surrounded by his guards. In vain Ayub called attention to the fact that the Emir prayed in the mosque as before. In vain he told the Toledans how he flung himself down and prayed with his head turned toward Mecca five times a day. The fact could not be gainsaid that he wore the Gothic crown, the golden circlet of Christian power, about his turban. How could a pious Moslem wear the crown of a Christian King without transgressing the law of the Koran?

All Abdulasis had meant to do was to satisfy the caprice of the woman he loved. But his enemies in Seville had sent couriers on swift horses to Damascus. They carried letters to the Khaliff. And the letters said that the Emir of Abdulasis had cast off the faith of the Prophet. They said that he wore the crown of the dead Gothic King. They said he was preparing to seize all the land of Spain by right of the Christian infidel woman he had married, Egilona, the widow of Don Roderick.

In his splendid palace in Damascus the Khaliff Suleman read the letters which the couriers brought from Spain. And he stroked his beard and spoke a few words to his vizier. That very night his messenger sped back on the way to Seville. And a fortnight later,

one evening when the Emir Abdulasis and the fair Egilona sat in
their gardens drinking in the fragrance of orange-blossoms, and
listening to the song of the nightingales, a weary Berber horseman
rode into the palace courtyard and asked for the Emir Ayub. And
when Ayub came he drew from his turban a missive sealed with the
Khaliff's seal, and handed it to him. Ayub read and bowed: "The
will of the Commander of the Faithful, who it Allah's viceregent on
earth, be done!" he said in a broken voice.

The nightingales were still singing among the rose-bushes when
the assassins came on the Emir of Abdulasis and Egilona, beneath the
light canopy of purple cloth which shielded them from the falling
dews. Egilona's white arms about Abdulasis' neck, she was pleading with him to make the golden circlet he wore around his turban
more than a mere symbol of power. And Abdulasis thought "How
she loves me!" and his heart grew soft. It was at that moment,
when the vision of royal power rose up dazzling before his mental
eye, that four naked Nubians, black as pitch, stole softly over the
grass, so softly the lovers did not hear them. Their bare feet trod
so lightly on the soft green turf of the garden, they moved so
noiselessly, so stealthily, that in the dim half-light which precedes the
dawn, they seemed like some ghastly vision and not like living men.
Two blacks flung themselves on their victims with a sudden bound,
their bright poignards flashed, and Abdulasis and Egilona perished,
hardly knowing they died, so unexpectedly had death come to them.
The Nubians grinned. One stooped and drew Egilona's filmy veil
of delicate silk from her brow and callously wiped his dagger on it.
Another tore from the Emir's jewelled turban the plain golden
circlet, the crown of Roderick the Goth, which had caused his death
—he had strict orders from Ayub to bring it to him!

Their bodies were flung into the palace courtyard, and when night
fell, they were buried by Ayub's orders beneath one of the stone
slabs of the court-yard pavement. To this day, in the Alcazar garden
where they met their death the orange-blossoms open beneath the
moon, and the nightingales sing the same songs of love and passion to
which Abdulasis and Egilona listened in the dim, dead years of their
golden past!

MOSTASIUM

On the seventh day, while the Mongols stormed Bagdad and the
blood of the slaughtered ran red down the streets that sloped to the
Tigris, a gray shadow flitted restlessly up and down the winding
stairway of the Tower of Gold. It was the Khaliff Mostasim. His
sons had died on the walls, the captains of Hulagu the khan were
dicing for his women, fair as the sheltered egg, on whom neither sun-
ray nor moonbeam ever had fallen directly, but he had shut himself
up with that which he loved above all else—his treasure.

In the vault of the Tower were five great cisterns filled with gold pieces, each piece of gold worth two hundred *maskin*. In the lower stories the floors were laid with silver bars, and bags of gold coin were stacked against the walls like bags of wheat in a granary. In the upper stories were woven silks beyond price, precious metals wrought into shapes that doubled their value, and jewels.

A night and day had passed since the wailing *"Hura, hura!"* of the Mongols, and the cries and curses of the Bagdadees had died away. The Khaliff Mostasim, seated on one of the sealed cisterns, was eating the last of the dried dates and drinking the last of the jug of water he had carried with him into his retreat. Suddenly there was a crash of axes, the brazen gate of the tower fell inwards, and Hulaga appeared. He waved back his followers, bidding them keep the door, and approached Montasim, who continued to eat his dates—for was he not the offspring of the Prophet, and Hulagu a yellow infidel dog? But the Tartar looked at him with contempt.

"Had you turned the gold of your tower into steel, into arrowtips and spear-heads and sword-blades, old man, I might not be standing before you!" he said. The Khaliff made no reply, but when Hulagu went on, "And now show me your treasure," he led the way, and showed the Mongol khan the incredible riches of his golden hive. And while he let the sounding golden coins roll through his trembling, caressing hands as a child lets drops of water flow through his fingers, Hulagu smiled. But when they reached the topmost tower chamber, where the sun fell slantwise into great crystal bowls filled with jewels that sent forth blue, red and green sparks when the sunrays touched them, the miser's pride gave way. "Do not rob me of my treasure!" he cried and writhed like a toothless gray snake at the Mongol's feet.

"I grant your prayer," said Hulagu. "Your treasure shall be your own as long as you live. But—for drink you shall have the contents of your cisterns and the golden honey of your hive shall be your food. And when the feet of Death climb the stairway to your jewel-chamber, you may try to buy him off with rubies and with pearls!"

He turned and descended the stairs and gave orders that the entrance to the Tower be closed with solid masonry, bidding his scribe remind him to visit it again in a week's time.

And when Hulagu had the stone blocks removed from the tower entrance after a week had gone by, the body of the Khaliff Mostasim lay on the floor of the vault. In his despair he had torn his garments from him, and he seemed like a golden statue with a silver beard, his arms outstretched as though crucified. The rare jewels which had escaped his stiffening fingers, though, were still alive, their hidden fires revealed by the light which streamed in through the open door.

THE IDOL OF SOMNATH

The great temple-fortress of Somnath, whose hideous idol, a great statue of the god Siva, drew pilgrims by the thousands to the city from the surrounding country all the year around, had just been taken by the soldiers of the Mohammedan Sultan Mamood of Gnazni. And as he rode at the head of his emirs toward the great Brahmin shrine, the old warrior's eyes flamed fire. At last he would have the pleasure of smashing another of the idolatrous Hindoo images. Once more he would deserve the name by which he was called, "Mamood the idol-breaker!" It had been weary work, a three full days of slaughter. The first day, the Moslems had flung their scaling-ladders against the towering walls and rushed up with the cry of Allah Akbar!" But the Hindoos had fought fiercely. When the moon, fair bride of night, shed her rays on the battlements, the flames of war were still not quenched in blood. On the second day the work of death was renewed. At last as the Moslems scaled the walls, they were pushed headlong down again by the spears of the defendants, who wept while they thrust, for they had taken leave of their god Siva, and only wished for death. On the third day an army of Hindoo idolaters had appeared on the horizon. There were long columns of foot-soldiers, great lines of elephants, and clouds of horsemen. But the old sultan had fallen on them tooth and nail, and had driven them in headlong flight. When the defenders of the temple fortress, who had watched the battle from their towers, saw the defeat of their countrymen, they had crowded out of the sea-gate, down to the vessels in the labor and had hoisted sails while the winds of fortune held. But Mamood had succeeded in taking and sinking many of their boats, and sending the souls of their occupants down to Gehenna, the place of eternal fire, before they could escape. Then, with his son, his nobles and emirs, he had ridden through the great Somnath gates and entered the town of the idol-worshippers.

But meanwhile, in the great temple itself, a cruel little human tragedy, one that nothing in common with the battle between Hindoo and Moslem, had been taking place. Its prelude, however, had occurred the morning of the third day, when Somnath was taken by the foe. At daybreak that day a beautiful young Hindoo girl had been washing her graceful brown limbs in the smooth curling water of the sea, where it rolled gently along the pebbly shore, at no great distance from the city. It was a secluded spot, and the Mohammedan soldiers were encamped on the further side of the town. So Mahal felt no fears, and had performed her ablutions with serene confidence.

But no sooner had she stepped from the refreshing flood and veiled her lovely form in a scarlet *jumna,* than a tiger leaped from the spur of jungle which ran down to the sea not far from where she had been bathing. The terrified girl gave a shriek as the beast stopped some ten feet away from her and lashed its tail preparatory to make a final bound. But while her face was still hidden in her hands, she heard the great cat's roar break and change to a hollow gurgling sound. She was still untouched. His cruel claws had not struck her to the ground. His hot, fetid breath did not fan her cheek. She removed her hands—and saw before her a handsome youth, who was leaning on the bow he had just discharged, while the tiger was tearing the earth a few yards away in its dying agonies, the arrow which had pierced to its brain projecting from its eye.

For a moment Mahal shrank from the stranger. Did he not wear the garb of a Moslem soldier? Was he not an enemy to her and her faith? But his kindly smile reassured her. And when she had stammered her thanks he said, as his eye looked with favor on her charms: "Your city is doomed. But take this ring"—and he drew from his finger a rich gold band set with a dazzling emerald—"it will ensure your safety when the soldiers of Allah enter. Any Moslem to whom you show it will lead you to me, and I will that not a hair of your head is touched. And now farewell!" He mounted his horse, tied to a nearby tamarind tree, and in a moment had passed from sight. Mahal sighed as she returned to the city. She almost hoped the Moslem army would enter for a villain, none the less a villain because he was hoary with gray-hairs, dogged her foot-steps. Mahal was the wife of a dying man and—the Chief Brahmin of the Temple of Siva, the gross and disgusting Prayatcha, was persecuting her with his attentions. Coarse and bloated, his shorn scalp hid the frost of age. But the ignoble wrinkles of his forehead showed that time already had sowed the furrows for the seed of death! The old voluptuary's legs were shrunken but his eyes were still bright with passion. As Mahal entered her hut she saw that her husband was dead. Beside him stood the Brahmin. He turned as he heard her footstep. With an oily voice he said, as he laid an affectionate hand on her arm: "Daughter, come to Siva's temple tonight! There we will talk over your burning. The widow must mount her husband's funeral pyre, as you know, but, perhaps . . ." He did not finish, but looked at her with evil suggestion.

Mahal's lovely head sank on her breast. When she looked up, Prayatcha had disappeared. The bride of only a few short weeks had been prepared to follow her husband out of life. She had steeled herself to mount the funeral pyre. She had not loved the sickly man thrust upon her by her father's will, but her duty seemed plain. But now, since she had met the young Moslem soldier on the beach—she did not feel so sure. And she dreaded her visit to Siva's temple. What did the gross and oily priest have in mind? She had not misread his evil glances. She knew she could not trust him. And yet—if she did not go to the temple she might never again see the handsome young stranger, who had promised to help her with a voice as soft and gentle as the dews of the summer night.

It was late that night, when, with hesitating steps, she drew near the great temple, at the moment when the Sultan Mamood, surrounded by mounted torch-bearers, was entering the city gates. For Somnath had fallen after the flight of its defenders. It had opened its gates to the victor without another sword-stroke, though Mahal was unaware of the fact. Siva's temple, a massive building, consisted of one great aisle, its arching roof upheld by hundreds of granite columns. At the end of the aisle stood the giant statue of Siva, a misshaped figure of stone. It was covered with jewels, and its eyes were formed of two enormous rubies. The body of the statue measured ten feet from side to side, and its limbs were in proportion. One lamp only hung in the temple. Its light was reflected on the jewelled idol in such a way that it gleamed with an effect of supernatural splendor. The most revolting abominations, the most depraved of secret rites common to the Brahminic religion were practised nightly in the great temple. But this sanctified vice was hidden from the public eye. As Mahal drew near the image, she heard a hollow sound and suddenly Prayatcha stood before her. With the false smile habitual to him he said: "Stand behind yonder pillar, my daughter, until the sacred rites of Siva have been performed! Then we will talk!" And thrusting her behind one of the massive granite columns he struck a gong on Siva's altar with a silver mallet.

At once a bevy of temple dancing-girls rushed into the great open space before the statue. Joined by Brahmin priests, with a tinkle of silver anklets and bangles, they danced with many obscene antics before the idol. Mahal looked at their performance with innocent bewilderment. The lovely Hindoo girl did not blush, for though a vague instinct within her own soul made her feel that, somehow, these gestures and postures were not right, she thought they were observances peculiar to the worship of the god. But soon the actions of the dancing-girls and their priestly partners made even the innocent Mahal's guileless and candid soul shudder and then . . . as the temple of religion seemed to turn into a shrine of the most revolting indecency, the great lamp was extinguished! Mahal's awe had already yielded to disgust and terror. When she heard laughter which thrilled her with loathing echoes from the temple shadows, she turned to grope her way out. It was at this moment that a soft but revolting voice whispered in her ear:

"Come to Siva's arms, sweet Mahal! It is the hour of dawn, and the god awaits you!"

Mahal's heart beat more quickly. The voice was disguised, yet she had heard it before. Ah, now she knew—it was that of the Brahmin Prayatcha! The web of trickery and deceit in which the scoundrel was trying to enmesh her was torn by a clear gleam of understanding.

"Infamous man," she cried with righteous indignation, "did you think to make me the victim of your unholy longings! Your religion is a sham! Your god is a deceiver! Your temple is polluted!" But Prayatcha did not give her time to say more. Despite her struggles, he clapped one hand over her mouth to prevent her from screaming. With the other he applied to her nostrils a cloth saturated in a *stupefying* drug. In another moment Mahal hung senseless in his arms.

When she awoke from the stupor into which she had fallen, she found herself lying against a closed door at the bottom of a short flight of stone steps, at whose top shone a bright light. These steps she at once ascended with desperate resolution, for she was filled with alarm at finding herself imprisoned, as she knew she must be, somewhere within the temple. At the head of the stairs she entered a circular chamber, about six feet in diameter. Its floor was covered with a costly Persian rug, and the light in the room was so intense as to be painful to her eyes. It was flung back from some invisible source by reflectors made of clusters of jewels. The walls of the room were thickly hung with strings of pearls and long chains of gems, and uncut jewels of every kind and color were piled in heaps on the Persian rug. Mahal could hardly move without treading on treasures worth a king's ransom. The wealth of the world seemed concentrated in this one little room!

As Mahal gazed with wide-opened eyes at the riches which surrounded her on every side, a panel door in the wall slowly opened, and her Brahmin abductor stood before her. His deep, dull eye was lit with an expression of triumphant malice. As the door by which he had entered slid back into place in its hidden grooves, he approached the victim and cried: "Be mine and all the wealth of Siva—for you stand in the bosom of Siva's holy statue—shall be yours! Refuse! . . ."

"Do your worst," cried Mahal, with flashing eyes, "do you think a woman has so little self-respect, so little sense of honor and decency as to be bribed to consent to her own degradation?"

"Your fate be on your own head!" replied the exasperated Brahmin. Seizing a silver mallet, he raised it to strike a gong which hung from an iron bar crossing the chamber about six feet from the floor, when . . . a strange noise came from without. The great image vibrated and shook to its very foundation. The jeweled room seemed to move as though tossed by a wave. But while the guilty Brahmin sank to his knees and raised his hands in an attitude of supplication, the lovely Hindoo girl stood unmoved. The noise grew louder, the walls of the chamber trembled. And suddenly, among the voices which came to her from without was one which rang on lovely Mahal's ear like sweetest music. It was the voice of the young stranger who had rescued her from death by the seashore.

In the great hall of the Temple of Somnath, while white-robed Brahmins crowded about him, Sultan Mamood of Gnazni had ordered the great image of Siva to be destroyed. In vain the Hindoo priests had offered the servant of Allah untold sums in gold and silver coin if he would spare their idol. Mamood's heart remained unmoved. And his dying son, Prince Ali, was heading the willing soldiers whose strokes echoed through the great hollow body of the accursed image.

Suddenly there was a tremendous crash! With a clatter of stone fragments, a whole section of the idol's hollow body fell to the temple floor. And before the astonished gaze of the Sultan and his officers, who rubbed their eyes, so startled were they, an unexpected picture was revealed. In the yawning cavern of the idol's belly, a cavern whose walls gleamed and glowed with untold gems, where diamonds, emeralds and rubies shot forth flames white, green and red, stood a lovely Hindoo girl. About her feet were heaped hillocks of pearls that gleamed with a creamy or rosy lustre. Her face smiled with the rapture of one whom the gods have delivered from a great danger. Beside her knelt a Brahmin priest. Prince Ali at once recognized Mahal. Pushing aside his soldiers, he leaped to the entrance of the cavity and held out his hand. And Mahal yielded to him her own, on which blazed the stone he had given her. Yet before she leaped lightly down from her curious prison Mahal turned, and her eyes darkened with indignation. She pointed to the despicable Prayatcha, who, still overcome with terror, his gross body quaking with fear, knelt in an attitude of supplication.

"You have saved me from pollution and death at the hands of yonder reptile!" she cried. "In another hour I should have been what I shudder to contemplate!" She buried her face in her hands, overcome by the revulsion of her feelings. The foul Brahmin, shrinking from the scornful glances of the honest Moslem soldiers, was dragged like some loathsome toad from his den of infamy. Five minutes later this pillar of Siva's shrine was hanging from the top of one of the great granite columns of the temple he had so frequently profaned. Mahal's belief in her Hindoo gods, Siva, especially, had been rudely shaken. He was a god whom she could no longer worship. This made it easy for the pious *mollahs* whom Prince Ali

sent to instruct her in the law of Islam to win her to their faith.
Mahal became a true believer and never, as Ali's wife, and secure
in the tender affection he lavished on her, did she regret that she had
turned to Allah and his Prophet. As for the Sultan Mamood, Allah
had indeed rewarded his refusal to sell his honest convictions for the
Brahmins' gold. For the immense treasures in Siva's belly exceeded
by far the gold in the hands of the Hindoo priests.

THE Middle Ages, the "Dark Ages," are the centuries in which the West is "settling down" on the ruins of the Roman empire and laying the foundations for modern institutions. It is a vast period. Christianity spreads over all the Western world, while Islam spreads in the East. Slavery grows milder and becomes serfdom. The feudal system and the "family" of Christian kings develops. The emperors struggle with the popes for world rule, and everywhere there is the constant strife of conflicting ideas as the nations slowly and gradually work up from ignorance to light. The Middle Ages are usually held to end with Columbus' discovery of America in 1492, when the Modern Age begins. The revival of classic learning, the Renaissance, the great struggle between Protestantism and Catholicism and the political development of the nations climax in the American and French Revolutions, and the establishment of the ideal of democratic government.

Humanity During the Middle Ages. The individual human being during the Middle Ages, as in ancient times, treads the same round of personal hopes, dreams and desires. Times change, nations change, new religions spring up, but man remains the same. In the stories which follow a few *human* glimpses at the vast Medieval peep-show—for the world always has been a "stage"—are given. From the days of the fusion of Latins and Barbarians we have a simple *true* tale of the escape of a Roman-Gaulish boy, of good family from degrading "serfdoms" in Barbarian captivity. It makes us feel the uncertainty of life at a time when a personal quarrel between two kings could plunge hundreds of innocent people into slavery. Now, when nations quarrel, enemy nationals are only subjected to temporary captivity. Our next tale aims to show how literally the Christian world of the year 100 took the visions of the Apocalypse. It tries to call up the thrill of anguish and exaltation those who went before us felt when they saw in their mind's eye earth's graves about to open, and the bones of the dead gather for the terrors of the Judgment Day. The legend that follows is one of the most touchingly *human* history has inspired, for it is more than historic—it is the tale of every man who, whether he has or has not worn a crown has *outlived himself*. The next tale is one which expresses the very soul of medieval *chivalry*. It shows the high plane on which the true knight placed the mistress of his heart. It shows the knighthood's idealization of the beloved in its purest and brightest colors. It shows, also, the noble and exalted response such devotion woke in a woman's breast. And—it shows the brutal cruelty with which a husband could resent what he considered an affront to his honor. Our next story is a very loveable and human one. It gives us the reaction of a simple *Western* soul to the sense-lure of the East. If we forget its medieval setting we can parallel it in our own life and time. For, though its heroine is the "Saracen Virgin," it is not a *religious* struggle that it portrays. Any navy boy who has been haunted by the memories of far Eastern lights-of-loves after he has come back to the home farm or town, and has forgotten them and found happiness in an honest affection for one of his own race and faith, has lived the same tale.

Our last story gives us a picture from that fantastic Aztec civilization of Mexico which was revealed to Europe as one of the results of Columbus' great discovery. It makes us feel its strange mixture of high culture and cruel barbarity, and we shudder at the heartlessness which held a promise made more sacred than a young life, and the pity that cut short its breath with a strangler's noose of fragrant roses.

ATTALUS AND THE COOK

(Retold from the Chronicle of Gregory of Tours, 533 A.D.)

Now Theuderic and Childebert, the two kings of the Franks, had made a treaty. Each swore that he would do nothing against the other. And each took hostages from the other, that there be less danger of each breaking his word. Many sons of great families of Roman descent passed into the hands of the two Frankish kings, but soon they fell to quarreling once more—all the hostages were declared *slaves!* Many escaped from slavery, and found their way home again, others were not able to escape. Among the latter was a youth named Attalus, nephew of the holy Gregory, Bishop of Langres. He, too, had been declared a slave, and turned into a horse-boy. He was held captive by a Teuton in the land of Trier.

At last Gregory sent out serving-men to look for him. They found him and offered the Teuton gifts if he would release him. But the latter scorned their gifts and said: "A lad of such good family will have to be bought for ten pounds of gold!" Then, when the messengers returned to their master, the latter's cook, named Leo said: "Give me leave of absence, and I may be able to bring him back out of captivity." This pleased his master the bishop. He gave him leave, and Leo went to the district where the boy was held as a slave and tried to steal him away secretly, but could not. So he found a man and said to him: "Come along with me to the Teuton's house and sell me to him as a slave. The price I bring shall be your gain. All I want is to be free to move about within his house."

So the man swore an oath to do as he asked, and sold him to the Teuton for twelve gold pieces. The man who had bought him asked what the new slave could do. Leo answered: "I know about all that goes on a noble table. I do not think another man on earth equals me in my art. Even if you were to give the king a dinner there is none who can invent royal dishes so skilfully as myself." So his master said: "Very well. On Sunday I will ask my neighbor and my relatives to my house. See to it that you prepare a meal that will astonish them, so that they say: 'No we never ate better in the king's own palace!'" "Let my master give orders that many hens be brought me," said Leo, "and I will do as he says." Sunday came, and the cook prepared many dainty and savory dishes, and all who feasted praised the meal.

Then the Teuton was kind to the cook, and he was given charge of all his master's stores, and divided all the food among the household. But when a year had passed and his master felt quite sure of him, Leo went out to a meadow near the house with the horse-boy, Attalus. There he lay down with him on the grass, but far away and with his back to him, so that none should notice they were talking and said to the boy: "We must think of home now! This night, when you have driven the horses into the corral, do not fall asleep. Be ready to come the minute I call you, and we will set out together." For the Teuton had invited many friends to a feast, among them his son-in-law. When they rose from the table in the middle of the night to go to bed, Leo followed the son-in-law, and handed him a flagon of sweet mead to drink. And the man said to him: "Tell me, cook whom your master trusts, when do you mean to take his horses and ride home?" He said this in jest. And Leo told the truth and replied: "I think of doing so this very night, God willing!" And the other man said: "I hope my servants will watch that you take nothing of mine!"

Then, when all were asleep, Leo softly called Attalus; they saddled the horses, and Leo asked the boy whether he had a sword. Attalus answered: "No, all I have is a short spear!" So Leo stepped into his master's room and picked up the latter's sword and shield. When his master asked who was there and what he wished, the other replied: "I am your slave Leo, and I am waking Attalus so that he may go and drive your horses out into the pasture, for he is sleeping as soundly as though he were drunk." His master said: "Do as you will," and fell asleep again. But Leo fitted out the boy with the weapons, and by the grace of God finding the door of the courtyard open, they mounted two horses and rode off with the others as well. When they came to the river Moselle they left their horses, swam the river on their shields and reached the opposite shore. It was shivery night when they came to a forest where they hid.

By the third night of their flight they had not had a bite to eat. At last, by the grace of God, they found a tree full of fruit, one of those trees called plum-trees. They ate, and somewhat strengthened, held on toward the land of Champagne. Then, as they were tramping along, they heard the hoofs of galloping horses and Leo said: "Let us fling ourselves down on the ground so that the people who are coming do not see us!" A big bramble-bush stood beside the road and they cast themselves down with swords drawn behind it so that they would have their weapons at hand if attacked. But when their pursuers had reached the bramble-bush they pulled up, and one of them, while the horses were stalling said: "Damnation, the scoundrels have escaped! They are not to be found! But by my sainted salvation, if I find them, I will hang one from the gallows and cut the other to pieces with the sword!"

The man who spoke was the Teuton, their master, who had ridden from the city of Rheims in search of them, and he surely would have found them along the road had not night fallen. Then the riders spurred their horses and rode on, but the fugitives reached the city that very night. There they asked to be directed to the house of the priest Paulellus. And as they crossed the street the bells were just ringing for mass, for it was the Lord's day. They knocked at the priest's door, and the boy Attalus told of how they had been pursued by his master. The priest said: "Then the vision I saw was a true one. For this very night I say two doves flying toward me, and perch on my hand, and one was white and the other black!" And the two runaways said: "May the Lord make allowance for us on this His holy day! We beg you to give us something to eat, for this is the beginning of the fourth day that we have tasted neither bread nor porridge!" So the priest hid Leo and Attalus, gave them bread dipped in wine and went to mass.

The Teuton had followed his slaves to the city, and there again tried to find them. But the priest fooled him and he returned home. The runaways regained their strength during the two days they were fed in the priest's house, and then left him to return to Bishop Gregory in Langres. The saintly man was happy when he saw them and wept on his nephew Attalus' neck. He set Leo and all his family free from slavery, and gave him landed property to have for his own, and on it, the cook, with his wife and child, lived a free man all the days of his life."

THE YEAR OF THE MILLENNIUM

The Greatest Terror the Christian World Ever Knew. When the year 999 after the birth of Christ drew to its close, the greatest terror that Christianity ever knew cast its shadows over every land in which human beings had accepted the cross and prayed to the Redeemer. For between the *last minute* of that year and the *first* of the next, all Christians believed that the world would come to an end, and that the Archangel Gabriel's trumpet would call the dead from their graves for the Judgment Day. For three months the churches stood open night and day, and every day was Sunday. Nowhere in the Christian lands were the fields sown. Trade and commerce stopped. The shops in the cities were closed. Men gave away all they possessed, for the time was at hand when they would need nothing. They kept only their best clothes, so that they might receive the Saviour properly when he came. Christmas that year was celebrated with unusual fervor throughout Christendom. Nowhere were guards and watchmen busy, for the fear of the Judgment to come prevented all evil-doing. The doors and windows of all houses were left wide open at night, for no one stole. The baker gave away his bread and the publican his wine. No one bothered to collect debts—what was the use? The churches were crowded, and confession absolution, mass and sacrament went on without a stop. At last came New Year's Eve. Let us take a look at Rome and see how it appeared on that eventful day.

THE MIDNIGHT MASS

Most of the people of Rome had crowded out into the open fields. There they stood looking up toward the sky waiting for what was to come. In one spot a crowd had gathered around a religious fanatic. He was a rich man who had dragged together a funeral pile of dry wood. Having set it aflame, he mounted an old arm-chair beside the pile and addressed the crowd:

"In the name of the Almighty God," said he, "as I have burned the bonds of all who owe me money, so will God draw a line through my own debts in the book of life! For any suffering I may have caused others, I now shall suffer myself! May purifying fire destroy this sinful body of mine! Mounting flames, let me rise with you to the skies!"

And with that he leaped into the flames and remained there with his hands clasped in prayer until he was choked to death by the smoke. In the Forum a man was digging at a great heap of refuse so that it might fall and bury him: "The hills shall cover us!" he sang joyfully as he dug. A pair of lovers leaped from the Sublicius Bridge into the Tiber river below, clasped in an embrace that the waves could not loosen. At noon the prisons were opened, and the prisoners received as heroes and martyrs. They were led into the houses of the rich and noble. Senators and knights waited on them at the table, and their wives washed their feet. And all said: "We are sinners and have nothing of which we can be proud! But these prisoners have suffered punishment while we went about free!" Never since the days that Christ walked the earth, was there such a display of Christian love and mercy. The sick in the hospitals begged to be carried out into the open, and their beds were set out in the streets and market-places. Birds were freed from their cages and horses from their stables. At first the horses ran about in the city. But soon some of them which reached the city gates caught a whiff of the fresh air of the fields, and ran off to look for a bit of green pasture. Others lay down in the streets and the children climbed on their backs. For the children were the only ones who showed no fear. They played about, enjoying their unusual freedom from restraint. For none had the heart to punish them. And since they did not know what all the excitement was about, they were happy.

With the coming of night the general fear and anguish increased. Masters and men fell on each other's necks, and begged each others' forgiveness. The masters regretted their harshness and cruelty, the servants bewailed their dishonesty. Enemies meeting each other on the streets embraced and wandered on hand in hand, singing hymns of praise like children. It was as though the golden age of humanity had returned! It seemed the realization of the thousand-year empire as foretold by the old fathers of the Church. And, more or less, the same scenes were repeated everywhere in the cities of Christendom.

In the Basilica Church of St. Peter, where the midnight mass—the last, perhaps that earth ever would hear!—was to be said, there Pope Silvester II stood before the high altar. The church was over-crowded, and all in it lay on their knees. The silence was so great that the rustling of the Pope's white sleeves as he moved about the altar could be heard. And there was still another sound. It was a sound which seemed to measure out the *last minutes of the earth's thousands of years of existence since the coming of Christ!* It echoed in the ears of those present as the pulse-beat does in the ear of a man with a fever, and its beat was loud and regular and never stopped. For the door of the church sacristy stood open, and what the great audience heard was the regular, uninterrupted tick, tick, tock of the great clock which hung within, one tick for every passing second.

The Pope was a man of iron will-power, calm and collected. He had probably left the sacristy door open purposely, in order to secure the greatest amount of effect at this great moment. Though his face was pale as death with excitement, as he did not move nor did his hands tremble.

The midnight mass had been said, and a deathly silence fell. The audience waited. The Servant of the Most High would probably now speak some words of consolation as he stood before the altar. But Pope Sylvester said not a word. He seemed lost in prayer, his hands raised to the sky. The clock kept on ticking. A long sigh came from the people, but nothing happened. Like children afraid of the dark, all those in the church lay with their faces to the ground, and did not venture to look up. The sweat of terror ran from many an icy brow, and knees and feet which had fallen asleep lost all feeling.

Then, suddenly—the clock stopped ticking!

Among the congregation the beginning of a scream of terror began to form in many a throat. And, stricken dead by fear, several bodies dropped heavily on the stone floor.

Then the clock began to strike. It struck one, two, three, four . . . It struck twelve . . . The twelfth stroke echoed out, and a deathly silence still reigned!

Then it was that Pope Sylvester turned around, and with the proud smile of a victor stretched out his hands in blessing over the heads of those who filled the church. And at the same moment all the bells in the tower began to peal out a glad and jubilant chime, and from the organ-loft sounded a chorus of joyous voices, young and older, a little uncertain at first, perhaps, but growing clearer and firmer moment by moment. They sang the *Te Deum Laudamus*—"Thee, God, we praise!"

The whole congregation united their voices with those of the choir. Yet it was some time before cramped backs could be straightened out, and before people recovered from the dreadful sight offered by those who had died of fright. When the *Te Deum* had been sung, men and women fell into each other's arms, laughing and crying and exchanging the kiss of peace. Thus ended the year 1000 after the birth of Christ!

THE TALE OF THE LIVING DEAD MAN

There once was a man who lived for many years after he was dead, and that is why his tale is both curious and sad. For it is better to die and be done with it, than to live after one is dead. Virgil, the Latin poet, truly said: "Once you are dead, and Minos, the judge of the dead has sat in judgment on you, then neither cunning nor a golden tongue, nor good deeds will restore you again to life!"

Norman William won the realm of England in the great battle of Hastings (1066 A.D.). There Harold, the last Saxon king of England, fell beneath his Golden Dragon banner, struck by an arrow in the eye, and with his fall the Saxons broke and fled. Some claim that Edith Swanneck, Harold's love, searched the battle-field by night while the monks of Waltham held the torches, until she found the dead king's body. Others say it never was found. However that may be, year in and year out, the rumor spread in England that King Harold lived, and that in his own good time he would appear, and that then the Normans would be driven out of England. But the years rolled by, and no Harold appeared. William the Conqueror died and was buried. His son William the Red, who followed him on the throne, was slain hunting in the Westminster forest. Some said it was a Saxon arrow that was pulled out of his back when they found him where he had died alone under a great oak. And after William the Red, his nephew Henry took advantage of his brother Robert's absence in the Holy Land, seized the royal treasure and the crown—and kept them.

Through all three reigns, an old Saxon, of whom nothing was known save that his wits were muddled, journeyed without rest, year in and year out, from one saint's shrine to another, and prayed at their altars. While the Norman kings succeeded each other on the English throne, while the face of the land changed, while Norman laws and Norman customs took the place of Saxon traditions and Saxon ways, while the peoples of the two races moved ever a little nearer each other, and became a little more used to each other, this old man wandered through the land. From Canterbury, to Exeter and Ely, and ever back again to the great Battle-Abbey of Waltham he went. When first he began his weary round, he stopped and told the people that he was Harold of England. But the men who had gathered to hear him talk would break out into jeers and laughter, and would stone him—for those were rough days. So, in time, the old pilgrim gave up his mad tale, and instead would tell how many steps a man had to take to walk from Ely to Canterbury or from Salisbury to Exeter. And he was proud of his knowledge. Then, one day, when King Henry rode into the castle of one of his knights, whom he had honored with a visit—for he was going to hunt the deer in his spreading forests—the old pilgrim happened to be standing with others, Saxon bondsmen and Normans, in the castle court. And—he shook his clenched hand at the King's Majesty and cried: "Away! A curse upon the Norman! Why comes he here?"

Of course he was at once seized and held and King Henry, turning to one of the bishops who rode in his train, said that he himself would sit in judgment on the man after the evening meal. So the mad old pilgrim was haled off and thrust in a dungeon till evening came. When they examined him, however, they found he carried about him in his wallet a scrap of parchment on which was written:

"This man is the bondsman of Rahere, King Henry's jester. Let no man ill-treat or injure him without warrant!" And the bishop to whom they brought the parchment scrap at once took it to King Henry, for like many others at court, he had little liking for the king's jester.

Now Rahere, the King's Fool, was no ordinary court jester. He was a clever and witty gentleman. Though, as an old chronicle says, "he was born of mean parentage, he had frequented the houses of nobles and princes in the flower of his youth," and finally had won King Henry's favor. In fact, the King thought so highly of Rahere's advice, and so relished his wit, that he gave him lands and manors, and Rahere could keep a company of a hundred fiddlers who played with silver bows for his entertainment.

Now when they brought the parchment to King Henry he at once called Rahere to him and said: "Who is this traitorous bondsman of yours?" And Rahere answered: "Wait, sire, until evening comes, and I will tell you. Nor do I think you will judge him over-harshly, seeing that not only is he a man of unbalanced mind, but is dead besides!" It was a strange speech of which the King could make but little, but then Rahere was given to saying strange things.

When evening came, the old pilgrim was led into the great hall of the castle. There King Henry sat among his barons and bishops, to pass judgment on him for his treasonable shout. And King Henry, who held Rahere's script in his hand, questioned the man himself. Said he, in Saxon—for he had married Edith, daughter of Edgar Eetheling, of Saxon blood royal, to better his claim to the throne, and he affected to favor his Saxon subjects—"Tell me, old man, who are you that fling treason into the King's very face when he rides abroad?" The old man looked about him in the hall, and when he saw the face of Rahere, the jester, his dull eye brightened. "Why," said he, "I am the bondsman of Rahere, yonder lord. And he has given me a paper to prove it. There is a penance I must do, and a debt I must pay, a great debt—but I know not to whom, for my mind is confused at times. Yet for the past forty years I have prayed at the shrine of every saint in England to find out." Again he looked at Rahere and the latter nodded. So the old man went on: "You see, it was long ago. I was trapped in Rouen by the Norman Duke. He had bones of saints hidden in a chest and, not knowing it, I swore on those bones to give him my kingdom of England. But what else could I do? Yet when I tell folk of it they stone me!" And the old pilgrim hid his face in his sleeve.

King Henry started. And one of the barons cried: "No, it cannot be! King Harold was slain at Hastings! I saw him lying beneath the Golden Dragon banner myself!" Then up spoke Rahere, and there was pity in his voice: "Have no fear, old man! I know that you were slain on Hastings field, forty odd years ago. But you speak before a king and not before churls. Do not fear to tell him your tale. You shall not be stoned."

Then the old man raised his head and stood erect. He was very tall, but thin and frail beyond telling, and it was plain that his age was great. And there was something pitifully proud in his bearing as he turned his sad eyes on King Henry: "I did not know that I had a king for a listener. I feared I should be stoned again, if I told my tale," he said. King Henry was a cold, hard man. He was selfish and grasping and there was little room for pity in his heart. But something stirred within him. He took from the table at which he sat his own cup of wine and held it out to the old pilgrim. And—and the latter drained the cup. Then happened a thing so slight it hardly seems worth telling and yet, after it had happened, there was not one in that great hall who did not know beyond all doubt that the old man really was Harold of England in the flesh. For when the pilgrim had drunk he did not stretch out his long arm and place the cup on the table. When King Henry the Norman drank, he set down his cup before him as was the Norman fashion, and his chamberlain took it away to refill it. But the old man merely thrust out his other arm, and beckoned behind him. He beckoned behind him as the Saxon kings had called their cupbearers ever since there had been Saxon kings in England. And then, for all it was a dangerous thing to do and might well cost him his life, a Saxon knight rose among the King Henry's Norman barons. He was of the blood of Earl Goodwin, the father of King Harold, and he strode to the old man and dropped on his knee before him. And he took the empty cup so imperiously held out to him, and carried it off as a Saxon cupbearer should at a royal banquet, pressed against his knee. King Henry fixed him with a glance, and then turned to the pilgrim:

"Sit, you who were once Harold of England—for such you must be if your own stubborn Saxons kneel to serve you!" And the pilgrim sat in the seat which was shoved forward for him, and stretched out his sandaled feet, cut and calloused by the hard earth of the highways. And the two kings looked at one another. But a strangled cry broke from the Saxon knight when he saw the cut and calloused feet, feet that were like a slave's, of the man who had been one of the greatest of kings. He remembered him in his glory, throned amid the Saxon thanes of England in his great hall in Westminster Palace, and again he became forward and tenderly raised the old man's feet, and placed beneath them the rich mantle he wore over his shoulder.

King Henry looked around at his Norman lords: "Is there one among you, gentles, who would risk his neck to serve me if I were mad and uncrowned, and Harold sat on my throne, and I yonder seat before him? Nay, nay," he went on, and laughed, though there was scorn in his laughter, as a chorus of loyal protest arose on all sides, "Nay, nay, not one of you unless, perhaps, it were Rahere, would be fool enough! But"—he paused and looked at Harold— "though he is nothing but a name, yet must I hold him a prisoner. He must be my guest for the rest of his life because," he looked around again at his barons, "ambitious men might use his name to trouble me. England was promised my father by King Edward the Confessor. And, whether it was a trick or not, Harold confirmed that promise on the saints' bones. And then he broke his oath! . . ."

The old man started up in his chair: "It was an oath better broken than kept," he said. "And yet, somehow, matters went wrong. Hastings was as good as won. Why did my house-carls, who stood so firm beneath the Golden Dragon, break their ranks when I had told them again and again that it was only a Norman trick?" And then his head sunk on his breast once more till King Henry's voice came to his ear:

"Tell us, old man, of the fight at Sanguelac?"* he said. But now there was a cunning look in the old man's eye. "Nay, nay," he answered, "too often have I been stoned for telling that tale. But I can tell you how many paces a man must take to tramp from Stamford Bridge to the Abbey of the Battle . . ." And then, quite suddenly and unexpectedly, he rose to his full height, and as the Saxon knight who had served him ran swiftly forward, he said in a strong, clear voice: "Way for the King!" and fell back in his kinsman's arms. Then as his soul was passing, he muttered in a low tone: "I have paid the fine!" That was all. King Henry shaded his eyes with his hand for a moment. "It is an awful thing to see a dead man die," he said. "May God grant him peace in a better world, for his fate has been hard beyond any known to man! Mad and yet half sane. Once the proudest king in Christendom and stoned as a crazy beggar-man by the lowliest of his own Saxons when he told them the truth!"

Nor did the Saxon knight who was kinsman to the doubly dead Harold suffer for his homage to the shadow of royalty who once had worn the crown. King Henry ever after showed him great favor and trust, for he argued that in a selfish world men who forget all else for loyalty's sake are rare, and that a monarch should attach them to himself, seeing that there are not many of them to be found.

THE STORY OF A HEART

In the golden days of the troubadours, gentle knights worshipped

* The Normans never spoke of the battle as the battle of Hastings. They called it *Sanguelac*— "the lake of blood."

I

fair ladies. It did not much matter whether they were married to others or not, for a chaste and honorable lady might give her hand to a husband and never break her wedding vows, while her heart belonged to another. So the young Chatelain of Coucy, a gallant knight and troubadour, had no scruples about falling in love with the Count of Fayal's young wife the first time he saw her.

After that he forsook his gay companions. He rode no more to jousts and tourneys. He gave up the hunt. Instead, he would sit for hours alone, on the bank of some stream, his eyes fixed on the running water. As the summer went by, he painted one poem after another on parchment, in beautifully colored letters. And when fall came, he sewed the crusader's white cross over his heart, that never had stopped beating fast and furiously since he had seen the young Countess. Then he mounted his horse, and set off with his men, together with thousands of other Christian fighters, for the Holy Land. But before he went, he took the verses he had painted on parchment, wrapped them in a square of fine blue silk and cast them in through an open window into the Countess of Fayal's room. And in the very first battle against the Seljuk Turks, the young knight's breast, seeing he made no effort to defend himself, was pierced by an arrow. He fell from his horse, and when his squire drew him out of the battle-press, he saw that he was bleeding to death. But de Coucy waved away all aid: "When my heart has ceased beating," he said to his squire, "take it out of my breast, and bury my body where I have fallen. But my heart you must place in the small golden urn you will find under my saddle-flap. Take it to the Countess of Fayal!"

His squire took ship for France, and through storm and tempest, he carefully carried the golden urn containing his master's heart. Though the hearts of all others aboard beat madly with fear, there was one on that ship which was at rest and did not beat. At last the squire found himself riding through the woods of Fayal, the golden urn before him on his saddle. Suddenly he heard hunting-horns, and the halloing of huntsmen, and a stag broke out of the thicket. And pierced by an arrow, it sank down dead before the squire's rearing horse. At the same moment, on every side, the Count of Fayal's men rushed from cover. But instead of turning to the stag, they all clutched at the golden case the stranger squire carried. The Count of Fayal rode up. "Sir," cried the squire, "protect me, if you are a knightly man! I carry with me the heart of my master, the Chatelain of Coucy!" The count looked at him, and waved his men away. "Keep your golden urn, since you are so loyal a squire," said he, and turned his horse. And the squire, about to ride on, as he touched spurs to his steed, cried: "Do not

let your men follow me in secret! The Countess of Fayal will thank
you for your kindness! It is to her that I carry the heart!"

At these words the Count of Fayal's face changed terribly. He
swung his charger around. "The Countess of Fayal is a lady whom
I know well. Here, give me this heart! I will carry it to her myself!" With that he tore the urn from the squire, hid it beneath
his mantle, and rode off followed by his band. His face was dis-
torted by black rage, and he pressed the still, dead heart against
his own wildly-beating living one. When he reached the castle the
stag which had been slain was at once handed over to the cooks to
prepare. But the Count himself brought the dead heart of the Chatelain de Coucy into the kitchen and said: "See that it is well cooked
and deliciously prepared with the richest spices!" And when he sat
down with his lady to meat, the knight's heart was brought in on a
golden platter, surrounded by a wreath of gaily-colored flowers. The
Count smiled: "Ever and always, of all that may fall into my hands,
the heart belongs to you, my dear!" he said to his lady. But no
sooner had the Countess commenced to eat of it than tears filled her
eyes, and she flung her head and arms across the table and wept
so that it seemed as though she would die of her weeping. Her
husband laughed with devilish glee:

"They say that even doves' hearts make those who eat them sad!
So it is not strange that this heart I dished up to you should have
moved you when you tasted it. For it is the heart of the Chatelain
of Coucy, the knight who wrote those tender songs of love which
you read, and reread in secret in your chamber at evening!" Then
the Countess rose, and clutching the table for support, answered
"You have done yourself an ill turn, my lord! I was true to you.
But now this heart has passed into me. I carry it about with me.
It lives in me. It works in me. Now I can love none other than
the one to whom it belonged. And after having tasted it I can
touch no other food!" And she lingered only a few days after that.
Growing paler and paler, she faded away, and yet it was as though
she were going through a second blooming, for she died with a smiling mouth and a brow that shone with radiant happiness.

THE SARACEN VIRGIN

GUILLAUME D'HERBILLY was a good Christian stone-cutter. He
liked to carve Virgins, apostles and prophets, Bathshebas in the
bath, Dalilah's cutting Samson's hair, and Susannahs among the
Elders for the churches. When he left for the Crusades with his
master, Count Etienne of Blois, he was moved partly by zeal to
recover Christ's tomb from the pagans, partly by curiosity to see
new things. Across the Alps, Dalmatia and Epirus to Byzantium,
thence to Antioch, and finally to Jerusalem he went. He fought

bravely beneath Jerusalem walls, and while the holy city was besieged, made the acquaintance of a Saracen lady. She lived in a square, white-washed house that stood amid gardens of fragrant flowers not far from the Crusaders' camp. She was a woman of evil life, but young and handsome. Carried away by her foreign charm, far from the sound of his native church bells, and because men think many things permitted in a strange land, Guillaume forgot his soul's safety in the pagan girl's tender amber arms. On his return to France, the holy city taken, he remembered this Saracen girl more vividly than the Holy Sepulchre.

The Count of Blois, when he got back, built a new chapel to the Virgin, but Guillaume, when he had finished carving her statue found, that unknowingly, he had carved it in the very image of the Saracen girl with whom he had sinned. And it soon turned out that Guillaume's Virgin was not a good one. When prayers were put up to her for one who was ill, he died. When the peasants prayed for rain, their crops were destroyed by drought. A woman who had made a novena, praying that a boy might be born to her, gave birth to two daughters. And—more terrible still—the young girls who prayed to Guillaume's Virgin that they might be delivered from temptation, invariably fell victims to it! For the beautiful statue, with its long tender eyelashes, was haunted by a demon. It was haunted by a devil because there was a devil in Guillaume. And the devil haunted Guillaume because he could not forget the kisses of the Saracen girl. So, as Guillaume fell more and more from grace, and became more and more dissolute in his habits, until he seemed to be a very Mohammedan himself, the deceitful idol he had carved multiplied her refusals to cure the sick, bless the fruits of the earth, and guard the virtue of honest maidens.

Now in all the French countryside there was no brighter maid than little Toinon, the goat-girl. Her soul was a treasure of innocence and goodness which might have filled the angels with delight. One day she came to the chapel to pray that the Virgin might cure her grandmother, who was ill. And Guillaume was there and saw her. For Guillaume often came to the chapel to renew his memories of the Mohammedan lady, and to enjoy the sight of his unvirginal Virgin. Toinon, with her innocent blue eyes and her golden hair, took his fancy. When she left the chapel he followed her and tried to make love to her—as he understood love. But she looked at him with such surprise, that he soon felt ashamed and left her. When she reached home, Toinon found her grandmother not yet cured, but sleeping and better. And the next day and the days after, as she came to the chapel to pray, the Saracen Virgin's face began to change. Little by little, it grew more and more Christian and kind. It seemed as though Toinon's prayers were gradually giving the Saracen Virgin a soul like her own innocent girlish one. And Guillaume, watching her from a corner, felt the demon influence of the statue diminish bit by bit as his heart became filled with an honest love for this little Toinon. At last, one day, Toinon, coming home, found her grandmother up and cooking a good soup. It was the first time that the Guillaume's Virgin had granted a prayer!

She had been released from her evil enchantment. So Toinon, full of happiness, hurried out to tell the neighbors the good news. And when she met Guillaume the stone-cutter on the way, and he tenderly yet respectfully asked her hand in marriage, she did not say no. From that day on Guillaume's Virgin performed all the miracles for which one could ask. And, strange to say, it was noticed after a time that her eyes, which before had been overlong and black, had turned oval and nearly blue. Her mouth, once a passionate red, like the heart of a pomegranate, had grown lily-pale, and her whole face had taken on a more honest, decent look— whether due to the departure of the devil which had haunted her, or to the effect of time and use.

A HANGMAN'S NOOSE OF ROSES

The Lord of Fasting,* the wise king of Tezcuco, so loved Xocotzin, called the Lady of Tula, whom he had raised from a concubine to a queen, and made the undisputed mistress of his heart, that he did whatever she asked, and even tried to anticipate her wishes. Now one day, without evil intent, Xocotzin complained to the king that some of the courtiers had made loose jests in her presence. And the king in his anger made a law condemning any one who spoke a licentious word in the palace to death. "Whether he be rich or poor, high or low, the veriest beggar or a member of my own family, he shall die!" said the Lord of Fasting.

Not long after this law had been made, the king's favorite son, Prince Willow-Tree-Planter returned, a youth of seventeen, from the priestly college where he had completed his education, and was assigned quarters in the great palace. And then, alas, one day, as a young *coco,* a palace serving-maid, passed through a hall in which he stood with some dignitaries, he jestingly called her by some endearing names which had reference to her firm young breasts.

The young maid, who thought that she would be put to death if she neglected to report the insult, pushed aside the door-keeper, and

---

* The King of Tezcuco was one of the subject kings of the great Aztec Emperor Montezuma (1519 A.D.), and "The Lord of Fasting" was not a *title,* but his own proper name. The Aztecs had many of these, to us curious proper names, such as: "Obsidian Snake," "Waterface," "Skyarrow," "Earring-Snake," "Black Flower," "Earthen Jug," etc.

ran at once into the Hall of Embassies, where she cast herself at the king's feet and sobbed forth her tale.

Then the Lord of Fasting knew that he had been caught in the unbreakable mesh of the web he himself had spun. At first his fear clutched at the hope that the slave-girl had heard amiss. But the ear-witnesses for whom he sent in secret, did not dare to lie, and confirmed her story. Then the king pronounced judgment on his own flesh and blood. In vain his nobles begged him to spare himself. In vain the Emperor Montezuma sent him messages. In vain the Lady of Tula knelt before his throne with her little ones, and sought to move him. For the first and only time he turned a deaf ear to her pleas and ordered her to be led away.

Yet he softened his cruel verdict so that the boy whom he loved above all his other children should not know of his approaching death. The young prince was led into one of the blossoming palace gardens, and there his comrades informed him that the king, his father, had forgiven him.

In a rapture of happiness the young prince adorned himself with roses, and his comrades, too, wound nooses and wreaths of flowers and cast them about his neck and then, still laughing, they quickly drew their nooses tight, so that he was suffocated by the intoxicating blossoms—at the supreme moment of his happiness, with a glad smile on his paling lips!

CHAPTER XVII

PICTURES OUT OF THE MONGOL EAST

LIKE the hordes of Atilla and the Turks, the Mongols of the Middle Ages are wild swarms of yellow horsemen who break out of Mongolian deserts and conquer the Asian world on a diet of meat and mare's milk. Great Khans or overlords like Jengis (1218-1227), Kublai (1269) who prayed to Christ, Mohammed, Moses and Buddha to be on the safe side, Timur, Baber (1505-1530), Akbar, the Mongol conquerers of India (1556-1605) are the great names of their days of glory. The pictures which follow give glimpses of Mongol life, barbarians and crudely cruel in the days of Jengis and Timur, and one less terrible, from the days of the great Mongol Emperor of India, Hoomayoon (1530-1556), whose father Babur invaded and subdued India in 1528.

The Mongol Soul. The soul of the yellow Mongol hordes, the "yellow peril" of the Medieval world, is that of the savage. Their life was the life of the savage huntsman, and *human* game was to them like any other they hunted. Blood and cruelty, dark superstition, greed and savage bestiality stain their earth progress until in Ottoman and Mongol Indian the refining influences of higher civilizations exert a softening effect. Then we find that the Mongol heart opens to the chivalrous impulse, and develops a capacity for human emotion. In the last tale of this group we also obtain an idea of the cruel suffering which the *caste* system of Brahminisms entailed on the *pariahs,* the caste of the outcasts, human creatures denied all human rights by the fanatic laws of a monstrous creed.

THE PASSING OF JENGIS KHAN

Jengis Khan was near death. During his last weeks he often had himself carried to his treasure-house. In public he pretended to despise pomp and splendor. He went about dressed in leather and iron In secret, however, he could sit for hours among his treasures, playing with flashing jewels, pearls and golden coins. Often he looked back on his long life. He realized that all the joys and ambitions that first had seemed so interesting and important to him had grown stale and flat with the passing years. And when he knew that he had not long to live, his thoughts turned more and more to his daughter Alang, for his son Hia was weak-brained.

One day he knew his end was very near. So he sent for Hia and Alang. When they came he sat up on his couch, propped against cushions and said: "Hia, I know that you are a fool! The Khan Marzuk had returned against my command, and means to seize the throne and your sister Alang. So you and Alang must be married. The marriage must take place in three hours' time. Then I will give you my seal ring and you shall be the Khan of Khans. But I shall die before night!" And this Jengis Khan said in spite of the fact that he knew Alang secretly loved Marzuk. The brother and sister bowed before him and went.

Hia dressed himself in splendid garments of silk and purple linen, and adorned himself with rich jewels. Then he mounted his horse and with his retinue rode through the streets. Two trumpeters went before him, blowing their trumpets and crying: "Long live Hia, Khan of Khans!" People came to the doors of their houses and pulled off their caps, and a few cried, "Long live Khan Hia!" But many looked displeased and said nothing, and the Tatar warriors among the crowd called out mocking words after the procession.

As Alang passed from her father's room to her own chamber she saw Marzuk standing in a window-niche. He smiled at her with glowing eyes and his white teeth shone.

"Why do you smile at me, Marzuk?" asked Alang.

"Because you are the fairest creation of Allah I have ever seen in my life!" he answered.

"If that be true, then why do you not kiss me?" she asked.

And Alang climbed to her chamber and sat down on a chest and looked out of the open window. Marzuk came in and looked at her unchanging face as she continued to gaze out on the whirling snowflakes. Then he bolted the door, lifted her high in his arms and kissed her, and his eyes gleamed like the eyes of a wolf. And Alang flung her arms around his neck and cried, "Marzuk!" and coiled up in his embrace like a serpent. "I hold the empire in my hand!" he cried. Alang laughed: "Do you not hear my brother's trumpeters and the people cheering him?" she asked. "The empire shall be yours, though you will have to kill my brother Hia. But you must swear that you will make me your first wife!" And then she laughed: "Who bolted the door from the inside? I do not remember bolting it. My maids will say: 'Alang has her lover in her chamber in bright daylight! . . . yet he is a hero and thousands obey his voice.'" But my brother Hia is returning with his courtiers and lickspittles. So you must come with me now, at once! We will go to my father and he shall give you his seal-ring."

Jengis Khan lay alone in his great bare room. For his slaves were sneaking along the long corridors of the great palace. They were breaking open locked doors, and hunting up and stealing costly garments and silver utensils and great elephants' tusks, which had been found in the far North, under the snows. And they dragged along their stolen goods, panting and perspiring, with guilty haste. They feared that any moment Jengis Khan might wake from his death-sleep and step out of his room among them. So they hastened most when they passed his door, though one impudent knave called out loudly: "I'll kill him if he comes out!" But the others pushed him and he fell on the ground, for he was loaded with long trailing bolts of silk. In the gloomy treasure-vault the wife of Jengis Khan was roaming about. She was selecting the most precious jewels and pearls, gems which could easily be hidden. And she put on one side great bags of gold coin, to take to her room. For when Jengis Khan died she meant to flee. She feared the new master, whether her son or another.

Jengis Khan's eyes were only half-closed. He whistled as he breathed. But he raised his eyelids when Alang and Marzuk entered. Alang called into his ear: "My lord father, this is my bridegroom! Give him your ring!" Jengis could not move a limb, but his eye-balls turned upward so that they could see the whites of his eyes, and he clenched his fist firmly on the ring.

But Jengis Khan did not move. His figure seemed to have shrunk and yet to have grown heavier.

"He is dead, Alang!" said Marzuk.

"If he is dead then we must open his hand while it still is warm and flexible, so that we can get the ring," said Alang. And she tried to open the clenched hand. But Jengis Khan's fist was so tightly clenched that the girl could not open it. Then Marzuk tried and exerted all his strength, but he could not open the hand either. Jengis Khan's eyes had remained fixed after the last slow movement he had made. One could only see their whites. Alang seized her lover's sword and cut into the finger-joint.

Marzuk turned away.

"It is for your sake that I do it!" cried Alang, and handed him the ring.

Then both went out of the palace and mounted their horses. The ring of Jengis Khan sparkled on Marzuk's hand. And all the Tartar warriors crowded around him, shouting joyfully, "Long live Marzuk, Khan of Khans!" while the snowflakes melted on their glowing faces. Hia was abandoned by all his followers. As he stood alone and deserted he was seized and at once cast into prison. But Marzuk spoke to the warriors and told them it was well that Jengis Khan had died. "For Jengis Khan favored the common people, who bend their backs and till the ground, who carry on trade and grow rich in stone houses. But I will turn the world into a smooth race-course, where my proud riders can play knightly games!"

THE PRICE OF POWER

Night, black night, without. Only a lamp burns dimly in the tent of Hadschi Berlas, the Tatar Khan. He lies stretched out across his couch, asleep. Suddenly a shadow crosses the light of the lamp. Timur stands before his uncle. There is a hollow whistling sound. With his left hand Hadschi Berlas' nephew, young Timur, tears away the head the saber in his right has severed. In the white light of dawn two figures mount the minaret tower. While Timur flings down the bloody head into the market-place, his astrologer Guines proclaims him Khan of Khans. Descending, he rides out into the plains. The emirs and *murzas* fling their caps up in the air, they cast themselves on the ground. They beat the earth nine times with their foreheads, in salutation to the new master.

PUNISHMENT AND REWARD

Tatar hordes break out of the desert steppes. Their heads are shaven. They have big ankles and ride wild, small-hoofed horses. Bows and quivers filled with arrows hang across their sides. Behind their squadrons trot camels loaded with women, children and provisions. They set out from the plains around Samarcand, and wherever they go they slay and destroy. They cannot pass through the hills into the Persian lowlands. So huge fires are built, and when the rocky mountain walls glow red-hot a river held in check by a dam is unloosed. The icy mountain waters strike the glowing basalt. It bursts, the road into Persia is free, and Persia is made subject to the Khan. And so it is everywhere. In Georgian Kars, the Tatars tear down the roses from their iron stakes and plant men on them instead. When in ten years' time the hordes—among whom Timur has ridden and fought in disguise—have conquered a third of Asia, the Tatar armies are recalled to Samarcand. There on the plain stands the throne of the Khan of Khans. It is empty till from the rear rank of one of the squadrons a small man rides forth. He is lame and drags one foot after him. But all the soldiers recognize him and call his name as he seats himself on the throne. That night great fires gleam on the plain. They gleam on the dead, the men and officers Timur had ordered impaled for neglect of duty, and on the drunken, who lie scattered about from the gardens of Samarcand to the extreme end of the great prairie, for Timur has given them their fill of fermented *kuymiss* to drink.

ON THE RUSSIAN STEPPE

A great silver cloud lies over the steppes of Muscovy. The Tatar host and the levies of the Russian princes met in battle. Wild Tatar shouts mingle with the Greek psalms of the Muscovites. The light Hungarian horsemen the Muscovites have hired break the Tatar center. But a new swarm of Tatar horsemen charges them in the flank. And while the steel battle-trumpets of the Muscovites call, the Tatar arrows sink with a splurging sound into the bellies of their foemen's horses, as though they were sinking into yielding sand-bags. Red clouds overhang the battlefield. Tatar horsemen ride up to khans in command of detachments, driving long rows of prisoners before them and crying "Prisoners? Slaves?" But the khans shake their heads, for Timur has ordered that no prisoners be taken, and the curved sabers flash.

A MESSAGE TO THE SON OF HEAVEN

Yakou Zeinabeddin, the son of Khan Yakou, rides to the land of the Chinese emperor. He rides on a mission. In time, with his two hundred Tatars, he reached Yung Ming Yung. There a black eunuch enters his tent to lead him to the palace. It is a huge building with many towers, from which hang silver bells that tinkle in the breeze. Zeinabeddin, with twenty *murzas,* enters a courtyard where oily eunuchs are drawn up in rows. He passes through a garden, and at last comes to a golden pavillon. The emperor sits on his throne, fan-bearers and parasol-holders about him. Suddenly there is a great blare of music, and all the Chinese present fall on their faces as a screen hiding the emperor is withdrawn. Over their prostrate bodies Zeinabeddin steps to the throne and receives from the Monarch's chancellor the talisman which is a sign of peace, a small square of white jade-stone, on which mystic signs are engraved. And holding the jade-stone in his hand, Zeinabeddin says, carelessly: "The Khan of Khans demands the provinces of Pazanfu and Panquinfu!" The Chinese emperor does not move a muscle of his face. He looks at and beyond Zeinabeddin. Then he speaks a word to his chancellor. The latter turns to the interpreter and the interpreter says to Zeinabeddin: "The Son of Heaven bids you tell your master that only his kindness of heart has thus far kept him from placing the little rice-bowl of the Tatar kingdom on his table!" Zeinabeddin at once begins to shout and stamp his feet. The twenty *murzas* draw their swords. But the gilded screen is contemptuously placed before the throne again, and as he looks around the court he sees it bristling with soldiers.

THE REPLY

It is spring again. The Tatar hordes sweep in tremendous floods toward the Chinese border. Their bows are slung across their backs. Their short, curved swords hang at their sides. The steppes lie bare behind them. They fling themselves in their thousands against the great wall of China which towers before them, white in the sun.

They break down a part of the wall, and flood the country. Two days later the Tartars howl with glee as they tear the gold earrings from the ears of the slain, while the captive Chinese emperor whom Timur has promised his life is borne apart on Tatar sabers in Timur's presence.

IN SAMARCAND

In Samarcand Timur has built him a splendid palace on the plain of Kjanegul, amid the fragrant rose-bowers. Artists from Bagdad have painted its dome with arabesques of a thousand colors. The courts are paved with marble, the walls are wainscoted with alabaster. Wise sayings from the Koran gleam above the archways—turquoise-blue green, pink and gold—of the doors. All the doors are of bronze. Bell-towers rise from the corners of the building. Below the palace is a vast underground hall. When the new palace is completed Miser Plek, one of Timur's five "Great Wives" conspires against him, and the Khan of Khans has her hung with a silken cord from the window of her chamber above the rose-bushes of the gardens.

BELL-CHIMES OF THE BOSPHORUS

The Tatar tents cover the plains near Constantinople. It is night. A messenger is led into the great silk tent of the Khan of Khans. He bows slightly and says that his master, the great Sultan Bajazet, will give battle on the morrow. Timur beckons an attendant, and the latter says: "The Khan of Khans makes you a present of a steed!" The Turkish *emir's* eyes glow. "Ask whether I may honor the gift by riding it in the battle!" The slave smiles: "The Khan of Khans will take it back tomorrow," he says. On the evening of the next day Timur enters the Sultan's tent, stepping on the fallen monarch's back. The Tatars build towers of the heads of the slain, towers that rise as high in the air as the minarets of Samarcand. The hordes roll over Constantinople. They set the tower bell-chimes ringing, and camp in the gardens along the Bosphorus. Their turbans are hung with jewels as though they were women. They cut themselves saddle-cloths out of the costly Persian praying rugs of the mosques. They wind chains of gold through their matted locks, and make reins for their horses out of them.

THE GARDEN OF GALBUDSAMUR FLOWERS

The Tartar hosts have turned. They are on their way to Egypt. When the Khan of Khans enters Tauris, where one of his sons is governor, he finds the gates unguarded. The palace gardens are bright with hundreds of lamps and lanterns. Musicians, loose women and drunken merry-makers are reveling among the bushes. The Khan of Khans dismounts. He leaves his saddled horse in the courtyard, with the *murzas* who have accompanied him. He enters the great hall of the palace. The windows are open on the rear gardens that stand out violet-blue in the first light of dawn. On a heap of rugs lies the governor, Timur's son, in drunken slumber. The floor is covered with wine-cups from which the spilled wine has run. In one corner a drunken drummer weakly raises his arm from time to time, and deals his drum a feeble blow. Everywhere, on rugs and on the stone pavement of the floor, lie wine-floundered revelers. A nightingale is singing on a branch before the window, but the sleepers do not hear her song. The Khan of Khans does not disturb his son, who lies with one arm flung carelessly across the white breast of some favorite of an hour. He steps out into the court and orders his tent set up in the garden.

In the morning, before he mounts, he sends for the prince: "I have but a few minutes to give you," he says. "What have you done since you have been governor here? Which provinces have you conquered? Which princes have you slain? Have you taken fortresses and blown up cities? Have you captured artists and builders and put up great buildings? Have you suppressed revolts? Have you increased your army? Haste to tell me, for I must go!"

The prince's eyes seek the ground.

"You have done nothing," says the Khan of Khans. "You have reveled. You have drunk. Your province and city is unguarded. You have not extended your boundaries. You have put wreathes of flowers on your head like a Greek!

The prince raises his head:

"Have you not celebrated feasts like no other Khan before you? Has not the plain around Samarcand been covered with the bodies of drunken soldiers? Is your harem not the largest of all?" he asked.

"I have *earned* my feasts," said his father, and his face grew dark and gloomy. "Do you know anything of the adventures of the spirit, the battles of the soul? Have you withstood temptation? Have you trodden the path of thorns which leads from thought to deed? I cannot bear the sight of blood, yet I must pour it out to rise like none before me have risen!"

The terrified youth begs for mercy. "I would send you to the deserts of Cipribet where I keep the *emirs* I have disgraced," Timur says, "but—I cannot let you live, for I have told you too much!" As the youth sinks to the ground Tatars bind him and carry him to a garden of Galbudsamur flowers. They are white and beautiful, but their fragrance poisons the very winds which blows them. There they lay him down.

THE WIND-ROSE OF THE ASIAN WORLD

The Tartar hordes flood over the Syrian cities of the Seacoast;

they break down the walls of Jerusalem; their arrows fall in thick clouds over Damascus. They cross the Red Sea and their catapults set Cairo afire. The Mamelukes who fall into their hands they hang up by the feet. When he sees his fortress crash to earth the Egyptian sultan flings himself from the top of the dam into the yellow flood of the Nile!

Again the Tartar hordes, the wild swarms of yellow horsemen, break out from Samacrand. They ride and ride. They cross the mountain passes into India. They cross the Indus. Their living prisoners the Tatars pile together into towers. Wet lime is poured among the mass of bodies, and wooden frames built around them. During long hours the towers sway to and fro in the plains, until finally they stand fixed and still. One Indian prince whom the Tatars capture is so handsome that all the women of the Great Khan's harem beg that he be spared. Timur smiles but—to honor his beauty—is rolled to death in silken rugs! Delhi falls amid rivers of blood as the Tatar sword strikes and strikes until arms drop with weariness. And on the morning after Delhi's fall the Khan of Khan's calls his astrologer Guines into his tent. When the astrologer comes the Great Khan draws out a wind-rose, a compass-card of the Asian world. And when messengers arrive to say that the last Hindoo rajah is hanging by his prayer-beads from the high window of his palace, the Khan of Khans fills in the last spot of white on the compass with red. "I have gained my end!" he says. "For the Asian world lies in my hand, it rocks to the pulse of my breath, there is not a man or beast in it that does not bow beneath my arrows!"

THE LIVER-EATER'S* PROPHECY

It was a time of famine in India, the splendid golden India of the Great Mogul, of the Emperor Humayoon, son of Akbar. And in time of famine it was the *pariahs*, the lowest, vilest and most degraded class of beings in the land from the standpoint of the Hindoos in the *castes* above them, who died first. Vuluvir the poor *pariah*

---

* The Hindoo *jiggerkhar* or "liver-eater" is a magician or witch supposed to be able to steal away another person's liver by means of the "evil eye," magic "looking over" and incantations. Looking at a victim, the *jiggerkhar* makes him unconscious, then steals from him something that looks like a pomegrante seed. This the *jiggerkhar* hides in the calf of his or her leg. When the magician throws this seed on the fire it spreads out to the size of a dish. Then the *jiggerkhar* breaks it up and hand it about to fellow-magicians, who devour it. And when the last morsel has been swallowed, the person bewitched will have died. The *jiggerkhar* teaches the incantations to his pupils and makes them eat the "liver-cake." But if the liver-seed is taken from the *jiggerkhar's* calf and eaten by the victim he will recover at once. Most *jiggerkhars* are women and all are able to perform many tragic feats.

with whom our story deals, was gazing gloomily at the mighty Ganges, which flooded past the door of his hovel. His beloved young wife, not yet fifteen, though the mother of three children, had just divided a handful of grain with her brood. Vulivir had followed a drove of oxen all morning long, collecting their dung, and after washing the ordure had secured enough *gram*—the small Indian bean—to keep body and soul of his loved ones together a few hours longer. To such straights was he reduced. But it would be wrong to say body and "soul", speaking of Hindoo *pariahs*. The *pariah* has no soul. He pollutes the earth, yet has nothing to hope for beyond the grave. Without any motive to preserve life, he has an equal dread of losing it. To be a *pariah* is to be damned both living and dead. While these thoughts crossed Vulivir's mind he saw a horseman dash into the river from the opposite bank, to cross the flood. But overborne by the current, it was not long before he began to sink, weighed down by his heavy clothing. It was then that the *pariah*, leaping into the water, swam out to him and succeeded in dragging him ashore. When he regained consciousness the man he had saved cried: "What, is it possible that a *pariah*, a Hindoo, who thinks the touch of another man not of his own race defiles him, recues a Mohammedan!" The *pariah* smiled sadly. "*Pariahs* do not think this," he said. "I am glad that the hand whose touch is a pollution to other Hindoos has saved a Mohammedan, who does not shudder to owe it his life!"

The stranger smiled. "Even high rank among Mohammedans yields to the laws of gratitude! *Pariah*, let me share your hut!" The *pariah* clasped his hands: "Such as it is—my wife and three children are dying in it of hunger—it is yours!" "Hunger?" cried the stranger. "See, my horse has found its way ashore. It carries a package of provisions, so we can cure their hunger." And taking from the back of the faithful animal, which now trotted up, a package of cold meats, rice and some bottles of Persian wine, the stranger entered the hut with the grateful outcast. There, by degrees, the sufferers were fed and revived. But—that very night the stranger himself fell into a hectic fever, which rose to delirium in the course of another day. But as the *pariah* and his wife uniting in giving him every tender care, he rapidly mended. During his illness the pariah had taken from the stranger's money-bag, which held some six thousand rupees, enough to buy food for them all, but not a rupee more. When quite restored to health, the stranger one day announced his departure. But when he attempted to thank his humble host, the latter would not hear of it, but said he and those dearer to him than life itself were the ones to be grateful. "You do not know whom you have sheltered?" asked his guest. "No, nor am I curious. Are you not my benefactor and a fellow-creature?" "Nevertheless, you shall know. I am the Emperor Humayoon. A rebel has driven me from my throne, and I must enlist the aid of some foreign prince to help me back on it." At once the *pariah* and his wife flung themselves at the Great Mogul's feet, but the latter said: "Take this ring, and this gold and may they keep you in the future from suffering such privations as you already have endured!" The ring he took from his finger and handed the pariah was a large ruby, of great value, and with it went a bag of two thousand gold rupees. Then amid their tears of joy the fallen emperor rode away.

By trading in cattle the Emperor's gold had purchased, the *pariah* grew rich in the course of a few years, and as he grew rich his daughter Yhahil grew in beauty and loveliness. Yet—no man, save some abject wretch of her own caste—would marry the daughter of a *pariah,* no matter how rich he might be. Marriage is the end and aim of existence for a Hindoo woman. Condemned to a frightful fate, poor Yhahil began to pine with this secret sorrow gnawing at her breast. The *pariah* grieved. Now he was even more an outcast—were that possible—than before. His riches placed a bar between his fellow-*pariahs* and himself, though they were unable to secure his daughter a husband of a higher caste. Many a *pariah* had tried in vain to win lovely Yhahil's heart. Unlike her father, however, most *pariahs* were on the level of the brute in intelligence, and "familiar with habits which outraged humanity." Yhahil could pity, but she could not love her *pariah* suitors. Yet one *pariah* youth was an exception to the debased rule of his race. He was good looking, he was intelligent, he even was refined. But—Yhahil did not love him, though he gladly would have died for her. One day he could contain himself no longer. "Yhahil," he cried, "why do you despise me?" "I do not despise you, Guatama," she answered, "but no one's heart is their own." Guatama shook his head. "Whom can you hope to marry if not a *pariah?*" he asked. "I must find a husband I love and a man of caste—or submit to the curse of maidenhood!" was Yhahil's reply. "Would you marry a Brahmin if only because he was a Brahmin?" "No, but I would not marry a *pariah* even though I loved him. I could have loved you, Guatama, were you not a *pariah!* If I marry I must live as a member of a respected community." And with that Guatama had to content himself. Celibacy is the greatest stigma a Hindoo woman can undergo. Yet Yhahil was willing to bear her shame unless she could find a husband who could raise among his fellows a head unbranded by pollution. Besides, could a gentle and refined girl look with anything but disgust on Guatama's occupation. It was not the poor wretch's fault, for only the lowest vocations were open to him. But—he worked as a scavanger in a nearby village! He collected cow-dung to plaster the floors of the lower-class Hindoo huts, he prepared the bodies of the dead for the funeral pyre, and did other degrading duties. Never, though the lovely girl occasionally admitted him to her presence, could she think of a man so busied without a sickening revulsion of heart. So even though her mother pleaded with her to unite herself with Guatama, she answered: "At least I have a choice of miseries in this world. And I would rather suffer those arising from an unwedded life, than those of a union which would make me wretched!"

But Guatama was soon to prove, and in a tragic way, that his soul could rise above the low level of the floors he laid in the Hindoo huts. One morning as Yhahil was bathing in the river, the attendant beside her screamed. Raising her eyes, she saw a huge crocodile nearby upon her. She sank fainting into her attendant's arms to be roused by a faint cry. It was Guatama, clutched in the monster's jaws. "I have saved you, Yhahil!" he cried and—a few bloody bubbles rising to the surface of the water testified at what cost. Yhahil shed bitter tears at home. She knew she could have loved Gautama had he not been a *pariah*. Yet her resolve to rise above her race was as changeless as ever. And she made up her mind to see whether, by taking a glance into the hidden future, she might not discover if there were any prospect of her hopes ever being realized.

Not far from the rich *pariah's* dwelling there lived a *jiggerkhar,* a fearsome old witch-woman with gray tangled locks. To her, though she was dreaded by the whole surrounding countryside, Yhahil went to have her future forecast. In a deep cave on the north side of a hill, where the golden sunbeams never entered, where no shrub grew among the rocks, but lizards and serpents glided among them instead, Yhahil, the pround *pariah* girl found the frightful hag whom she was seeking. Her hair was like the wiry grass that hangs from the crests of sun-scorched rocks, her wrinkles were so close together that a needle-point could not have been put between them. The skin clung to the bones of her face so that it was hard to tell what was skin and what was bone. Her lurid eyes gleamed dully beneath from fallen lids. When Yhahil drew near she flung a gold *mohur** into the hag's lap and cried: "Mother I have come to ask a favor!" The jiggerkhar silenced the howling blind *pariah* dog in her lap. "Since you know how to ask, it shall be granted, maiden," she said. "Tell me something of my future, mother, the future your eye pierces with the brightness of a star, though to me it is dim and hidden!" Yhahil continued. Then after greasing the greedy palm of the repulsive soothsayer with two additional gold-pieces, Yhahil followed her into her gloomy cave. There the witch

* A coin worth about thirty-five shillings or twenty rupees.

said to her: "You are a *pariah* girl who refuses to marry a man of her own caste! Yet you shall marry! . . . . Never," cried Yhahil, "I would sooner die than marry a *pariah!*"

"Yet you shall marry—and *not a pariah!*" And with that she had to be content for the time. Again and again she visited the old crone, and crossed her palm with gold, and again and again the latter repeated her first saying but told her nothing new. For though the *jiggerkhar* muttered her magic spells to compel the revelations of the hidden powers, she was for a time unsuccessful. But at last, one night, Yhahil, saw a sudden flash break the gloom of the cavern. A blue streak of light rose from the floor, and illumined the rocky chamber. The old woman stood behind the flame, which flung a gray quivering radiance on her frightful face and form. A snake was coiled around her neck, a three-foot *guana*, a lizard of the rocks, crawled at her feet, and though Yhahil grew pale, she listened eagerly to every word of the *jiggerkhar's* prophecy:

"Girl, your destiny has been weighed and spoken!" said the hag. "You will not live to waste away as a maiden, but shall die ennobled, the mother of beautiful sons and daughters! To do so you must go to the Mogul capital and there discover what fortune has in store for you! I have spoken!"

When Yhahil told her father that she wished to go to Delhi he eagerly fell in with her idea, for he welcomed a change of scene. And once settled in the Mogul city, Yhahil's personal charms did not long remain a secret. For the *pariah* women did not cover their faces when they walked abroad, and whenever Yhahil left the house a buzz of admiration rose in the surrounding streets. Then, one morning as she was walking through a crowded bazaar, she was accidentally struck down by a palanquin-pole. The person in the palanquin at once got out, had her lifted into his litter, and taken to her home. Her father, rushing out in alarm, was soon calmed when he found his daughter had suffered no more than a shock, and invited the courteous stranger who had first knocked her down, then picked her up, into his house. The latter accepted and, much to the *pariah's* delight, turned out to be the *Omrah** Sulim, son of Beiram Chan, prime minister to the Emperor Humayoon. The handsome young noble had been wavering in his affection between three fair Mohammedan ladies of the Emperor's court. Now he desired only lovely Yhahil. But—how could a Moslem noble stoop to marry the daughter of a Hindoo outcast? Nor did Sulim think it necessary. He felt sure that Yhahil would accept the kind of alliance he meant to propose to her. So one day while they were seated in a summer pavilion in the beautiful gardens in the rear of her father's house, he said: "Yhahil, would you be happy if you left your parents?" "But

---

* *Omrah,* a noble or high official under the Mogul Emperors of India.

I know of no reason why I should leave them," she replied. "Suppose you married?" "Could they not still be with me?" "Your husband might not like them," the young Omrah said, slowly. "If he could not like those I love then he would be no fit husband for me," answered the spirited girl. "But suppose you were living with one you loved, loved fondly and truly, without being bound by the compulsory obligations of marriage?" Yhahil smiled. "I never could be in such a position," she remarked. "Yhahil," said the young noble, earnestly, "could you not share my love free from those civil restraints which, as a poet has said, "so often chill the warm glow of hearts and make wedlock a round of dull, monotonous dissatisfaction?" Yhahil rose and answered proudly: "Sulim, I am a girl innocent of the world's ways! I know little of life's artifices! I have been impressed by your delicate attentions. Yet—the moment they cease being delicate, my respect for you will be at an end! I would rather be a *pariah's* wife than an *Omrah's* right-of-love!"

And dismissing the handsome young noble, Yhahil thereafter refused to receive him when he called. But the Moslem, roused by her opposition, had set his heart upon possessing her. One morning Yhahil left her home as usual with her attendant—but she did not return at the accustomed hour. And her father, only too well aware of what probably had happened to her, resolved in this hour of need, to appeal to the Great Mogul himself, the Emperor Humayoon, whom he once had befriended, to obtain justice on his daughter's ravisher.

The next day he hastened to the *Dewan Aum*, or Hall of Public Audience of the palace. When he entered he was dazzled by the splendor of the sight it presented. The Emperor Humayoon was seated on the famous *musnud*, the "peacock-throne." It was shaped like a peacock, and the bird's outspread tail was formed entirely of glittering diamonds, rubies and other precious stones. The walls and columns of the hall were of white marble, ornamented with flower-designs. And over the roof-arches Persian letters, silverbright against the dark polished marble said: "If there be a heaven on earth, it is here, it is here, it is here!" Beside the throne was a great luminous block of crystal as large as a great table. On this the Emperor sat when holding a private council with his ministers. Light filtered down in a soft, radiant glow through the gold-inlaid dome of the roof.

When the *pariah* attempted to draw near the emperor, however, a guard herded him back, and told him that he could not see the ruler in person, but would have to address a petition to him. And when the *pariah* insisted on advancing, the guard cried: "Another step and I shall cut you down!" The *pariah* stepped forward and then, crying "My blood be upon your head!" leaped aside as the guards hewed at the place he just had left with his scimitar, calling out in a loud, shrill voice that echoed through the great hall: "Justice, justice from the great Emperor of the Moguls!" Humayoon raised his head from the petition he was reading, and said with mild dignity: "Let him who demands justice approach!" And when the *pariah* rose after his prostration, Humayoon at once recognized him, descended from the *musnud,* and clasped him in his arms, to the court's surprise. Then he told them how Vulivir had saved his life. Seating him by his own imperial side on the block of crystal, he listened to his story. The *Omrah* Sulim was at once called before him, ordered to restore the stolen daughter to her father's home, and then taken to prison. At the Emperor's suggestion Vulivir abjured his Hindoo faith, which made him a worm to be trod upon while he lived, and blew him away into nothingness when he died, and became a moslem. Then Humayoon at once raised him to the rank of *Omrah,* and gave him splendid estates to support his new dignity.

Yhahil, to whose purity young Sulim had offered no offense when he had abducted her, though he had warmly pressed his suit, had forgiven him. She felt sorry to think he languished in prison. But when she asked her father to plead with the Emperor for his release he cried: "Surely the man who tore a child from beneath her father's roof by force is to be feared!" Yhahil smiled. In the East as in the West women know how practical considerations influence the hearts of men. "He sought to win me dishonestly when I was only a *pariah* girl," she said. "He may be glad to marry me as an *Omrah's* daughter. Besides—I love him!" When Mohomed Chan—for such was Vulivir's new title—preferred his request to the emperor, Humayoon had the young offender brought before him. Sulim was only too ready to marry Yhahil to atone for his scandalous offense. But when Mohomed Chan took him to his home to ask fair Yhahil's forgiveness she, like any other girl or any other age, received him with withering coldness. Not until he had passionately admitted his fault, not until he had cried: "I have wronged you, object of my soul's adoration! Will you not become mine?" did she relent and allow the young *Omrah* to clasp her to his breast. They were married the same day, and the Great Mogul himself honored the wedding by his presence, and the newly wed pair with his blessing. Thus was the *jiggerkhar's* prophecy fulfilled. Nor was there ever a happier married pair than the *pariah's* daughter and the Moslem noble's son.

CHAPTER XVIII

HUMAN NATURE IN THE RENAISSANCE

THE Renaissance or "rebirth," is the name given the fifteenth and sixteenth centuries. In them there was a new enthusiasm, a great "revival" of interest in the arts and literature of ancient Greece and Rome. The world was passing from the Gothic Age to Modern Times. In literature men no longer thought only of "divine" literature which, aside from the lays and songs of the knightly troubadours, had been practically the only kind cultivated. The study of the old classic writers roused an interest in "human" literature, literature which dealt with the world and the human beings in it.

The Sixteenth Century in the World at Large. In the sixteenth and part of the seventeenth century, the Renaissance spirit encouraged by popes and princes, led artists of every kind to create beauty in many ways. But with the coming of the Reformation and the breaking away of princes in every land from allegiance to the Roman Church, the great wars of religion began. In Holland, in France, in Middle Europe, during these terrible wars, both sides shed oceans of blood, insisting that their own particular *ladder of dogma* was the only one up which a Christian could *climb to heaven!* In our more tolerant age it seems that the most insane thing a man or nation can do, is to shed blood because of a difference of religious opinion.

The group of tales comprised in the present chapter is devoted only to *personal* and *human* glimpses of life in Renaissance Italy. For Italy was *the* land of the Renaissance, though its influence was expressed in France during the reign of King Francis I; in England in the "Tudor" art of King Henry VIII; and even in Spain. Our first tale is a human one of love and jealously and its consequences. Our second is one of the strangest ever told—a tale which shows the almost miraculous power human beauty had in an age when beauty was worshipped above all other things. The third and fourth tales are by actual Renaissance writers who set down stories of the life in their own day in a romantic manner. All in all, we may take it that these stories give something of the spirit of human life, its weakness and strength, its nobility and cruelty, in one of the most interesting periods history has known.

LA GIOCONDA

The soul of Italian Florence was the soul of the Renaissance.
Florence was a town that every Florentine loved. He loved it
more than money, wife or child. He loved it with a passion we do
not understand in our own less romantic days. It had been the life-
dream of Duke Lorenzo the Magnificent to make Florence beautiful.
When the gloomy monk Savonarola stood by his bedside and bade
him renounce all earthly love, renounce his love for *Florence*—the
dying sinner rebelled! All else he had given up eagerly, as a dying
Christian should for his soul's peace. But when the monk asked
him to give up his love for Florence—he turned to the wall and died
without a word!

It was in this beautiful Florence, this golden, laughing Florence
of the dead Lorenzo, that the Carnival was at its height in the year
1496. Out in the street the boisterous crowd of merry-makers was
celebrating. And in the great hall of the house of Messire Francesco del Giocondo, whose windows looked out on one side of the
great square, Giocondo's guests were gathered. They were going to
watch the Carnival procession. Francesco del Giocondo was a
merchant—but none would have suspected it. He was one of those
Renaissance merchants to be found in Florence, Venice and Milan,
who sold their goods the way a nobleman sold his sword, and to the
same customers—crowned heads. Francesco del Giocondo dealt in
jewels—no, not jewels, but in one jewel only, in pearls. And his
customers were popes and emperors, kings, dukes and princes.

His guests, for the most part rich and noble Florentines, were
chatting and laughing over the wine his servants poured into tall,
thin-stemmed Venetian glasses. They were helping themselves to
the fruits which stood in a gilded basket on the table about which
they were gathered. But Francesco's eye often strayed from the
window through which all were looking down on the street, to the
balcony at one side. A flight of steps led up to it from below, and
the members of the household used to come in from the street by the
balcony door. But no one noticed his distraction for now the great
Carnival procession reached the square on which one side of the
house fronted. To the accompaniment of glad shouts and a merry
chorus the big Carnival floats, surrounded by men carrying flags,
banners and devices, swept proudly into the square. Every guest
forgot his wine-glass and craned his neck to see, and when the float
of the goddess Venus, surrounded by nymphs, bacchantes and nereids
—among them the loveliest women of Florence—appeared, the approval was general. For during Carnival time—and at other times
as well—Venus, the goddess of love and pleasure, ruled the pleasure-
loving city. But, since Leonardo's death, Savonarola's power had

been increasing. He and his black Dominican monks, the Brothers of San Marco, frowned on pleasure—and demanded penitence. They bade the people of Florence exchange light loves for litanies, roses for remorse, kisses for confessions. The hot-blooded youth of Florence laughed them to scorn, but many of the more solid burghers obeyed, and the golden sun of Florence's joy in life was overcast by the black shadows of religious fanaticism.

And so it was not surprising that just as Venus' great gilded float with its light-lived beauties appeared in the square from one end, it ran headlong in a procession of the black monks of San Marco, headed by Savonarola, which had crossed the bridge over the Arno. With the meeting of the two opposing processions the flame of hatred between the two parties burst out. But this time heaven was with its own. Not only did the Gregorian chant—the terrible hymn *Dies irae,* "Day of Wrath"—bear down the confused shouting of the Carnival mummers. But in the lull of a moment, Savonarola stepped out before his pious band. He was a magnetic orator. He was a talker whose words burned conviction into every soul. When and while he spoke he could do with Florence what he would. And he launched so bitter, biting and hateful a denunciation at Venus, that voluptuous Ginerva ad Alta Rocca, a charming light-lived young noblewomen who had consented to play the part of the goddess of pleasure, trembled and blushed—and she did not blush easily! And the mob, even her own followers, with a great cry of penitence, began to tear down the hangings and decorations from the float and push the dryads and nymphs from their places. Ginerva herself, tears of repentance in her eyes, knelt before the monk, wrapping her gauzy veils about her in shame. Such was the power of Savonarola's eloquence!

Arrigo, a friend of the fair Ginerva, had seen her jostled from her throne to fall at the gloomy monk's feet, thrilled by his voice, overcome with remorse. He turned to Francesco del Giocondo and said: "May I bring her up? . . ." Francesco hesitated. After all, Ginerva was . . . He frowned. "But Mona Lisa will arrive at any moment," he said. "She will be kind to her," said Arrigo, "even . . . Mona Lisa is kind to every one!" So Francesco nodded a consent. A moment later the penitent Venus was supported up the balcony stairs and through the balcony door, and was drawing a deep breath in one of Giocondo's chairs. "Ah," she murmured, "penitence is so sweet a thing when one has sinned!" But five minutes later, when Mona Lisa, Messire Don Francesco's wife, appeared on the balcony, Ginerva was chatting merrily and singing *ritornelle,* those bits of verse fitted to some taking air which have been made up on the spur of the moment—with the other guests.

"Who gave you the iris flowers?" asked Francesco, as soon as he saw his wife's sweet, pale face framed in the doorway. He had at once gone to meet her, and he looked at the bunch of white flowers in her hand. "No one gave them to me. They were lying by the road and I picked them up. I love iris," answered Mona Lisa. "Did you see any one?" Mona Lisa glanced at him with quiet rebuke in her eyes, and when he tried to put his arm about her shrunk from him. "I have just come from confession," she said. And then she came into the room, greeting Ginerva and her husband's guests with her calm, quiet courtesy, and at Ginerva's request to let her have some clothes to wear home, going at once with her to her room.

When she had gone Francesco drew his friend Arrigo aside and into an adjoining room, a library one of whose sides was lined with two bookcases, a curtained niche between them. And he said bitterly to his friend. "Mona Lisa never changes—toward me! She is always cold, quiet and unmoved. Her lips never smile. Her eyes never glow with emotion. She is clear and cold and silent, every day —and every night! I cannot wake a spark of response to my own ardent love in her. And yet. . ." As he spoke he drew the curtain of the recess between the bookcases, — "Look at that picture, man!" The picture was the copy Leonardo da Vinci had made of his own original for the husband of the one sitter whom the great painter had loved with a deep, pure and mystic passion. "Do you see that mysterious, sweet and tender smile? What thought prompted that smile—or what man? The face she turns to *me* is always the same, pallid, cold and calm. Gladly would I burn in hell to know the secret of that smile, Arrigo!" Arrigo shook his head. "Francesco, you are fanciful! Take care you do not lose your wits," he answered, laying his hand affectionately on del Giocondo's shoulder. The latter pulled himself together, let the curtain drop and reentering the hall, clapped his hands for candles, which the servants brought and placed on the table. As they did so a stranger was let in at the door, who called out as he entered, "I fear I am late!" He was young and handsome. Bowing to Francesco, he explained that he was Giovanni del Salviati, arrived only that day from Rome on the matter of the great pink pearl which the Holy Father had ordered. If it were not too late? . . . Francesco, with dignified courtesy, and as though to make clear that a small matter of business should not be allowed to drive his guests from the house, turned to the others and said: "Do not reach for your cloaks, good friends! If you care to see my treasures, wait a few moments!" They readily followed his invitation and Piero de Tumoni added: "It always is a sight worth seeing, and one you grant us as seldom as you do a glimpse of Mona Lisa, your most beautiful wife!" Francesco's brow darkened. "That is another matter," he answered curtly, and drawing from his doublet a long gold chain ending in a locket, he opened the locket and drew from it an odd-shaped key. Then, stepping to a tapestry that hung on the wall, he pulled it aside and the door of a cabinet was revealed. "The Holy Father in Rome, the Doge in Venice, and the King of Portugal himself have no pearls like mine," he said. "They are so beautiful that I have made a special shrine for them. First I open this outer door," and he did so, "with this key. Then I press a hidden spring—with my back toward you, for it is a secret I alone know—and the second door flies open. Both locks were made by a skilled German locksmith, long since returned to his native land." Then Francesco stood aside, so that all could look into the narrow chamber in which two men at the most could stand at a time. "The small cemented windows in the roof are of thick, green, opaque glass. They fill the room with a mysterious green twilight, as though one were at the bottom of the sea. There, built against the walls of this little chamber is a narrow altar, and on that altar stands a treasure-box. That I open with another key." And Francesco took a small gold key from his chain and turned it in the lock of the casket. As he did so the four sides of the box turned down flatly on the altar itself, and a murmur of surprise went up from the onlookers. For the box had no bottom! Instead, where it should have been yawned an oblong black hole. Francesco smiled. "But where is your jewel-casket?" asked the Pope's messenger. Francesco went to the side of the marble altar, and a windlass creaked as he began to turn a handle.

"My pearls lie in the bottom of the Arno river. An arm of the Arno river flows beneath this house. There, on the cool, underground sands I keep my pearls. To raise them I use a windlass."

"And here they are already!" cried the Roman Salviati, as a golden casket came slowly up through the black hole which been had covered by the falsehood. The casket was resting on an oblong platform which settled into place with a final click of the crank, and Francesco pointed out the little holes bored in it. "The water oozes in and out of them as the current flows. It washes against the pearls as the waters of the sea once did." Then he carried his casket to the table, opened it, and showed the glowing, lustrous pearls to his guests, who crowded about to admire them.

A few moments later Mona Lisa and Ginerva, who had discarded her veils for the more substantial clothes she had borrowed from Francesco's wife appeared, while Francesco explained that pearls were as much a hobby as a business with him. "I've been collecting them for twenty years. I like to let them run through my fingers like flickering moonbeams, like little white stars. I hardly can bear to sell one of my beauties, and as soon as it is sold I feel I must have it back again." Then he went on, mysteriously, "Pearls sometimes grow ill, just like human beings, and their glow and luster fail. But I have a cure that never fails to restore them. What the pearl needs is to nestle close to some warm human body. So every night I wind the loveliest pearls about Mona Lisa's neck and bosom. And the fading pearls gather new life from the quickening beat of her heart. They grow radiant and glowing once more."

Mona Lisa, who stood a little apart from the others, sighed: "I loathe his pearls," she murmured softly to herself. "They do not seem like flickering moonbeams to me—but like tears shed in secret, the tears longing draws from sleepless eyes. I nourish his pearls with my heart's blood! They poison my soul, they suck my marrow! I feel them around me at night, as cold as hidden chains!" And she shivered slightly and drew her veil more closely around her.

At last Francesco held up a great round pearl. It glowed with a faint pink glow, as though the dawn had touched it with one rosy finger when it lay on some beach of silver sand. "Here is the rose-colored pearl His Holiness wanted. I do not care to sell it under 5,000 ducats of gold...." "The price does not matter," said Giovanni dei Salviati. "I have full powers to pay what price you ask, for His Holiness wants the pearl." Francesco held up the pearl by its slender chain. "Yes," he answered, "I know that—but I hate to sell it! But wait a moment," he went on, bringing the jewel nearer the candle-light. "Yes, there is a tiny lack-lustre spot! To-night my Mona Lisa shall wear it and—tomorrow it will be gone." He clapped his hands and a servant brought him a green bowl, half-filled with water. "It is sea-water from Pisa," he added. "My pearls always are given a last bath in it, for my mariner brings it fresh to me every week."

But while the others watched him carry back the little casket to its compartment, and place it on its platform, Giovanni, the Pope's messenger and Mona Lisa softly and noiselessly drew near each other. "Fiordalsia!" breathed the one, and "Giovanni!" the other. Then, as Francesco, turning around, caught sight of them, his wife calmly took the pink pearl from the bowl and passing the chain around her neck said: "If I am to wear the pearl I'll take it now, for I would go to rest." Francesco looked at her suspiciously. "So you were here?" he asked. "You spoke to me a moment ago, when I stood yonder," she answered. "Ah, yes, well.... it is getting late!" he added, absently.

The company now broke up. The gentlemen took their mantles, bowed to Mona Lisa and bade Francesco farewell. And Giovanni dei Salviato said: "But how about my pearl, Messire Francesco?" Francesco smiled. "You shall have it the first thing in the morning. And I feel like stretching my legs. Let me walk to your lodgings with you. Here, Sisto, give me the house-keys!" But as the servant came up with the keys and a torch, Giovanni said, hesitatingly, "I am not going directly to my lodgings," and Arrigo whispered to

Francesco. "Do not urge him. He has half-promised to stop in at Ginerva's house!" So Francesco contented himself with a final farewell, and then followed his guest out to lock up after them.

While Mona Lisa still stood fingering the rose-colored pearl, suddenly Giovanni was in the room again. He had hidden in the shadows, and while Francesco was ushering his guests out of the gate at the far end of the court, had softly crept up the balcony. Is there anything sadder than the broken-hearted explanations of two hapless lovers, torn from each other by a cruel fate they could not control? While Giovanni was off with the Duke Caesar Borgia's army in the Romanga, poor Mona Lisa, during his absence, in spite of her tears and prayers, had been hurried into a marriage with the wealthy Florentine jewel-merchant. "I did not dream it would be so hard to suffer the love of a man I did not love, Giovanni!" she said, and tears trembled in her eyes. To Giovanni the chance meeting seemed a miracle. "It is the finger of Providence, that points out the way to happiness for us!" he cried. "He brings me the pearl tomorrow. You must go to early mass at San Trinità Church. I will be waiting at the gate with a carriage and then—we take the road to Rome, to freedom, to happiness!" And a joy too great for words, the joy of a great release, brought to Mona Lisa's face that starry, mysterious smile which her husband Francesco never saw. For the moment she looked exactly like the picture Leonardo had painted. And then the smile changed to an expression of terror. "May the saints help us!" she whispered, "His step! On the balcony! Quick, hide in the hall, and when you have a chance—the piazza gate is still open. I'll try to hold his attention!" Giovanni disappeared. Francesco came in from the balcony: "Was some one speaking?" he asked as he entered the room, "Ah, it is you!" he went on and then—he saw Mona Lisa's smile! For the moment she had forgotten him, and the mysterious, radiant smile, like clear, deep water whose bottom no one can see, shone on her face. Francesco started, but as he spoke the smile faded. "She has put on her mask again," said he to himself and aloud, "I must lock the piazza gate." "Let the servant do it," said his wife, but Francesco shook his head. He went out on the balcony again, walked down a few steps, and then stooping against the railing, shook his keys in the air. Mona Lisa, deceived, swiftly passed into the hall and whispered: "He is locking the piazza gate! Hide in the niche at you right hand, here in the room! Piccardia, my maid, shall let you through her room and down the steps that lead to the court!" And as he passed her, her lover took her in his arms for a moment. She knew the exquisite joy and anguish of a kiss that might be the last he would ever give her. As he disappeared Francesco, who peering from the balcony had seen them in each other's arms, stepped a few paces further down the stairs. Then, as

though he were calling from the court he shouted. "The whole stairway is full of flowers!" A moment later he entered the room, flinging
a handful of red flowers on the floor. The doors of the jewel-cabinet
had been left open, though the curtain before them had been dropped
again. Giovanni had slipped behind the curtain. But when Mona
Lisa returned from the flowers saying, "Crimson flowers, flowers of
the Evil One!.... Do come, Francesco!" her husband answered
playfully: "How longingly you say 'Do come,'.... and, can I believe
my eyes, you are blushing like some innocent young girl instead of
a staid married woman!" Then, with false tenderness he added, "Yes,
I'll come, but first I must close the windows!" Closing one window
after another, Francesco finally locked the balcony door—cutting
off Giovanni's way of escape. And he locked the door on the court,
though Mona Lisa, with growing fear, begged him to come to bed.
Merrily he answered: "No, my little Lisa, such a passionate longing is
nothing for old married folk like ourselves," and stopping before the
curtain that hid the jewel-cabinet, he said it hung crookedly, and
suddenly jerked it aside. But only the closed door confronted him.
And Mona Lisa and Francesco both knew in their hearts and souls
that Giovanni was inside. But then, while Mona Lisa started in
terror, Francesco said, quite innocently, "I nearly forgot to lock the
jewel-cabinet!" Lisa tried to hold him back. "It is locked, Francesco," she said. "Ah, no," said he, "but now it is!" he added, as
he turned the key in the lock. Then Francesco, as she fell back exhausted on the couch at one side of the wall, stepped to the balcony
door, unlocked it and looked out on the Arno, flowing silver beneath
the moonlight. The serenade some lover was singing beneath his
sweetheart's window came to their ears. And Mona List in an
agony of helplessness, thought to herself; "He is imprisoned in the
jewel-cabinet! He will suffocate there! God help me, what shall
I do!" But now, pretending that the song had awakened all his love
longing for her, the cruel Francesco played with his unfortunate wife
as a cat does with a mouse. He lavished endearments on her. He
took her in his arms—knowing that every word he said could be heard
by the lover hidden in the jewel-cabinet—and brought the wretched
woman to the edge of madness. And when Giovanni, unable to bear
the torture of this love-making, cried out in savage, ringing tones:
"Open the door" Francesco refused to admit that he heard him, and
drowned his voice in roars of laughter. Then, making Mona Lisa
say again and again "I love you, Francesco!" and at the cost of
many kisses, he promised her the key to the jewel-cabinet. But he
did not give it to her. Instead, going to the balcony, he flung the
one and only key which could unlock the cabinet into the Arno—
to prove to her, as he said, that he loved her even more than all his

pearls! And as Mona Lisa fell unconscious across the couch he smiled a sinister smile and left the house.

Mona Lisa had fallen into her deep and horrid swoon on the last night of the Carnival. She opened her eyes on the gray dawn of Ash-Wednesday. Her step-daughter, pretty little Dianora, had just tiptoed through the room to take a look at her new boat, moored to the house, Piccardia, her maid, had just opened the windows. Only slowly, as the bells for early mass began to ring from San Trinità Church, did Mona Lisa begin to remember what had happened. And not till her eye chanced to fall on the door of the jewel-cabinet did full realization of what had taken place flood her mind. She sat up and wrung her hands. "I have slept! The hours have passed and I have not done a thing to save him! The key! But the key is in the river." Then she rushed to the cabinet. "Giovanni" she cried, it is Fiodalisa!.... Have patience only one little moment more!.... I will have the door torn down!" She shook the door, she beat upon it with her fists: "Giovanni, answer, in God's name, answer! Say something, a single word, my Vannino!" And then, suddenly she cried, "He is dead!" And she fell back from the door, murmuring tonelessly, "He is dead, dead! My Giovanni is dead!" Now her step-daughter Dianora appeared on the balcony. "See what I found in my boat, mother!" she cried gaily and—held up the golden key Francesco thought he had flung into the Arno! Feverishly Mona Lisa took the key from the child and hurried her off to mass. And then, tottering to the cabinet, she unlocked the first outer door. But—as she hesitated, trembling, at the second, she heard Francesco's steps on the balcony stairs. Swiftly and silently she reclosed the outer door and hid the key in her bosom. Francesco came in with a deadly white face. He said: "I went to Messire Salviati's house this morning to bring him his pearl. But the handsome rascal was not at home. Some love adventure kept him out, no doubt!" Mona Lisa smiled as though nothing had occurred. "See what I have," she said and held up the key. "Why....that is my key, the one I flung into the river!" Francesco gasped, in surprise. "Yes, it fell into Dianora's boat and ....it was brought to me a few minutes after you left the house." Francesco stared at her. "Who gave it to you?" he asked. "My maid, Piccardia. She came home late from the Carnival!" And Francesco groaned to himself: "That is why she smiles....she released him!" And when he added, aloud, "Give me the key!" Mona Lisa, still smiling her angelic smile, answered: "Of course. It has no value to me. But if you care to give me the pearls that Madonna Lucrezia Borgia has ordered, I shall be glad to wear them." A demon broke loose in Francesco's soul. "He is alive!" he panted, turning away his head, and then "But, perhaps he was not there at all! Could any woman smile as she does—after what I did to her—

unless he were alive?" And when Mona Lisa repeated, "Do you wish to give me the pearls," in her calm, sweet voice, he went slowly to the cabinet. He hesitated a moment, but opened the first door, while Lisa, who had followed, stood behind him. As he pressed the inner spring and the second floor door flew open, he started back. And then Mona Lisa suddenly cried in a voice ringing with devilish suggestion "Did some thief break in? Seize him, seize him, my Francesco!" And as Francesco, stung to action by her words, leaped into the inner compartment, Lisa with a single bound flung herself against the door so that it crashed shut with a ring of steel. Then, while Francesco's cries of "Lisa, Lisa!" rose, she turned the key in the lock of the outer door, and sank in a heap against it. "It will be hours before any one comes, Francesco!" she muttered. "You called up in me the demon who lurks in every woman's soul. You taught me how to toy with horrors, and killed what was human in me! Now you have your reward!" Suddenly she got to her feet. "But this time the key shall be lost forever! It shall not be found again to bring you back to life!" And staggering to the balcony, Mona Lisa with a desperate strength flung the key far out, and saw it fall in a glittering arc into the Arno, before she again collapsed. When they found her the beautiful Mona Lisa had gone mad!

TOO BEAUTIFUL!

It was in the year the Grand-Duke Ferdinand de Medici ascended the throne of Florence, that a woman whose face was covered with a death's-head mask was placed on trial before the judge of the criminal court. Shrouded in a long mantle, reaching to her ankles, its hood drawn down over her forehead, this figure with its terrifying death-mask, and funeral robe and cowl, seemed a ghost about to attend a carnival of the dead. This woman was Rosaura Montalboni. For the fourth time she stood before the chair of justice, accused of a crime which, strange to say, was its own defense. But of what was she accused?

She was accused of being so beautiful that when she stepped to her window in the morning, the people crowded the streets until that sedan-chairs and coaches were unable to pass, the merchants forgot to display their goods, and magistrates, city officials, soldiers and those who had work to do stood lost for hours in admiration, without thinking of their duties. Rosaura Montalboni was accused of being so beautiful that when she went out to buy of the silk-dealers and jewellers, they refused to charge her for her wares. They laid their riches at her feet and begged her to take what she wanted. The man whose shop was visited was ruined.

She was accused of being so beautiful that since she had established herself on the *right* bank of the Arno river, a whole row of palaces had arisen there, while the *left* shore had fallen into a decline, because of the nobles, rich merchants and great ship-owners who had deserted it.

She was accused of being so beautiful that when she entered the church of Santa Maria del Fiore, the worshippers turned their backs on the altar to look at her. Damnation and suffering instead of salvation and comfort was what they took with them when they left.

When the fishermen drew the corpse of some pale youth from the Arno of a morning, it was sure to be that of an unhappy admirer who had killed himself for Rosaura's sake. When the watchmen at night came across the body of a knight clad in rich satins, with a dagger-thrust in his heart, swimming in a pool of his own blood, it was certain that Rosaura was the cause of his death. She had turned her head to glance at him, perhaps, and excited a rival's savage jealousy. When wealthy fathers died suddenly and unexpectedly, all knew that they had been poisoned because of Rosaura—for any one in Florence would gladly have poisoned father, mother, brother and sister, to win a smile from Rosaura's lovely eyes!

Once there had been a famine in the city. The maddened people ran amuck and rushed raging to the Montalboni palace, whose mistress bathed in milk, watered the flowers of her garden with wine, and gave banquets day by day, while the people died of starvation. When the howling mob had broken through the gates, and put the richly-clad servants to flight, Rosaura stepped down the marble stairway quite alone. Her wonderful golden-blond hair fell down over her shoulders. She fanned her rosy face with her diamond-studded fan—and the mob fell on its knees, as though the Madonna had appeared! The leaders kissed the hem of her robe, and the starving crowd withdrew. Rosaura had given them a kindly smile and they were satisfied.

Three times she had been brought to court because of her beauty, on the complaint of embittered fathers whose sons had fallen victims to Rosaura's charms. Three times Rosaura had been accused of being "too beautiful." The judges heard the complaints, cited the guilty defendant to appear before them, and convinced themselves that the accusation was true in every respect. It was truer than true. Rosaura was even more beautiful than she was accused of being. Twice the judges verdict ran: "The accusation is justified, the crime is proven, and the accused is freed!"

Her beauty was a great crime, yet it was its own greater excuse. When she looked her judges in the eye they forgot the law; when she wept they swore she was innocent. When she smiled they were ready to declare *themselves* guilty. The third case was that of the administrator of the ducal treasury. He had laid hands on the treasure entrusted to his care and, after he had squandered it on the beautiful Rosaura, had killed himself. Mercy could no longer be shown her. The lovely lady was once more brought into court. By a majority of one the verdict ran that she be banished from Florence for all time, and that her beautiful body be branded with a red-hot iron by the common hangman.

The pillory at which she was to be punished had been erected before the notorious Pizzi palace. An enormous multitude crowded the great square and the roofs of the houses from which the platform could be seen. The lovely lady, more enchantingly beautiful than ever, was led forth; and the hangman seized his red-hot iron and tore the silken gown from Rosaura's shoulder in order to stamp it with the badge of infamy. And then—when he saw her smooth, white shoulder before him, he forgot that he was the hangman, and instead of the hot iron he pressed his hot lips against it!

His mistake cost the hangman his head; but it saved Rosaura, for no one could be found to carry out the judgment of the court against that round, snow-white shoulder! Every one who saw her thought only of kissing her, not of disfiguring her with a glowing iron. The strange tale came to the ears of the Grand-Duke. Cosimo de Medici at that time was an old man, and had turned very pious. Perhaps it was piety which moved him, when on his request, the lady having been brought before him, he pardoned and annulled her sentence. From that time forward Rosaura Montalboni was allowed to be as beautiful as she chose. None dared enter complaint against her. None ventured to accuse her radiant eyes, her smiling lips, the seductive dimples in her blushing cheeks, and that smile which captivated the senses.

When Cosimo de Medici died, Ferdinand de Medici ascended the grand-ducal throne. Now Lorenzo Frascati, his boyhood friend, had become a painter and Ferdinand a prince, yet the ruler did not forget his former companion. He brought him from Padua to his own palace, so that he might share his power and his joys.

Lorenzo Frascati was a youth with a happy disposition, inclined to merry pranks, as painters mostly are, and the amusing fancies which occurred to him whiled away many an hour for the Grand-Duke. But suddenly Lorenzo grew serious and thoughtful, his merry jests ceased, and the prince found it hard to cheer him. Ferdinand had built a new chapel on the bank of the Arno, and in order to provide Lorenzo with a congenial occupation, told him to decorate the interior of the building as his own good taste might dictate. So Lorenzo shut himself up in the chapel from morning till night. Even when he left, he locked the door after him so that his work might not be seen until completed. But once, when Lorenzo had spent three whole days in the chapel, and would allow no one to enter it, his assistants were alarmed. They hurried to the Grand-Duke and informed him that some misfortune must have overtaken their master, seeing that he had spent three days in the building without food or drink.

Then the Grand-Duke himself hastened to the spot. After repeated knocking brought no response, he had the chapel door broken down by force, and entered the building whose interior none but Lorenzo thus far had seen. He looked about him with astonishment. Without exception, the sacred walls and ceiling showed the portrait of one and the same woman. The features of the saints rising to heaven with palm branches in their hands, the smiling angels, the repentant Magdalens, and the Madonna over the altar all had the self-same enchantingly lovely face. And this face which filled the entire church was none other—than the face of Rosaura Montalboni!

Lorenzo himself, however, sat in the pulpit, and his staring glance passed from one picture to the other. He knew neither his friend the Grand-Duke nor any of those who accompanied him—he saw nothing but the pictured phantoms of his imagination. He had gone mad, and remained mad as long as he lived! The Grand-Duke had the plaster torn from the frescoed walls, and when the chapel had been reconsecrated, shut it up that none might even pray in it. The prince was very young, a mere boy, and as yet was unaware of the magic which lurks in woman's eye, and how difficult it is to withstand it. For now Rosaura Montalboni was called before the tribunal for the fourth time. But this time a mask in the form of a death's-head hid her face. The radiant glances of her lovely eyes, and the bewitching smile of her red lips should not again move her judges.

"Are you that beautiful Rosaura Montalboni who drags down to destruction young and old with the magic of your face?"

This was the question the judge asked the death's-head.

And the death's-head answered: "I am she!"

"Is is true that those who look at you are made mad by your beauty?"

"It is true," replied the death's-head, turning its grisly, skeleton face to the questioner.

"Do you know the number of those who have gone to their deaths for your sake, in order to rid themselves of an existence which had become a curse?"

The death's-head sobbed bitterly. And though no tears rolled from its empty sockets, the sound of weeping came from beneath its motionless jaw-bones.

"Rosaura Montalboni, give ear to the judgment which this court pronounces upon you: For the rest of your natural life you shall be kept in solitary confinement, apart from all other prisoners. And lest your beautiful face serve to seduce your jailors or their superiors, you shall wear the death mask as long as you live. All who look at

I

you will shudder and turn away, and be filled with fear instead of love when they see you!"

Did Rosaura Montalboni turn pale when she heard this verdict? Did her red lips twitch with pain and horror? The death mask was rigid and immovable: no one could say. Francesco de Medici reigned as Grand-Duke of Florence for nine and thirty years, and died in the nine and thirtieth year of his reign. He was succeeded by Duke Cosimo the Third. When he ascended the throne the new Grand-Duke granted a general pardon to all those languishing in the prisons of the state. It was the duty of the judges to examine the documents relating to each case, in order to pass on the individual crimes and offences, and decide whether the pardon was deserved. And they found that among the prisoners was a woman whose only crime had been that she was *too beautiful!* For this crime she had been condemned to life-long imprisonment, and the wearing of a death-mask in perpetuity.

A pardon was granted her. Yet, when her mask was removed, they saw the same deathly pale and wilted face, with sunken eyes, and wrinkled skin clinging to the bones, shown by the death-mask itself. And that was Rosaura Montalboni, who years before had been forced to do such cruel penance because she was "too beautiful"!

FOR HER CHILDREN'S SAKE

One of the most touchingly human tales of all the many stories of the Renaissance is that told by an old Renaissance writer himself, the good Matteo Bandello de Castelnuovo, Bishop of Agen (d. 1560). It is one that reflects credit on both its hero and heroine, and may be accepted as a true tale of an actual happening.

Luchino Vivaldo was a young noble of Genoa, whose every wish was granted almost before he expressed it, so that he had grown used to having his own way in most matters. Now one day, as he was passing through the street, he saw a lovely girl of sixteen whose sight roused such a fire in his heart that he could think of no one else. He began to pass and repass in front of her house, merely to enjoy the pleasure of saluting her, and made a point of meeting her wherever he could. But though at first she had innocently replied to his greetings and compliments, the young girl soon realized that Luchino had an unworthy purpose in mind. So she was careful to appear but seldom in the street. When Luchino greeted her, she acted as though she did not see him, and spoke to her companions; and if she saw him coming a ways off, she went into the house and did not venture out again until he had passed.

Now there is a pretty custom in Genoa. A young lover takes a bouquet of flowers, jasmines, citron-blossoms, pomegranates or other blooms and, when he meets the girl he loves in the street, he hands it to her. And she, in return, gives him whatever flowers she may be wearing in her bosom, or holding in her hand. In Genoa this is called "having an understanding." It means that the two lovers "understand" each other, and that there is love between them. So one day Luchino bought him a fair boquet of carnations—and it cost him a golden ducat to do so, for it was in the dead of winter and the flowers out of season—meeting Gianchinetta, for that was the girl's name in the street, he stopped her. Then, standing in the snow, begged her to accept the beautiful flowers. But Gianchinetta blushed, and then answered reproachfully: "Messire Luchino, I am a poor girl and it would hurt my good name to become your light-of-love." And with that, refusing the flowers, she shut herself up in her house. For though she was of humble birth, and had but few clothes to wear, Gianchinetta had a pure and noble mind. This repulse nearly drove Luchino mad. He tried one thing after another to realize his desire, but all in vain. He sent Gianchinetta many messages and gifts but the first brought no reply and the last were returned. He offered her whatever she wanted. He even offered to marry her to some one and give her a dowry of a thousand gold ducats—if only she would yield what he asked. But the higher his passion burned, the colder and more unkind she became. Thus two years went by without the desperate lover being able to realize his desire. And then— Gianchinetta married a poor lad who made a living as a seaman aboard the galleys!

Did this put an end to Luchino's evil endeavors? Not at all. It is true that his relatives made him marry a wealthy girl of an aristocratic Genoese family. Yet, for all his wife was beautiful, her charms could not dampen the fires which Gianchinetta had kindled in his heart. So Luchino continued to persecute her with his attentions as before. But, though the story of his infatuation was known all over Genoa, Gianchinetta's virtue was so well established that she enjoyed universal respect. As for Luchino he did not care what people said of him.

Gianchinetta, in course of time, had three children and managed to feed and bring them up as well as might be on her husband's earnings. And then the galley on which he sailed had the bad luck to be captured, on a trip to Sardinia, and her husband was imprisoned with the rest of the crew. This misfortune overtook Gianchinetta at the very time a famine had broken out in Genoa, and it was hard to get a bag of grain even for nine gold pieces. Gianchinetta, whose husband could not help her, saw her little ones starving before her eyes. And after much thought she resolved to yield herself to her lover, and let him have his way, so that her children might live. When she had made this resolution, she went to Luchino's palace and met him coming down the marble steps. And to Luchino's exceeding surprise, she flung herself at his feet, weeping bitterly and said: "Lord, I am ready to do whatever you ask! I am ready to do all you have so often required of me in vain. I surrender my body to your will, and only ask that of your generosity that you will not let my children die of starvation!"

And then Luchino showed what manner of man he was at heart. For he raised up Gianchinetta, comforted and encouraged her, and answered: "Dear Gianchinetta, God forbid that your childrens' hunger should force you to do what all my love was unable to accomplish! I could not bear the thought that to save your three innocents from hunger, you should grant me what the great affection I have had for you since the first day I saw you has not been able to bring about!"

And when he had said this he led Gianchinetta to his wife—who often had pitied him because of his unfortunate passion—and after he had told her what had happened, he begged *her* to provide for Gianchinetta and her children, so that no shadow would rest on her fair fame. And thus he turned a sinful and unholy passion into an honorable friendship.

WHY ALL MEN WERE CALLED "SIR" IN GENOA

Giavanni Sercombi, another Renaissance novelist, has left us a pretty tale of his own times. It may well be founded on an actual fact, for the great Italian cities, Venice, Genoa and others, were often places of refuge for the sons of Greek emperors, and for Greek nobles who had to flee from Constantinople in consequence of the bloody palace revolutions and changes of dynasty which were so frequent during the last century of the Greek empire's existence.

There once was an Emperor of Constantinople called Nicephorus, who had a fifteen year-old son named Alexios. Now Alexios was a wild and head-strong boy. He fell into bad habits, associated with evil companions and, in short, was beginning to turn into a regular ne'er-do-well. Naturally, his father remonstrated with him. But instead of taking what he said in good part, the young hot-head secretly ran away from the palace, and hid himself aboard a Genoese ship as a castaway. When he discovered this the emperor swore that if he ever returned he would throw him into prison. But Alexios, who had been found and forced to earn his passage before the mast, in due time arrived in Genoa. And there when he came ashore, he called himself "Pennyweed." Soon the money Pennyweed had brought from Constantinople began to run short. When he had sold everything he had, about the only means of livelihood left him—for he never had learned a trade—was to roll dice with other outcasts. It was one of the accomplishments to which his father had objected, but in this way, and by picking up an old job here and there, he managed to eke out a wretched existence in Genoa for some three years, and often enough went hungry to bed.

Then one day, by some chance, when he had a few silver shillings in his pocket, he saw a handsome falcon. His heart went out to the noble bird, for he had loved to ride out falcon-hunting in his princely days, and without further thought he bought it. And he kept the bird so well that soon there was not a handsomer falcon to be seen in all Genoa. One day as Pennyweed was walking along the street with his falcon on his fist, a Genoese nobleman named Spinetta del Fiesco saw the bird. It pleased him and he said: "Pennyweed, sell me your falcon!" And Pennyweed, who under his rags had the instinct of a great gentleman, answered: "My lord, I will not sell you my falcon! But if you have taken a fancy to it, I will be glad to let you have it as a gift." Spinetta was indignant: "What," cried he, "have I not money enough to buy your bird?" And Pennyweed answered: "You have money a-plenty, but this bird is not for sale. You only can have it as a present!" Then the arrogant and haughty Spinetta flew into a rage. "You rascally knave," he shouted, "how dare you tell me that this falcon cannot be bought with my good money! Do you think I will let people say that a lubberly street beggar had made Spinetta del Fiesco a present?" And in his rage he took the falcon from Pennyweed's fist, and beat the latter's cheeks bloody with it, and then wrung the unfortunate bird's neck. Flinging it at Pennyweed's feet he said: "There, scoundrel, there's your gift falcon!"

Now Spinetta was so great a lord and so powerful in Genoa that no one had dared say a word while he was beating Pennyweed, but had merely looked on and kept silence. But Pennyweed, who had been cruelly beaten and insulted, merely because of his wish to be courteous, and because as a gentleman he could not make business of selling things, cried: "Alas, how have I fallen, I who am the son of the Emperor of Constantinople! How low I have sunken who, if I stood in the palace of Blachernae, would be honored by more great lords and barons than there are people in all Genoa! And, wretch that I am, I lost it all because of my own folly! If I thought my father would take me back again, even though it were my death, I would go to him!"

And after thinking deeply, he said to himself: "My father is growing older. If God takes him to Him, then some other will seize his throne and land, and what will become of me, poor worm? Yes, though my father kill me, I must go back to him!" So he went down to the harbor, and soon found a ship that was sailing for Constantinople. And when he said that he only wanted to work his passage there, and asked for no wages, he was at once taken aboard. In due course of time, with favoring winds, the vessel reach Constantinople.

When they went ashore, Pennyweed asked one of the other sailors to go to the palace and inquire after a certain Tedeo. And if Tedeo wanted to know why he asked for him, he was to say: "A youth who came in our ship wants to know if you will not come to him." The sailor did as he was asked, and when Tedeo received the message he came down to the wharf, saw Pennyweed and at once recognized in him the young Prince Alexios. After he had answered all Alexios' questions about his father and the court, he took him to a tailor-shop and had him clothed in the costliest garments. Then he led him to the palace, and took him to a certain room where he told him to wait. Then Tedeo went into the Emperor, who sat at meat and said to him, "What a fine thing it would be, Your Majesty, if we knew whether your son Alexios were dead or alive!" And the Emperor answered: "You speak the truth. I would give up all I own to get him back again, good or bad. For, after all, he is my only son!" And he sighed deeply and a tear trickled down his gray beard. So Tedeo returned to Alexios, and led him in to his father. Alexios flung himself at the Emperor's feet and was forgiven, and when his father died soon after, was at once crowned Emperor.

When the citizens of Genoa heard that a new Emperor had been crowned in Constantinople, they sent three of the greatest nobles of Genoa as ambassadors to congratulate him. And one of the three was the same Spinetta del Fiesco who had beaten Alexios because of his falcon. The Emperor received them, and at once recognizing Spinetta del Fiesco asked him: "My lord, have you ever treated a fellow-being unjustly?" Then Spinetta swore by the Holy Trinity he never had. But the Emperor shook his head at his answer: "It cannot be," he said slowly, "that in all your life you never wronged another. Sometime in your life you must have wronged a fellow-being," he said. Then Spinetta remembered Pennyweed's falcon. And he said: "You are right. I recall that once I wronged a vagabond named Pennyweed in Genoa. He had a fine falcon and wanted to make me a gift of the bird. But since he would only give and not sell it, I took the falcon and beat his head bloody with it and killed the bird. And, so far as I know, that is the only wrong I ever did any one."

"And was it not a great wrong?" asked the Emperor Alexios. "Yes," said Spinetta, frankly, "for since the bird took my fancy I should have accepted it as a gift. And I should have thanked the vagabond who stood there naked and in rags with the gift of a robe. Yes, I did very wrong!" Then the Emperor said: "Yet I owe you a greater debt of gratitude than any one else in the world! For I was the man who offered you the falcon. Your name is Spinetta del Fiesco, and you beat me about the head with my falcon in the market-place, and I went by the name of Pennyweed. What you did made me see myself as I was. It made me return to my father. And thus I am grateful for your insult, which took me back here. For your insult turned me from a vagabond into an emperor. And any favor you ask of me shall be granted!"

When the three ambassadors, laden with splendid gifts, returned to Genoa, and told their tale in the council-chamber, the Council of Genoa decided that thereafter every person, without exception, should be addressed as "Sir" in their city. He should be addressed as "Sir" whether he went in silks or in rags. For how was it possible to tell just who any one might really chance to be? Had not the son of the Emperor of Constantinople himself stood naked in the market-place? And so, for many centuries, this custom was observed in Genoa, and the lowliest beggar in the streets was addressed as "Sir."

CHAPTER XIX

PICTURES FROM THE AGE OF THE RELIGIOUS WARS

THE golden sun of Renaissance joy in life set in the shadows of battle's thunder-clouds. With the coming of the Reformation the dogs of war were unleashed. Europe became one vast battlefield. In the Netherlands, in France, in England (where the Cavaliers represented the Catholic party and Cromwell's Puritans the Protestants), and throughout Middle Europe men called on the same God to help them in the bloody work of forcing their own idea as to how he should be worshiped on their fellowmen. Not until the Peace of Westphalia, which ended the Thirty Years' War (1648), did religious wars drop into the background, though persecution for opinion's sake continued in nearly all lands and among all creeds.

Those who lived by the Sword. Many a reader knows from his own experience how brutalizing and debasing an influence actual war exerts on the human individual. There are things about military life that are fine: companionships and friendships formed under conditions which tests the souls of men: heroism, self-sacrifice, the surrender of life for an ideal. But—the life itself is an unnatural one. Its high moments are developed against a black and blood-red background of existence. And in the age of the Religious Wars, during the sixteenth and seventeenth centuries, ,the fighting—and the plundering, burning, violating and murdering was done by lawless bands of professional soldiery. There were no "national" armies in those days. The soldiery who in the name of the God of Luther and Calvin or the God of the Roman pope and the Catholic princes, slaughtered, slew and outraged, often were the scum of a very scummy earth. It is from these struggles of *intolerance* that the following pictures have been drawn. They give glimpses of individual soldier life from a purely *human* angle.

THE INNOCENT AND THE DAMNED

"I must have the girl," said François de Bernage to his confidential valet Lazare, the aider and abettor of all his mad, fantastic, head-strong follies. "I must have her, I tell you! Ever since I saw her face that day when the Huguenot dogs were coming out of their conventicle, and her masque dropped in the mud as she rode by, it has haunted me. I cannot live without her!" Lazare smiled. The words were familiar. He often had heard them before. But this time François was in earnest.

Only twenty-five, the heir to vast estates, he was a perfect product of that vicious finishing school in depravity known as the court of King Henry III of France (d. 1589). François de Bernage's incredible amorous adventures excited attention even in the corrupt Paris of this day. Loyal to his king, and faithless to the ladies who were the mistresses of his heart in bewildering succession, he regarded himself as a good Christian. He even had mass said for his dogs, so attached was he to the king's own faith. But his last escapade had been too much for King Henry. An affair with a maid-of-honor of the Duchess of Guise had ended in the unfortunate girl's death. He had been banished from Court, and sent to Bourges. There, with his company of a hundred men-at-arms, he had been ordered to join the Catholic army under Perrier, which was holding the country against the Huguenots. But, one day, before he had come to Bourges, he had seen a lovely young Huguenot girl, Madeleine de Gardefort, with golden hair and timid, violet-blue eyes. Since then he had felt he could not live without her. And now, after several vain attempts to meet her, to make himself acceptable—an utter impossibility—to her stern Huguenot father, he had determined to have her abducted rather than suffer the agonies of what, though he did not realize it, was the first genuine passion he ever had known.

When his master had spoken Lazare drew aside the curtain before the door, and Aspar, the *Stradiot* corporal, entered. The Stradiots were light Albanian mercenary horsemen. They were among the best pillagers and plunderers in that mixed and godless host gathering in Bourges, and shrank from no manner of profitable crime. They cut off the heads of their dead enemies, Turkish fashion. It was together with Aspar that Lazare meant to carry out the abduction of Madeleine de Gardefort, in order to make his master happy.

The young nobleman brought a gleam to Aspar's eye when, after some explanations, he pushed over a heavy netted purse filled with gold to that ex-slaver and ex-galley slave and said: "There will be more if you bring me the girl!" But, after the two men had left François' reflections were gloomy ones. Even in those days, when the terrible hatred between Catholics and Protestants justified almost anything *either* party did against the other, a noble in the king's army could not abduct a young, innocent girl of noble birth without making a stir, even though she were a Huguenot. And—Madeleine was a god-child of the Duchess of Ferrara. If his men were caught in the act they would be hung, and he would have to let them hang, for he could not appear in the matter. If they were successful, he might have to pay dearly himself. If it were discovered that he kept her in his tent, there at Bourges, the arch-bishop might claim her, to try her as a heretic. But—the die was cast!

The following morning the two abductors were ready. Lazare had bought a recruiting order from Colonel Perrier's lackey. It entitled him to an escort of ten riders. He also had gotten a camp scribe to forge a safe-conduct with a perfect signature of Admiral Coligny, the Huguenot leader, in case they fell in with any Huguenots. Besides ten *Stradiots*, led by Aspar, they had two huge, thin Macedonian greyhounds. And Lazare took Madeleine's mask, which François had kept, for as he told his master: "If these hounds were in Paris, and they sniffed one of your surcoats, they would run you to earth here. They are very powerful, their black hide makes them invisible at night, and they can strangle a man before he can utter a single cry!"

The party rode first to Gardefort, the chateau of Madeleine's father. There, hiding in the nearby woods, they surprised one of the castle maids and terrified the girl into confessing that her mistress had gone to visit a friend, Madame de Cueuves, in the Chateau of Rochepente. As soon as they had this information Aspar, rising high in his stirrups, had flung the poor creature into the deep meadow pool. He had watched her rise twice and, as she came up for the last time, thrust her back with a javelin. But when, toward night-fall of the next day they drew near the Chateau of Rochepente, it was evident there was something on Aspar's mind. Was it remorse? Oh, no, for Aspar did not know that there were such things as remorse or a conscience. But he said, gloomily, to Lazare: "I did wrong in the matter of that cursed girl! I left her basket in the meadow. Now they will find the basket in one place and the body in another, and will know that her death was no accident. It was a stupid blunder!"

Not far from the castle of Rochepente, they loosed the greyhounds and let them smell of Madeleine's mask. At once the dogs began to course the great plain before the chateau, drawing narrower and narrower circles, until at last they all stopped in the same place. It was the iron gate of the out-tower which protected the castle draw-bridge. Aspar recalled his hounds with a soft, long call like a jackal's howl. They now knew that Madeleine was inside. The great moat of the castle—something rarely the case—surrounded it completely. Lazare sounded it, and found it had an uniform depth of twenty feet. On the opposite bank the castle walls rose steeply into the air to a height of fifty feet. Two small gates, at two different points, which gave on the water, were the only weak spots in the defence. For Rochepente was one of those fortified chateaux to subdue which cannon were necessary.

As soon as it grew dark enough, they managed to open one of the gates of the great park which bordered the chateau on one side, and reached the moat. And there, where a great bay window overhung the water, Lazare could see people passing within the room by the light of torches. The light was so bright that Lazare even made out Madeleine's face, and heaved a sigh of relief. "Well, there she is," he said to Aspar, "all we need do now is to get her!" And he added, annoyed: "To think she is only twenty feet away, and we cannot lay hand on her!" As he spoke, Madeleine seated herself in the window, and began to sing. Her white robe showed against the outer darkness like a radiant cloud, and her hair shone like molten gold. In the silence of the night the sound of her lute rose on the air, accompanying her voice as she sang a sweet, tender song by Nanini, one of those songs of which the lovely Mary Stuart, Queen of Scots, was so fond. The music of the song rose pure and clear, like the sighing of a crystal which has been struck. The strings of the lute sobbed with deep notes, or murmured softly and gently like a murmuring brook. And the two ruffians without, vile beyond telling, the innocent blood they had shed the cleanest among the many stains which soiled their depraved souls, listened with rapture. They let the heavenly music enter into them. For a moment, with invisible threads more delicate than those of star-rays, it bound them to a supernatural world which filled them with delight. Then the voice died away, the lute fell silent, and they woke to reality once more. But for a moment, both felt sad, sad and—though they did not know the feeling of guilt, guilty. Lazare was the first to shake off his torpor.

"This Lady Madeleine is a very amiable person," he said. "Not only is she going to make us rich, but no sooner do we get here than she treats us to a serenade!" And Aspar was dumfounded by her beauty. Never, so he told Lazare, had he seen so lovely a woman. She would bring her own weight in gold in the slave-market of Constantinople or Algiers. She was a pearl beyond price.

Gradually all the windows of the chateau grew dark, and silence spread over it. And lynx-eyed Aspar, seeing a light still flickering in a certain room of the second story, after a careful look declared that he had made out the silhouette of Madeleine. "The third window of the second story, to the right," he told Lazare, "is the girl's room." Then one of Aspar's *Stradiots* took off every stitch Lazare and Aspar had on, and rubbed their bodies with oil. Hanging their daggers from their necks, they let themselves into the waters of the moat, each with a rope around his middle whose end was held by a man on the bank. Swimming rapidly, the oil on their bodies preventing the cold water from chilling them, they came to the watergate under the draw-bridge tower. The lock of this gate Aspar succeeded in forcing with his dagger, and gliding with bent head beneath the arch, he and Lazare found they were standing on the flagging of a narrow channel, along which the water ran, and in which a boat was moored to an iron ring. At the opposite end of the channel an iron gate which opened on a courtyard was not even locked. When he saw this Aspar said to Lazare: "Go back to the men, and tell them to put the hounds in the water with you, and to give you the girl's mask! Be sure you do not get it wet. I will go on ahead. The hounds will lead you to me and we will put them on the girl's trail." Soon Lazare rejoined him, after having crossed three different courtyards, in a vestibule. There the valet took down a crystal night-lamp which stood in a niche, and then they began their search. They strayed through long corridors and passages which seemed endless, and in which the hounds disappeared. They did not dare call them, and from minute to minute feared that a chance meeting with some servant, the waking-up of some frightened old woman, or the trembling ray of their lamp might betray them. In the confusion of rooms, chambers and corridors, they dared open no doors. They passed through different rooms in which people were sleeping. But so carefully did they shield the light of the lamp, and so softly did they walk, that they awoke no one. The wind blew through the draughty corridors. It puffed out the tapestries behind the walls and made them look as though men were hidden behind them. And the two wretches would feel the hand of fear clutching their throats. But at last, following the hounds, they reached a huge square chamber with doors opening on it from all sides. And here the hounds, with sudden eagerness, led them to a narrow stairway whose walls were hung with tapestry. They climbed it and soon felt rugs under their feet, and knew they were on the second story. The hall they now had entered was lined with bronze and marble busts, standing on pedestals of green porphery, and the light of their lamp was reflected by the gilded frames of pictures, and by enameled vases in which were growing plants. But suddenly, directly opposite where they stood, Lazare and Aspar saw two men completely nude rise from the ground to confront them. They promptly prepared to defend themselves—and then saw that a great Venetian mirror against the wall, standing between two doors, was reflecting their own figures. For a moment they stood there, Aspar glancing speculatively at the riches spread out before his eyes, Lazare reflecting on the dangers of their adventure. But now the hounds began to sniff and scratch at a certain door. At once Aspar calmed them with a few soft words, and they stretched themselves out along the wall, their muzzles between their forepaws as though sleeping. "We have reached the place," said Aspar, "the girl is behind that door!"

Lazare softly opened it. The hinges did not creak. In the pale light of an alabaster night-lamp he saw the great draped and canopied bed, and raised one of its curtains. No doubt because of the dim

light of her night-lamp Madeleine, who was fast asleep, had turned
her face away from it. She was breathing easily, one of her arms
was stretched out over the covers, and her golden hair flooded the
pillow. But they did not stop to enjoy her beauty. Swiftly raising
the bed-curtains, Aspar's hand closed on Madeleine's mouth, while
Lazare held her feet. In another moment she had been gagged with
a delicate chemise the *Stradiot* saw lying on a chair, was rolled up in
her coverlet, her hands and feet tied with strips of linen. Bundled
up as she was, she looked like some white mummy suddenly brought
to life, her eyes unnaturally wide and staring, and full of the horror
of the tomb, seemingly the only living thing about this motionless
corpse.

It may have seemed a terrible dream to Madeleine. For these two
naked men who busied themselves about her looked more like demons
than human beings. She shut her eyes, thinking she had a nightmare. But the hounds had entered the room, and one of the beasts
touched her cheek with its cold muzzle. Then she opened her eyes
and writhed, for she was now wide awake, and her flesh ran cold with
terror. Lazare, having found a chest of carved wood, hurriedly
tumbled out its contents on the floor. And since in his master's service he had become very familiar with the intimate habits of women,
he had soon chosen among the clothes scattered about the room whatever Madeleine would need for her trip with them. Putting them in
the chest he said to Aspar, who was listening at the door: "There
is just enough room to put her in on top of these things. We would
do well to carry her out in this chest. Then she will not get wet
and catch cold!" Aspar thought it an excellent plan. Once the moat
had been crossed, they could draw up the chest with ropes, now that
they had a boat. So they laid her in, shut down the cover, and pushed
the lock so that it would not rattle. Lazare then lifted it, and put it
on Aspar's shoulder, who walked off swiftly like some shop-porter
carrying a bundle of stuffs. The thought of François' gold ducats
made his load feel easy. In front of him went Lazare, his bare dagger in one hand, the lamp in the other. Thus, without waking a soul,
they went back the way they had come, and reached the postern gate
which would let them out into the moat. But here they cursed. The
gate had been locked. "It must have been the wind," said Aspar,
but Lazare thought they had been trapped. A dog began to bark in
one of the courts they had left, and they decided not to seek some
other way out, but to force the gate. Aspar succeeded in doing so
with Lazare's dagger, and placing the chest in the boat and swimming
beside it, they floated it to the far side of the moat. There Aspar
whistled. His *Stradiots* hoisted up the chest and then the two men,
who held the hounds in their arms. The news they had was good.
Not a soul had stirred in the chateau, and not a soul had stirred in

the plain. It was clear that no one even knew they were in that part of the country. Soon they were on their way, stopping only, after a few hours' hard riding—the chest had been tied to the back of one of the horses—to allow Madeleine to dress herself with the aid of a peasant woman in a wayside hut. Aspar told her that her life and honor were not in danger. He was taking her to Poitiers—this for the benefit of the peasant woman—where she could write to her people with regard to a ransom. Two days more of rapid pushing on brought them to Bourges where—so relaxed had discipline become—the whole party was able to enter without giving a countersign, and Madeleine was safely installed in the tent of François de Bernage, without any one knowing she was there. François was absent at the time, on a mission to the Admiral de Coligny, but Madeleine was expected. Moved by a curious access of pity, François, some time before, had picked up a Moorish gipsy girl on the roadside. She was struggling among a group of black-armored French "riders," who were about to hang her as a witch because of a small black crow she carried in her bosom. François as usual thinking of Madeleine, felt sorry for the little creature who seemed like some bedraggled little bird herself. He bought her of the riders for ten ducats of gold, and she had since lived in his tent. He had ordered her, before he left Bourges, to see that Madeleine was treated with every consideration, but to tell her nothing. The little Maughrabine, devoted body and soul to François, followed his instructions to the letter. She looked on Madeleine as one of those beautiful captives who are the glory of a harem. She served her on bended knee, but told her nothing. So Madeleine read her Bible and wrote letters to her father. They were not sent, but even if they had been, would not have reached him, for he had been killed in the battle of Montluc.

We must tell the remainder of our tale in brief. François de Bernage returned. His beautiful, innocent captive at first suffered, then returned her ravisher's love. But—with a stubborn remnant of Huguenot pride, she would not let him know she loved him! And François, who suffered agonies because of it, who begged her again and again to give him her heart, could win no word of love from her. It drove him mad at times. And yet, in the enameled medallion of the Order of St. Michel which he wore—he was a knight of the Order—she sewed a little note. It said only: "François, I love you and have given you my heart!" And she had signed it, "Madeleine." So while he longed to have her tell him she loved him more than he ever had longed for anything in his life, he carried her confession of love about him day by day, utterly unknowing he did so. But their unhappy tragedy was reaching its climax. The despicable scoundrel who commanded the royal forces in Bourges was a Colonel Perrier. He was a bit of human scum, a Parisian "marauder," floating for the moment on the tide of royal favor owing to the unspeakable complaisances of his wife. He traveled with an enormous convoy of baggage-wagons, lackeys, actresses and cooks. The Vidame de Senlis, an experienced soldier, a man of the purest and most fanatic virtue, whose spare time was spent in religious exercises, and who did not deign to honor the orgies of Colonel Perrier with his company, was the real brains of the army. But Perrier, whose only thought was to rob, pillage and plunder, who was amassing treasure at the expense of friend and foe, had made his plans with regard to François. To him François was a handsome golden bird, ripe for the plucking. The haughty young noble's first thought, when meeting his generalissimo, had been to withdraw from his horrible suppers, where wine and debauchery preceded dicing for high stakes. But Perrier let fall an observation which showed he knew of Madeleine's presence in François' tent. The fat Colonel spoke of the complaints which were being made, even at King Henry's Court, where the Duchess of Ferrara was insisting that something be done about her god-child's strange case. But he, the Colonel, would look out for François, hinted Perrier. So François curbed his price, and played and lost his golden ducats to Perrier until he owed him some 35,000 livres. And then, Perrier offered to stake his debt and 15,000 more livres—against Madeleine! He had once caught a glimpse of her, and she had taken his fancy. The blood rushed to François' head. He half-drew his sword, then—agreed to the wager, and lost. As he rose from the table his eye happened to look down and there, on the ground by Perrier's chair, lay three cards which showed that the Colonel had cheated him. Foaming with a rage, François drew his sword, but the wily scoundrel already was disappearing through a door and his guards and lackeys were rushing up. Madeleine was already in his hands, and François had sold his honor in vain! His first thought was to recapture her, sword in hand. But it was madness to make the attempt. Then, his brain on fire, he made his resolution. He returned to his tent, armed himself, mounted his great charger and, accompanied by Lazare, rode out of Bourges. After all, Perrier would not dare harm her. He could win her back again with gold or steel. He had determined to go over to the Huguenots. And he left orders with the lieutenant of his company of a hundred men-at-arms to rejoin him in the morning at the Huguenot camp. He could safely do so, for he was generous and liberal with his men to a degree, and they adored him, and would follow wherever he chose to lead.

Poor Madeleine, led to Perrier's tent, had turned on the monster with a strange, fierce courage astonishing in so gentle a creature. After she had torn his face with her nails till he could hardly see, the brute, in his rage, turned her over to his lackeys. And just as wretched François was riding through a street, he caught a glimpse of Madeleine. She was tossing about among a great crowd of lackeys, Spanish footmen and camp followers, who were all clutching at her. François cut down three men and tried to force his way into the throng. But more and more Spaniards came up. He and Lazare were powerless against their hundreds. He rode on. And then, safely out of Bourges, he fell in with a small party of Huguenot horsemen. They were led by a Huguenot noble who had been betrothed to Madeleine and he, recognizing François, sent a bullet through his brain before he could wave his white scarf and explain that he had gone over to the Reformed cause. And it was Madeleine's Protestant suitor who, bending over his dead foe, opened the enamel medallion of the Order of St. Michel, and found enclosed in it a blonde tress and a strip of parchment with the words: "François, I love you and have given you my heart!" signed with Madeleine's name. It was her Huguenot lover who found on the dead body of her Catholic lover the confession the latter would have sold his soul to have known, and which might have changed the course of two lives and brought them happiness instead of tragedy.

The *Stradiots* of Perrier's army had the pleasant custom of impaling the head of their dead enemies on the spikes of the stockade which surrounded their quarters. And there Madeleine's head, easily to be recognized by the long blonde curls, was found the following day. For in a great attack the Huguenots took Bourges and, the Vicomte de Seulis having been killed, scattered Perrier's army to the winds. Yet fate had been kind to Madeleine in the manner of her death. A merciful heart-stroke had saved her from the ultimate outrage. The brutes who were squabbling over her suddenly found they were fighting for a bit of lifeless clay. In ten Breton village churches, and in ten parishes of Anjou, François' widowed mother had masses said thrice a day for the repose of his soul. No candles burned and no mass was said for the helpless Huguenot girl. But, perhaps, in the paradise of love divine, these unhappy earthly lovers found the happiness they did not know on earth!

IN THE HEYDAY OF THE GREAT GOD LOOT

Three centuries ago was the heyday of the great god Loot. He ruled the Thirty Years' War, the most long-drawn-out war of spoilation and plunder known to history. The prospect of unlimited fighting and unlimited looting drew the best fighting-men of Europe to Germany. There, according to religious conviction or personal preference, they enlisted on one or the other side, with the Catholic emperor or the Swedish king or one of the Protestant princes. The prospects of plunder were equally alluring on either side. In the armies of the Protestant princes were to be found Englishmen, Scots,

Danes, Swedes, Finns and even Laplanders. Under the Imperial banners served Irishmen, then as now eager to fight in any cause that would offer an excuse for fighting, Walloons, Spaniards, Italians, members of almost all the Slavonic races, Croatians and Mohammedan Stradiots. Even Cossacks appeared with the Imperial armies in 1636, showing themselves on the banks of the Rhine for the first time in the history of Western Europe! They had been sent to reinforce the imperial general Count Gallas, whose troops were stationed in Alsace; but the atrocities they committed and their general insubordination were such that they were soon dismissed. One hundred and seventy-eight years later, during the Allied campaign of 1814 against Napoleon, their descendants lived up to the reputation of their sires.

In the armies of the Thirty Years' War, in which so many different nationalities were represented, the great god Loot reigned supreme. From the high commanding officers down to the horse-boys everyone looted whenever and wherever he had a chance. A battle won or a city sacked might make a man rich beyond the dreams of avarice; and just as in Napoleon's armies the man in the ranks might hug the illusion that he carried a *marechal's* baton in his knapsack, so the mercenary of the Thirty Years' War might hope to rise to high command (and greater possibilities for plunder) in a day when captaincies and colonelcies could be purchased for a price in good red gold.

Gold is shy. It hides away in times of war. But the military treasure-hunters of the sixteenth century knew how to coax it out of its hiding places. As the war went on and all that was valuable disappeared, the soldiery on both sides worked hard to make hidden things come to light. When a troup of soldiers entered a village the farmers were put to the torture to make them give up what they might have. The soldiers gave them the water-torture (it was called "the Swedish drink"). They rubbed the bare soles of their feet in with salt and had goats lick them. They drew a horse-hair through their tongues and gently moved it up and down. They tied knotted ropes around their foreheads and tightened them at the back of the heads. With a thousand fiendish variations of cruelty they worshipped the great god Loot. Men, women and children suffered.

And, although the red-letter days of looting, the days of battle and the sack of cities were frequent enough during the Thirty Years' War, every day was "looting day" in a sixteenth and seventeenth century army. There was no such thing as a commissariat in our modern sense of the word, hence a daily routine of plunder—at the expense of the peasant—was necessary to the armies' very existence. And when we consider that an army of 130,000 persons, camp-followers, women and children, stripped the country through which they passed as bare as the proverbial locust, it may be imagined how thoroughly the looting was done.

It was after some victorious battle or the plundering of some wealthy town that the soldier showed himself in all his glory. In the camps the tents of the sutlers were crowded with the victors, drinking and singing. The soldier laid out the proceeds of his spoil in new clothes. He bought himself handsome plumes for his hat, scarlet hose with gold galoons, colored mantles and new boots or shoes. Or he purchased a mule for his wife or mistress to ride, and dressed her in ermine and silks. Grooms and horse-boys sometimes rode clad in satin from head to foot. During the winter of 1630 the Croatians, "Crabats" as they were often called at the time, had plundered to such effect in Pomerania, that their belts were heavy with gold, and they used the surplus of precious metals they had looted to make breast-plates of hammered gold and silver which protected their chests. At times the spendthrift fancy of the soldier of fortune took an erratic turn. It was noticed in the battle of Lützen that one of Count Pappenheim's cuirassiers had covered his steed with a network of golden stars; the housings of another were hung with more than three hundred silver moons. Plate, both gold and silver, was often melted and made into long chains. The owner, according to an old custom, could easily twist off the individual links and use them to pay a score. Another soldier use for precious metals was their employ in the form of scapulars or amulets. The "Siderists," or astrologers of the day, who were supposed to be skilled in star-gazing, cast gold and silver medallions under "stallar conjunctions," which protected the wearer against shot and steel.

It might almost be said that the prospect of plunder was the mainspring of action in the contending armies during the Thirty Years' War, which those on both sides claimed to be fighting—for the sake of the "Prince of Peace"! The soldier's pay was small and he received it either irregularly or not at all. As a rule his devotion to the cause he defended was slight. His honor as a soldier, his sense of attachment to the flag to which he had sworn faith, his professional pride, which made him feel that the soldier was the lord of a world tottering to its fall, were practically all that differentiated him from the robber and murderer of his time. Loot represented to him what sorry poetry and romance there was in his life; it meant wine, dicing, a companion to cheer him when he lay in camp; it stood for fine garments and heron-feathers on his cap, for blooded horses and splendid weapons, and advancement in rank. And in the bloody lottery of battle and siege the poorest soldier might reasonably expect to win his fortune. There were individual cases in plenty to justify the hope of the great majority.

A striking story is that of a soldier in the infantry regiment of General von Holtz, forming part of the army of the Elector of Bavaria. This fellow had formerly been a musketeer, but had come down to trailing a pike, a decided come down. For a soldier of the time, speaking of the "miserable pikemen," declares them to be almost useless in battle. "Whoever cuts down a pikeman whom he might have spared," he says, "murders an innocent, for although these poor draught oxen are supposed to protect their brigades from an attack by cavalry in the open field, they can harm no one of their own free will, and any one who runs himself upon their long pikes deserves to be speared. I have witnessed many a sharp encounter in my day, but seldom have I seen any one slain by a pikeneer."

Be that as it may, the pikeneer in question was lucky enough, in a skirmish as Herbsthausen, to capture a barrel of French gold dubloons, so large a barrel that he could hardly carry it off. He secretly left the regiment, fitted himself out like a prince, bought a coach and six handsome horses, and hired a coachman, and several lackeys and pages as well as a valet, all clad in splendid livery to wait on him. With these he repaired to Munich, where he stopped at the finest tavern in the city, and lived with the utmost luxury, spending his time eating and drinking and going driving in his fine coach. With gloomy irony he called himself "Colonel Scamp." This mode of living he kept up for about six weeks, during which time it chanced that General von Holtz, the commander of his regiment, happened to stop at the same tavern on his way through the city. Mine host had much to say concerning the wealth and the distinguished qualities of Colonel Scamp, yet the general could not remember having ever encountered this name among the cavaliers of the Holy Roman Empire or soldiers of fortune. His curiosity induced him to send the stranger an invitation to dinner.

Colonel Scamp accepted the invitation, and when the sweets and confections were served at the end of the meal, he had a covered dish brought on which contained five hundred newly minted French *pistoles* and a gold chain worth a hundred ducats. These he begged the general to accept with the words: "I trust Your Excellency will consent to receive this little gift and bear me in kindly remembrance!" General von Holtz showed some reluctance to receive so generous a present from a stranger, but the liberal colonel insisted, adding: "The time will soon come when Your Excellency will see that it was incumbent on me to make him this gift. I consider it a good investment, and hope in return to induce Your Excellency to do me a favor which will cost you nothing." General von Holtz thereupon accepted the golden chain and the money, promising, as was the custom, to repay the courtesy should occasion arise. The general continued his journey and the self-made colonel went on living as before. When he passed a guard-post the soldiers presented arms in his honor, in recognition of which he would throw them a handful of dollars. At the end of the six weeks all his money had been spent. Thereupon he sold his coach and six, his fine clothes and linen and drank up the proceeds. His servants left him and he was at last reduced to one poor suit and not a cent of money. The inn-keeper, who had made money by his guest, was now desirous of getting rid of him. He presented him with fifty silver *reichstaler*, but my colonel stayed until they had gone the way of the rest. The inn-keeper then sacrificed another five *reichstaler* and forbade his servants to sell him anything. The spendthrift hastened to the next tavern and spent his money there. When Colonel Scamp at last realized that the game was up, he made his way to his regiment, which lay at Heilbronn. When he arrived he was at once ironed and threatened with the gallows for desertion. It was then that he begged to be brought before the general, gave his assumed name, and recalled to him the dinner in the Munich inn. General von Holtz could do no less than order him to be freed. Upon giving him a sharp reprimand, however, for having thrown away so great a sum of money foolishly, the soldier replied that his whole life he had wanted to know what it felt like to be a great lord, and that by means of the loot he had taken he had been able to gratify his desire.

When the Swedes took the strong castle of Marienburg, which commands the city of Würzburg, they gathered in "the greatest booty that ever was found in any one conquest in the whole war. The soldiers got here so much money that they did not know what to do with it, and the plunder that they got here and at the battle of Leipzig, made them so unruly that had not the King been the best master of discipline in the world, they had never been kept in any reasonable bounds." Some idea of the greatness of the loot taken at the storming of Marienburg may be gained from the fact that "The bishop's treasure, and other public monies not plundered by the soldiers, was told out by the officers, and amounted to 400,000 florins in money, and the burghers of the town in solemn procession, brought the king *three tons of gold* as a composition to exempt the city of Marienburg from plunder!"

The sovereign princes sent their silver plate and the blooded steeds in their stables to the generals for presents to induce them to remove their plundering hordes of soldiery into another territory. In the same way the cities sent sums of money and barrels of wine to the colonels of regiments and the captains of troops; and the villages saddle horses and golden tresses to the cornets and corporals, though toward the end of the war such presents largely ceased, because everything had already been plundered or given away. At the close of the war some of the greatest generals received the proclamation of peace with bitter anger. They had not amassed enough loot! When the messenger came to the Swedish commander, General Wrangel, with news that peace had been concluded, he drove him from his presence with curses, tore his hat from his head and trod it underfoot. He was not yet as rich as he wished to be. Another of the Swedish leaders, Count Königsmark, carried back to Sweden with him so many wagonloads of gold and valuables that the interest on his loot brought his family a yearly income of 130,000 dollars, equal to 600,000 or 700,000 American dollars to-day.

But for sustained, *continuous* looting the record of the Thirty Years' War has still to be beaten. And its like will never be seen again, for the heyday of the great god Loot is over forever, and his glory has departed!

THE ARMY WIFE

The Swedish general, his lordship the Count of Königsmark, sat in his tent. Before him stood the first lieutenant of a regiment of Teuton dragoons which had entered the Swedish service after the death of its leader, the Protestant Duke of Weimar. The young soldier, Bernard König, was one of the wild children of the terrible Thirty Years' War. His parents had been killed in the sack of a small town, and he had been carried away in a sutler's cart that followed the dragoon regiment. Now and again, one among the little wretches who grew up as horse-boys, with a precocious knowledge of evil such as the world of to-day does not dream of, had enough strength of character, enough fibre and stamina, to rise from the moral slime and ooze of his surroundings. If he had a soldier's gifts there was nothing to prevent his rising high. Bernard was one of these waifs of war who had survived the physical and moral vicissitudes of camp life. At twenty-five he already was a first lieutenant and—Königsmark had sent for him to give him command of the regiment. Its colonel at the time had just been killed in a duel.

"And now, Bernard, tell me how the army feels, and what the men want. Peace negotiations already are under way. If we are still to strike a blow at the Emperor we cannot put it off!" The Swedish King Gustavus Adolphus had come into Germany with the high resolve to sacrifice all he had to defend the religion of the Reformed Lutheran princes against the Catholic Austrian Emperor.

And, as in the case of most other wars, before or since, the struggle soon moved from the lofty ground of the ideal to the low level of personal gain. The peasants all over the countryside, the industrious cities and their workers might be ruined, the human sword and cannon-fodder itself, brutalized by the unspeakable "standing army" conditions of the time, might be used up with great rapidity—but, as usual, there was a small group of men, the profiteers of blood, who drew their dividends on the slaughter and destruction of their fellow-beings, and dreaded seeing their profits come to an end. Count Königsmark was one of these men. He had started life as a poverty-stricken son of a petty German noble family. He became one of the worst birds of prey that ever winged his way through the wretched Middle European lands. The professional soldiers, diplomats, money-lenders and financiers who profited by the Thirty Years' War did not wish to see it end. And Königsmark, as he sat in his tent that morning, was anxiously going over the possibility of making one more great haul of "loot," before the War came to an end. Bernard, who had a young wife in his tent, the gentle daughter of a village parson who had chosen to follow her young husband on his wild and dangerous career against her father's prayers, felt as Königsmark did. The young officer gladly would have left the army and settled down somewhere to try to build up a ruined estate—there were plenty of them—but first he must have something to begin life with in the war-blasted land of his birth. And, if he could make Königsmark see his idea, the best one to secure a last great haul of loot before peace came, he himself could look forward to starting a peaceful life with his wife Judith with greater confidence. So he answered his general's question as follows:

"The greatest treasures in the world, Your Excellency, millions in gold, jewels, costly furniture and plate, are heaped up together in one spot. The War has passed them by, and the soldiers would go wild with joy if you were to lead them to this gold-mine. For the deserters say that all the Emperor Ferdinand's treasures have found their way to Prague. There are hundreds of the greatest Austrian nobles in the city, with their wives and children. Each one of them would pay a ransom of more than a thousand ducats gold. And it is all so easy to take. The Imperialists are careless, for the priests tell their soldiers that the saints themselves guard Prague. So my riders say that if they could first pluck the imperial eagle bare, they could more easily resign themselves to peace!" Count Königsmark patted Bernard on the shoulder and replied: "You have the right idea, and if all falls out as it should, you shall not lose!"

Toward the end of June Königsmark suddenly appeared before Prague. In the gray dawn he broke into the poorly guarded outworks, and as the first golden sunrays gilded the church-towers and the bells rang for mass, his soldiers were flooding the streets. The imperial fortress, the whole aristocratic quarter of Prague, had fallen into his hands. Yelling and roaring, the wild soldiery flung itself into the great mansions and palaces which with their contents, already had been distributed as spoils of war before the town was taken. And all the hard-riding veterans had longed for around their camp-fires was theirs: noble prisoners, gold, jewels and splendid furniture past counting.

In one great palace, splendidly fitted up, Colonel Bernard König lay with his horsemen. The owner, luckily for him, was absent in Vienna. But his trembling major-domo had shown the intruders the absent proprietor's silver chests, the filled store-rooms, and the great wine-cellar. In the rooms on the ground floor the soldiers took up their quarters. They sat on chairs of gilded leather, and toasted each other in Spanish wine from silver hampers. Their horses stamped their feet in the stables which opened on the great inner courtyard, and ate themselves fat with the oats and grain fed them.

In one of the magnificent chambers of the upper story, Bernard's young wife Judith bent over her little son. "They have put you in a cradle of alabaster and silver, you poor homeless boy!" she said. "The walls of your bedroom are marble, and the pictures of nobles and great gentlemen in purple mantles, with gold chains of honor, look haughtily down on you from their gilt frames. They seem to ask: 'Who is this stranger child and where does it belong?' And no one knows. When you grow up some day you will ask in vain: 'Who was my mother?' For the spot where her home once stood is now a black ruin. If you come to the village where she dwelt you will hear the people curse her. For she disobeyed her old father, and went off with a wild soldier, one of the soldiermen whom every peasant hates!"

Then she lifted the child out of its cradle as she heard the sound of approaching footsteps: "Here is your son, dear lord," she called out to Bernard as he entered. "You have made the poor parson's daughter happy as your wife, and this other little bit of life is her thanks! Now you must care for both of us. Take him in your arms and me as well, for you are all we two poor outcasts have on earth! You are our last hope and refuge!"

"He is going to be a fine, sturdy boy," said Bernard, as he looked at the little fellow with a happy smile. "There, you little rascal, try and cheer up your mother! See, he is opening his eyes, and in his own language he is telling you not to spoil the blessing he has brought our lives with sadness and gloom." And when the boy began to scream, Piepes, the colonel's horse-boy, devoted to him and his wife, took the child from his arms and tossing him up and down in the air until he yelled with delight, took him into the next room.

The colonel looked around at the walls. "The haughty gentlemen on the walls do not approve of uninvited guests like ourselves. But now that peace is on the way, we may look forward to beginning life anew, a different life and a better one. We will go back to our own land and settle down. We will do our share of planting and building up after the many years of destruction. And the taking of Prague has given us the means to make a good start." So Judith forgot her misgivings, and began to look forward to the happy future her husband painted in eloquent words.

But—her misgivings were only too well justified. In the fall couriers brought the news to Prague that at last the peace between the Emperor and the Swedes had been signed. And Bernard handed over the command of his company to his lieutenant. With three armed servants and his horse-boy Pieps—Judith with their boy and one servant-maid in a comfortable traveling-coach—he rode through the Bohemian hills on the road back to their homeland, to begin again the new life their hopes and dreams had pictured. The skirmishing between the armies was at an end, and besides, here and there along the road across the mountains, were posted small Swedish pickets. And then, one fair September morning—Judith had left the coach and was walking along the road with her Bernard, who was leading his horse, while behind them walked the horse-boy carrying his master's carbine—it happened. At the very moment the bells were ringing out the glad news of peace from the steeple of a little village they could see far below in the valley, a troop of imperialistic horse came along the road. In their leader, who wore a cornet's red sash, Bernard recognized a life-long enemy, who tried to rob him of his wife and his soldier honor. The imperialistic riders hesitated when their captain shouted "Fire!" for after all, peace had been declared. But he himself discharged his pistol at Bernard, who stood with Judith's arms around his neck. The one shot killed them both, and the two lovers sank down in the dust of the roadside, still clasped in each other's arms. And then a second shot rang out. It came from the carbine which the horse-boy, his hair on end, had suddenly raised and pointed. The horses of the cavalrymen reared, while the steed of the imperialist officer dragged the dead murderer's body along the ground as it fled.

THE Age of the Baroque is the Age of Absolute Monarchy. It is the age of kings who rule by divine right, and in most cases grind down their people with ruinous taxes to support glittering courts and the mad wars of royal ambition. The second half of the seventeenth and the earlier eighteenth centuries, in particular reveal these monarchs in nearly every European land.

When the Courts Ranked the Countries. Louis XIV of France, the "Sun King" is the model for most of the other kings. And Charles XII of Sweden is a military despot, too, and half a madman. To pursue the phantom of military glory and heroic adventure on the battlefield was his dream. He conquered lands and gave their crowns away to push on to ever more fantastic adventures. Almost a dime-novel king, he held the loyalty of his ruined and despairing Swedes to the last. Charles II, the Baroque Stuart, like Augustus the Strong of Poland and Saxony, and a host of lesser royalties were glorified royal skirt-hunters, and their subjects suffered so that they might hang their mistresses with diamonds. Peter the Great was a barbarian who tried to civilize his people though he remained a savage himself. The Hapsburgs in Spain and Austria, the Turkish sultans, the Pope and the Italian princes all placed their *personal* princely or royal pleasure before the peoples' good. Magnificence and wretchedness, luxury and starvation, splendor and squalor went hand in hand when Courts ranked the People in the age of kings "by divine right."

Pictures of Baroque Life. Our baroque vistas are four in number. The first is a study, based on authentic Spanish sources, of a soldier type found in various countries at various times: the gallant military adventurer who after a colorful, extravagant worldly existence, turns from earth to heaven and tries to make the pious labors of his later days atone for youthful follies and excesses. Our third tale gives a thoroughly *human* picture of the contrasting magnificence and misery of a genuine Baroque court—that of the splendor-loving Augustus the Strong, King of Poland and Elector of Saxony who, like other kings of the time, condemned his unfortunate subjects to wretchedness so that he might duplicate the glories of Versailles in every detail. The delightful glimpses of Baroque Paris and the Whitehall of Charles II (our second and fourth "vistas") are from the "Diaries" of John Evelyn, whose pictures of the life and manners of his time are among the most interesting and authentic known to History.

THE SOLDIER MONK

(1597-1651)

Don Tiburcio de Redin, the soldier monk, was a hardy adventurer. He was one of those men who, after seeing life in the school of war, returned from Flanders, Italy and the Indies, thinking the world their oyster. They had little respect for law and few principles. They acknowledged no right but that of their own will. They were quick to bare their blades at the slightest word offensive to their *punta de honor* ("point of honor")—their guiding star. They lived lives of license, but in old age often settled down to saving their souls.

Don Tiburcio de Redin was a Navarrese, born in Pamplona, August 11, 1597. His father was Don Carlos de Redin, Lord of Redin and Baron of Biguezal. His mother was Doña Isabel de Cruzat, of the lords of Oriz and Gongora, a woman of masculine character and strong temper. It is said that after Don Martin, her second son, had risen to be Grand Prior of Navarre and Viceroy of Sicily, he was visiting his mother in Redin, and ventured to *raise his voice* while she presided at the table! Incensed at his lack of respect, she cast the knife she held in her hand at him with such fury that, had he not dodged, he might have been severely wounded. Don Tiburcio favored his mother in disposition.

When fourteen years old Tiburcio asked permission to enter the army, and it was cheerfully given. So in company with his brother Miguel, a captain of Spanish infantry, the boy served through the Italian campaign against the Duke of Savoy, from 1613 to 1617. In spite of his youth he showed headstrong bravery, and for his prowess at the assault of the fortress of Vercelli he was made a knight of Santiago, and received his commission as ensign in his brother's company. Three years later he was made "war captain at sea," and appointed to what was called the *carrera de Indias,* the "Indian Service," in South America, which in the sixteenth century offered greater opportunities to the gentlemen of Spain than the "Indian Service" of Great Britain affords her sons to-day. He held this position till 1624, and showed himself as brave on water as on land.

But "in him the wrathful mood did so predominate, that he yielded to it with untold vehemence and rushed into terrible extremes." While his ship was returning from the Indias (Spanish South America was so called), the heat of the tropic day on the Spanish Main led Don Tiburcio to take a siesta in his chair on deck. No sooner had his eyes closed, than two soldiers near him started quarreling. He rose, settled their quarrel and closed his eyes. Again about to fall asleep, he was annoyed by the shouting of the soldiers, who were again quarreling. And again, with less patience than before, he reduced them to silence. Yet when they roused him the third time, he sprang up and made for the man he considered the more guilty. The latter, who knew his captain, was so frightened that without waiting he leaped from the capstan bar into the sea. But ferocious Don Tiburcio leaped right in after him, and overhauling him in the water, gave him a severe drubbing, then and there!

Don Tiburcio left the "Indian service" to take command of a company of two hundred and fifty pikemen. With them he fought in Portugal, distinguishing himself under the Marquis of Hinojosa. And in 1624, while in command of the *banderas,* infantry companies stationed at the port of Cadiz, he obtained the king's (Philip IV) permission to raise a special company for service in the "armada of the South"—the fleet sailing for South America. As this fleet was not as yet ready to put to sea, he solicited employment in the "oceanic armada" to be sent to the Philippines.

Serving with his usual bravery in the "oceanic armada" until 1638, his feats of arms the admiration of his comrades, rumors of his courage reached the king's ears. Once, when he came to court, Philip gave him a gold chain. But he had a genius for getting in trouble with the authorities.

Once Don Tiburcio, entering the house of a married lady whom he admired, but who did not return his affection, was set upon by her indignant husband and his servants. Their loud cries roused the neighborhood. Hundreds crowded about the house, cursing the offender, and demanding his head. Don Tiburcio—his conscience may have been ill at ease—saw that discretion was the better part of valor. He gave leg-bail and escaped. But as he hurried off, his pride blushed. A stain had been cast on his honor by his undignified flight! So he hurried on to Cadiz, and pretending he could do the king a great service—his lively imagination enabled him to paint it in detail—he got four vessels of war from the general of the armada. With these, not losing a moment, he ascended the river toward Seville. His decks were cleared for action and his cannon loaded. For he meant to chastize the citizens by *bombarding their town!* Luckily the governor of Seville chanced to hear of his progress, went to meet him, and after much persuasion induced the insulted soldier to give up his idea. A slight official reprimand was the sole consequence of Redin's boldness.

And his final disregard of the powers that were could not be overlooked. Both the king, Philip IV, and his prime minister, the all-powerful Count-Duke of Olivares had promised Don Tiburcio the post of "Absolute Governor" of a new Catalonian *armada* being fitted out in Barcelona. But his appointment was delayed from week to week, and Don Tiburcio's patience passed with the passing days. He reminded both king and minister several times, but without success. So one morning he stationed himself in the middle of the square of *las Cuatro Calles* in Madrid, through which the minister was accustomed to pass every day in his coach, on his way to inspect the work being done at the royal palace of Buen Retiro.

When the coach was abreast of Don Tiburcio he ordered the coachman to stop, saying he wished to speak to his master. When no attention was paid him, the resolute place-seeker ran along with the horses, and cut their traces. By this simple means he brought the coach to a standstill. He then stood on the step and abused the minister of state for his delay in carrying out the king's wishes, and reproved him for his denying him an audience. He added: "If your excellency does not attend to the matter of my appointment soon, I shall be obliged to seek you in your house!"

The Count-Duke de Olivares held the whole power of the Spanish kingdom in his hands at the time. He was haughty and tyrannical. Self-admiration was his ruling trait. But fear helped him to dissimulate. He listened with apparent calm to his indignant interlocutor, and promised to have the matter attended to at once. But it was out of the question that a man of his character would overlook such a piece of bravado. Don Tiburcio soon had word that the *aguacils* were after him hot-foot. He hurried to Cadiz and sailed at once for the Indies.

He had been in Panama but a few days when the new Viceroy of Peru arrived there from Spain. He had orders to seize Don Tiburcio and send him back, but to show him the respect due a prisoner of quality, he bound him to his word of honor to sail for Spain, and at the same time offered him the command of a vessel of war to bring him home. In the Indian seas the Dutch fleets then rode triumphant, plundering the treasure galleons that brought the gold of the New World to Cadiz. A Dutch ship was known to be lurking outside the harbor of Panama at the very moment. Don Tiburcio realized that some splendid deed of daring alone would restore his credit at court. He laid his plans accordingly. Instead of a ship of war he chose a huge, unwieldy carrack, which he heavily freighted with sand so that she rode deep in the water, as though she carried a rich cargo. *He had all the guns spiked,* and thus prepared, drilled his crew in the rôle they were to play, and set sail.

Two days out, the Dutch vessel drew near, as he had expected. Don Tiburcio dipped his ensign and cried out the Dutchman to ask for quarter. This they readily promised, pleased with so easy a capture! The enemy captain boarded the Spanish ship with a number of men, and was told the Spanish captain lay ill in his cabin. The Hollander entered and found Don Tiburcio stretched out on his bed. But as soon as he saw his visitor he flung off his bed-clothes and felled him with a pistol shot. The shot was a signal for most of the Spanish soldiers, who were waiting at their posts, to leap into the Dutch vessel, Don Tiburcio leading them. The remainder fought bravely with the Dutchmen who had already boarded them. Soon the remnant of the Dutch crew upon their own decks were subdued, and when those in Don Tiburcio's ship attempted to turn the guns on the Spaniards alongside, they found them spiked and had to surrender.

Don Tiburcio arrived safely in Cadiz with ships and prisoners, and sent word of his success to Madrid. As he had foreseen the king was pleased. He called him to court, made up his difference with the Count-Duke, and confirmed the long-delayed nomination to the command of the Catalonian fleet. Soon after, however, while still in Madrid, an event occurred which changed Tiburcio's whole life and made a monk of the soldier.

This, strange to say, was the result of a street row between the lackeys of the Princess of Carignan and those of some other noble family. Don Tiburcio could never resist the prospect of a fight. Hearing of this delightful brawl, he sallied forth with his own servants to the *Puerta del Sol* (Gate of the Sun) selected as the battle-field. It is not known whether he meant to help the weaker of the two gangs, or whether he intended to attack both. The latter would have been quite probable. Sad to say, he no sooner reached the scene than his head was struck by a flying stone and he fell from his horse, covered with blood and to all appearances lifeless.

In the course of a slow recovery from this injury he became intensely religious, and the entire current of his thought was turned from earthly to heavenly things. When well again he entered the Capucin convent of Tarazona, July 26, 1637, under the name of Brother Francisco of Pampeluna. The next year he became a full-fledged monk. For seven years he devoted himself to good works in various Spanish monasteries, with occasional flashes of his old fighting spirit. Once he found four soldiers threatening a poor widow woman in her town house in Cortez. Humbly and repeatedly he begged them to desist. They only mocked him. At length, losing patience, he took his staff, and in spite of swords and armor gave all four soldiers a terrible beating and threw them down a flight of stairs.

Until 1651 Don Tiburcio worked as a missionary in many fields. He baptized thousands of savages, founded churches, especially in the American colonies of Spain, and spread the faith. He died on his way back from Spain, of the gout, which had long tormented him, and was buried in the Cathedral church of La Guayra. The citizens of the town prided themselves greatly on the fact, and when in 1677 it was decided to remove his body to Spain, the people rose in arms and the project could not be carried out.

WHAT AN ENGLISH TRAVELER SAW IN THE FRANCE OF LOUIS XIV

"In August (1649), the Regiment of Picardy, about 1200 horses and foot (amongst them was a captain I knew), having come to Calais, I took horses for myself and servant, and under their protection marched to Boulogne. It was a miserable spectacle to see how these tattered soldiers pillaged the poor people of their sheep, poultry, corn, cattle and whatever came their way. But they had such ill pay that they were ready themselves to starve!

"In Paris I went to see a dromedary, a very monstrous beast, much like a camel, but larger. There was also dancing on the rope, but surprising above all was the water-spouter. He, drinking only fountain-water, rendered out of his mouth in several glasses all sorts of wine and sweet waters. For a piece of money he discovered the secret for me. On March 11th I went to the *Châtelet* or Prison. A malefactor was to have the "question" or torture given him to make him confess a robbery with which he was charged. First they bound his wrist with a strong rope with one end of it made fast to an iron ring in the wall, four feet from the floor. Then his feet were bound with another rope, fastened five feet farther than his utmost length to another ring on the floor. Thus hung, yet lying silent, they slid a horse of wood under the rope which bound his feet, which so exceedingly stiffened it, as to sever the poor fellow's joints in miserable sort, drawing him out at length in an extraordinary manner, he having only a pair of linen drawers on his naked body. When he would not confess . . . they put a higher horse under the rope to increase his torture by extension. And then the executioner with a horn (such as they drench horses with), stuck the end of it into his mouth, and poured two buckets of water down his throat, which so prodigiously swelled him as would have pitied and affrighted any one to see it! . . .

. . . .

"On September 7th I went to visit Mr. Hobbes, the famous philosopher of Malmesbury. From his Paris window we saw the whole equipage and glorious cavalcade of the young French monarch, Louis XIV, passing to Parliament, to take the kingly government on him, now being in his 14th year, and out of his minority. First came the captain of the King's Aids, 50 in all, richly liveried; next the Queen Mother's Light Horse, 100, the lieutenant covered all over with embroidery and ribbons, before him riding four trumpeters in black velvet full of lace. Then came the King's Light Horse, 200, richly habited, with four trumpeters in blue gold-embroidered velvet, in front of whom rode the Count d'Olonne, his belt gold-embroidered, with pearls. Next came the Grand Prêvot's company on foot with the Prêvot on horseback. After them came the Swiss (Swiss guards) in black velvet toques, led by two cavaliers in scarlet satin, after their country fashion, which is very fantastic. They had in their caps heron plumes with a band of diamonds, and about them twelve little Swiss boys with halberds. Then . . . came grandees, governors of places, and lieutenant-governors of provinces, magnificently mounted and habited . . . the whole troop covered with gold, jewels and rich caparisons, followed by sixty trumpeters in blue velvet and as many heralds . . . then marshals and many of the nobility, and the Count d'Harcourt, the King's Master of the Horse, alone, carrying the King's sword in a scarf, which he held up in a blue sheath studded with fleurs-de-lis (lilies). Then came abundance of footmen and pages of the King, new-liveried in white and red feathers. And lastly, appeared the young King himself on an Isabella barb (Arab horse) . . . in a suit so covered with rich embroidery that one could perceive nothing of the stuff under it. He went almost the whole way hat in hand, saluting the ladies and those acclaiming him, who filled the windows with their beauty and the air with the cry of "Long live the King!" Great persons of the Court, French and Scotch guards—between their files various princes of the blood, dukes and lords—the Queen's Guard of Swiss, pages and footmen, the Queen-Mother herself in a rich coach, more guards, and an innumerable company of coaches full of ladies and gallants concluded the procession. In this equipage passed the monarch to Parliament, henceforth exercising his kingly government."

THE MAN WHO ATE FOR SEVEN

In the merry days of Augustus the Strong, King of Poland and Elector of Saxony, whose baroque court rivalled in splendor with those of Louis XIV of France and Philip IV of Spain, there lived in a tumble-down barrack of a house in the city of Dresden an elderly nobleman. He was as poor as a church-mouse, but filled with the pride of birth. And he had brought up his pretty daughter Banise to look down on food. This, perhaps, was a good thing, for often enough they had but little to eat. In fact, poor Banise never had eaten a real square meal in her life and, though no one would have suspected it, an ordinary earthly hunger was often the true source of her dreamy, gentle and melancholy glances. But in time she came to look on eating as a coarse, plebeian habit, which refined and well-bred persons ignored as far as possible.

Once in a great while delicate Banise, who hung her head like a little white snowdrop, attended one of the great court balls which King Augustus liked to give. Only once in a while, for she had but one good dress, a trifle old-fashioned, of faded rose-colored brocade, and she liked to let enough time go by for it to have been forgotten before she wore it again. And at one of these court balls a captain in His Majesty of Poland's army fell in love with the pretty and timid girl, and began to pay court to her. Banise, shyly at first, but gradually finding that she liked her admirer, received his visits with pleasure, and came to a vague understanding with him. It was vague because a magnetic bond of union between them was missing. This magnetic bond was not of steel but of gold. Banise and her father had nothing. The captain had only a very slim captain's pay —and Augustus the Strong paid his soldiers with startling irregularity, since he himself was often embarrassed for money. The captain did not need to go hungry, in view of the endless feasts, festivals and banquets the Elector was constantly giving, and he looked on his debts as one of the necessary evils of being an officer and a gentleman. But—he did not want to make life hard for poor Banise, so he waited until—one of King Augustus' masters of the horse drowned! It happened during a wild night ride from Pillnitz, where a great drinking-bout had been held, to Dresden. In crossing the Elbe the master of the horse had fallen from his steed, and that had been the end of him. His Polish Majesty himself and his ladies were known to have fallen from their horses after similar festive occasions, even though they did not drown. Banise's captain was one of the first to announce himself as a candidate for the vacant post. If he secured it, he would marry Banise. But—not being a good lickspittler, or used to making his way at court by way of petticoat favor, his prospects of getting the post were scant. Besides, the lieutenant of his company, a wealthy young fellow of good family, had begun to lay siege to Banise's heart, and this worried the captain not a little.

While the matter of the vacant post was still hanging fire, King Augustus the Strong gave a great "redout" in the palace. It was one of those entertainments where everyone appeared disguised in a peasant costume, and the Elector himself, with a farmer's belt studded with diamonds, played the part of "the host." The "hostess" on this occasion was the beautiful Madame de Dehnhoff, and the highest cavaliers and ladies of the court waited on the "guests." Banise had coaxed her father to put on his one shabby black velvet suit, and got into her own rose-colored brocade. It would attract no attention amid the splendid processions of masked "peasants" in their bright, fantastic costumes glittering with gold and precious stones. But the captain, who had planned to meet his sweetheart there, could not go —he was on duty that night, while his lieutenant was free!

On the night of the great peasant ball the poor captain sat with five comrades, all out of sorts as he was, in the smoky guard-room, playing cards and cursing his luck. Suddenly, like a star fallen from heaven, a splendid apparition stood among them in the candle-light. It was the company's lieutenant, radiant with good humor and the good food and the good wines which he had been absorbing. He was dressed in what was supposed to be a peasant costume, but which down to his very pumps and socks, was entirely of fire-red satin. On his head he wore a red cap with a red cock-feather in it, and he looked like the Devil himself. But when the unfortunate officers in the guard-room leaped up with a stifled curse on their lips, he soon soothed them. Out of the kindness of his heart he had found a way to do them a good turn, he said. Each one of the six was to put on his costume in turn, and enter the ballrooms. There he could make his way to the great buffet-tent, where stood the most wonderful array of good things to eat and drink, satisfy his hunger as quickly as possible, and return to the guard-room to give the next man his chance. All the officers of the regiments were tall, well-built young fellows. The red costume fitted them all, and—though the captain had a vague suspicion that his lieutenant's offer hid some trick—he fell in with it like the rest. For he thought he might catch sight of Banise, and have a few words with her.

One after another, the young officers slipped into the red costume, murmured their names indistinctly as they passed the post at the ballroom door—their costumes was a passport in itself—and made for the dinner-tent. There each one of them fell upon food and drink with a lion's appetite, and cleared away tremendous quantities of the choicest eatables. Before very long the enormous and unnatural appetite of the masked red-satin farmer boy began to excite astonishment, and soon it had aroused universal curiosity. Like some bottomless jar the red-satin fellow filled himself with the best there was to eat and drink. Then he disappeared just long enough to let out another notch in his belt, presumably, and returned with the insatiability of a caterpillar or a locust to his work of destruction. Roasts and cold meats, jellied pastries, every kind of vegetable dish, and sweets of all sorts vanished in this body, which seemed to be all stomach.

Naturally the attention of the Elector himself, who was playing the "host" at the entertainment, was drawn to this wonder of nature. He asked who the man was and—how many times he had appeared

I

in the dining tent. So his courtiers figured and compared notes, and told him that the red-satin farmer had thrown himself on the food like a devouring lion no less than—*seven times!* Now when the other officers all had returned to the guard-room well filled and content, the captain got into the red-satin costume, and "The Sevenfold Eater," as the rest of the company had begun to call him, appeared again. Not without a shudder did most of those present look at him, and Augustus the Strong could no longer control his curiosity. He stepped up to his fiery red "guest," and asked him to take off his mask. Since this was a request which had to be obeyed, the captain did so. But the Elector did not recognize his face. He asked him for his name, and at once added—unusual physical feats always impressed the prince, who could bend a silver dollar between thumb and forefinger—that he would be glad to show himself grateful for the amusement he had given him. Then the captain took heart, and giving his name and rank, at the same time begged for the vacant post of the drowned master of the horse. Augustus laughed. So uniquely talented a man said he, needed a well-paid position. The captain rose from his knees as master of the horse to the King of Poland and Elector of Saxony, and after many expressions of thanks was graciously dismissed by his sovereign. Of course, his first step was to hunt up his beloved Banise.

But when he found her leaning against a dark-red velvet window-curtain in her washed-out, rose-red dress, like a fading rose-leaf hanging from a purple mantle, and tried to tell her of his, or rather their good fortune, she received him with icy disdain. And when he persisted she waved him away, took her father's arm and disappeared. After that, for months she showed him the same coldness and haughtiness, until at last the captain, embittered though still loving, and quite at a loss to explain her treatment, stopped trying to see her. He did not know that Banise, brought up from childhood to look with scorn on those who yielded to the temptation of food had watched his *sevenfold* appearance in the dining-tent, and the giant meals he had devoured on each occasion with horror!

Seven times! Could she love a man who yielded so completely to his baser animal nature? The delicate consideration, the tenderness and gallantry he had shown her were all deceit! As soon as he thought he could safely indulge in his brutal lust for food, screened by a mask, he had done so. He had trampled underfoot all her holiest ideas of decency and good conduct. And would not a man who exceeded the boundaries of what was human in one direction show himself coarse and insatiable in every way, once he could take liberties under his own roof? Yet, after Banise had proved to herself that she was doing the only right thing in keeping this monster at a distance, she would often burst into bitter tears.

Time went on. The summer came in which King Augustus the Strong celebrated the wedding of his Crownprince to an Austrian archduchess with unheard-of splendor. A radiant summer sun gilded the magnificent processions, the water-festivals and mountain-festivals, the great hunts, mythological plays, the caroussels in Pillnitz on the Elbe, in the Plau grounds, in the Dresden palace and "Bear-pit," and in the Great Gardens. The sunbeams shone on the jewel-covered gowns and dresses of brocade, silk and cloth-of-gold of the court cavaliers and ladies, on the richly harnessed, satin-coated horses, the shimmering pavilions, coaches, tents, banners and wreaths. But while Augustus the Strong lived with his court in profusion and luxury, there was starvation among the country folk and the city toilers. The crops had been a failure, and though the monarch bought grain abroad to relieve the people, it passed through so many middle-men that when it came to be sold the poor could not buy it. And, though they were noble, Banise and her father were among the poor. Day by day they had less to eat, and the poor girl was often at her wit's end to know how they would get their next meal. And then, one day, the captain called on her. But now, since she had suffered so, the little fanatic looked at the fresh, strong, well-nourished master of the horse with positive hatred. And to cap the climax, the unfortunate man began to tell her about a great banquet at the palace of Field-Marshal Count Flemming.

There had been endless eating and drinking, until the Piles, who could not carry their liquor like the Saxons, even forgot to show their king the proper respect. Banise looked at him with angry eyes. She said: "Sevenfold gluttony and wine-bibbing! I hate it like death itself, as well as those who practice it!" And this she accompanied with such a hateful glance, that after a few unsuccessful attempts to regain his composure the unfortunate master of the horse left his lady-love in a hurry. By mistake, in making his way from the house, he got into the kitchen. And he saw a great light!

The next day at noon, when Banise had just finished cooking a thin gruel-soup, there came a knock at the door. In front of it stood a basket. In the basket lay two delicious-smelling capons, roasted brown, and a number of fresh white rolls. Father and daughter looked each other in the eye. But neither had strength of mind enough to admit that they were tempted beyond their principles. They sat down to their water-gruel and made the best of it. Usually the old man rested after dinner in his armchair. To-day he could not sit still. After wandering aimlessly about the room for a time, he told his daughter that he would take a walk, and off he went. And at last Banise decided to put the tempter's basket, which she had set inside the kitchen, back into the hall again. Before she did so, however, she lifted the cover—and saw that one of the savory brown capons had disappeared! Alas, how could he have done it, her proud, aristocratic father! Inconceivable! No, it could not be. Now all was lost, family honor, pride of birth, morality, decency, and all the rest! But her laments, the tears running down her little cheeks, had increased her own ravenous hunger. The remaining capon sent up a most enticing smell. And, almost without thinking, she put her hand into the basket, tore off a leg, devoured it with indescribable relish, and thought, "Oh, what a dishonorable creature you are!" But—the rest of the capon and five little rolls followed the leg. And thereafter, day by day, Banise and her father sacrificed their principles—for day by day a freshly-filled basket stood in front of their door. "The kind Electress may have heard of our need," her father said, in an embarrassed way, "and the proudest noble in the land may accept help from his sovereign!" But both of them knew better.

And gradually, as Banise grew more rosy-cheeked, more plump and more pretty than ever before, her views with regard to eating and hunger underwent a remarkable change. And she no longer thought of the master of the horse with the repulsion and horror she once had felt for him. She met him again, and when she gave him her hand to kiss, did not wonder whether he would like to eat it, as she used to do. All in all, even his gluttony at the great ball did not seem so terrible when she remembered that once she had eaten a whole capon . . . terrible, terrible! And so, when one day he asked her whether she would not be his wife, she felt so embarrassed that she could do no more than nod her head in agreement. But he sighed, and said that though he was very happy, he must admit that his position was not all that it might be. He had debts, which would have to be paid off gradually, and the salaries of court officials were very irregularly paid. But he knew his Banise. He knew her noble heart. He knew she would be glad to suffer care, trouble and *hunger* if only they could do so together! At the word "hunger" Banise's eyes filled with tears. Yes, she would be glad to share all his troubles and if heaven so willed it, though God forbid it be so!—yes, if absolutely necessary she—would—even—go—hungry—with him! And then she began to sob as though her heart would break. At that her lover could play a part no longer. Laughing, he took her in his arms, and touched by her innocent sorrow, he admitted that he had been the doctor who had led him to take a more natural and healthy view of life by using nature's own medicine—good food! And he would add only one thing. She need not fear his terrible gluttony. He no longer had a sevenfold appetite. Only with regard to his love for her was he a man who still could eat for seven!

WHITEHALL IN THE DAYS OF THE "MERRY MONARCH"

"This day (Jan. 29th, 1660) His Majesty King Charles II came to

London after a sad and long exile. . . . It was also his birthday, and with a triumph of above 20,000 horse and foot, brandishing their swords and shouting with inexpressible joy, the way strewn with flowers, the bells ringing, the streets hung with tapestry, fountains running with wine, he was received. Mayor, Aldermen and all the Companies, lords and nobles clad in cloth-of-gold, silver and velvet, windows and balconies set with ladies, trumpets, music and myriads of people flocking . . . I stood in the Strand and beheld it and blessed God!

"I saw the magnificent entry of the French Ambassador Colbert, received in the Banqueting House. I never saw a richer coach than that which he came in to Whitehall. Standing by His Majesty at dinner in the presence, was a rare fruit called the King-pine, growing in the Barbadoes and West Indies. His Majesty having cut it up, was pleased to give me a piece off his own plate to taste of . . . I walked with the King Charles through St. James' Park to the garden (March 4th, 1670), where I both saw and heard a very familiar discourse between His Majesty and Mrs. Nelly, as they call a certain impudent comedian (Nell Gwynne). She was looking out of her garden on a terrace on the top of the wall, and His Majesty standing on the green walk under it. Thence the King walked to the Duchess of Cleveland, another lady of pleasure and curse of our nation. . . . This evening (Jan. 11, 1682), I was at the entertainment of the Morocco Ambassador at the Duchess of Portsmouth's glorious apartments at Whitehall. There was a great banquet of sweetmeats and music. . . . The Ambassador and his retinue behaved themselves with extraordinary moderation and modesty, though placed about a long table, a lady between each two Moors. Among the ladies were the King's natural children, Ladies Litchfield and Sussex, and the Duchess of Portsmouth, Nelly, etc., concubines and cattle of that sort, as splendid as jewels and excess of bravery could make them. . . ."

"Following His Majesty this morning (Oct. 16th, 1683), through the Gallery at Whitehall, I went with the few who attended him into the Duchess of Portsmouth's *dressing-room*, within her bed-chamber! There she was in her morning loose garment, her maids combing her, newly out of bed, His Majesty and his gallants standing about her. But what engaged my curiosity was that the rich and splendid furniture of this woman's apartment has now been twice or thrice pulled down and rebuilt, to satisfy her prodigal and expensive pleasures, while Her Majesty's does not exceed some gentleman's wives in furniture and accommodation. . . . What contentment can there be in the riches and splendor of this world, purchased with vice and dishonor . . . ?"

"King Charles II died on February 6th, 1685. He gave up the ghost half an hour after eleven in the morning . . . in the fifty-fourth year of his age. He was a prince of many virtues and many great imperfections. . . . He took delight in having a number of little spaniels follow him and lie in his bed-chamber, where he often suffered the bitches to puppy and give suck, which rendered it very offensive indeed and made the whole court nasty and stinking. He would doubtless have been an excellent prince, had he been less addicted to women, who made him restless, and always in want to supply their unmeasurable profusion, to the detriment of many indigent persons who had signally served both him and his father. . . ."

CHAPTER XXI

In the magnificence of the Baroque seventeenth, and the earlier eighteenth centuries was sown the seed of the revolutions which were to substitute, toward the end of the eighteenth century, the ideal of *democracy* for that of *kingly* rule by divine right.

The Character of the Rococo Age. Humanly speaking, in nearly every land the Rococo Age was one in which a towering, glittering, golden superstructure of royal, noble and priestly luxury and extravagance was built up on a foundation of wretched, toiling, suffering and starving humanity. This human foundation for the mad luxury of kings and nobles began to break down within itself. The breaking-down agency was the spread of *revolutionary doctrines*—the equal rights of man, the theory that kings were *not* a divine institution—Heaven knows, they did nothing to encourage the idea that they were one of God's blessings!—and that nobles and priests were not, *as such, privileged classes.* The essence of democracy, the theory that one man is as good as another, whether his ancestors hung on a gallows or from a family tree, came to the wretched peasants *from above,* from the writers and even some of the nobles themselves. The peasants realized this new ideal in the French Revolution, after our own War of Independence had shown them—in a more humane and noble way—that no tyrannical king could get the better of a nation bent on being free.

Rococo Facets. There are as many *facets* (the small, individual triangular planes or surfaces with which a gem is cut) to Rococo life, as there are to a diamond, hundreds of them. In the following pictures we shall try to give a few of the most interesting of the *many human* facets of Rococo existence.

SHIFTING CRYSTALS OF THE ROCOCO KALEIDOSCOPE

THE FIRST ROCOCO COMMANDMENT

"Any one who did not live before 1789 never knew the pleasure of living," said the famous Tallyrand, who was a gay young cleric in the days of Louis XV, and ended his life as the world's foremost diplomat of the old school. And, the art or "pleasure" of living in

Rococo days was regulated by certain fixed rules of good form and etiquette—in the fashionable court and noble circles, the only ones which counted. Courtesy, *external* courtesy, was the first of Rococo Commandments. When she ascended the scaffold, Queen Marie Antoinette happened to step on the executioner's foot: "Excuse me, I hope I did not hurt you," she said at once. The height of bad manners was *for a wife to love her husband!* It simply was not done. "You have been married six months and still love your husband? My dear, that's something a milliner can indulge in, but not a marquise," was what the society dowager said to the eighteenth century débutante. And the great lord, whether layman or priest, was not supposed to give money a thought. Money was vulgar. It was not discussed. The superintendents of great estates might force the wretched peasants to stuff their hungry mouths with grass to wring from their toil the *louis d'or,* the "golden Louis" the gold coins named "Louis" after the kings of France) their lay or clerical masters squandered over the gaming-tables or on their mistresses. But it was beneath a nobleman's dignity to take an interest in *how* he got his gold! When Louis XVI reproached Archbishop Dillon with the tremendous debts he ran up, the prelate carelessly replied: "Sire, I will inquire of my intendent—for, of course, I do not concern myself with such things—and then will have the honor of reporting to Your Majesty how my affairs stand!" When the Cardinal-Prince of Rohan went into bankruptcy (it was a bankruptcy of some 50,000,000 livres) the proud Grand Almoner of France boasted that "Only a king or a Rohan could treat himself to a bankruptcy on such a scale!" The whole end and aim of fashionable existence was to make life easier and pleasanter, not more difficult, and to live "politely."

THE WELL-BRED ROCOCO WIFE

A well-bred wife in good society, or a mistress whose title was nearly as well established as that of a wife, one who knew the laws of tact and good form, was always especially attentive and considerate of her husband's lady love of the moment. A model example was the Countess de Boufflers, who was the friend of the last Prince of Conti. Rousseau, the philosopher, said of her: "She is a Frenchwoman as regards her bust, but the rest of her is cosmopolitan." The Countess de Boufflers looked with a complaisant eye on the Prince's little infidelities with the easy-going nymphs of the Paris *Opéra* and with other ladies, and thus made herself far more secure in her position than she would have had she indulged in scenes of jealousy. Madame de Deffand, a Rococo lady, has described the social code of her day: "We knew how to live and how to die in those days. We ignored illnesses. If we had the gout we walked erect in spite of it, without letting anyone know we suffered. We concealed our sufferings *out of consideration for others!* We knew how to ruin ourselves with a smile, like those gamblers who have such control over themselves that they do not change countenance, no matter what they may lose. We had ourselves carried out hunting half-dead. We thought it better form to die at a ball or at the theater than in bed. We enjoyed life, and when the hour of departure came, we prided ourselves on making our exit in good form."

GLIMPSES OF THE ROCOCO SOUL

During the American War of Independence Lafayette and the Duke of Lauzon were once quartered in a Virginia hermit's home. Merely because he was bored, the Duke, as was his habit, addressed the most tender compliments to the hermit's daughter, until finally she said to him: "I am surprised to hear you speak as you do, for I have heard you are married, and have a wife in France." "Married?" answered the Duke, "yes, that's true, but I am so little married that it hardly is worth while mentioning. Just ask Lafayette!"

The old Marshal-Duke of Richelieu, one of the worst libertines of Rococo France, was famous for his cynicism. Once he surprised his wife in the arms of his groom. He bowed to her and said, in a reproachful tone of voice: "But Madame, think how embarrassing it would have been for you if some one else had entered the room!" Then he dismissed the groom. After he had become a widower, he planned to marry Princess Elizabeth of Lorraine, but the project was supposed to be a secret. Somehow the same groom got wind of it, and thinking the Duke had forgotten the incident already mentioned, went to him and begged to be taken back into his service. The old Marshal looked at him with surprise: "How did you find out I meant to marry again?" he asked.

The Abbé Voisenon was one of the merry writers of those licentious *contes* (tales) in which the eighteenth century delighted, and of comic opera texts. He always said he was on the point of death. After half a century of folly he did retire to his country home, the Chateau of Voisenon, to prepare to die. He had a lead coffin brought in and put in the hall. "There," he would say, "is my last riding-coat!" The coffin stood invitingly open, but death did not arrive. Voisenon made the acquaintance of some country neighbors and of the village priest. He hunted, played cards and read Voltaire, saying that he was reading his breviary. Though he lived merrily, peasants round about said he was a phantom and not alive. And he himself would say: "I look like a family ghost!" At times he would take to his bed not expecting to get up again. "Farewell, my friends," he would cry, "it is all over! Come to my funeral to-morrow!" The next day, arriving dressed in mourning, they would find Voisenon at the table, trying to make his doctor drunk. But one day he actually seemed dead. The doctor gave him up. The frightened servants ran to the village to get the last sacraments for him. While they were gone the Abbé de Voisenon recovered and rang. No one answered. He grew angry, had a terrible spasm and then—got up, dressed, took his gun and went off hunting. On his way the Host was carried past, followed by the whole village, and he knelt, as was his custom. But no one saw him. When the procession had passed he went on to the woods. While he was shooting a rabbit, the priest reached the Chauteau, ready to minister to the dying man. But he could not be found, not even in his coffin. At last his valet, who had gone out into the fields to look for him, found him: "But Monsieur l'Abbé," he said, "do you not know that the priest is waiting to give you extreme unction?" His last hour finally did come. It was not an hour of penitence. The village priest, holding up the crucifix, admonished him to make his peace with God. "No, my affair with God is broken off, my dear *curé,*" said the sacrilegious *abbé.* "I herewith return his letters and his picture!" The "letters" was the breviary of the Church, the "picture" was the crucifix. And thus Voisenon died.

How The Men Who Destroyed the Older Order in France Felt Toward It. In one of the most weird and fantastic tales ever told, a modern Teuton author has embodied the feeling of the ardent French "Red Republican" of the first French Revolution with regard to royalty and kings. Better than any amount of historical fact it lets us see the bitterness, the blackness of a hatred such as only centuries of oppression and tyranny could have aroused. The lighter side of the Court life of the Rococo Age and the darker pages of popular wretchedness are discussed in "The Intimate Romance of History," and in the "History of the World." This tale shows how the average human being, the average Frenchman who destroyed the gilded glories of the Bourbon monarchy in France felt about what he had destroyed.

ROYAL HEARTS

The Duke Ferdinand of Orleans* returned toward the end of Sep-

* Ferdinand Philip Louis Charles Henry, Duke of Orleans (1810-1842) was the son of Louis Philippe, Duke of Orleans, afterward King of France. He was amiable and popular. It was the age of French colonial expansion in Algeria. "Colonization" was one of the great topics of the day. But when he had a love affair with pretty Jenny Colon, a working-girl, the Parisians, who liked him, only said: "Every one colonizes in their own way!" A man who knows him personally has recorded many incidents of his kindness and generosity, and has declared "The Duke of Orleans was one of the most charming men I have known."

tember, 1841, to his Paris *hôtel,* after a stay in the country. There his valet handed him on a great gold platter all the correspondence which had gathered during his absence, and among these letters one in particular attracted the Duke's attention. It read as follows:

Dear Sir:

I have a large number of pictures which I intend to sell to you at a high figure. The sum will be nothing, however, compared to the wealth which your family has piled up by its thefts. The extraordinary *material* value my paintings have for the royal house, aside from any other consideration, should make you grateful for the chance I offer you to secure them. I am an old man with few wants, and expect to hand over the money you give me to the society of "The People of the Mountain," honest Frenchmen who maintain the traditions of the men who executed Louis XVI. Driven from France, they are now established in Geneva. I expect to turn the money over to them for the express purpose of encouraging the murder of kings. You may not like the use I make of the money, but every one has a right to do with his own money what he will. I know positively that you will buy my pictures; in fact, you will find it absolutely necessary to do so.

MARTIN DROLING.

The spoiled scion of royalty was impressed by the curious letter. He told his adjutant, Count de Touailon-Geffrard, to make some investigations, and it turned out that Martin Droling was a quiet old painter, over eighty years of age, who now seldom or never left his dingy studio in the Rue des Martyres. In his youth he had painted and exhibited frequently, mostly kitchen interiors. One of his kitchen interiors, in fact, had been bought by the State and hung in the Louvre.

Then the Duke of Orleans laughed, said something about "this droll Droling" and paid no further attention to the letter. But a few days later he received a second one. It read:

Dear Sir:

I cannot understand why you have not yet turned up at my place. I repeat that I am an old man. It would be best if our business were wound up as soon as possible, lest death interfere with our closing the deal. So I shall expect to see you not earlier than eleven-thirty to-morrow morning at my studio. Do not come before then, for I am a late riser and have no mind to crawl out of bed at some unearthly hour on your account.

MARTIN DROLING.

The Duke said to his adjutant: "I think we will obey Mr. Droling's orders. Have a carriage waiting to-morrow morning, my dear Touaillon, so that we get to his place at least half-an-hour before the time he sets. I think he will be all the funnier if he is angrier!" So the next morning the Duke and his adjutant panted up four flights of stairs in a dirty tenement court until they saw a big, yellow door with an old name-plate marked "Martin Droling." After knocking and hammering a long time, a goat-like voice at last cried: "What's the matter? Who are you?" "Get up, Papa Droling, get up!" cried the Duke, highly amused. "You have company!" "I'll get up when it suits me and not a minute before," was the answer. But the Duke and his adjutant were full of good humor. They flung themselves against the door till it shook, they beat on it with their canes, and kept shouting: "Get up! Get up! Company! Out of bed!" At last steps neared the door. "You can go as far as you like," said the voice, "but you'll not get in until I have washed, dressed, and eaten breakfast!" The Duke pleaded, prayed and cursed. All in vain. At last he settled down to wait, telling his adjutant that at last he was getting an idea at first hand what it meant to wait for an audience in a royal anteroom. Finally the door opened, and a small, pallid man, clad in the costume of the first Consulate, whose little face peered out from an enormous black cravat, opened the door. "I am Martin Droling," he said. "What do you want?" When the Duke told him he had asked them to call, he pulled out a silver watch like a turnip and said: "I asked you to call at eleven-thirty. But you have been playing your silly jokes here for the past half-hour, and each one of my pictures will cost you just a thousand francs more because of it. I'll teach you good manners! And now which of you is Mr. Orleans?"

The adjutant was shocked. "Mr. Droling," he said bowing in the Duke's direction, "His Royal Highness, the Duke of Orleans stands before you!" The little man fairly snorted with rage: "Call the gentleman what you like, but kindly allow me to call him by his *right* name! And who are *you*, by the way? Will you be kind enough to introduce yourself?" The Duke revelled in the sight of his adjutant's speechless amazement. Then, in his most charming manner, he said: "Permit me, Mr. Droling, my adjutant, Count de Touaillon-Geffrard, Lieutenant-Colonel of the Second Regiment of Cuirassiers."

Droling made a short bow. "My dear sir," he said, "I do not know you and I do not care to make the acquaintance of people of your sort. I did not invite you here, and have no intention of receiving you. So kindly take yourself off again." The Duke of Orleans, like most princely personages, was more or less dependent on the members of his suite. But that did not make him any the fonder of them. The way in which Droling treated his adjutant, who was very proud of his crusading ancestors, so amused the Duke that he could hardly keep from laughing. He asked Touaillon to go and wait for him in the carriage and said: "After all, Mr. Droling need receive only persons who are agreeable to him." But now the raging adjutant had a sweet revenge. For as he turned to go he heard Droling say: "If you imagine for a moment, Mr. Orleans, that you are agreeable to me, you are very much mistaken. I find you most unsympathetic, and only asked you here because we have business to transact with each other. Kindly enter!"

The Duke entered and looked around the studio. There were some empty easels and some sketches on the walls, while old, dusty costumes were scattered around on chests and chairs. He saw no sign of a picture, and with an air of resignation sank down on a small painter's stool in the middle of the room. But with a cry of rage the little man shrieked: "Did I ask you to sit? Your worthy family does not even seem to have learned the first elements of good manners, Mr. Orleans! What would you say if I sat down in *your* home uninvited? Besides, you are sitting on *my* chair!" This time the Duke really was surprised, but Droling hastily flung down some rags from an old leather chair, moved it forward and said with great formality: "May I beg you to seat yourself here!" Then, after getting two glasses of Venetian crystal and treating his visitor and himself to an excellent glass of Port, the old man was at once interested when the Duke mentioned his "Kitchen Interior" in the Louvre. "How do you like the picture?" he asked. And the Duke, who never had seen it, praised it in general terms. "I am sorry you approve of such truck," the old man sighed. "Only the brown garbage-pot has a suggestion of King Louis XIII about it," he added.

"Of King Louis XIII?" repeated the Duke, astonished. He began to think the old man was mad. So he decided, first of all, to tell him the truth—that he had not seen the Louvre pictures. When he had made this admission the old man shook his head: "Well, it is easy to see that you are a member of the royal house," he said. "What else could one expect?" and he looked at his guest with the greatest contempt. The Duke felt uncomfortable. "How about our business?...." he murmured. And the old painter nodded his head. "You may believe me when I say that I exceedingly dislike to have my pictures pass into the possession of a family so abominable as the Valois-Bourbon-Orleans family," he said to the Duke. "But, in the first place, no one else would pay so high a price, and besides, Mr. Orleans," and he grinned at the Duke, "the pictures contain— in a somewhat unusual form, it is true—what your royal house had for centuries regarded as its holiest possession!"

"I fail to understand you," said the Duke.

Martin Droling grinned again: "You will understand me, Mr.

Orleans, when I tell you that—my pictures contain *the hearts of the kings of France!*" Now the Duke was convinced Droling was mad. But the latter already had hopped up from his chair, and had dragged forth a picture from behind a screen which hid it. He dusted it off with a rag, put it on an easel and then cried out like a barker at a circus: "Here is the heart of one of the most celebrated kings who sat on the throne of France, one of the greatest scoundrels who ever walked the earth: the heart of King Louis XI!" The Duke looked at the picture.

It showed a great, dead tree, from whose branches hung a couple of dozen naked, partly decomposed human beings. In the dark wood of the trunk was engraved a heart, with the letters: "L. XI." The Duke thought the picture was directly and cruelly truthful, but it cast out a repulsive odor of decay, and he felt as though he must hold his nose. The Duke of Orleans knew the history of France, and especially that of the royal family well enough to recognize at once what the picture showed. It was the famous "Garden" of his pious ancestor, King Louis XI, who loved to hang people. That the painter had offered this picture to him seemed singularly tactless. For the young Duke, while in command in Africa, had been most humane. Only Droling's age and supposed madness enabled him to remain civil. "I must confess the workmanship is excellent. But I am not enough of an ancestor-worshiper to grow enthusiastic about all the horrible things done by my half-barbarous forbears. The idea of the picture is singularly lacking in good taste...." The old man grinned. "Yes, but your reproach does not apply to me. Your own grandfather suggested the idea of the picture to me. You must blame him!"

"What do you say?"

"The father of your own father, who is king of France to-day, my good friend Philippe-Egalité of Orleans.* On our way back from the execution of your uncle, the sixteenth Louis, he gave me the idea. But any one could see that the picture shows the repulsive heart of Louis XI! It is not artistic. His was one of the largest of all the hearts and had a horrible odor. It always gave me a head-ache when I sniffed it. Will you have a pinch of snuff?" The painter took out a large gold snuff-box and held it out to his guest. And the Duke

* Louis-Philippe-Joseph, Duke of Orleans (1747-1793) called Philippe-Egalité (Equality) was a debauched voluptuary, an intimate friend of that royal drunkard, Beau "fat friend," the Prince of Wales (King George IV of England). He "threw in" with the people in the French Revolution and voted for the death of Louis XVI as "Citizen Orleans," a member of the Revolutionary Convention. Selfish in his pursuit of pleasure, he was courteous and considerate of his friends. He was among the "Moderates" put to death when the "Terrorists" got the upper hand.

who, as a matter of fact, liked snuff, took a good pinch and thrust it into his nostrils.

"It is a good mixture," said the old man. "Prince Gaston of Orleans, Queen Anne of Austria and King Charles V. Well, how do you like it? It must be amusing to inhale the best part of your venerated ancestors in a pinch of snuff!"

"Mr. Droling," said the Duke, "I can only praise your wine and your snuff. But, if you will excuse my mentioning it, I don't understand a word of what you say!" "What is it you do not understand?" "I do not understand what you are telling me about my ancestors who are supposed to be hidden in your paintings and in your snuff." The old man crowed. "Stupid like all the Orleans!" he cried. "You are even more stupid than your grandfather, who was enough of an ass to go over to the Moderate party, the Girondins, instead of sticking to the red Jacobites! Well, he paid for his disloyalty on the guillotine! So you do not understand, Mr. Orleans? I say my pictures have been painted with the hearts of the kings of France. Do you understand that?"

"Yes, Mr. Droling, but...."

"And out of this snuff-box and others that I have, I snuff up what is left of the royal hearts after I have used them in my painting! Do you understand that?" The Duke frowned. "You needn't shout, Mr. Droling, "I'm not deaf," he said. "But still I do not get the connection." The painter signed, but did not answer for a moment. Then he went to a closet and took from it a couple of small copper nameplates, which he handed to the Duke. "There are thirty-one others in the drawer. I make you a present of all of them. They go with the pictures," he said.

The Duke looked carefully at the inscriptions on the two copper labels. Then he opened the closet drawer and studied the rest. The inscriptions showed that the name-plates came from the urns which had contained the hearts of the kings, princes and princesses of the blood royal of France. And, gradually, the Duke began to understand.

"How did you get hold of them?" he asked. Quite against his will, there was something arrogant in his tone of voice. "I bought them," replied the old man in the same tone. "You know painters often take an interest in all sorts of old junk!"

"Then sell these name-plates to me!" said the Duke.

"I've made you a present of them, man! You can hang them at the bottom of my pictures. I will show you which are which. This," and he took a label from the Duke's hand, "belongs under one of my jolliest pictures. Wait a minute and you shall see it!" Another picture was drawn from behind the screen and placed on an easel. And the old man drummed on the copper label with his fingers and

announced: "This is the heart of King Henry IV, the first Bourbon!
It was a little damaged by the dagger-thrust of Ravaillac, a man of
admirable principles!"

The painting showed an immense kitchen, almost entirely occupied by an enormous oven with many range-holes. On all these range-
holes, from which the flames leaped upward, stood cooking pots in
which living human beings were boiling. Many were trying to climb
out, others were screaming and cutting horrible faces. A dreadful
fear and terror was reflected in all the starving features. The brown
hearth showed a painted heart with the initials "H. IV." The Duke
turned away. "I do not understand it," he said.

Droling laughed. "And yet your worthy ancestor's fine phrase
may be read in every school-book: 'I want every peasant to have a
hen in his pot of a Sunday.' See, those were the chickens the King
himself had in his kitchen pots! Try another mixture," he added,
pulling out another snuff-box and holding it out to the Duke. "It is
a good one: Henry IV and Francis I. Try it, it will make you feel
like a bird of prey!"

"Do you mean to tell me," said the Duke, slowly, "that this brown
snuff is made of the hearts of those two kings?" "Indeed it is, I
mixed it myself!" "But where did you get the hearts?" "I bought
them, I tell you. Do you want to have the details? Very well!"

"Petit-Radel—did you ever hear of him? No, of course not, you
are uneducated, a true Orleans, as I noticed at once. But your grandfather was well acquainted with Petit-Radel, the architect. One day
Petit-Radel was commissioned to destroy the silly old royal tombs in
the funeral vaults of the Abbey of St. Denis and Val-de-Grace, and in
the Jesuit Church in Saint Antoine street as well. He made a good
job of it. Your grandfather told me about it. 'Go along with him
and you will be able to buy mummy cheap!' he said. Do you know
what a mummy is, Mr. Orleans? No? Well, mummy is mummy. It
is the remains of bodies which have been embalmed and which are
used as colors. And they are expensive coloring matter. You can
imagine how pleased I was at the chance of getting some fine mummy
cheaply. In the Jesuit Church we found the urns with the embalmed hearts of the kings and princes. Petit-Radel smashed the
urns, and I bought the copper labels and the hearts.' '

"And you mixed colors out of these hearts?"

"Why, of course! That's all a royal heart is good for! No, I
exaggerate, it makes good snuff, too! Take a pinch: Henry IV and
Francis I!" But the Duke declined. "I thank you, Mr. Droling,"
he said. The old man shut his snuff-box. "Suit yourself, but you
will never have another opportunity to inhale snuff made of royal
hearts. And," he continued, "every heart of the family Valois-

Bourbon-Orleans is included in my collection. Whose heart would you like to see?"

"Louis XV," answered the Duke, at haphazard.

Soon another picture stood on the easel. It was very dark. "You seemed to have used a great deal of mummy in this one, Mr. Droling," said the Duke. "No, the king's heart was very small—no more than a boy's heart, for all that it beat sixty-four years. But I used other hearts as well in this painting: those of the Regent, the Duke of Orleans, of the Pompadour and the Dubarry. The picture covers a whole period!" The picture showed a confused throng of gentlemen and ladies who were all slinking, moving and crawling past and over each other. Some wore nothing at all. Others wore the costume of their day, with high *toupets,* perukes, jabots and laced coats. But all their bodies—instead of having living heads—ended in death's-heads, covered with a thin, parchment-like skin. Their movements had something sickly, animal, doggish even. The actual painting was masterly, but there was something strangely like-less in the expression of the individuals and of the crowd as a whole. And this strange mixture of life and death, of man and beast, was so skillfully harmonized that the picture made a deeply terrible impression on any one who looked at it. "It is a horrible picture," said the Duke with conviction. The old painter crowed with delight. "Isn't it? Repulsive, absolutely disgusting! In a word, *truly royal!*" Then he grew serious: "It cost me agonies to paint this picture, Mr. Orleans," he said. "There is no torture like that of being compelled to explore the depths of royal hearts. Well, take a look at another picture!"

The Duke went to the screen and took out the first picture which came to hand and raised it up on the easel.

"Ah, you have gotten hold of the heart of King Charles IX! There was none of them who thirsted for blood as he did!' '

The Duke saw a broad river, which rolled slowly along between flat banks under a twilight sky. An endless flood of human wreckage was carried along by the waves of the turgid stream, a flood of corpses. Quite in the foreground, standing erect in a boat, was a logger who directed the terrible drive of felled human logs. He was a lean figure, wrapped in a mantle of royal purple, his pale face disfigured, his mad gaze staring straight ahead. With a great boathook which he pushed into the ooze, he drove his terrible freight downstream. The next picture the Duke looked at was even more terrible. We will not attempt to describe the corpse in dissolution at which two magnificently painted vultures were tearing. The Duke turned away, pale with horror. The old man clutched his sleeve: "It is the finest of all my pictures! It shows your great ancestor, King Louis XIV. Did you not recognize him? It was he who said: "I am the State!" And there you have that State—corrupt, decayed, gone into dissolution!"

The Duke sat down in a chair. He poured himself a glass of wine and drank it saying: "If you will permit me, Mr. Droling. Your art calls for strong nerves!" The painter stepped up to him and held out his own glass. "Please pour me some, too, Mr. Orleans! And let us drink to my final release from my curse. For now I am free at last!" the old man added in a trembling voice. "All these terrible hearts have been painted up. What little is left of them is in my snuff-boxes. My life-work is done. When you send for the paintings this afternoon, have all my tools, my brushes, easels and what not taken away too, as a favor! Oh, the joy of being free again, of never having to see these horrors any more!" He moved his little painting stool close to the Duke's chair, and seized the latter's right hand in both his own. "You are an Orleans! You are the son of the King of France! You know how greatly I hate your family! Yet I am so happy at this moment that I almost forget the terrible sufferings I have endured together *with* your family for centuries! Never has a human being led a more terrible existence than I have. This is my tale:

"When I had bought the mummied royal hearts at the suggestion of your grandfather, Philippe of Orleans, I first painted the "Kitchen Interior" you saw in the Louvre. And, to show my contempt for the king, for the first time I used some of the mummy color, a bit of the heart of King Louis XIII, on the garbage-pail. It was a taste-less jest. For at that time I did not hate your family as I do to-day. I hated the King, Louis XVI, and his Austrian wife, but not more than any other Parisian. And Philippe was my good friend. His hatred for his own family was greater, far greater than mine. He suggested that I use these royal hearts to express the *thought* content as well as the *material* content of my pictures. It was he who suggested that I paint King Louis XI's "Garden" to express that king's heart in a worthy manner.

"At the time I was delighted with his suggestion. In all I had thirty-three hearts, and eighteen of them were king's hearts. In eighteen pictures I could paint the history of France as expressed by the hearts of its kings! Can you think of anything more alluring for an artist? I studied the history of my country, and at the same time set to work. Your grandfather supplied me with all the books on French history obtainable, besides secret memoirs, diaries, and documents of every kind. For years I immersed myself in your family's blood-stained history . . . but no matter how horrible I made each picture which was to express the quintessence of a royal heart, it always fell below the terrible truth! The crimes of the Valois, Bourbons and Orleans were so stupendous that it seemed almost impossible to express them artistically. And out of my tortures to do justice to my subject grew my hatred and my loathing for those who had plunged me in such agony of soul. I could have murdered your grandfather! One day he rushed into my studio. He had become a traitor. He had gone over to the Gironde, the Moderates. He begged me to hide him. He could have found no one in all Paris who would have delivered him to the hangman with greater delight! I at once sent my servant for the soldiers, and kept him under lock and key until they dragged him away. He was guillotined ten days later. As my reward I had begged to be given his heart!"

The Duke interrupted him: "But you could not possibly have painted with the fresh heart!"

"No! But I had time, all the time in the world! I had to use up all the other hearts first. I had your grandfather's heart embalmed and dried. I let it lay for thirty-six years. It made a splendid mummy color. With it I painted my last picture. Wait, I will show it to you!"

He jumped up and dragged another picture from behind the screen. "Here Mr. Orleans! What you *see,* I have often heard *beat—beat on that same chair* in which you are sitting—*the heart of your grandfather, the Duke of Orleans, Philippe Egalité!*" The Duke instinctively put his hand to his chest. He felt as though he must hold fast to his own heart before this horrible old man tore it from his breast. He hardly dared raise his eyes to the picture.

The picture's background was formed of an iron railing with many spikes. It ran the whole length of the canvas. In the foreground many hundreds of poles had been thrust into the ground. Each of these poles, as well as each of the spikes of the railing, was crowned with a human head. The poles were arranged in heart-form, and in such a way that the railing, in its two upper half-circles, showed the outlines of a heart. And the inner radius of the heart was completely filled with the poles. It looked as though death-flowers were growing out of the brown earth. High above the poles, however, in the grayish, yellow air, floated a vague, misty, grimacing face, which was really nothing more or less than a single demoniac grin. And this grimace, more clearly examined, was also a chopped-off head. It was also heart-shaped: it had the characteristic heart-shaped form of the heads of the members of the house of Orleans. The Duke never had known his grandfather, but the resemblance of this pear-shaped face to that of his father and his own at once struck him. And while he stared at this exhibit of guillotined heads, the old man's voice seemed to come to him from a distance:

"Yes, Mr. Orleans, all of them are portraits! Oh, the trouble it cost to get pictures of all these people! Do you want to know to whom the heads belonged whose sight your grandfather up there—

he is *all heart* now, look at him!—is so *heartily* enjoying? They belong to all those whom *he himself* brought to the guillotine! There is the Duke of Montpensier and that is the Marquise of Clairemont. There are Neckar, Turgot, Beaulieu-Rubin. There is his cousin, Louis Capet, whom you call King Louis XVI. Wait, I will give you the list!"

He dug in his coat pocket and brought out a faded little memorandum book. "Take it, Mr. Orleans! It is Philippe Orleans' legacy to his grandson, heir to the throne of France. It was his betting book. He kept strict note of all those whom he brought to guillotine. For, you know, that was his *sport!* It was for the sake of his *sport* that your grandfather became a red republican! Here, take his royal notes! The hangman gave them to me for a hundred sous!"

The Duke took the booklet, but the letters swam before his eyes. And the little old painter went on: "Only to look at that picture makes you shudder. Ah, the man with whose heart it was painted was a fellow of another stamp! His heart would laugh could he see you, laugh as it laughs in the picture. In truth, I have painted him a fine memorial. But now, Mr. Orleans, perhaps you have an idea of what I have suffered!"

"You see, I took over the *soul* of each of your ancestors into my own. They have all dwelt in this broken old body which stands before you, the Louis and the Henrys, the Francises, Charleses and Philips! I was possessed by them, like a man possessed by devils! I had to commit all their crimes over again. That was my work. I spent months feeling my way into the hells of their royal fantasies, in plunging into the poisonous *abysses* of their thoughts . . . And when I began to use the hearts as snuff, then, at last, was I able to do justice to my task. For it seemed as though the soul of the king whose heart I drew into my nostrils took possession of my brain. And all that was left for my own poor little self to do was to set down his blood-stained royal caprices on canvas—in colors made of his own royal heart. Yes, Mr. Orleans, in me you see all your ancestors! They all come to life again in my brain. All of them, from your grand-father back to Philippe V, the first Valois, who put the crown of the Capets on his head with his blood-dripping fingers. And I was the artist. I was the type of the woman whom they all possessed and outraged—for the artist is a woman! He coaxes thoughts to himself like a wanton, yields himself up to them, and then bears his works under awful tortures. Yes," he said, and his voice was full on the cutting bitterness of self-contempt: "I am the living wanton of the dead kings of France! And now, Mr. Orleans, to you, the last living member of your race, I present my bill for the nights of love . . . their fruits are yours in return! It is your forefathers' fault if they are not more beautiful!"

On a sheet of white paper he handed the Duke a list of the paintings and their prices. The Duke folded it and put it in his pocket.

"I will send you the money this noon, and have the pictures called for at the same time," he said. "Just show the people all you want taken away. I am obliged to you, Mr. Droling. Will you shake hands with me before I go?"

"No," said Martin Droling, "you are an Orleans!"

The Duke bowed in silence, and left him.

On July 13, 1842, Duke Ferdinand of Orleans died in consequence of a fall from a carriage. In his will a peculiar clause, by which he left his heart to the painter Martin Droling, 34 Rue des Martyrs, attracted attention. No doubt King Louis-Philippe, in virtue of the private laws of the royal hours, did not allow this clause to be executed. But it could not have been carried out in any event, for the old painter had died months before. His pictures seem to have disappeared completely, and in order to get a glimpse of the hearts of the French royal family it is necessary to go to the Louvre in Paris, and look at Droling's "Kitchen Interior," No. 4339 in the catalogue.

The Eighteenth Century in Other Lands. The hatred against royalty and the privileged classes was not so bloodily expressed in other lands and the suffering of the people was not so extreme as in France. *Absolutism in Spain*—where a fat-witted king and a vile queen maintained a flagrantly dissolute court while the country went to ruin became identified with *patriotism,* when Napoleon tried to add the land to his string of conquered kingdoms. In Naples, a king and queen who rank among the lowest specimens of the human race, were for a time kept on the throne by England. But little by little, during and after the Napoleonic Age, constitutional government, democratic and popular representation did away with despotism everywhere. The last great absolute Monarchs of Europe, the Russian Tzar, and the Turkish Sultan, were swept away as a result of the War to end War. With them went the last of the despotism of royalty and the aristocratic privilege of the eighteenth century. Before bringing "The Romance of Human Life Through the Ages" to an end, we will give two more glimpses of eighteenth century life. One shows how the medieval spirit of intolerance still lingered in men's souls, and how slavery was still a commonplace of existence in the days when the United States threw off the tyrant's yoke. The other emphasizes a truth that applies to all ages: that the happiness of human beings does not depend on circumstances or surroundings, that it can rise above suffering and death, if only it is founded on *love!*

GALAFAS

(A Tale of the Dunkerque Galleys)

The galleys—we still hear the expression, "he works like a galley-slave" to indicate hard labor—were eighteenth century French war-vessels whose motive power was furnished by banks or tiers of oars twenty-five feet long or more, each oar manned by three men. The rowers were criminals or slaves and often condemned "to the galleys" for life. Many of the slaves purchased on the king's account were Turks. And it is of one of these Turks, a Turkish galley-slave aboard the Dunkerque galley "The Palm," that the following true tale has come down to us. One day two thieves, among other things, stole from the Cathedral of Dunkerque the silver box containing the holy oils for the administration of the sacrament of extreme unction. They carried the box to the Turkish galley-slave Galafas in his *baraque*,* and he bought it of them. When the thieves admitted to Galafas that what they had stolen was *robe santa,* "a holy thing," Galafas was a little worried, and thought he had better change the form of the silver box. He emptied out the holy oils and greased his boots with them, so that they should not go to waste. Then he made a hole in the ground under his *baraque* and there hid the flattened box. Unfortunately, one of the thieves was taken and convicted of the theft. He was asked what had become of the box, and confessed that he had sold it to Galafas, the Turk. When he led them to Galafas' *baraque* the latter quite frankly admitted having bought his plunder. Asked where the box was he showed its hiding-place. The Bishop of Dunkerque was at once informed so that he himself might hasten to carry back this precious and holy relic which none other had a right to touch. So the bishop with his priests soon hurried up in his surplice and with his cross, in procession. They dug in the earth according to the Turk's directions. And they found the box, flattened out by blows from a mallet. Then not seeing the holy oil, they asked the Turk what he had done with it. "I greased my boots with it," said the Turk, innocently. "If I had only had some lettuce I would have put it on that, for I tasted the oil and it was very good!" And with that the clergy all began to cry: "Sacrilege, sacrilege!" And this made the Turk, who had no idea of what it all was about, laugh heartily and make fun of them. But he soon found out it was no laughing matter. Then they made him take off his shoes. The bishop himself took them off, for who else would have dared lay his profane hands on these shoes sanctified by the holy oils.

---

* During the winter, when the galleys did not put to sea, the galley-slaves lived in rows of huts along the docks to which the galleys were moored. These huts were called *baraques*. There many of the slaves receivers of stolen goods, in which they did business.

Finally, with many ceremonies and palpitations of the heart, Galafas' shoes, together with the hammered-out box, and all the earth which the box might have touched, were gathered up in an altar-cloth. Four priests each took one corner of the cloth, and singing penetential psalms carried it to the cathedral, where all was buried beneath the altar. Galafas' *baraque* was demolished, and a heap of stones was piled up on the spot where it had stood as a record of the sacrilege committed. Galafas himself was put in the galley, chained with double chains and handcuffed. There, for a time, nothing could be done about punishing him because of a conflict of jurisdiction.

The Council of War of the galleys claimed the right of judgment, and the clergy contested its claim. Besides, the king had decreed that no other tribunal of justice in the kingdom could seize a slave or convict working on the galleys unless he were freed from the galleys by the king's pardon. And the slave or convict had his choice. He could accept or refuse his pardon, but in the latter case he had to remain in the galleys for life. The clergy of Dunkerque begged the king to pardon Galafas, which he did readily enough. One day they came to him and congratulated him for getting a royal pardon instead of being tortured. Galafas, not knowing the trap they had laid for him, joyfully accepted his pardon, and the major of the galleys had him unchained and putting his letter of pardon into his hand, told him he was free.

With one bound Galafas was off the galley. But the clergy, whose only fear had been that Galafas would refuse his pardon, had every avenue of escape covered, so that the poor Turk was at once seized and taken to the city prison. In vain he showed his pardon. His Majesty only had pardoned him as a galley-slave, he was told, and not for the crime of sacrilege which he had committed. Then the Court tried him at the bishop's request with all due formality and Galafas, convicted of a sacrilege of the worst kind, was condemned *to be burned alive and have his ashes scattered to the four winds!* Now Galafas appealed to the Parliament of Douai, and was taken to Douai to have his sentence confirmed.

Meanwhile much time had gone by, and during it the other Turks rowing on the galleys had managed to get a letter sent to Constantinople. The letter was given into the hands of the Grand Seignior, the Sultan, himself, and the latter at once sent for the French ambassador. If Galafas were burned alive for a crime which he did not even know was a crime when he had committed it, the Sultan declared, he would see to it that five hundred Christians, *French slaves,* were done to death in exactly the same way! Naturally the French ambassador at once sent couriers post-haste to his court. And the French king hastily ordered the Parliament of Douai *not* to confirm the Dunkerque sentence! Instead, Galafas escaped with being beaten along the length of the Dunkerque wharf; and was condemned to the galleys for life. This was lucky for him, for shortly after he was released, whether to please the Grand Seignior, or because of four hundred livres he paid for his freedom. He returned to his own land, and thus ended the affair of the sacrilege of Dunkerque. And from beginning to end, poor Galafas never quite realized the horror of the crime he had committed so innocently.

A LOVE THAT CAME TOO LATE

The Princes Diane de Talmont, one of Queen Marie Antoinette's closest friends, had lived at the French Court from the time she was a young girl. In the course of an early love affair, in which her heart really was engaged, her lover, a poor gentlemen, shot himself because family opposition made their union impossible. After that Diane de Talmont lived the gay, flighty, irresponsible life of her circle, and had many love affairs. She sent the Marquise de Cabris, who had stolen one of her lovers, a challenge and would no doubt have exchanged pistol-shots with her had not Madame de Pompadour interfered. And at the age of twenty she so turned the head of the Young Pretender, the Stuart Prince Charlie, that he could only be removed from Paris and her vicinity by force. He barricaded himself in his house in the Rue Richelieu, and defended himself with cannon until his powder gave out. When he was taken a picture of Diane de Talmont, clothed only in royal ermine, was found on his heart. Enough to say, she was one of the most loving and best beloved young ladies at Court, one of those richest in public and private adventures of all sorts. And this not only in her younger years, during the reign of King Louis XV, but until the whole "old order" came to an end in 1792. It was then that something she never before had noticed—the people—took a hand in her life.

It should be mentioned that at eighteen the beautiful Diane had been married to the Prince de Talmont, but that neither had availed themselves of marital privileges and remained mere acquaintances. Their marriage was a "marriage of convenience," arranged by their parents, to unite two great fortunes, and since it was unblessed by children each went his and her own way. The Prince de Talmont was a quiet gentlemen. He did not care for Court life, and spent most of his time on his estates in southern France when he was not in the field with the army. The princess lived her Paris life of love affairs, adventures and intrigues at Court. And so both of them had grown old, nearly sixty, before, one night, they met in the last place in the world they ever would have expected to meet— in jail!

The Prince, who had hastened from the country to rally around his king when the Revolution began, was one of the first to be thrown in jail, together with his wife. Hurried from their separate suites in the Hotel de Talmont to a dark prison in the dead of night, the two old people sat on a wooden bench together and—perhaps for the first time in their lives—clung to each other and wept, united by the same feelings. The Princess excused herself to her husband because her toilette had not been attended to, and he made excuses of the same kind to her. And each noticed a curious thing which softened their hearts. The Prince saw that the Princess' old wrinkled face looked just like that of the old nurse of his boyhood days, and the Princess noticed that the Prince resembled John, her faithful old coachman. Both, under the masks they had worn all their lives, discovered their real human faces.

The world was too busy in those days establishing the doctrine of liberty, freedom and equality, to pay much attention to imprisoned aristocrats. Universal love of mankind had to be raised to the throne. Aristocrats were thought of only when it seemed necessary to hustle them to the guillotine and out of a world into which they no longer fitted. Meanwhile, they were left to the tender mercies of some hangman who abused them. The Prince and Princess de Talmont had fallen into the hands of a fellow of this kind. For a bed they had a bundle of straw. Water, bread and salt were their only food, seasoned with curses. The two unfortunates had been dragged from their palace in such haste that they had not been able to take a little money with them, and thus make their hard lot easier.

And yet, what they endured gave them something they never had known before. In the Prince de Talmont there developed a great, glowing affection for this poor woman, old and ugly, who tried to tend him, brush the straw from his coat, and fill him with hope and confidence. A profound inner passion, a feeling of great and holy joy overpowered him when he felt the old woman's head resting on his shoulder, when she thrust her poor, bony hands into his own with a gentle, affectionate gesture.

And the same thing had happened to Diane. She had passed through life without ever giving her husband a thought or a glance, lost in the follies of her old world, which had so utterly passed away. When she saw him suffer and hunger in prison without ever uttering a complaint, when she saw how tenderly he waited on her, putting his arm under her head and trying to make her hard couch a trifle softer, and how he tried to show himself a man for her sake, she began to love him deeply. These two old married people, who all their life long never had found time to get acquainted, in their cold, dark prison, with death staring them in the face, deprived of all that had formerly made up their lives, came to know a great happiness. It was, heaven be praised, a happiness not dependent on external things. It was a happiness which may come to beggar as well as to a king, to a prisoner as well as to a jailer, the happiness growing out of a deep, all-embracing love.

Now by chance, the Prince de Talmont, who had been a passionate collector of fine porcelain, had happened to have in his coat-pocket a tiny group of figures, a very rare bit, on the night of his arrest. He had picked it up at a great bargain that very day, and it had accompanied him to jail. As soon as he thought it safe, he determined to offer it to the jailor, explain to him that as a work of art he could get its weight in gold for it, and obtain a mattress, a bottle of wine and some white bread for Diane in exchange. In sacrificing his little treasure, the Prince thought only of her. The group was one somewhat too "free" for the taste of our own time, but neither of the old folks, as they bent over the little figures of shepherds and shepherdesses, gave this a thought. And it was when Diane said to her husband that he should not give up so valuable a possession for her sake, that he slowly, almost timidly, confessed that he would be glad to sacrifice far greater possessions and even life itself for her. In short, the two old married folks made each other the most tender and touching declarations of love, and hugged each other with tears in their eyes, when they realized that God had granted them this blessing in the present condition they were in.

Then the Prince de Talmont showed his porcelain figures to his jailor. The latter, in private life was a cobbler. Aside from thinking that all aristocrats should be treated like dogs, he was a simple creature. And in the delicate, frivolous little toy he saw only something horribly indecent. It was another sign of the depravity of this class, which even in jail amused itself with things of the sort. Without even taking up the bit of porcelain, he knocked it rudely out of the Prince's hand crying: "You old swine!" He was delighted when the delicate work of art struck and broke into a thousand fragments on the hard stone floor. But the two old folks did not listen to the flood of curses he poured on them. Silently they turned to each other, and closing their ears to his words, gently stroked each other's hands, and looked toward the ceiling, where a confusion of gray spider-webs filled every corner.

Not long after the Prince de Talmont and his wife died on the scaffold, whose steps they mounted hand in hand. Once more, before all the people, whom they no longer saw, and whose presence was as indifferent to them as that of a pack of dogs or other animals would have been, they embraced each other long and tenderly. They gladly left this world in which, as it seemed to them, only beasts reigned, happy to be delivered from the growling and roaring that sounded around them. When the head of the Princess, who was guillotined first, fell into the basket, the Prince flung himself quickly under the blade. There he touched his forehead with the blood of the woman he loved who, before she had bowed her head, had smiled at him for the last time. He was eager to follow her into a world where he asked only to be reunited to one whom on earth he had loved too short a time, though with all the strength of his soul!

CONCLUSION

The eighteenth century saw the real end of the old order throughout the world. Great men might for a time arrest the progress of the democratic ideal. A Frederick the Great might establish the autocratic ideal on a basis of sound statesmanship: his successors had to give it up to the People! A Napoleon could make military glory the foundation of despotic rule: he could not found a dynasty! Louis XVIII, the brother of Louis XVI, could not bring back the old times when he succeeded Napoleon, nor could the "citizen king" Louis Philippe. And as soon as military glory deserted poor Napoleon III, the French cast him out and returned to the republican form of government. In England, Spain, Italy, Belgium, Holland and the Scandinavian lands, kings now are merely "costume figures." They are puppets who are driven about in gilded carriages, who wear their royal crowns and ermine on occasion, and go through ceremonial forms—for a salary! Their power has passed to their parliaments. They exist only because people like traditions. And in Europe, in particular, a king to the people at large often seems a necessary luxury, one of those things a well-regulated nation should have; one of those things to which good folk can point with pride and say: "We have one, too!" But no "divinity" hedges a salaried employee and—if you look beyond crown and robes, a modern constitutional king is nothing more.

A modern king's greatest value to-day, perhaps, is the *social prestige* association with him is supposed to give those who enjoy the privilege. And, curiously enough, as a rule the proud, independent citizens of republics are those who will make every sacrifice to bask in the sunshine of foreign royal favor. The poor yearn to possess millions, the millionaire longs for the social prestige he thinks royalty or aristocratic associations confer. In a way the romance of history, the romance of human life through the ages, comes to an end with the establishment of the ideals of *democracy*. Wealth is useful, but it is not necessarily romantic. And when, with democracy, wealth becomes the great social lever, we find the citizens (and especially the citizenesses) of republics entertain the world at large by trying to *buy* a romance—in the shape of supposed "social distinction"—whose soul has fled! The head of one branch of a family whose fortunes were founded on the New York real estate purchased by its founder, an honest pedlar, was stung by this aristocratic bee. He deliberately expatriates himself, puts in a lifetime and spends a fortune "hanging" about royal and nobiliary precincts. He dies but—the great work has been accomplished: there is a *title* in the family! A long series of "international" marriages, often contracted with utterly worthless and degenerate wearers of noble names, shows how eagerly the "free and equal" nationals of republics chase titled "distinctions." And even bargains in royalty may be picked up in these days when little kings keep the auto-tank filled for the hurried trip to railroad station or dock to take the road into exile. But bargain-counter rushes of this sort, presentations at the Court of St. James, title-worship and kowtowing, are not romance. Neither do they represent the mental attitude of the great majority of people, especially in the United States.

The great middle classes of every nation represent that nation at its best. It is in its "highest" and "lowest" classes of society that a nation is always least representative. And the great sane and sensible bulk of any nation may well afford to smile at the vagaries of the society title-hunters who chase the shadows of a romantic past in unromantic individuals of the present whom the accident of birth has given a right to call themselves kings, princes, dukes, counts, lords or what not. True romance lies in the past. And the real romantic "past" of humanity may be said to end with the American and French Revolutions. They did away with "romance"—and a thousand and one crimes, cruelties and abuses that flourished together with it—and substituted for it the less romantic but more practical ideals of individual liberty, and "a free field and no favors" for all. Whether those ideals have found their highest development in the life of our own day is another question, but the ideals themselves are ours to have and to hold.